THE ANALYSIS AND SOLUTION OF

PARTIAL
DIFFERENTIAL
EQUATIONS

CONTEMPORARY UNDERGRADUATE MATHEMATICS SERIES
Robert J. Wisner, Editor

THE NATURE OF MODERN MATHEMATICS. Karl J. Smith

MATHEMATICS FOR THE LIBERAL ARTS STUDENT, SECOND EDITION. Fred Richman,
Carol Walker, and Robert J. Wisner

INTERMEDIATE ALGEBRA. Edward D. Gaughan

ALGEBRA: A PRECALCULUS COURSE. James E. Hall

COLLEGE ALGEBRA. Edward D. Gaughan

TRIGONOMETRY: CIRCULAR FUNCTIONS AND THEIR APPLICATIONS. James E. Hall

MODERN MATHEMATICS: AN ELEMENTARY APPROACH, THIRD EDITION. Ruric E. Wheeler

A PROGRAMMED STUDY OF NUMBER SYSTEMS. Ruric E. Wheeler and Ed R. Wheeler

FUNDAMENTAL COLLEGE MATHEMATICS: NUMBER SYSTEMS AND INTUITIVE GEOMETRY.
Ruric E. Wheeler

MODERN MATHEMATICS FOR BUSINESS STUDENTS. Ruric E. Wheeler and W. D. Peeples

ANALYTIC GEOMETRY. James E. Hall

INTRODUCTORY GEOMETRY: AN INFORMAL APPROACH, SECOND EDITION. James R. Smart

MODERN GEOMETRIES. James R. Smart

AN INTUITIVE APPROACH TO ELEMENTARY GEOMETRY. Beauregard Stubblefield

GEOMETRY FOR TEACHERS. Paul B. Johnson and Carol H. Kipps

LINEAR ALGEBRA. James E. Scroggs

ESSENTIALS OF ABSTRACT ALGEBRA. Charles M. Bundrick and John J. Leeson

AN INTRODUCTION TO ABSTRACT ALGEBRA. A. Richard Mitchell and Roger W. Mitchell

INTRODUCTION TO ANALYSIS. Edward D. Gaughan

DIFFERENTIAL EQUATIONS AND RELATED TOPICS FOR SCIENCE AND ENGINEERING. Robert
W. Hunt

THE ANALYSIS AND SOLUTION OF PARTIAL DIFFERENTIAL EQUATIONS. Robert L. Street

A PRIMER OF COMPLEX VARIABLES WITH AN INTRODUCTION TO ADVANCED TECHNIQUES.
Hugh J. Hamilton

CALCULUS OF SEVERAL VARIABLES. E. K. McLachlan

PROBABILITY. Donald R. Barr and Peter W. Zehna

THEORY AND EXAMPLES OF POINT-SET TOPOLOGY. John Greever

AN INTRODUCTION TO ALGEBRAIC TOPOLOGY. John W. Keesee

EXPLORATIONS IN NUMBER THEORY. Jeanne Agnew

NUMBER THEORY: AN INTRODUCTION TO ALGEBRA. Fred Richman

THE ANALYSIS AND SOLUTION OF
PARTIAL DIFFERENTIAL EQUATIONS

ROBERT L. STREET
Stanford University

BROOKS/COLE PUBLISHING COMPANY
Monterey, California
A Division of Wadsworth Publishing Company, Inc.

ISBN: O-8185-0061-1
L.C. Catalog Card No.: 73-75562
Printed in the United States of America

1 2 3 4 5 6 7 8 9 10—77 76 75 74 73

Partial differential equations play an important role in applied mathematics and the physical and engineering sciences. This book is intended to serve as a text for elementary courses in partial differential equations. The plan and content of the book were selected to provide a guide to the theory, properties, and relations to physical problems of these equations.

The reader will find that problem formulation and solution are considered as essentially separate actions in the text. Emphasis is placed on the importance of correct problem formulation through the use of physical reasoning and the qualitative mathematical concepts of existence, uniqueness, and continuity of solutions. The full range of tools and concepts that can be made available to the beginning student is then employed in problem solution. An attempt is made to give perspective to the relations between analytic and numerical methods and between qualitative and quantitative methods and results. Rigorous developments are given for most concepts, but useful heuristic proofs and physical reasoning are not shunned.

In order to provide insight to more advanced topics, as well as practice in their use, the book goes further in scope and detail than most beginning textbooks. As a result, the instructor has the opportunity to choose a range of material that suits his particular course plan and references. Furthermore, after completion of his formal course work, the reader is able, and hopefully inclined, to read further on his own in a book whose notation, style, and level are familiar to him.

In a one-semester, 2-hour-per-week course or a one-quarter, 3-hour-per-week course, the material in Chapters 1 through 6 can be covered completely. Some instructors may find it desirable to include parts of Chapter 8 on transforms and Chapter 9 on characteristics in the first course in lieu of Chapter 6. A course covering Chapters 1 through 6 will give a grounding in the essentials of partial differential equations, including:

1. background and introductions to physical problems leading to partial differential equations.
2. classification and properties of various equations.
3. the method of separation of variables in simple and generalized forms.
4. the role and use of ordinary differential equations (and their theory).
5. existence, uniqueness, and continuity of solutions.
6. Fourier theory.
7. eigenvalues, eigenfunctions, and eigenfunction expansions.

For best understanding and appreciation, Chapter 10 on numerical methods should not be attempted until Chapters 1 through 6 have been completed.

A liberal number of problem exercises appear at the end of each chapter. The working of a significant portion of these problems is essential to a full understanding of the book's content. The reader is forewarned, however, that many problems involving partial differential equations are conceptually difficult and require long solutions. It is wise to plan well and execute carefully. Speed is no virtue in the attempted solution of these problems, and successful solutions will result from use of patience and care in handling the assignments.

The presentation is designed to provide a complete basic guide and to allow the instructor to utilize his classroom time for amplifying particular points and setting the desired emphasis of his course—be it rigorously mathematical or engineering oriented. The reader should have a good background in basic college calculus; neither advanced calculus nor complex-variable theory are essential prerequisites. A prior or concurrent course in ordinary differential equations is highly desirable but again is not essential if the reader has had some experience with simple harmonic motions (as most engineering and science students have). The appendixes provide much of the basic background material needed.

The reader should pay particular attention to the references gathered at the end of each chapter and should refer to them often. The references refer to sources of material for this book, to alternative or parallel approaches to those used here, to advanced texts or monographs on particular subjects, and to current literature. The reference numbers are used in the text as keys to particular references.

My interest in partial differential equations was first stimulated by the teaching of Professor Paul W. Berg of Stanford University. Indeed, the systematic approach to initial-boundary-value problems that he taught me has been carried through in this work. In particular, Sections 3.2, 3.4, and 5.1 bear most clearly the imprint of the teaching and approach that he and James L. McGregor subsequently set forth in their book *Elementary Partial Differential Equations* (San Francisco: Holden–Day, 1966). Of course, in the preparation of an elementary book such as this, the works of many authors have been drawn upon, particularly the classic works of Courant and Hilbert* and of Churchill.† These sources of material are acknowledged in the text.

I am deeply indebted to my wife for her encouragement, patience, and work in the typing of drafts, which no finite amount of gratitude can repay; to my daughters for being quiet when necessary and delightful otherwise; and to Ashby Longwell for her long-term assistance in preparing the manuscript and for setting such high standards of presentation. Mrs. Longwell, Emily Winstrom, and Kay MacLaury all contributed ably to the typing of the final manuscript and have my great appreciation. The comments, criticisms, and suggestions of my Stanford colleagues and students have been invaluable in preparing the book from sets of classroom notes. I would also like to thank Professors Courtney Coleman of Harvey Mudd College, Robert E. Lynch of Purdue University, and John S. Maybee of the University of Colorado for their helpful reviews of the manuscript. Finally, I am appreciative of the years of patient encouragement from Jack N. Thornton of Brooks/Cole Publishing Company and Dr. Robert Wisner of New Mexico State University, Consulting Editor for this series of books.

Robert L. Street

---

* R. Courant and D. Hilbert, *Methods of Mathematical Physics*, Vols. I & II. New York: Interscience (a division of John Wiley & Sons), 1953 & 1962.

† R. V. Churchill, *Fourier Series and Boundary Value Problems*, 2nd ed. New York: McGraw-Hill, 1963.

CONTENTS

THE ANALYSIS AND SOLUTION OF

PARTIAL
DIFFERENTIAL
EQUATIONS

CHAPTER 1

PHYSICAL SYSTEMS AND PARTIAL DIFFERENTIAL EQUATIONS

1.1 THE PARTIAL DIFFERENTIAL EQUATION

Physical systems in many fields of applied science and engineering can be described in terms of mathematical systems composed of equations containing partial derivatives. These equations usually may be grouped into (a) equations descriptive of the system as a whole and (b) appropriate auxiliary (or side) condition equations that depend on the physics of the particular system. These sets of *partial differential equations* are the subject of this book.

A large number of interesting physical problems can be described by relatively simple equations (in particular, the second-order equations that are listed below). In what follows, we restrict our attention to a few of these basic or classical equations and their physical origins. Even so, a wealth of physical problems are represented, and we do develop methods to deal with some problems involving propagation of electric and radio waves, hydrodynamics, ocean waves, heat conduction, vibrations in solids, propagation of sound waves in a gas, diffusion, and nuclear reactor neutron flux. Partial differential equations and their appropriate auxiliary conditions can be studied in their classes according to their solution characteristics, but without reference to their physical origins. However, in an introductory exposition it is instructive to relate our problems to physical origins. Indeed, the physical systems described by our mathematics serve both as our motivation to solve problems and as an intuitive guide to the proper behavior for the mathematical solutions.

If u is a function of several variables such that its value is $u(x, y, z, t)$, the partial derivative of u with respect to x evaluated at a point (x_0, y_0, z_0, t_0) is denoted by

$$\frac{\partial u}{\partial x}(x_0, y_0, z_0, t_0)$$

or by

$$\frac{\partial u}{\partial x}\bigg|_{(x_0, y_0, z_0, t_0)}$$

The notations

$$p = u_x = \frac{\partial u}{\partial x}, \quad q = u_y = \frac{\partial u}{\partial y}, \quad r = u_{xx}, \quad s = u_{xy}, \quad t = u_{yy}$$

are used extensively for convenience and brevity.

A partial differential equation is an equation involving several independent variables $x, y, z, \ldots$, a function u of these variables, and the partial derivatives of the dependent function u with respect to the independent variables. Symbolically,

$$F(x, y, z, \ldots, u, u_x, u_y, u_z, \ldots, u_{xx}, u_{yy}, \ldots, u_{xy}, u_{xz}, \ldots) = 0 \tag{1.1}$$

The *order* of the partial differential equation is defined to be the order of the highest partial derivatives appearing in the equation. Thus

$$u_{xyz} + xu_{xx} + yu_{yy} + u_x + u_y = 0 \tag{1.2}$$

is of third order, whereas the equation for stress u in a plastic body [1]*

$$(u_{xx} - u_{yy})^2 + 4(u_{xy})^2 = K \tag{1.3}$$

is of second order.

A function u is called a *solution* to a partial differential equation, such as (1.1), (1.2), or (1.3), whenever the equation becomes an identity in the independent variables $(x, y, \ldots)$ upon substitution of u and its appropriate derivatives in the partial differential equation. For example, if

$$u_{xx} - u_{tt} = 0 \tag{1.4}$$

then

$$u_1(x, t) = \sin \pi x \cos \pi t$$

$$u_2(x, t) = \sin 2\pi x \cos 2\pi t$$

$$\vdots \tag{1.5}$$

$$u_n(x, t) = \sin n\pi x \cos n\pi t$$

are all solutions, as is easily seen by direct substitution. The result (1.5) reveals an important characteristic of partial differential equations that is common to ordinary

---

* The numbers in brackets refer to references listed at the end of each chapter.

differential equations, too: a single equation, like (1.4), for one function u may possess many *particular* solutions. Thus one of our first concerns in any problem will be to develop, as was hinted above, certain auxiliary conditions that will serve to isolate or characterize an *individual* solution for a given problem. We note now only that these individual solutions are usually composed from some subset of the totality of all particular solutions to a given equation.

The partial differential equation (1.1) is called *linear* if the functional relationship F is algebraically linear in the variables $u, u_x, \ldots, u_{xx}, u_{yy}, \ldots, u_{xy}, \ldots$ and the coefficients of the variables are functions only of the independent variables. The second-order partial differential equation in two independent variables (x, y)

$$\alpha_1 u_{xx} + \alpha_2 u_{xy} + \alpha_3 u_{yy} + \alpha_4 = 0 \tag{1.6}$$

is linear if the α_i are specified functions of only (x, y). Otherwise when the α_i depend on $(x, y, u, u_x, u_y, \ldots)$, (1.6) is *nonlinear*. Thus (1.3) is a nonlinear equation. One class of nonlinear equations of particular interest is linear with respect to the derivatives of highest order; for example,

$$u_x u_{xx} + 2uu_{xy} + u_y u_{yy} = 0$$

or with f being a function of (x, y) alone,

$$u_{xx} + u_y u_x = f$$

These equations are called *quasi-linear* because they can be classified as to type and studied qualitatively as though they were linear. The simple equation of supersonic flow

$$(c^2 - u_x^2)u_{xx} - 2u_x u_y u_{xy} + (c^2 - u_y^2)u_{yy} = 0 \tag{1.7}$$

is a quasi-linear equation. In general, (1.6) is quasi-linear when the α_i depend on (x, y, u, u_x, u_y) only. A general theory for nonlinear partial differential equations has yet to be developed. There is a relatively complete and simple theory for linear equations, however, and a somewhat less complete theory for quasi-linear equations [2]. Fortunately, many significant physical systems can be described by linear partial differential equations, in particular, by second-order equations whose form is

$$\alpha_1(x, y)u_{xx}(x, y) + \alpha_2(x, y)u_{xy}(x, y) + \alpha_3(x, y)u_{yy}(x, y)$$
$$+ \alpha_4(x, y)u_x(x, y) + \alpha_5(x, y)u_y(x, y) + \alpha_6(x, y)u(x, y) + \alpha_7(x, y) = 0 \tag{1.8}$$

Many important linear partial differential equations of second order are not as complex as (1.8), and we shall spend a majority of our time dealing with equations like the following special forms of (1.8):

$$u_{tt} = c^2 u_{xx} \qquad \text{The Wave Equation}$$

$$u_t = k u_{xx} \qquad \text{The Heat Equation}$$

$$u_{xx} + u_{yy} = 0 \qquad \text{The Laplace Equation}$$

$$u_{xx} + u_{yy} = G \qquad \text{The Poisson Equation}$$
$$\qquad\qquad\qquad\qquad [G \text{ may be a function of } (x, y)]$$

The first two equations received their names from their early physical application to wavelike motions (vibrations, for example) and to heat conduction in solids, respectively. The last two equations find their greatest applications in the field of potential theory and were named after the great French mathematician Pierre S. de Laplace, who developed the foundations of potential theory, and the French mathematical physicist Simeon D. Poisson, who made important contributions to the field.

1.2   THE MODEL CONCEPT

A physical system is an object or collection of matter on which attention is concentrated in the analysis of a problem. Usually a system is composed of matter of *fixed identity* that is viewed as being separated from everything external to the system (the *surroundings*) by an imagined *boundary*. In the case of heat conduction in a sphere, the system is the sphere, the boundary covers the surface of the sphere, and the external environment (heated air or a constant temperature water bath, for example) is the surroundings. In some cases, it is convenient to modify our point of view and to speak in terms of a "control system" or *control volume*, which is a volume fixed in space through whose boundary matter, energy, etc., may pass.

Every system has certain characteristics by which its physical condition may be described—for example, mass, pressure, temperature, and thermal conductivity. In the system concept, we focus attention on an object of immediate interest (the system) and then observe both the interactions between system and surroundings and the changes in system characteristics.

The system-surrounding interactions and the internal state of the system are governed by physical laws, such as Newton's Second Law, which in its simplest form for a single particle says

$$a = \frac{F}{m} \tag{1.9}$$

where a is the acceleration of the particle, F is the vector force acting on the particle, and m is the particle mass. In addition, suppose that the future state or condition of a system depends, as we might imagine, on the time that the particular process under examination begins and on the system state at that time. We will then find it necessary not only to observe and prescribe conditions in the surroundings (i.e., at the boundary in particular) but also to establish some description of the initial state of the system, its boundary, and the surroundings. Thus auxiliary boundary and initial conditions arise normally in our description of a system and supplement the governing physical laws.

Theoretical predictions of the behavior of physical systems are sought by constructing a *mathematical model* or system whose solutions have values that approximate measured values in the physical system. Unfortunately, the creation of a tractable mathematical model—that is, one whose solution can readily be found— requires the introduction of assumptions, most of which are restrictive in nature and produce simplifications. The determination and application of the solution for a particular mathematical model must be made in the light of these assumptions. In constructing a mathematical model, one must achieve first a concise and fairly realistic description of the physical system and then a precise translation of its characteristics into mathematical terms. In our work each physical problem leads to a mathematical model composed of (a) a differential equation or equations and (b) an appropriate set of auxiliary boundary and/or initial conditions. The dependent, unspecified variable (or variables) in the model equations is the mathematical representation of the physical characteristic whose behavior is to be predicted— for example, the temperature distribution $T(x, t)$ in a thin, heated bar or the displacement $y(x, t)$ of a vibrating string in a piano.

Let us consider a particularly simple physical system: a small mass m attached to a fixed point by means of a linear spring of unstretched length l_0 and spring constant k (the force exerted by a linear spring is proportional to the amount it is stretched or compressed and acts in the opposite direction; k is the proportionality constant). The situation is depicted in Fig. 1.1a; the system is pictured in terms of a boundary enveloping the mass in Fig. 1.1b. Figure 1.1b shows the forces acting on or through the system boundaries. The position of the mass at any time t is described by a coordinate $x(t)$, measured from the unstretched position of the spring. If the mass is released from the position $x = 0$, we know intuitively and experimentally that some sort of motion will ensue. In particular, the motion is governed by the scalar form of Newton's Second Law, (1.9) above. The only forces acting along the x axis are the spring force $F = -kx$ and the weight mg. The mathematical model of our physical system begins with an equation $m(d^2x/dt^2) = -kx + mg$, since d^2x/dt^2 is the acceleration of the mass. What else is needed? Does the motion depend on (a) how it started and (b) where it started? The answers are, of course, *yes*. Question (a) is answered by prescribing $dx/dt(0) = V_0$, the initial velocity of the mass. Question (b) is answered by prescribing $x(0) = x_0$, the initial position of the mass. It would appear that a complete model is given by

$$\frac{d^2x}{dt^2} + \frac{k}{m}x = g, \qquad t > 0 \tag{1.10}$$

$$x(0) = x_0$$
$$\frac{dx}{dt}(0) = V_0 \tag{1.11}$$

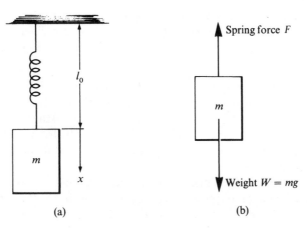

(a)   (b)

FIGURE 1.1

where the position $x(t)$ is the dependent, unspecified physical characteristic to be predicted. Here (1.10) is the differential equation, whereas (1.11) is a pair of auxiliary *initial* conditions. That (1.10) and (1.11) are a complete mathematical model is well known; the motion of the mass is called *simple harmonic* and the solution is

$$x(t) = \left(x_0 - \frac{mg}{k}\right) \cos \left(\frac{k}{m}\right)^{1/2} t + \frac{V_0}{(k/m)^{1/2}} \sin \left(\frac{k}{m}\right)^{1/2} t + \frac{mg}{k} \tag{1.12}$$

It is interesting to ponder the relationship between the obtained solution (1.12) and the given data, as well as the statement, made above, that (1.12) is *the* solution.

The solutions of a mathematical model of a physical system *should have values that approximate the measured values* of the characteristic variables of the physical system. These variables have values at all times. Thus at least one solution to the model equation set must exist. Most (but not necessarily all) physical systems have a single, unambiguous state at any given time. Accordingly, the mathematical model should have at most one solution. However, while our mathematical formulation needs to be sufficiently well prescribed to exclude unwanted solutions, the formulation should not be overprescribed and thereby exclude all solutions. For example, if we prescribe, in addition to the conditions already given, $x(5)$ arbitrarily for the model (1.10) to (1.11), no solution will exist in general.

Finally, physical values are measured data. Because perfect accuracy is not possible in measuring these values, physical values used as data in mathematical models are approximate, and tolerances are given on the degree of precision in a data set. Unless a variation of the given data for a model in the small tolerance range leads to an equivalently small change in the solution, the mathematical model cannot realistically correspond to a physical phenomenon. It is particularly easy to see that small changes in the data $[m, g, k, x_0, V_0]$ for the model (1.10) to (1.11) produce small changes in the solution (1.12), for example.

Therefore there are three qualitative requirements that a mathematical model must meet in order to conform to physical reality:

1. *Existence: at least one* solution to the model equation set must exist.
2. *Uniqueness:* there must be *at most* one solution.
3. *Continuity:* The solution must depend continuously on all the given data (e.g., the equation coefficients α_i and the data prescribed along the boundaries or initially). Alternatively, solutions corresponding to data that differ by small amounts should also differ by small amounts (the solutions must be stable against perturbations in the data).

A mathematical model is defined to be mathematically *well posed, properly posed,* or *correctly set* when it satisfies the preceding three requirements of existence, uniqueness, and continuity. However, the true test of a mathematical model is the comparison of its solution with actual experimental results from the physical system. This test, unfortunately, cannot always be realistically performed because of a lack of such experimental results.

As a word of caution, it should be pointed out that Courant and Hilbert [2] give several examples of physically realistic phenomena leading to "improperly posed" problems. There is virtually no theoretical basis for even systematically classifying, much less formulating and solving, such problems; but they are still important and arise from real situations. Improperly posed problems have particular importance in the application of the new, powerful numerical analysis techniques, which employ approximate representations of the usual equations. As an example, numerical, finite-difference methods [3] are being employed in the analysis of problems for which the initial and boundary data are known only approximately or, more significantly, cannot be accounted for either rigorously or accurately in the computation scheme.

1.3   PROBLEM FORMULATION; PROBLEM SOLUTION

In each *problem* that we study we face the specific task of obtaining results that predict the behavior of a physical system. *Problem formulation* is the act of constructing an appropriate mathematical model for a particular physical system whose behavior we are to predict. *Problem solution* is the mathematical process of obtaining useful information about the unknown, dependent variables in a mathematical model.

The useful information obtained in a solution can take several forms. It may be in the classical form, in which the unknowns are described in the solution explicitly by some mathematical expression as continuous functions of the independent variables. This form is called the *closed-form solution*. The mathematical expressions are typically integrals, infinite series, power series, or other algebraic combinations of functions of the independent variables. However, a considerable amount of numerical computation may be required to obtain actual numerical values. On the other hand, in this era of ever more complex problems and advanced numerical computation methods, *numerical solutions*—that is, solutions obtained by approximation techniques such as finite differences—are common. Usually a numerical solution is a tabulated or graphed set of numerical values of the dependent variables at individual, discrete points in the time-space domain of the problem. Thus while physical state variables have values that exist *physically* at every point and vary continuously from point to point, we can compute only a finite set of corresponding solution values to the numerical model, no easy general functional relationships being available to describe the dependent variables of the model.

In very complex problems we may be able to obtain only very limited amounts of useful information about the solution, such as numerical bounds on the solution. This type of information is, in fact, of great value for many situations and is developed here in certain special cases where it is of immediate value or interest.

The attack on a physical problem is naturally divisible into the formulation and solution phases. Referring to the criteria cited earlier for the performance of a mathematical model, we are reminded of the need for careful formulation. Our results depend crucially on the accuracy of our formulation; clearly, improper formulation leads to meaningless solutions.

Problem formulation is accomplished by:

1. *Achieving a concise description of the physical system.* We must describe the system, its boundaries, environment, and dependent variables in terms of the independent variables.

2. *Reducing the physical system to a mathematical model.* We must make idealizations and simplifying assumptions. Some subjective decision must be made

regarding what influences are pertinent and what are not; one wants to use the minimal number of idealizations and assumptions to get the simplest model that adequately predicts the physical system behavior.

3. *Demonstrating the adequacy of the model by proving the existence, uniqueness, and continuity of the solution.* Contrarily, we may demonstrate that these criteria are not appropriate in some situations. The demonstration of existence, uniqueness, and continuity of the solution is usually based on the properties of the model equations, including the initial and boundary conditions; accordingly, the demonstrations can be made without explicit knowledge of the solution—that is, before it is obtained.

Because one tends to look at the closed-form solution as evidence, in itself, of the existence, uniqueness, and continuity of a solution, these three qualitative questions are often overlooked in the quest for numbers when closed-form solution forms are available. However, where only numerical solutions are available, failure to reach at least some tentative conclusions about the solution's existence, uniqueness, and continuity can lead directly to nonsensical results. The numerical methods in Chap. 10 employ approximations to the basic differential equations so that the question of the adequacy of the mathematical model is compounded further by the question of whether or not the approximations leading to the *numerical model* are valid.

Following problem formulation, problem solution requires application of one or several of many methods that we shall develop for generating solutions to specific equations and auxiliary conditions. Unfortunately, step (3) above and finding the solution are by far the most difficult of the processes necessary in solving a physical problem. Many difficulties arise because of poor handling of (1) and (2) above; how this can happen will become clear as we derive equations and auxiliary conditions in Chap. 2. In many cases, (3) cannot be explicitly accomplished. It is then convenient, expedient, and perhaps imperative for us to proceed directly from (2) to an attempt to find a solution. A most useful existence proof is one that leads both to proof of the existence of a solution and to the explicit, written-out solution. In the reverse process, we infer existence when we have succeeded in obtaining a solution. This can be done with rigor only when the solution is in closed form. Similarly, but with no justification, we might be tempted to infer uniqueness from our failure to construct more than one solution.

The methods of obtaining the actual solution are quite different in the cases of closed-form and numerical solutions. Until we reach Chap. 10 and discuss finite-difference methods, we are concerned primarily with finding closed-form solutions (e.g., Secs. 4.6 and 9.4 provide exceptions).

In solving ordinary differential equations, we seek to find a general solution that contains certain arbitrary constants that are used to satisfy the auxiliary conditions, a *general solution* being the collection of *all* solutions to an equation. The general solution of a partial differential equation contains arbitrary functions that must be determined in order to satisfy the auxiliary conditions. In most cases, we cannot find the general solution for partial differential equations; and when we do, the general form contains arbitrary functions that simply cannot be evaluated for general auxiliary conditions. However, for linear equations, a valuable procedure is to compose a solution from a collection of particular solutions, such as (1.5) above. The particular solutions can then be combined with arbitrary multiplying constants in a series. The auxiliary conditions are used finally to determine the values for the set of multiplying constants so that the conditions are satisfied and a unique solution is obtained.

1.4   SUMMARY—SCOPE AND OBJECTIVES

In many practically important situations in the physical and engineering sciences, attempts to describe and predict the behavior of physical systems lead to the formulation and solution of mathematical models. We are going to study mathematical models composed from partial differential equations and auxiliary conditions that arise naturally from analysis of physical systems.

We focus our attention first on the proper formulation of mathematical models in a number of typical, yet simple, physical systems. We test the expected behavior of the model by trying to ensure that its solution meets the qualitative criteria of existence, uniqueness, and continuity. Then we develop methods of solution leading to both closed-form and numerical results.

This work deals primarily with linear, second-order partial differential equations in two independent variables. The theory and applications of these equations are both typical of partial differential equations as a whole and ideally amenable to an elementary treatment. In order to provide a broad base for extension of the concepts discussed, certain sections and problems are devoted to nonlinear problems, greater numbers of independent variables, and equations of higher order. In fact, most of the methods given here can be generalized to handle the last two areas. The subject of first-order equations is treated briefly in Chap. 9; an elegant and useful theory with physical interpretations exists and is treated in depth by Courant and Hilbert [2].

Our objectives are to learn the characteristics of partial differential equations, to understand the bases of partial differential equation theory, and to develop methods, both analytical and numerical, to obtain solutions to a wide range of mathematical models of physical systems.

REFERENCES

1. W. F. Ames, *Nonlinear Partial Differential Equations in Engineering.* New York: Academic Press, 1965.

2. R. Courant and D. Hilbert, *Methods of Mathematical Physics*, Vol. II. New York: Interscience (a division of John Wiley & Sons), 1962.

3. J. E. Welch, "Computer Simulation of Water Waves—Hanging Ten the Hard Way," *Datamation*, Vol. 12, No. 11, November 1966, pp. 41–47.

PROBLEMS

1.1   If $u(x, y) = (x^2 + y^2)^{1/2} - x/y$, verify that

$$u_{xy} = u_{yx}, \qquad y \neq 0$$

1.2   If u is a function of the two independent variables x and y, what properties must u possess so that

$$u_{xy} = u_{yx}$$

always? (*Hint:* A brief review of basic calculus is in order.)

1.3   Determine the order of the following equations and whether they are linear, quasi-linear, or nonlinear equations.

(a) $u_{xyt} + x^2 u_{xx} + y_{yy} + u_x + u_t = 0$ (b) $u_{xx} - u_{yy} + u_t^2 = 5$

(c) $u_x - u_y + u_t = u^2$ (d) $u_{tt} = (u_{xx} + u_{yy})^2$

1.4   Construct partial differential equations for u as a function of (x, y, z) according to the following specifications:

(a) first order, nonlinear   (b) third order, quasi-linear

(c) second order, linear

1.5   If $u(x, y) = \frac{1}{2} \ln (x^2 + y^2)$, show that

$$u_{xx} + u_{yy} = 0$$

Is u a solution to the partial differential equation? For all x and y? Why or why not?

1.6   If $u(x, y, z) = (x^2 + y^2 + z^2)^{-1/2}$, show that u is a solution of

$$u_{xx} + u_{yy} + u_{zz} = 0$$

1.7   Explain the chain rule of partial differentiation with respect to s and t for the function u of the variables (x, y, z), where x, y, z are each functions of s and t.

1.8   If $u(x, t) = h(\xi) + l(\eta)$, where h and l are twice-continuously-differentiable functions of a single variable and $\xi = x + ct$ and $\eta = x - ct$, show that

$$c^2 u_{xx} - u_{tt} = 0$$

that is, u is a solution of the wave equation.

1.9   Deduce an infinite set of particular solutions to the equation

$$c^2 u_{xx} - u_{tt} = 0$$

Do the particular solutions that you generated have the same form as the solution in Prob. 1.8? Can they be put into the same form? [*Hint:* Compare Prob. 1.8 to Eqs. (1.4) and (1.5).]

1.10   Verify that

$$u(x, y) = A \sin \lambda x \cosh \lambda y$$

is a solution of

$$u_{xx} + u_{yy} = 0$$

Are the values of A and λ restricted in any way?

1.11   Select the linear equations from the following list:

(a) $u_x u_y - 3u = x$

(b) $u_{xx} + u_{yy} = (ku)_x$, where k is a function of (x, y).

(c) $x^2 u_{xx} + y u_{yy} = xy$

(d) $u_{xy} + u_x u_{xx} = u_{xxx}$

(e) $y u_{xxy} + e^x u_x + 3 = 0$

(f) $u_{xx} + u_{yy} + \lambda \ln u = \ln x$

   Does the value of λ affect your answer?

(g) $3xu_x - 4yu_y + (x^2 + y^2)u = 0$

(h) $u_{xx} + 2u_{xy} + 4u_{yy} + 5u_x + 4u_y = 0$

(i) $u_y = -2 (\ln u)_x$

(j) $(ku_x)_x = u_y + ku$, where k is constant.

   How is your answer affected if k is a function of x?
   If k is a function of u?

1.12   Verify by direct substitution that Eq. (1.12) is the solution to the mathematical model described by Eqs. (1.10) and (1.11). Plot $x(t)$ versus t for the following cases if $g = 32.2$ and $k/m = 10$. [Note that g has the units ft(sec)$^{-2}$ and k/m has the units (sec)$^{-2}$ in the foot-pound-second system.]

(a) $x_0 = 0$ ft, $V_0 = 0$ ft/sec   (b) $x_0 = 3.22$ ft, $V_0 = 0$ ft/sec

(c) $x_0 = 3.22$ ft, $V_0 = -3.18$ ft/sec   (d) $x_0 = 0$, $V_0 = 3.18$ ft/sec

How do the results of the various cases differ?

1.13   Through the use of series approximations show the order of error Δx introduced in (1.12) by errors in the given data of

(a) Δk (b) Δm (c) Δg (d) Δx_0 (e) ΔV_0

Can you conclude in each case that small changes in data produce small changes in the solution—that is, that the solution is continuous with respect to the data?

1.14   Make a list of five physical systems that you believe can be described by mathematical models. For the systems on your list, do the following:

(a) Describe which systems will have mathematical models governed by partial differential equations and the physical processes involved—for example, heat transfer, fluid flow, etc.

(b) Explain why the models of your systems should have unique solutions.

(c) Describe a reasonable set of boundaries for each system and the conditions to be met there. What initial or starting conditions are necessary?

(d) List representative dependent and independent variables for each system on your list.

1.15   Carry out items (a) through (d) of Prob. 1.14 for the following physical systems:

(a) the atmosphere of the earth.   (b) the oceans of the earth.

(c) the flow of blood through the human liver.

CHAPTER 2

EQUATIONS AND
AUXILIARY CONDITIONS

2.1 INTRODUCTION

In this chapter specific equations and conditions are derived to construct explicitly the mathematical models described in Chap. 1. First, the classical second-order equations—the heat, wave, and Laplace (Poisson) equations—are derived, together with some reasonable auxiliary conditions, from physical principles. Second, complete mathematical models of physical systems are presented in the form of initial-boundary-value problems that incorporate the classical second-order equations with two independent variables.

The derivations given in Sec. 2.2 lead to differential equations of only three types: *parabolic*, *elliptic*, and *hyperbolic* equations. In addition, certain combinations of boundary and initial conditions are associated naturally with each particular type of equation. In Sec. 2.6 a closer examination of the general, linear second-order equation in two independent variables (1.8) shows that it can be transformed to a simple form corresponding to one of those obtained in Sec. 2.2. In fact, (1.8) is shown to have *canonical forms*—that is, transformed forms in which the coefficients α_1, α_2, and α_3 of the second-order derivatives have only the values $+1$, -1, or 0. There are only three possible forms, and each has an invariant meaning with regard to the type and behavior of the equation solution.

In the fourth section of this chapter, the groundwork is laid for finding solutions to the problems described in Sec. 2.3 through a discussion of linearity and the concept of superposition. We also give a brief discussion of nonlinear problems and their complexities in Sec. 2.5.

2.2   THE CLASSICAL SECOND-ORDER EQUATIONS

2.2.1   Physical Problems Leading to the Heat Equation

Derivation of the Heat Equation

The flow of heat in a conducting solid forms the basis for our first attempt to deduce a mathematical model employing partial differential equations. Heat flow is energy in transition from one mass to another as the result of a temperature difference.

Consider a solid, shown in Fig. 2.1, with a distribution of temperature at some time t. The solid is taken to be isotropic; that is, its structure and properties in the neighborhood of any point are the same relative to all directions through the point. We make the assumption that the temperature distribution and material properties are continuous throughout the solid. Now let dS be the area of a small element centered on some point P within the solid (Fig. 2.1). The *flux* f_n is defined as the rate at which heat (heat per unit area per unit time) is transferred across dS at P in the direction of the outward normal, unit vector n; it is easily shown that the flux distribution is also continuous. Experiments have shown that for heat flow by conduction in a solid,

$$f_n = -K\frac{\partial u}{\partial n} \tag{2.1}$$

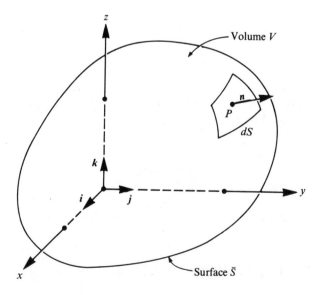

FIGURE 2.1

where $u(x, y, z, t)$ is the distribution of temperatures in the solid in which dS is located, $\partial/\partial n$ denotes differentiation in the direction of the outward normal to dS at P, and $K(x, y, z, u)$ is the *thermal conductivity* of the solid medium. For many practical purposes, K is constant. From (2.1), the fluxes across surfaces parallel to the coordinate axes are given by

$$f_x = -K\frac{\partial u}{\partial x}, \quad f_y = -K\frac{\partial u}{\partial y}, \quad f_z = -K\frac{\partial u}{\partial z} \tag{2.2}$$

Now let us choose an arbitrary fixed control volume V with surface $\bar{S}$ in a solid (Fig. 2.1). Because energy must be conserved, it is easy to conclude that the change (per unit time) in the amount of heat stored within V must be equal to the net amount of heat flowing in through the surfaces $\bar{S}$ plus the heat generated by any sources of heat within V in the same unit time period. In summary, we have:

1. The amount of heat flowing *into* the volume V per unit time is given by the summation of the fluxes through each dS of $\bar{S}$—that is, by the surface integral (note the minus sign)

$$-\iint_{\bar{S}} f_n \, dS \tag{2.3}$$

2. The heat stored within the volume V at any time is given by the volume integral

$$\iiint_V \rho c u \, dx \, dy \, dz \tag{2.4}$$

where ρ is the *density* of the solid (mass per unit volume) and c is the *specific heat* (heat per unit mass per unit of temperature). Both ρ and c can be functions of (x, y, z, t, u), but many times they are independent of either u or t. From (2.4), the change in heat storage per unit of time is

$$\frac{\partial}{\partial t}\left(\iiint_V \rho c u \, dx \, dy \, dz\right) \tag{2.5}$$

3. If $A(x, y, z, t, u)$ is the rate of heat generation (heat per unit volume per unit time) by sources at a point as a function of time, position, and temperature, then the heat generated by sources in V per unit of time is given by the volume integral

$$\iiint_V A \, dx \, dy \, dz \tag{2.6}$$

Because energy is conserved, the sum of (2.3) and (2.6) must equal the change in storage (2.5); thus

$$\frac{\partial}{\partial t}\left(\iiint_V \rho c u \, dx \, dy \, dz\right) = -\iint_{\bar{S}} f_n \, dS + \iiint_V A \, dx \, dy \, dz \tag{2.7}$$

Equation (2.7) can be simplified, first, by noting that the control volume V is fixed in time and space so that

$$\frac{\partial}{\partial t}\left(\iiint_V \rho c u \, dx \, dy \, dz\right) = \iiint_V \frac{\partial}{\partial t}(\rho c u) \, dx \, dy \, dz \tag{2.8}$$

and, second, by applying the Gauss theorem of vector integral calculus [1].*

If the flux at a point is expressed as a vector in terms of the cartesian unit vectors i, j, k (see Fig. 2.1) and the flux components along the coordinate directions [see (2.2)], then

$$f = f_x i + f_y j + f_z k \tag{2.9}$$

The flux normal to a surface dS at a point P is then obtained from the dot product of f with the outward, normal unit vector n to dS at P; $f_n = f \cdot n$ is therefore the component of f in the direction of n as desired. Thus

$$\iint_{\bar{S}} f_n \, dS = \iint_S f \cdot n \, dS \tag{2.10}$$

and the Gauss theorem (Appendix 1) for transformation of a surface integral to a volume integral is, in this case,

$$\iint_{\bar{S}} f \cdot n \, dS = \iiint_V \operatorname{div} f \, dx \, dy \, dz \tag{2.11}$$

in which

$$\operatorname{div} f = \frac{\partial f_x}{\partial x} + \frac{\partial f_y}{\partial y} + \frac{\partial f_z}{\partial z} \tag{2.12}$$

Accordingly, combining (2.7) to (2.8) and (2.10) to (2.12) gives us

$$\iiint_V \left[\frac{\partial}{\partial t}(\rho c u) + \frac{\partial f_x}{\partial x} + \frac{\partial f_y}{\partial y} + \frac{\partial f_z}{\partial z} - A\right] dx \, dy \, dz = 0 \tag{2.13}$$

Because the control volume V is arbitrary, (2.13) must hold for all possible V. Hence application of the law of the mean [1] to the volume integral with a vanishingly small V shows that the integrand in (2.13) must be identically zero; that is,

$$\frac{\partial}{\partial t}(\rho c u) + \left(\frac{\partial f_x}{\partial x} + \frac{\partial f_y}{\partial y} + \frac{\partial f_z}{\partial z}\right) = A \tag{2.14}$$

provided only that the integrand is continuous, which is reasonable for the problem as formulated. Carslaw and Jaeger [2] point out that (2.14) is in fact valid even for inhomogeneous and nonisotropic solids.

When ρ and c are not functions of t, (2.14) reduces to

$$\rho c \frac{\partial u}{\partial t} + \left(\frac{\partial f_x}{\partial x} + \frac{\partial f_y}{\partial y} + \frac{\partial f_z}{\partial z}\right) = A \tag{2.15}$$

* A summary of vector relations is given in Appendix 1.

Then introduction of (2.2) into (2.15) produces

$$\rho c \frac{\partial u}{\partial t} = \frac{\partial}{\partial x}\left(K \frac{\partial u}{\partial x}\right) + \frac{\partial}{\partial y}\left(K \frac{\partial u}{\partial y}\right) + \frac{\partial}{\partial z}\left(K \frac{\partial u}{\partial z}\right) + A \tag{2.16}$$

When K and A are both functions of position only, this equation is linear, and some special cases have been solved in which K varied spatially. If K depends on temperature, (2.16) is nonlinear. When K depends on u alone, application of the chain rule of differentiation gives

$$\rho c \frac{\partial u}{\partial t} = K \nabla^2 u + A + \frac{\partial K}{\partial u}\left[\left(\frac{\partial u}{\partial x}\right)^2 + \left(\frac{\partial u}{\partial y}\right)^2 + \left(\frac{\partial u}{\partial z}\right)^2\right] \tag{2.17}$$

which shows the nonlinearity clearly [2]. The notation "nabla-squared" ∇^2 represents the Laplacian operator

$$\nabla^2 = \frac{\partial^2}{\partial x^2} + \frac{\partial^2}{\partial y^2} + \frac{\partial^2}{\partial z^2} \tag{2.18}$$

In many cases (when the temperature gradients are relatively small), K is approximately constant and (2.16) reduces, in the absence of sources, to

$$\frac{\partial u}{\partial t} = k \nabla^2 u \quad \text{or} \quad u_{xx} + u_{yy} + u_{zz} - \frac{1}{k}u_t = 0 \tag{2.19}$$

where

$$k = \frac{K}{\rho c}$$

is called the *thermal diffusivity.*.

Equation (2.19) is the heat equation for conduction in three space dimensions. It is a second-order, linear partial differential equation (recall that k is a constant and $A = 0$). Under conditions in which the temperature u in a solid varies only in the x direction and with time t, (2.19) becomes

$$u_{xx} - \frac{1}{k}u_t = 0 \tag{2.20}$$

The diffusion of sewage pollutants in lakes, streams, and oceans, as well as other diffusion problems, is also modeled by equations similar to (2.16) or (2.19). For diffusion processes, the conductivity K is replaced by a diffusion coefficient D that is determined experimentally. Diffusion problems are discussed in Chap. 8.

Determination of Auxiliary Conditions

An analysis of the physical system pictured in Fig. 2.1 has led to an equation for our mathematical model of heat conduction in a solid. The dependent, unspecified variable is u—the temperature distribution in the solid. Previous discussions suggest that auxiliary conditions are needed to complete the model. The derivation of the model equation shows two identifiable quantities in this problem: the temperature distribution u and the heat flux f. With this in mind, we again turn to the physical system and seek reasonable conditions that lead to a mathematical model with the unique solution we expect on the basis of experimental evidence.

Initial Condition. As a start, the temperature u throughout the body must be known at $t = 0$. We suppose that the initial temperature $u_0(x, y, z)$ is a continuous function and that the solution $u(x, y, z, t)$ is such that

$$\lim_{t \to 0} u = u_0 \tag{2.21}$$

or in more common notation

$$u(x, y, z, 0) = u_0(x, y, z) \tag{2.22}$$

at every point in the solid. Henceforth the notation of (2.22) is used for initial conditions, and *in this book a condition of the type* (2.22) *always implies that the limit in* (2.21) *exists*, as it must for any physically realistic problem. The flux can be calculated from (2.22), so no initial condition need be specified for f. Furthermore, it does not seem reasonable that we could specify the rate of change of temperature u_t at $t = 0$ because u_t is governed in the solid by (2.16) for example and therefore could not arbitrarily be given. Thus (2.22) is the only initial condition for this problem.

Boundary Conditions. A large number of conditions may exist at the boundaries of the solid. A detailed physical discussion is given in [2]. The conditions usually arising include

1. *Prescribed surface temperature:* If $\bar{S}$ is the surface of the solid in Fig. 2.1, the prescribed temperature would be

$$u(x, y, z, t) = T(x, y, z, t) \text{ on } \bar{S}, \qquad t > 0 \tag{2.23}$$

Equation (2.23) holds for $t > 0$ because it is possible that at $t = 0$ the initial state of the solid is not matched to its environment at the boundary—that is, possibly

$$u(x, y, z, 0) \neq T(x, y, z, 0) \text{ on } \bar{S}$$

Physically one can imagine this condition being generated by dropping a red-hot steel ball into ice water.

2. *Insulated surface:* If $\bar{S}$ is perfectly insulated, there can be no heat flux f through $\bar{S}$. Accordingly, from (2.1), since $K \neq 0$,

$$\frac{\partial u}{\partial n} = 0 \text{ on } \bar{S}, \qquad t > 0 \tag{2.24}$$

3. *Cooling by forced convection*—that is, by a draft: Suppose that a fluid at temperature u_S flows rapidly past the surface $\bar{S}$. Then experiments show that

$$K\frac{\partial u}{\partial n} + H(u - u_S) = 0 \text{ on } \bar{S}, \qquad t > 0 \tag{2.25}$$

is the boundary condition. Here H is a coefficient dependent on the fluid properties and velocity *and* on the shape of $\bar{S}$. Equation (2.25) is called Newton's law (of cooling) [2]. It describes a linear heat-transfer process at the surface in which flux is proportional to the temperature difference between the surface and the environment. The condition may arise physically in other ways (see the Problems). A highly nonlinear condition arises if radiation occurs from $\bar{S}$ to a medium of constant temperature u_S by the Stefan–Boltzmann law; then

$$K\frac{\partial u}{\partial n} = \alpha(u^4 - u_S^4)$$

Physical reasoning shows that only one of the foregoing boundary conditions can be enforced at any time on *a given region of the boundary*. For example, if $\bar{S}$ is insulated so that (2.24) holds, simultaneous convection cooling is not possible, for (2.25) requires, in general, that $u_n \neq 0$ in violation of (2.24). Consequently, the complete mathematical model for heat conduction in a solid is given by a *partial differential equation*, say (2.16), *one initial condition* (2.22), and any *one boundary condition* from among (2.23) to (2.25) or variants thereon. All the boundary conditions may apply in a single given problem, but each to a different part of $\bar{S}$. For example, for conduction in a long, thin, cylindrical steel bar, we may fix the temperature at the left end of the bar, insulate the longitudinal surface, and impose a convection condition at the right end.

It is important to look back now to see that in *this particular case* (heat conduction in a solid), very few restrictive assumptions were made. In fact, the entire derivation was built from the results of experiments and mathematical hypotheses drawn from these results. Consequently, it is expected (and true) that the mathematical model gives a highly accurate description of the behavior of the physical system. We discuss the mathematical adequacy of the model in Chap. 6.

2.2.2   Physical Problems Leading to the Wave Equation

Derivation of the Wave Equation and Auxiliary Conditions for a Membrane

Let us examine the physical process of the vibrations of a membrane—for example, a drumhead. The membrane is assumed to be a very thin, perfectly elastic film that is uniform or homogeneous; in other words, its mass per unit area ρ and thickness τ are constant throughout the film. In fact, the membrane is so thin that while it resists stretching (like rubber), it offers no resistance at all to bending (see Sec. 5.3, where bending resistance is considered).

The most obvious way to mount the membrane is to stretch it uniformly and tightly and then clamp it to a fixed boundary support, whose general form is given by the simple closed space curve $\bar{M}$ and whose trace in some (x, y) plane is $\bar{M}_T$. If $\bar{M}$ lies entirely in the (x, y) plane, no external forces are acting on the mounted membrane and it is at rest, then the membrane will be flat. Taking this to be the reference position, we describe transverse (to the plane) motions of the membrane by $z(x, y, t)$, where the z axis is perpendicular to the (x, y) plane.

For our purposes, it is convenient to imagine a more general mounting for the membrane in which the membrane boundary can move freely over a cylinder with base curve $\bar{M}_T$ and walls aligned with the z axis [3]. Then the membrane remains uniformly and tightly stretched, no resistance is offered to stretching, or distortion of the membrane tangent to (along) the boundary edge $\bar{M}$, and we shall later have the freedom of imposing the various boundary conditions that arose in the previous section.

The physical system is shown in Fig. 2.2. The situation may be summarized as follows:

1. Our idealized membrane of density ρ (mass per unit area) is, as a consequence of its lack of resistance to bending, perfectly flexible. Accordingly, the stress (force per unit length per unit thickness of membrane of thickness τ) across any line drawn in the membrane surface is a tension T, perpendicular to the line and tangent to the surface of the membrane.

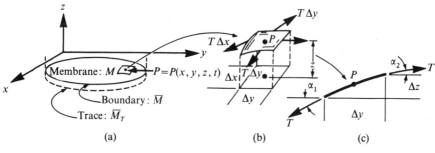

FIGURE 2.2

2. This tension T is independent of direction at any point in the membrane. This condition is a result of the assumed homogeneity of the membrane and the generalized boundary support prescribed above, for any unbalanced directional tension is relieved by a lateral readjustment of the membrane along the boundary.

3. The deflection $z(x, y, t)$ of the membrane is assumed to be such that the angles of inclination of the membrane surface at any point are small and the squares of the derivatives z_x, z_y, etc., can be neglected compared to unity. This is called the *small amplitude assumption*; it is widely used in vibration, water waves, and acoustic theories. Mathematically, the assumption helps us achieve a linear equation, but it also imposes strong restrictions on the range of motions that should be represented by our vibration model. Fortunately, in many applications, the results of small amplitude theories have been found to be useful even when the size of the disturbance is nowhere near small.

4. The lateral motion of membrane particles is negligibly small. In particular, if the particles move essentially only in the transverse direction, the membrane thickness τ does not change, so that there is no extension of the membrane during vibration. This is all true only to the extent that the small amplitude assumption holds.

A brief discussion of the preceding postulates is profitable. Consider the elemental side view (Fig. 2.2c). We consider $T(x, y - \Delta y/2)$ and $T(x, y + \Delta y/2)$ as representative of the tension forces per unit length acting on the elemental faces. In view of the postulates given, $T(x, y - \Delta y/2) \Delta x \cos \alpha_1$ and $T(x, y + \Delta y/2) \Delta x \cos \alpha_2$ are the only forces acting in the y direction on the element. Furthermore, since the element does not move in the y direction, application of the scalar form of Newton's Second Law (1.9) (extended in this case to elements of a continuous medium) to the y direction yields

$$T\left(x, y - \frac{\Delta y}{2}\right) \cos \alpha_1 = T\left(x, y + \frac{\Delta y}{2}\right) \cos \alpha_2 \tag{2.26}$$

Geometrically,

$$\cos \alpha_1 = \left.\frac{1}{\sqrt{1 + z_y^2}}\right|_{x, y - \Delta y/2} \qquad \cos \alpha_2 = \left.\frac{1}{\sqrt{1 + z_y^2}}\right|_{x, y + \Delta y/2}$$

After expanding the square roots by the binomial expansion [1] and neglecting terms of the order z_y^2 and higher in accordance with the small amplitude assumption, it follows first that, to the order of approximation used,

$$\cos \alpha_1 = 1 \qquad \cos \alpha_2 = 1$$

and second, from (2.26), that

$$T\left(x, y - \frac{\Delta y}{2}\right) = T\left(x, y + \frac{\Delta y}{2}\right) \tag{2.27}$$

A general development would show that (2.27) holds in any arbitrary direction throughout the membrane (recall that the directional orientation of the membrane on the (x, y) plane was arbitrary); thus, to the order of approximation used here,

$$T = \text{constant} \tag{2.28}$$

as a result of the small amplitude assumption. Similarly, the area of a displaced small element (such as shown in Fig. 2.2b) is

$$dA_d = \sqrt{1 + z_x^2} \sqrt{1 + z_y^2} \, dx \, dy \tag{2.29}$$

But clearly the result of expanding the square roots in (2.29) by the binomial expansion, neglecting terms of the order z_x^2, z_y^2, etc., in accordance with the small amplitude assumption, is

$$dA_d = dx \, dy$$

Therefore the original area

$$A_0 = \int_M dx \, dy$$

and the displaced membrane area

$$A_d = \int_M dA_d = \int_M dx \, dy$$

are equal; this result demonstrates the dependence of postulate d above on the small amplitude assumption.

Application to an element of the scalar form of Newton's Second Law (1.9) in the z direction leads now directly to the equation of the vibrations; the equation is formally

$$z_{tt} = \frac{F_z}{m} \tag{2.30}$$

where z_{tt} is the acceleration, F_z is the net force in the z direction, and m is the mass of the element under consideration, namely, the element in Fig. 2.2b. Its mass is $\rho \, \Delta x \, \Delta y$; from Fig. 2.2c, the vertical forces due to $T(x, y - \Delta y/2)$ and $T(x, y + \Delta y/2)$ are

$$-T\left(x, y - \frac{\Delta y}{2}\right) \Delta x \sin \alpha_1 \quad \text{and} \quad +T\left(x, y + \frac{\Delta y}{2}\right) \Delta x \sin \alpha_2$$

Since T is a constant and, to our order of approximation,

$$\sin \alpha_1 = z_y\left(x, y - \frac{\Delta y}{2}\right) \quad \text{and} \quad \sin \alpha_2 = z_y\left(x, y + \frac{\Delta y}{2}\right)$$

it follows that the sum of the forces due to $T(x, y - \Delta y/2)$ and $T(x, y + \Delta y/2)$ and, similarly, to $T(x - \Delta x/2, y)$ and $T(x + \Delta x/2, y)$—the tensions acting on all four faces—is

$$
\begin{aligned}
& -T\,\Delta x z_y\!\left(x, y - \frac{\Delta y}{2}\right) + T\,\Delta x z_y\!\left(x, y + \frac{\Delta y}{2}\right) \\
& -T\,\Delta y z_x\!\left(x - \frac{\Delta x}{2}, y\right) + T\,\Delta y z_x\!\left(x + \frac{\Delta x}{2}, y\right)
\end{aligned}
\tag{2.31}
$$

An additional force per unit mass $F(z, x, y, t)$, acting in the vertical direction on each unit mass in the membrane, can be included for generality; $F(z, x, y, t)$ can represent, for example, the effect of gravity ($F = -g$ if gravity acts in the negative z direction) or a variable pressure force (then $F = -p/\rho$, where p is a force per unit area).* Combining (2.30) and (2.31) and introducing $F(z, x, y, t)$ and $m = \rho\,\Delta x\,\Delta y$ give

$$
\begin{aligned}
\rho z_{tt} = T\bigg[& \frac{z_y(x, y + \Delta y/2) - z_y(x, y - \Delta y/2)}{\Delta y} \\
& + \frac{z_x(x + \Delta x/2, y) - z_x(x - \Delta x/2, y)}{\Delta x} \bigg] + \rho F
\end{aligned}
\tag{2.32}
$$

In the limit as $\Delta x \to 0$ and $\Delta y \to 0$, we obtain

$$
z_{tt} = \frac{T}{\rho}(z_{yy} + z_{xx}) + F(z, x, y, t)
\tag{2.33}
$$

Commonly, (2.33) is written

$$
z_{tt} - c^2(z_{xx} + z_{yy}) - F(z, x, y, t) = 0
\tag{2.34a}
$$

or

$$
z_{tt} = c^2 \nabla^2 z + F
\tag{2.34b}
$$

where $c^2 = T/\rho = $ constant and ∇^2 is the two-dimensional Laplacian [see (2.18)].

Equation (2.33) is called the *Wave Equation*. Here it is the equation for transverse vibrations of a uniform, flexible membrane under the small amplitude assumption. The equation is of second order and linear as long as F is not a nonlinear function of z or its derivatives. Interesting special cases and variations of the wave equation (2.33) will be discussed below, but we first turn to a discussion of auxiliary conditions appropriate to the vibration process.

Boundary Conditions. Recall that postulate 4 above requires that any membrane particle retain its original x–y coordinates at all times and move only in the z direction. It follows that the physical condition of the membrane at any time t can be described then in terms of the position z—the dependent variable of the problem—or perhaps in terms of the slope of the surface along any normal $z_n = \partial z/\partial n$. At the boundary of a finite-size membrane, the most obvious natural condition is a fixed boundary, such as for a drum. Thus the first natural boundary condition is

$$
z(x, y, t) = f(x, y) \text{ for } (x, y) \text{ on } \overline{M}_T, \qquad t > 0
\tag{2.35}
$$

* In fact, $F = -p\cos\alpha/\rho$, but $\cos\alpha = 1$ to the order of approximation used here.

where $f(x, y)$ is a prescribed function on $\overline{M}_T$. Variations of (2.35) would include

(a) Plane, fixed boundary:

$$z(x, y, t) = 0 \text{ for } (x, y) \text{ on } \overline{M} = \overline{M}_T, \qquad t > 0 \qquad (2.36)$$

(b) Boundary with a prescribed time-dependent motion q:

$$z(x, y, t) = q(x, y, t) \text{ for } (x, y) \text{ on } \overline{M}_T, \qquad t > 0 \qquad (2.37)$$

Other boundary conditions are found by examining the support mechanism at the edge of the membrane. A section along a plane normal to the boundary edge of a membrane is shown in Fig. 2.3. Here the support mechanism is represented by the forces F_n and F_z (per unit length along the boundary) in the outward normal and z directions, respectively, where n lies in the x–y plane. A summation of forces acting in the n direction shows, by virtue of postulate 4 regarding the fixed x–y location of $\overline{M}$ and the small amplitude assumption, that

$$F_n = T \cos \alpha_2$$

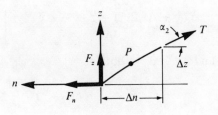

FIGURE 2.3

Then, if terms of the order of z_n^2 are neglected, $\cos \alpha_2 \approx 1$ and

$$F_n = T$$

as expected. Application of Newton's Second Law in the vertical direction gives, for a membrane slice of width Δd perpendicular to the (n, z) plane,

$$F_z \Delta d + T \sin \alpha_2 \Delta d = \rho \Delta n \Delta d z_{tt}(P) \qquad (2.38)$$

In this case, $\sin \alpha_2 = -\Delta z/\Delta n$ to our order of approximation. Accordingly, by dividing (2.38) by Δd and letting Δn approach 0, we find

$$F_z - T z_n = 0 \qquad (2.39)$$

The possible physical interpretations of (2.39) include

1. A free boundary support such that the membrane is constrained laterally but not vertically; then $F_z = 0$ so

$$z_n(x, y, t) = 0 \text{ for } (x, y) \text{ on } \overline{M}_T, \qquad t > 0 \qquad (2.40)$$

2. A constant or time-dependent force applied at the boundary; a specified function $h = h(x, y, t)$ is possible, so

$$z_n(x, y, t) = \frac{h}{T} \text{ for } (x, y) \text{ on } \overline{M}_T, \qquad t > 0 \qquad (2.41)$$

3. Attachment of the membrane at the boundary to a continuous linear spring such that $F_z = -kz$ (see Sec. 1.2); then from (2.39)

$$z_n(x, y, t) = -\frac{k}{T}z(x, y, t) \text{ for } (x, y) \text{ on } \overline{M}_T, \qquad t > 0 \qquad (2.42)$$

As in the case of heat-conduction boundary conditions, physical reasoning quickly establishes that only one of the preceding boundary conditions can be enforced at any time on a given region of the boundary. On the other hand, at least one condition is always required.

Initial Conditions. Without question, the initial position of the membrane must be known at $t = 0$. Physically, the initial position $z_0(x, y)$ must be a continuous function; this initial condition can be written

$$z(x, y, 0) = z_0(x, y) \text{ for } (x, y) \text{ in } M \text{ and on } \overline{M}_T \qquad (2.43)$$

that is, at every point on the membrane. Note that in this derivation for a membrane, as in the heat conduction case, we have allowed for possible mismatches between initial and boundary conditions at $t = 0$ by requiring the latter to hold only for $t > 0$.

The question now arises, "Is another initial condition appropriate for the vibration problem?" From the discussion of Sec. 1.2, experience with second-order ordinary differential equations, and physical intuition, the answer is *yes*. First, second-order equations usually require two appropriate conditions. Second, the development of a vibration depends crucially on the initial velocity of the vibrating body. In particular, if $z_0 = 0$ and the membrane has no initial velocity, then no vibration can occur unless some external forces act. On the contrary, an initial velocity clearly would initiate motion of the membrane even in the absence of an initial displacement. Consequently, a second initial condition is required. We specify the rate of change of membrane position with time; that is,

$$z_t(x, y, 0) = V_0(x, y) \text{ for } (x, y) \text{ in } M \text{ and on } \overline{M}_T \qquad (2.44)$$

where the vertical velocity V_0 must be a continuous function on physical grounds.

In summary, the physical process of small, transverse vibrations of a membrane is described by a mathematical model composed of a *partial differential equation*, say (2.33) in general, *two initial conditions* (2.43) and (2.44), and any *one boundary condition* at each point of the boundary from among (2.35) to (2.42). A review of the derivation of the vibration model shows that the derivation rests on a generalization of Newton's Second Law, a mathematical expression derived from experimental results, and several very restrictive assumptions or idealizations. This is in contrast to the case of heat conduction, in which few restrictive assumptions were made. Here, however, the small amplitude assumption was used; it severely restricts the size of motions that the model can describe. Also, the membrane was assumed to offer no resistance to bending; this is a rather severe idealization. When bending resistance is present, a fourth-order partial differential equation is obtained (see Sec. 5.3). Because of the restrictions implicit in the construction of the mathematical model, its description of the behavior of any real membrane (as opposed to the simplified one prescribed) may be inaccurate. In Chap. 6 the mathematical adequacy of the model is discussed.

Additional Considerations

The wave equation, as typified by (2.33), is of great importance in the mathematical models of a large and varied number of physical systems. In the problems and the applications of later chapters, wave equations will be seen to be part of the model for such cases as the flow of electricity in wires, longitudinal waves in bars, tidal waves, sound waves, and electric field waves in a wave guide. In this section we examine first a simplification of the wave equation (2.33) to its two-dimensional form (one space and one time dimension as independent variables) and second a coordinate transformation useful in problems involving some circular symmetry.

One of the most interesting mathematical models in partial differential equation theory is that for the vibration of a string. The physical system is simple, yet all the important characteristics of wave equations are retained. The derivation of an equation and auxiliary conditions for the transverse vibration of a string exactly parallels that of the membrane. In fact, we need not repeat the derivation, since it suffices to point out the few differences and then summarize the new results.

The idealized vibrating string is uniform in composition, perfectly elastic, and lies along the y axis. It offers no resistance to bending. The vibrations must be such that the slope of the string is small, and they must occur only in the (z, y) plane. The density *per unit length* of the string is ρ, while tension T is now defined as the *total* force acting in the string. All the postulates and arguments given for the membrane hold except those related to adjustments at the boundary. They are not applicable now because, for the string, the tension cannot possibly have a direction outside the (z, y) plane.

From (2.28), we deduce that the tension T in the string is constant. Application of Newton's law (2.30) to an element of string gives, approximately,

$$z_{tt} = \frac{T(y + \Delta y/2) \sin \alpha_2 - T(y - \Delta y/2) \sin \alpha_1}{\rho \, \Delta y} + F(z, y, t) \tag{2.45}$$

where $F(z, y, t)$ is again a general force per unit mass acting in the z direction on the string. As in the case of the membrane, according to the small amplitude assumption,

$$\sin \alpha_1 = z_y\left(y - \frac{\Delta y}{2}\right) \quad \text{and} \quad \sin \alpha_2 = z_y\left(y + \frac{\Delta y}{2}\right)$$

Thus in the limit as $\Delta y \to 0$, (2.45) becomes, exactly,

$$z_{tt} = \frac{1}{\rho}(Tz_y)_y + F(z, y, t) \tag{2.46}$$

If $c^2 = T/\rho = \text{constant}$, (2.46) becomes

$$z_{tt} = c^2 z_{yy} + F(z, y, t) \tag{2.47}$$

Equation (2.47) is another wave equation [see (2.33)] and the equation for the small transverse vibrations of a string.

The natural boundary conditions for a string of length l, lying between 0 and l along the y axis, are obtained directly from simplification of (2.37) and (2.39). Thus

(a) for a fully constrained end,

$$z(0, t) = g_0(t) \quad \text{or} \quad z(l, t) = g_l(t), \qquad t > 0 \tag{2.48}$$

(b) for a laterally constrained end,

$$z_y = \frac{F_z}{T} \quad \text{at either } y = 0 \quad \text{or} \quad l, \qquad t > 0 \tag{2.49}$$

Appropriate variations on (2.48) and (2.49) parallel (2.35), (2.36), and (2.40) to (2.42).

Physical reasoning for the string is the same as that for the membrane with regard to initial conditions. Therefore, for a string between 0 and l, the *two* appropriate initial conditions are

$$z(y, 0) = z_0(y) \qquad 0 \leq y \leq l \tag{2.50}$$

and

$$z_t(y, 0) = V_0(y) \qquad 0 \leq y \leq l \tag{2.51}$$

Thus the physical process of small transverse vibrations of a string is described by a mathematical model composed of (2.47), (2.50), and (2.51), and any *one* of the boundary conditions (2.48) or (2.49) imposed at each end of the string. The limitations of the membrane model are inherent in the string model, too.

In (2.19) and (2.34b), the Laplacian operator ∇^2 arose. In problems with circular or spherical symmetry, the (x, y) or (x, y, z) coordinates used earlier in ∇^2 are not convenient. It is better if polar, cylindrical, or spherical coordinates are used. This may be accomplished in two ways. First, the proper coordinate system may be used in the derivation of the equations and auxiliary conditions (see, e.g., the Problems). Second, a change of variables can be introduced into the final results—that is, into (2.19) or (2.34b). Here we consider, as an example of the second method, the use of polar coordinates for a vibrating circular membrane; other examples are the subject of Problems at the end of the chapter.

The transverse vibrations of a circular membrane are modeled by the differential equation (2.34b), by the boundary conditions (2.37) or (2.39) as appropriate, and by the initial conditions (2.43) and (2.44). For a circular membrane, the x–y coordinates are replaced by r–θ coordinates, defined by

$$x = r \cos \theta \quad \text{and} \quad y = r \sin \theta \tag{2.52a}$$

where

$$\theta = \tan^{-1} \frac{y}{x} \qquad r = (x^2 + y^2)^{1/2} \tag{2.52b}$$

A circular membrane of radius R then lies in the region $[0 \leq r \leq R, 0 < \theta \leq 2\pi]$ as shown in Fig. 2.4.

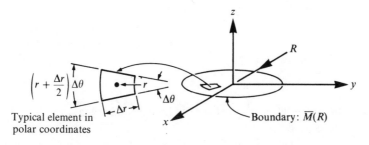

FIGURE 2.4   A circular membrane; polar coordinates.

The initial and boundary conditions for a circular membrane are easily converted to polar coordinates. Equations (2.43) and (2.44) become

$$z(r, \theta, 0) = z_0(r, \theta), \qquad 0 \le r < R, \;\; 0 < \theta \le 2\pi \tag{2.53}$$

and

$$z_t(r, \theta, 0) = V_0(r, \theta), \qquad 0 \le r < R, \;\; 0 < \theta \le 2\pi \tag{2.54}$$

Equation (2.37) becomes

$$z(R, \theta, t) = f(\theta, t), \qquad t > 0 \tag{2.55}$$

and (2.39) becomes

$$z_n(R, \theta, t) = \frac{F_z(z, \theta, t)}{T}, \qquad t > 0 \tag{2.56}$$

since $\partial/\partial n = \partial/\partial r$ at $r = R$.

In (2.34b), $\nabla^2 z = z_{xx} + z_{yy}$, and it is necessary to find $z_{xx} = f(r, \theta)$ and $z_{yy} = g(r, \theta)$. According to (2.52) and the chain rule of differentiation,

$$\frac{\partial z}{\partial x} = \frac{\partial z}{\partial r}\frac{\partial r}{\partial x} + \frac{\partial z}{\partial \theta}\frac{\partial \theta}{\partial x}$$

$$= \frac{\partial z}{\partial r}\frac{x}{(x^2 + y^2)^{1/2}} + \frac{\partial z}{\partial \theta}\frac{-y}{(x^2 + y^2)}$$

$$= z_r\left(\frac{x}{r}\right) - z_\theta\left(\frac{y}{r^2}\right) \tag{2.57}$$

Now, from (2.57),

$$z_{xx} = \left(z_r\frac{x}{r}\right)_r\frac{\partial r}{\partial x} + \left(z_r\frac{x}{r}\right)_\theta\frac{\partial \theta}{\partial x}$$

$$- \left(z_\theta\frac{y}{r^2}\right)_\theta\frac{\partial \theta}{\partial x} - \left(z_\theta\frac{y}{r^2}\right)_r\frac{\partial r}{\partial x} \tag{2.58}$$

Performing all the indicated operations in (2.58) and using the chain rule give

$$z_{xx} = \frac{y^2}{r^3}z_r + \frac{2xy}{r^4}z_\theta + \frac{x^2}{r^2}z_{rr} - \frac{2xy}{r^3}z_{r\theta} + \frac{y^2}{r^4}z_{\theta\theta} \tag{2.59}$$

Similarly,

$$z_{yy} = \frac{x^2}{r^3}z_r - \frac{2xy}{r^4}z_\theta + \frac{y^2}{r^2}z_{rr} + \frac{2xy}{r^3}z_{r\theta} + \frac{x^2}{r^4}z_{\theta\theta} \tag{2.60}$$

Accordingly, since $x^2 + y^2 = r^2$, the sum of (2.59) and (2.60) is

$$z_{xx} + z_{yy} = \nabla^2 z = z_{rr} + \frac{1}{r}z_r + \frac{1}{r^2}z_{\theta\theta} \tag{2.61}$$

Finally, Eq. (2.34b) can be written according to (2.61) in terms of the independent variables (r, θ, t):

$$z_{tt} = c^2\left(z_{rr} + \frac{1}{r}z_r + \frac{1}{r^2}z_{\theta\theta}\right) + F(z, r, \theta, t) \qquad (2.62)$$

If the vibrations of the membrane are symmetric about the origin—that is, z is independent of θ, then z_θ and $z_{\theta\theta}$ are zero. Equation (2.62) becomes

$$z_{tt} = c^2\left(z_{rr} + \frac{1}{r}z_r\right) + F(z, r, t), \qquad 0 < r < R, \quad 0 < t$$

But this equation and (2.62) are singular at the origin $r = 0$ and thus do not model the vibration phenomenon there. It is sufficient on physical grounds to apply these equations only for $r > 0$ and to insist that z be bounded and continuous at $r = 0$. However, in order to find an explicit expression at $r = 0$ in the case of no θ dependence, we expand the term in parenthesis above in a Taylor series (Appendix 1); that is,

$$\left(z_{rr} + \frac{1}{r}z_r\right) = z_{rr}(r, t) + \frac{1}{r}[z_r(0, t) + z_{rr}(0, t)r + O(r^2)]$$

Since the singularity arises from the coordinate system and not the physics of the membrane, we must have

$$\lim_{r \to 0}\left(z_{rr} + \frac{1}{r}z_r\right) < \infty$$

that is, there is no infinite acceleration at the origin. Therefore it follows that

$$z_r(0, t) = 0$$

and

$$\lim_{r \to 0}\left(z_{rr} + \frac{1}{r}z_r\right) = 2z_{rr}(0, t)$$

whence

$$z_{tt}(0, t) = 2c^2 z_{rr}(0, t) + F(z, 0, t)$$

Now we can complete the mathematical model for the case in which z is independent of θ:

$$z_{tt} = c^2\left(z_{rr} + \frac{1}{r}z_r\right) + F(z, r, t), \qquad 0 < r < R, \quad 0 < t \qquad (2.63a)$$

$$z(R, t) = f(t), \qquad t > 0$$

or

$$z_r(R, t) = \frac{F_z(z, t)}{T}, \qquad t > 0 \qquad (2.63b)$$

and

$$z_r(0, t) = 0, \qquad t > 0$$

$$z(r, 0) = z_0(r), \qquad 0 \le r \le R \qquad (2.63c)$$

$$z_t(r, 0) = V_0(r), \qquad 0 \le r \le R \qquad (2.63d)$$

2.2.3   Physical Problems Leading to the Laplace and Poisson Equations

The Equations and Some Auxiliary Conditions of Hydrodynamics

A fluid is a coherent material that offers little resistance to change of shape (or shearing). *Fluid mechanics*, which is the study of the statics and dynamics of fluids, is an essential part of such fields as oceanography, meteorology, and aeronautics.

In the majority of flow problems, it is not possible to obtain both a precise formulation and an exact solution by use of a mathematical model; simplifications are necessary. Two assumptions are particularly common; they lead to the definition of the ideal fluid and the methods of hydrodynamics that are concerned with the application of the fundamental physical laws to the ideal fluid.

The *ideal fluid* is assumed to be both inviscid and incompressible. Thus although all real fluids experience small shearing forces or internal friction when undergoing deformation—that is, are viscous—the ideal fluid does not. Similarly, although gases are usually considered compressible—that is, their density is a function of pressure—the ideal fluid is not compressible. To a good approximation, air and water are ideal fluids in many applications. Where viscous effects and compressibility are important, other methods and approximations are needed [4].

The essential physical laws for ideal fluid flow analyses are the *conservation of mass* and *conservation of momentum laws*. The Eulerian system of hydrodynamics, in which the fluid motion is described by the velocity field in the fluid region at each instant of time, is adopted. We also assume that our ideal fluid has a uniform, constant density. The flow at any point is described in terms of the fluid pressure p, the fluid density ρ, and the fluid velocity components u, v, w in the (x, y, z) coordinate directions, respectively. The equations of motion are derived in a manner analogous to that previously outlined for heat (Sec. 2.2.1). For example, because the fluid is incompressible and has a constant density, the net mass of fluid passing in and out of a control volume is constant—that is, mass is conserved. A similar conservation law applies for the linear momentum of the fluid [4, 5]. The equations obtained from a derivation based on these two conservation laws are a set of coupled, nonlinear partial differential equations. For example, in two dimensions, the conservation of mass leads to

$$u_x + v_y = 0 \tag{2.64}$$

while

$$u_t + uu_x + vu_y = -\frac{1}{\rho}p_x \tag{2.65}$$

and

$$v_t + uv_x + vv_y = -\frac{1}{\rho}p_y - g \tag{2.66}$$

(where g is the acceleration due to gravity acting in the negative y direction) arise from conservation of the x and y components of momentum. The solution of this formidable equation set, called the continuity equation and Euler's equations of motion, respectively, is difficult.

In the particular case of ideal fluid motions starting from rest under the action of pressure forces or moving boundaries, the fluid velocities can be expressed in terms of the continuous partial derivatives of a scalar function ϕ. Thus, in two dimensions, $\phi = \phi(x, y, t)$ and

$$
\begin{aligned}
u &= \phi_x \\
v &= \phi_y
\end{aligned}
\tag{2.67}
$$

The function ϕ is called the *velocity potential* in analogy with the scalar potentials of electric and magnetic fields whose derivatives describe force fields. A flow is termed *irrotational* if a velocity potential exists [4, 5]; there are wide applications for this concept.

Now, (2.64) to (2.66) are considerably simplified. The first equation becomes

$$
\phi_{xx} + \phi_{yy} = 0
\tag{2.68}
$$

upon introduction of ϕ. This is the two-dimensional *Laplace Equation*, which we may write

$$
\nabla^2 \phi = 0
\tag{2.69}
$$

This equation is linear. Interestingly, the remaining equations (2.65) and (2.66) can be integrated if first we introduce ϕ into the time-derivative terms and use the relation $u_y = v_x$ that follows from (2.67). Then

$$
\phi_{xt} + uu_x + vv_x = -\frac{1}{\rho}p_x
$$

$$
\phi_{yt} + uu_y + vv_y = -\frac{1}{\rho}p_y - g
$$

whence integration of the first with respect to x and the second with respect to y gives

$$
\begin{aligned}
\phi_t + \frac{1}{2}(u^2 + v^2) + \frac{p}{\rho} &= F_1(y, t) \\
\phi_t + \frac{1}{2}(u^2 + v^2) + \frac{p}{\rho} + gy &= F_2(x, t)
\end{aligned}
\tag{2.70}
$$

in which F_1 and F_2 are arbitrary. From (2.70), it follows that $F_1(y, t) + gy = F_2(x, t)$. If this equality is to hold for all x and y, then $F_1 + gy$ cannot be a function of y, while F_2 cannot be a function of x. Accordingly, $F_1 + gy = F_2 = G(t)$ alone. This arbitrary function of t may be absorbed into ϕ without disturbing (2.67); thus the single equation

$$
\phi_t + \frac{1}{2}(u^2 + v^2) + gy + \frac{p}{\rho} = 0
\tag{2.71}
$$

known as the Bernoulli equation, replaces the Euler equations of motion (2.65) and (2.66). If ϕ is known as the solution to (2.69), p can be found directly from (2.71).

The equation describing two-dimensional, irrotational flow of an ideal fluid is the Laplace equation (2.69) when the flow is described by a velocity potential $\phi(x, y, t)$. The other unknown in the problem is the pressure p, which is known as a function of ϕ and the independent variables via (2.71).

Only a brief discussion of auxiliary conditions for fluid flows can be given here. An obvious natural boundary condition is that the velocity of fluid normal to a fixed surface must vanish—that is,

$$\phi_n = 0 \tag{2.72}$$

along a fixed, solid boundary. There is no similar restriction on the flow *along* the boundary; the frictionless fluid slips without restraint over the boundary. On the contrary, experiments show that the velocity of *real* fluids relative to a wall is always zero; in other words, both the normal and tangential velocities vanish. This no-slip condition represents an essential difference between real and ideal flows [5].

Suppose that the fluid is bounded on one side by a free surface—that is, by another fluid of negligible density which is at rest (say the interface between water and air). The fluid velocity normal to the surface must be zero, but now the surface location is unknown and may be moving. Furthermore, at the interface the pressure in the air is known (usually constant) so that (2.71) must be satisfied and it is nonlinear!

Since a further coherent, general discussion of appropriate auxiliary conditions is beyond the scope of this book, we shall later treat certain special problems and develop mathematical models on an individual basis.

Other Physical Systems

There are other physical systems whose mathematical models are based on Laplace or Poisson equations and for which we already have suitable background.

Suppose that we examine the steady-state conduction of heat—the case where at any point in the solid none of the properties of the system changes with time. Then, in particular,

$$u = u(x, y, z)$$

and

$$A = A(x, y, z, u)$$

alone, and (2.16) becomes

$$\frac{\partial}{\partial x}\left(K\frac{\partial u}{\partial x}\right) + \frac{\partial}{\partial y}\left(K\frac{\partial u}{\partial y}\right) + \frac{\partial}{\partial z}\left(K\frac{\partial u}{\partial z}\right) + A = 0 \tag{2.73}$$

When K is constant, (2.73) can be written

$$u_{xx} + u_{yy} + u_{zz} = -\frac{A}{K} \tag{2.74}$$

or

$$\nabla^2 u = -\frac{A}{K} \tag{2.75}$$

Equations (2.74) or (2.75) are called *Poisson Equations*. When $A \equiv 0$, they become the Laplace equation

$$\nabla^2 u = 0 \tag{2.76a}$$

The conduction of heat in a thin, flat plate with insulated top and bottom surfaces can be described by

$$u_{xx} + u_{yy} = -\frac{A}{K} \tag{2.76b}$$

since no fluxes occur in the z direction.

All the boundary conditions previously derived for heat conduction remain valid, except that they are no longer functions of time. An initial condition is no longer appropriate. The complete mathematical model for steady-state heat conduction in a solid is given by *a partial differential equation*, say (2.75), and any *one boundary condition* on each segment of the solid's surface.

Next consider the time-independent state of the thin, flexible membrane examined above. From (2.34b), we have

$$\nabla^2 z = -\frac{F}{c^2} \tag{2.77}$$

where $F = F(x, y)$; (2.77) is a Poisson-type equation. As in the heat conduction case, the initial conditions are no longer applicable, but the boundary conditions derived above are still appropriate if they are time independent.

Equation (2.47) reduces to a particularly interesting result when $z_{tt} = 0$ and $F = -g$. Then we have the case of a string under the influence of gravity alone; that is,

$$z_{yy} = \frac{\rho g}{T} \tag{2.78}$$

If we take the fixed-end boundary conditions (2.48) and set $g_0 = g_l = 0$,

$$z(0) = z(l) = 0 \tag{2.79}$$

Now (2.78) can be integrated to give

$$z = \frac{\rho g y^2}{2T} + c_1 y + c_2 \tag{2.80}$$

Using (2.79) shows that

$$0 = c_2$$

and

$$0 = \frac{\rho g l^2}{2T} + c_1 l$$

Thus

$$c_1 = -\frac{\rho g l}{2T}$$

and the solution for the shape of the string is

$$z = \frac{\rho g}{2T}(y^2 - ly)$$

or

$$z = \frac{\rho g l}{2T} y \left(\frac{y}{l} - 1 \right) \tag{2.81}$$

2.3   THE COMPLETE MATHEMATICAL MODEL

Earlier we found the equations and auxiliary conditions that arise naturally in physical problems. Now we focus attention on three simple cases and formulate for each a mathematical model that appears to be complete on physical grounds. Chapters 3 through 5 are concerned with methods for finding solutions to these models. Then, in Chap. 6, our discussion of the qualitative questions of existence, uniqueness, and continuity will produce the necessary mathematical evidence that the models given here, as well as many others, are in fact well posed.

First, consider heat conduction in a long, thin, cylindrical bar (Fig. 2.5a) made from a material whose thermal diffusivity k is a constant. The bar has a length l_1 and its surface is insulated. The bar ends are subjected to appropriate boundary conditions. The x axis lies along the bar. In this case, $f_y = f_z = 0$ at the surface of the bar because of the insulation. When uniform conditions (in y, z) are applied across the ends of the bar (at $x = 0$ and l_1), no transverse gradients exist in any cross section $x = $ constant; hence $f_y = f_z = 0$ everywhere in the bar. Equation (2.20) is appropriate for this heat flow when no heat sources are present in the bar. Possible complete models are summarized in Table 2.1 (page 34).

Second, consider steady-state heat conduction in a thin, rectangular plate (Fig. 2.5b). Assume that K is constant in the plate, whose dimensions are (l_1, l_2, Δ). The top and bottom surfaces (the planes $z = 0$ and $z = \Delta$) are insulated, while each

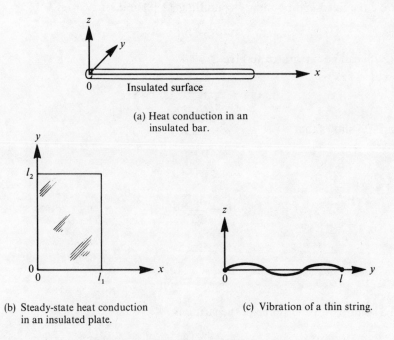

(a) Heat conduction in an
insulated bar.

(b) Steady-state heat conduction
in an insulated plate.

(c) Vibration of a thin string.

FIGURE 2.5   Simple physical problems.

of the four edges is subjected to a natural boundary condition. The appropriate equation is (2.76) with $A = 0$ when no sources are present in the plate. Complete models for this case are summarized in Table 2.1.

Finally, consider the vibrations of a uniform, thin string (Fig. 2.5c). The string is as described in Sec. 2.2.2 above. The assumptions of small amplitude theory are invoked to give (2.47) as the equation for the complete models summarized in Table 2.1; there $F(y, t) = 0$.

Table 2.1 illustrates simple versions of mathematical models we have derived from physical reasoning and laws. Each model has a second-order, linear partial differential equation. In each case, one boundary condition is required physically at each natural boundary of the system. For the heat conduction cases, the problems have been simplified by imposing the zero-heat-flux condition over a large part of the boundary—that is, by insulating the lateral boundary and letting the ends or edges be governed by other physical conditions. The models involving time t have an open-ended domain $0 < t$ in contrast to the finite region usually associated with problems purely in the space domain. This leads to the requirement for two initial conditions (specified at $t = 0$) for the wave equation problem, since it is physically unreasonable to prescribe the system state at a future time. A problem whose partial differential equation is second order in t and that has two initial conditions specified at $t = 0$ is called a Cauchy-type problem.

From Table 2.1 it is clear that certain types of boundary conditions appear and are appropriate in all the models. These common conditions are classified as boundary conditions of

1. the first type, or the *Dirichlet* condition: the dependent variable is prescribed along the boundary.

2. the second type, or the *Neumann* condition: the normal derivative of the dependent variable is prescribed along the boundary.

3. the third type: a relation between the dependent variable and its normal derivative is prescribed along the boundary.

These classes correspond to the groups in Table 2.1. The third type incorporates the first two, since they are recovered, for example, in the limit as either $H \to 0$ or $K \to 0$ in the Group 3 condition for the Laplace problem in Table 2.1. As an idealization, it is also possible to consider infinite space domains for physical problems. This moves the applicable boundary conditions to infinity (note the contrast with the infinite t-domain specification), where they then may not actually influence the solution if attention is being focused at or near a particular finite point in the space domain.

Finally, Table 2.1 suggests, as does [6], that pure boundary-value problems are usually associated with the Laplace (and Poisson) equation. On the other hand, initial-boundary-value problems arise in connection with the wave and heat equations.

2.4 LINEARITY AND SUPERPOSITION

We denote by L the partial differential operator whose general second-order form derives from (1.8) when $\alpha_7(x, y) \equiv 0$; that is,

$$L[u] = \alpha_1 u_{xx} + \alpha_2 u_{xy} + \alpha_3 u_{yy} + \alpha_4 u_x + \alpha_5 u_y + \alpha_6 u \qquad (2.82)$$

TABLE 2.1 Typical Initial-Boundary-Value Problems in Rectangular Regions

Equation Form		Laplace	Wave	Heat
Physical system		Steady-state heat conduction in a thin plate, no sources	Small transverse vibrations of a uniform string	Heat conduction in a thin round bar, no sources
Independent variables		x, y	y, t	x, t
Dependent variable		$u = u(x, y) = $ temperature	$z = z(y, t) = $ displacement	$u = u(x, t) = $ temperature
Domain of independent variables		$0 \leq x \leq l_1,\quad 0 \leq y \leq l_2$	$0 \leq y \leq l_2,\quad 0 \leq t$	$0 \leq x \leq l_1,\quad 0 \leq t$
Governing equation		$u_{xx} + u_{yy} = 0$	$c^2 z_{yy} - z_{tt} = 0 \qquad c^2 = \dfrac{T}{\rho}$	$k u_{xx} - u_t = 0 \qquad k = \dfrac{K}{\rho c}$
Boundary conditions	Group 1	$u(x, 0) = T_1(x), \quad 0 < x < l_1$ $u(x, l_2) = T_2(x), \quad 0 < x < l_1$ $u(0, y) = T_3(y), \quad 0 < y < l_2$ $u(l_1, y) = T_4(y), \quad 0 < y < l_2$	$z(0, t) = f_1(t).$ $z(l_2, t) = f_2(t),$	$u(0, t) = T_1(t),\quad 0 < t$ $u(l_1, t) = T_2(t),$
Possible types:	Group 2*	$u_y(x, y_i) = f_{11}(x)$ $u_x(x_j, y) = f_2 f(y)$	$z_y(y_i, t) = S_i(t)$	$u_x(x_j, t) = f_j(t)$
	Group 3*	$K u_y(x, y_i) + H[u(x, y_i) - u_s] = 0$ $K u_x(x_j, y) + H[u(x_j, y) - u_s] = 0$	$z_y(y_i, t) = \dfrac{F_z(z, t)}{T}$	$K u_x(x_j, t) + H[u(x_j, t) - u_s(t)] = 0$
Initial conditions	Number required	None; this is a pure boundary-value problem	2	1
	Types	Not applicable	$z(y, 0) = z_0(y), \quad 0 \leq y \leq l_2$ $z_t(y, 0) = V_0(y), \quad 0 \leq y \leq l_2$	$u(x, 0) = T_0(x), \quad 0 \leq x \leq l_1$

* May replace Group 1 on one-for-one basis with $x_j = 0$ or l_1 and $y_i = 0$ or l_2.

34

and $\alpha_i = \alpha_i(x, y)$ as before. The operator L carries out a transformation process on the designated dependent variable. When the α_i are continuous, $L[u_i]$ in (2.82) defines a transformation of the set of functions $\{u_i\}$ with two continuous derivatives with respect to (x, y) into the set of continuous functions $\{L[u_i]\}$. For example, if

$$L = \frac{\partial^2}{\partial x^2} - \frac{1}{k}\frac{\partial}{\partial t} \tag{2.83}$$

then

$$L[u] = 0$$

is a partial differential equation with dependent variable u and is an alternative way of writing (2.20). Furthermore, if

$$B[\ ] = [\ ]_x|_{0,t} = \frac{\partial}{\partial x}(0, t)$$

then

$$B[u] = u_x(0, t) = g(t) \tag{2.84}$$

is one of the boundary conditions for heat conduction in an insulated rod (see Table 2.1).

An operator L having the property that

$$L[c_1 u_1 + c_2 u_2] = c_1 L[u_1] + c_2 L[u_2]$$

for two functions u_1 and u_2 in a specified set of functions and constants c_1 and c_2, is called a *linear operator* on the specified set of functions.

EXAMPLE 2.1   Show that $L = \partial^2/\partial x^2 + \partial^2/\partial y^2$ is a linear operator on the set of functions $\{u_i\}$ with two continuous derivatives with respect to (x, y).

$$L[c_1 u_1 + c_2 u_2] = (c_1 u_1 + c_2 u_2)_{xx} + (c_1 u_1 + c_2 u_2)_{yy}$$
$$= c_1 u_{1xx} + c_2 u_{2xx} + c_1 u_{1yy} + c_2 u_{2yy}$$
$$= c_1(u_{1xx} + u_{1yy}) + c_2(u_{2xx} + u_{2yy})$$
$$= c_1 L[u_1] + c_2 L[u_2] \qquad \text{Q.E.D.}$$

EXAMPLE 2.2   Show that $N = (\partial^2/\partial x^2)^2$ is not a linear operator with respect to $\{u_i\}$.

$$N[c_1 u_1 + c_2 u_2] = [(c_1 u_1 + c_2 u_2)_{xx}]^2$$
$$= c_1^2 u_{1xx}^2 + 2c_1 c_2 u_{1xx} u_{2xx} + c_2^2 u_{2xx}^2$$
$$\neq c_1 N[u_1] + c_2 N[u_2] \qquad \text{Q.E.D.}$$

EXAMPLE 2.3   Show that $N = \log(\ )$ is nonlinear, also. Clearly,

$$\log(c_1 u_1 + c_2 u_2) \neq c_1 \log u_1 + c_2 \log u_2$$

because

$$\log\left[(u_1)^{c_1}(u_2)^{c_2}\right] = c_1 \log u_1 + c_2 \log u_2 \qquad \text{Q.E.D.}$$

Other operators are examined in the exercises; however, it should be clear that the operator L, defined in (2.82), is in fact a general *linear partial differential operator* on the set of functions with two continuous derivatives with respect to (x, y). Thus (1.8), written as $L[u] = -\alpha_7$ (α_7 is a given function of the independent variables), is a *linear partial differential equation*. If $\alpha_7 \equiv 0$, $L[u] = 0$ is a *homogeneous* equation and $u \equiv 0$ is a solution to homogeneous equations. When $\alpha_7 \not\equiv 0$, the equation $L[u] = f$ is termed *inhomogeneous*. In retrospect, the requirements that (a) the terms of (1.8) be algebraically linear in the dependent variable and its derivatives and (b) the coefficients of these terms be functions only of the independent variables are seen to be sufficient to ensure that (1.8) is linear. Many of the equations derived earlier in this chapter are linear in their important applications. As a result, it is important to know the properties of linear expressions and the complexities introduced by nonlinearities.

If $\tilde{u}$ is a solution of the homogeneous, linear equation $L[u] = 0$ so that, in particular, $L[\tilde{u}] = 0$, then, for the constant c,

$$L[c\tilde{u}] = cL[\tilde{u}] = 0$$

Thus, as $\tilde{u}$ is a solution, $c\tilde{u}$ is also a solution. In addition, if L is a linear operator on the set of functions $\{u_i\}$ and $\{c_i\}$ are a set of constants, then

$$L[c_1 u_1 + c_2 u_2] = c_1 L[u_1] + c_2 L[u_2]$$

and

$$L[c_1 u_1 + c_2 u_2 + c_3 u_3] = L[c_1 u_1 + c_2 u_2] + c_3 L[u_3]$$
$$= c_1 L[u_1] + c_2 L[u_2] + c_3 L[u_3]$$

Now, by induction, the *Principle of Superposition* follows: If $f_1, f_2, \ldots, f_N$ are N functions of the independent variables, $c_1, c_2, \ldots, c_N$ are N constants, L is a linear operator, and $u_1, u_2, \ldots, u_N$ are N solutions to

$$L[u_i] = f_i, \qquad i = 1, 2, \ldots, N$$

then

$$u = \sum_{i=1}^{N} c_i u_i$$

is a solution of

$$L[u] = \sum_{i=1}^{N} c_i f_i \qquad (2.85)$$

This statement of the principle can be verified by direct substitution. Under appropriate circumstances for the convergence of series, we can let $N \to \infty$ in the preceding equation. Two valuable corollaries can be drawn from (2.85).

First Corollary: If $u_1, u_2, \ldots, u_N$ are solutions of $L[u_i] = 0$, then

$$u = \sum_{i=1}^{N} c_i u_i$$

is also a solution of $L[u] = 0$ for *any* c_i.

Second Corollary: If v is a solution of $L[v] = f$ *and* u is a solution of $L[u] = 0$, then

$$w = u + v$$

is a solution of $L[w] = f$.

Under the proper conditions (convergence of series, etc.), the corollary results can be combined in a profitable manner such that

$$w = v + \sum_{i=1}^{\infty} c_i u_i \tag{2.86}$$

is a solution of $L[w] = f$ and the c_i are an infinite collection of arbitrary constants that can be used to satisfy auxiliary conditions in initial-boundary-value problems.

Solutions to linear equations can also be combined in the form of integrals. As an example,

$$u(x, t) = e^{-\lambda^2 kt} \cos \lambda x \tag{2.87}$$

is a solution to (2.20)—that is, to the one-dimensional heat equation

$$u_{xx} = \frac{1}{k} u_t \tag{2.88}$$

The summation by integration of (2.87) is

$$\tilde{u}(x, t) = \int_{-\infty}^{\infty} e^{-\lambda^2 kt} \cos \lambda x \, d\lambda$$

$$= \sqrt{\frac{\pi}{kt}} e^{-x^2/4kt} \tag{2.89}$$

and (2.89) is also a solution to (2.88).

Clearly, the precise conditions under which the infinite series and integral summations are valid need to be spelled out. However, in lieu of a general development, we shall establish the necessary rules and tests as the need arises in the subsequent chapters.

2.5   NONLINEARITIES

The derivations of equations and boundary conditions in Sec. 2.2 led to examples of nonlinearities in spite of the simple and idealized problems under consideration.

In the case of heat conduction, (2.17) showed the nonlinearity arising when $K = K(u)$ alone. In fact, if, as is physically reasonable, $\rho = $ constant and $c = c(u)$ alone, then, according to (2.14), (2.17) would be

$$\rho c u_t + \rho c_u u u_t = K u_{xx} + A + K_u (u_x)^2 \tag{2.90}$$

for a spatially one-dimensional problem.

Equation (2.90) contains nonlinearities with respect to both independent variables.

In the case of the transverse vibrations of a string, elimination of the small amplitude assumption leads to a complicated system [7]. If v and z are the displacements in the y and z directions, respectively, the partial differential equation (2.47) is replaced by two equations

$$\begin{aligned}(T \sin \theta)_x &= \rho z_{tt} \\ (T \cos \theta)_x &= \rho v_{tt}\end{aligned} \tag{2.91}$$

where from appropriate stress-strain relations

$$T = T_0 + EA\{[(1 + v_x)^2 + z_x^2]^{1/2} - 1\}$$

and also $\tan \theta = z_x/(1 + v_x)$; that is, θ is the angle of inclination of the string with the horizontal.

In the case of fluid flow, even the ideal flow equations (2.65) and (2.66) are a highly nonlinear system. Only in the case of irrotational flow can a linear equation be found—for example, (2.68). However, the nonlinear Bernoulli equation (2.71), which gives a $p = p(\phi)$ in general, becomes a nonlinear boundary condition when a free surface boundary is present in the flow. Of course, even if $\phi_t = 0$, $g = 0$, and $p = 0$ in (2.71), it remains a nonlinear boundary condition because the location of the free surface boundary is always an unknown in such problems.

In Sec. 2.4 the groundwork was laid for obtaining useful solutions to mathematical models through the use of the principle of superposition. Unfortunately, the principle is based on the linearity of the model equations; thus when nonlinearities are present, the principle no longer holds. Similarly, the Laplace and Fourier transform methods (see Chap. 8) also depend on linearity. The loss of such methods is the primary damaging effect of nonlinearities.

Furthermore, there is no new general principle to replace the superposition principle or the Laplace and Fourier transforms when nonlinearities are present. As a result, the limited theory of nonlinear partial differential equations is based on a collection of more-or-less special cases in which various methods of attack, including transformations of variables, exact methods, similarity solutions, approximate methods, and numerical methods, have been successful. A comprehensive discussion is given in [7]. Some consideration to nonlinear problems is given here in Chap. 10.

2.6   CLASSIFICATION OF EQUATIONS AND REDUCTION TO CANONICAL FORM

Problems involving different physical systems were studied in Sec. 2.2. In each case, the partial differential equation of the resulting mathematical model was a second-order, linear equation of distinct character. In fact, in the equations derived no mixed derivatives appear, and the equations were one of three types. These are typified by (let $c = 1$ and $k = 1$)

$$u_{yy} - u_{tt} = 0$$

$$u_{xx} - u_t = 0 \qquad (2.92)$$

$$u_{xx} + u_{yy} = 0$$

Recall that the set of natural auxiliary conditions associated with each of these simple equations was distinct.

Because of the apparent pattern in the results of Secs. 2.2 and 2.3 (even though our sample was admittedly very small), it appears worthwhile to see if the more general, linear, second-order equation (1.8) can be classified as to type and if some transformation can be made to bring (1.8) to standard or canonical forms. If this were possible and the canonical forms were closely related to (2.92), a study of the very simple forms (2.92) would suffice to illustrate the significant properties and behavior of the general equation and its solutions.

We begin by recasting (1.8) in the form

$$au_{xx} + 2bu_{xy} + cu_{yy} = F \qquad (2.93)$$

where now $u(x, y)$ and the coefficients a, b, and c are functions of x and y only. The equation is linear if $F(x, y, u, u_x, u_y)$ is linear; we consider only the linear case here. We group terms involving the independent variables, u, and its first derivatives in the single functional form F because only the derivatives of the highest order matter in the qualitative evaluation of equation properties and behavior. We assume that u, a, b, and c are all at least twice continuously differentiable.

Now we propose a real change of variables

$$\xi = \xi(x, y)$$

$$\eta = \eta(x, y) \qquad (2.94)$$

that takes $u(x, y)$ into $u(\xi, \eta)$, and we seek to reduce the complexity of (2.93) in some significant way. The real functions $\xi(x, y)$ and $\eta(x, y)$ are also assumed to be at least twice continuously differentiable in some prescribed x, y domain. The change of variables (2.94) is introduced into (2.93) in the usual manner. First, according to the chain rule of partial differentiation [1, p. 86],

$$u_x = u_\xi \xi_x + u_\eta \eta_x$$

$$u_y = u_\xi \xi_y + u_\eta \eta_y$$

$$u_{xx} = u_{\xi\xi}\xi_x^2 + 2u_{\xi\eta}\xi_x\eta_x + u_{\eta\eta}\eta_x^2 + u_\xi\xi_{xx} + u_\eta\eta_{xx}$$

$$u_{xy} = u_{\xi\xi}\xi_x\xi_y + u_{\xi\eta}[\xi_x\eta_y + \xi_y\eta_x] + u_{\eta\eta}\eta_x\eta_y + u_\xi\xi_{xy} + u_\eta\eta_{xy}$$

etc.

It follows that

$$au_{xx} + 2bu_{xy} + cu_{yy} - F = Au_{\xi\xi} + 2Bu_{\xi\eta} + Cu_{\eta\eta} - G \qquad (2.95)$$

where

$$A = a\xi_x^2 + 2b\xi_x\xi_y + c\xi_y^2 \qquad (2.96)$$

$$B = a\xi_x\eta_x + b[\xi_x\eta_y + \xi_y\eta_x] + c\xi_y\eta_y \tag{2.97}$$

$$C = a\eta_x^2 + 2b\eta_x\eta_y + c\eta_y^2 \tag{2.98}$$

$$G = F - u_\xi[a\xi_{xx} + 2b\xi_{xy} + c\xi_{yy}] - u_\eta[a\eta_{xx} + 2b\eta_{xy} + c\eta_{yy}]$$

Thus we really have the linear transformed equation

$$Au_{\xi\xi} + 2Bu_{\xi\eta} + Cu_{\eta\eta} = G \tag{2.99}$$

In order to reduce (2.99)—for example, to make A and C zero—we must find solutions to (2.96) through (2.98). However, (2.96) and (2.98) are both of the form

$$a\Phi_x^2 + 2b\Phi_x\Phi_y + c\Phi_y^2 = 0 \tag{2.100}$$

which can be factored into the two equivalent equations

$$a\Phi_{1x} = \{-b - (b^2 - ac)^{1/2}\}\Phi_{1y} \tag{2.101a}$$

$$a\Phi_{2x} = \{-b + (b^2 - ac)^{1/2}\}\Phi_{2y} \tag{2.101b}$$

in which Φ_1 and Φ_2 are independent solutions of (2.100) if (2.101a) and (2.101b) are distinct. The character of our simplifying transformation (2.94) is now seen to depend crucially on the sign of the *discriminant* $b^2 - ac$.

There exists a direct analogy between (2.93) and its discriminant and the equation of second degree in plane geometry [1]

$$\bar{A}x^2 + \bar{B}xy + \bar{C}y^2 = G = -Dx - Ey - F$$

and its discriminant $\bar{B}^2 - \overline{AC}$. Accordingly, we expect here to treat the three cases corresponding to the possible signs of the discriminant and to find canonical forms analogous to the geometric forms: ellipse ($\bar{B}^2 - \overline{AC} < 0$), hyperbola ($\bar{B}^2 - \overline{AC} > 0$), and parabola ($\bar{B}^2 - \overline{AC} = 0$).

The Jacobian of the transformation (2.94) is

$$J = \frac{\partial(\xi, \eta)}{\partial(x, y)} = \begin{vmatrix} \xi_x & \xi_y \\ \eta_x & \eta_y \end{vmatrix} = \xi_x\eta_y - \xi_y\eta_x \tag{2.102}$$

For one-to-one transformations whose Jacobians must be different from zero in the domain of interest, it is possible [1] to solve (2.94) uniquely for $x(\xi, \eta)$ and $y(\xi, \eta)$, and they will possess the same continuity properties as ξ and η (see above). Furthermore, under these conditions, we have, from (2.96) to (2.98),

$$B^2 - AC = (b^2 - ac)(\xi_x\eta_y - \xi_y\eta_x)^2$$

$$= (b^2 - ac)J^2, \qquad J^2 > 0 \tag{2.103}$$

As (2.97) is now related to (2.96) and (2.98) through (2.103), the sign of $b^2 - ac$ becomes the governing factor in our search for canonical forms and (2.97) need no longer be considered. Because $J^2 > 0$ in (2.103), the sign of $b^2 - ac$ remains invariant under the transformation, and thus *the type of our equations is not altered by the change of variables* (2.94).

We now consider the simplification of (2.93) through the transformation (2.94) for three cases: $b^2 - ac > 0$, $b^2 - ac = 0$, and $b^2 - ac < 0$. The discriminant $b^2 - ac$ is assumed to remain of one sign throughout the domain of interest. Our discussion is relatively brief; more comprehensive presentations are found in [3, 8, 9].

Case 1. $b^2 - ac > 0$ (and $B^2 - AC > 0$)

Let $A = C = 0$ in (2.99); this guarantees that $B^2 \neq 0$. However, (2.96) and (2.98) must be satisfied. This is done by setting $\xi = \Phi_1(x, y)$ and $\eta = \Phi_2(x, y)$, where both Φ_1 and Φ_2 are real functions as defined in (2.101). From (2.103), it follows that $B \neq 0$ anywhere. Thus we may divide (2.99) by $2B$, and recalling that $A = C = 0$ now, reduce (2.99) to

$$u_{\xi\eta} = G_1(\xi, \eta, u, u_\xi, u_\eta) \tag{2.104}$$

throughout the x–y region of definition of the solution functions $\xi = \Phi_1$ and $\eta = \Phi_2$. Interestingly, the simple transformation $\xi = r + s$ and $\eta = r - s$ changes (2.104) to

$$u_{rr} - u_{ss} = \tilde{G}_1(r, s, u, u_r, u_s) \tag{2.105}$$

This result is equivalent to that obtained by setting $B = 0$ and $A = -C \neq 0$, then solving the coupled equations obtained from (2.96) to (2.98).

Both (2.104) and (2.105) are canonical forms for $b^2 - ac > 0$; as might be expected from the geometric analogy mentioned above, equations with such canonical forms are called *hyperbolic* equations. For hyperbolic equations, the transformation equations (2.101) are distinct. If their distinct solutions Φ_1 and Φ_2 are written in terms of the level curves [1]

$$\Phi_1(x, y) = \text{constant}$$

$$\Phi_2(x, y) = \text{constant}$$

the solutions for the level curves are given by the integrals of the ordinary differential equations (obtained directly from (2.101a) and (2.101b) because $dy/dx = -\Phi_x/\Phi_y$; see [1, p. 95])

$$\frac{dy}{dx} = \frac{b(x, y) + [b^2(x, y) - a(x, y)c(x, y)]^{1/2}}{a(x, y)}$$
$$\frac{dy}{dx} = \frac{b(x, y) - [b^2(x, y) - a(x, y)c(x, y)]^{1/2}}{a(x, y)} \tag{2.106}$$

which are known as the *characteristic equations*. The two families of integral curves $\Phi_1(x, y) = c_1$ and $\Phi_2(x, y) = c_2$ are called the *characteristics* of the *hyperbolic partial differential equation*. Second-order hyperbolic equations always have *two* distinct families of characteristics. They are considered in greater detail in Chap. 9.

Case 2. $b^2 - ac = 0$ (and $B^2 - AC = 0$)

When $b^2 - ac = 0$ and hence $B^2 - AC = 0$ [see (2.103)] in the whole region of study, it is sufficient to set $A = 0$ because then $B = 0$ immediately. In addition, the characteristic equations (2.106) now merge and Eqs. (2.101) are no longer distinct. Thus we take

$$\xi(x, y) = \Phi_1(x, y)$$

and let $\eta(x, y)$ be some arbitrary function that is independent of $\Phi_1(x, y)$—that is, so $J \neq 0$.

It follows [3] that as long as a and c are not simultaneously zero, $C \neq 0$ [see (2.98)]; hence we divide (2.99) by C to obtain the canonical form

$$u_{\eta\eta} = G_2(\xi, \eta, u, u_\xi, u_\eta) \tag{2.107}$$

throughout the appropriate region where Φ_1 and η are defined. Equations having the canonical form (2.107) are called *parabolic* equations. Clearly, they have only *one* family of characteristics because the characteristic equations (2.106) are identical when $b^2 - ac = 0$.

In certain cases, (2.107) becomes degenerate; that is, the solution can be obtained by treating (2.107) as an ordinary differential equation with ξ as a parameter. For example, suppose that $G_2 = G_2(\xi, \eta)$ in (2.107). Then it is solvable by integration; that is,

$$u_\eta = \int^\eta G_2(\xi, \rho)\, d\rho + f(\xi)$$

$$u(\xi, \eta) = \int^\eta \int^\tau G_2(\xi, \rho)\, d\rho\, d\tau + \int^\eta f(\xi)\, d\rho + g(\xi) \tag{2.108}$$

which is the general solution. In fact, whenever G_2 is *not* a function of u_ξ, (2.107) is degenerate. Hence, following Petrovsky [3], we introduce a restricted definition of parabolicity and hereafter require that for an equation to be of parabolic type, $b^2 - ac$ equal zero *and* the coefficient of u_ξ in the canonical form (2.107) be nonzero.

Case 3. $b^2 - ac < 0$ (and $B^2 - AC < 0$)

From (2.103), the conditions $B = 0$ and $A = C$ are compatible with $b^2 - ac < 0$. Accordingly, from (2.96) to (2.98), a transformation (2.94) that satisfies the following coupled simultaneous equations

$$a(\xi_x^2 - \eta_x^2) + 2b(\xi_x\xi_y - \eta_x\eta_y) + c(\xi_y^2 - \eta_y^2) = 0$$
$$\tag{2.109}$$
$$a\xi_x\eta_x + b(\xi_x\eta_y + \xi_y\eta_x) + c\xi_y\eta_y = 0$$

is required. This system (2.109) can be further transformed [8] to a pair of first-order partial differential equations known as the *Beltrami Equations*, whose solution, although it exists, is no easier to find than the solution of the original equation (2.93). However, the canonical form achieved by setting $B = 0$ and $A = C\ (\neq 0)$ is

$$u_{\xi\xi} + u_{\eta\eta} = G_3(\xi, \eta, u, u_\xi, u_\eta) \tag{2.110}$$

which is the canonical form for *elliptic*-type equations.

If the coefficients a, b, and c of (2.93) are analytic,* we can proceed with an analysis paralleling those given above and complete our discussion of the role of $b^2 - ac$ by using (2.106). Hence let $a(x, y)$, $b(x, y)$, and $c(x, y)$ be analytic functions

---

* A function $f(x, y)$ is termed *analytic* in a region if $f(x, y)$ can be represented by a power series in the given region.

in some given region of interest. Thus the coefficients of Φ_{1y} and Φ_{2y} in Eqs. (2.101) are also analytic and, because $b^2 - ac < 0$, are complex conjugates. Then the solutions Φ_1 and Φ_2 of these equations can also be assumed to be complex conjugates; in terms of their level curves, we write

$$\Phi_1(x, y) = \phi(x, y) + i\psi(x, y) = \text{constant}$$

$$\Phi_2(x, y) = \phi(x, y) - i\psi(x, y) = \text{constant}$$

(2.111)

where $\phi(x, y)$ and $\psi(x, y)$ are real functions. Furthermore, the characteristic equations (2.106) are distinct, but the integrals of (2.106) that are the characteristics of an elliptic equation are *complex*. Thus although hyperbolic equations have two families of real characteristics and parabolic equations have one such family, elliptic equations have *no real characteristics* but have two families of complex characteristics.

Now Φ_1 and Φ_2 could be used to make $A = C = 0$. Doing so has no benefit here, since the ξ and η transforms then are not real. If we set $\xi(x, y) = \phi(x, y)$ and $\eta(x, y) = \psi(x, y)$, (a) the Jacobian J is nonzero, (b) $A = C$ and both are nonzero, and (c) ξ and η satisfy (2.109), as direct substitution shows. Thus $B = 0$, $A = C$, and the canonical form for (2.93) is still (2.110) because we may divide the transformed equation (2.99) by $A = C$. Finding the functions ϕ and ψ—that is, the explicit solutions to the characteristic equations—requires integration of (2.106), which may be difficult but certainly is possible in principle.

In summary, there are three canonical forms for the general, linear, second-order equation (2.93), which is then always one of three types. The type depends solely on the sign of the discriminant $b^2 - ac$. The general equation is reduced to canonical form by a real change of variables. It is usually difficult to find the change of variables ξ and η in the general case even though the equations they satisfy are known and it can be proved that such ξ and η exist [6, 8]. We have not attempted to develop methods to find ξ and η explicitly because, for our purposes, it is enough to know that the transformation to canonical form can be made. To establish this point by concrete example, the exercises include a number of simple problems in which ξ and η are to be determined. Although hints are given so that ξ and η are easy to find and no general methods are suggested, many of the pertinent points in the foregoing discussion are reemphasized in these exercise examples.

Table 2.2 gives a summary of the preceding results and, using a common set of independent variables, illustrates the close relation between the canonical forms and the equations in Table 2.1 [see (2.92) also]. We see that the three partial differential equations from Table 2.1 incorporate the essential features of the much more general canonical forms. Accordingly, we may focus our attention on the three simple equations and expect to gain an understanding and appreciation of the significant properties and behavior of the three types of equations: hyperbolic, parabolic, and elliptic.

Finally, although we do not probe further, the classification of quasi-linear equations and equations with greater numbers of independent variables, for example, is possible by extension of what we have already learned [3, 9]. In fact, do you think that our derivation of canonical forms would be altered if the coefficients a, b, and c in (2.93) were functions of (x, y, u, u_ξ, u_η)? The equation would then be quasi-linear.

TABLE 2.2 Summary of Canonical Forms and Related Linear,
Second-order Equations with Two Independent Variables

Equation Type	Hyperbolic	Parabolic	Elliptic
Value of $b^2 - ac$	> 0	$= 0$	< 0
Canonical form	1. $u_{\xi\eta} = G_1(\xi, \eta, u, u_\xi, u_\eta)$ 2. $u_{\xi\xi} - u_{\eta\eta} = \bar{G}_1(\xi, \eta, u, u_\xi, u_\eta)$	$u_{\eta\eta} = G_2(\xi, \eta, u, u_\xi, u_\eta)$ Coefficient of $u_\xi \neq 0$	$u_{\xi\xi} + u_{\eta\eta} = G_3(\xi, \eta, u, u_\xi, u_\eta)$
Representative equation of physical system [see (2.92)]	Wave Equation $u_{\xi\xi} - u_{\eta\eta} = 0$	Heat Equation $u_{\eta\eta} - u_\xi = 0$	Laplace Equation $u_{\xi\xi} + u_{\eta\eta} = 0$
Number of families of real characteristics	2	1	0

REFERENCES

1. W. Kaplan, *Advanced Calculus*. Reading, Mass.: Addison-Wesley, 1952.

2. H. S. Carslaw and J. C. Jaeger, *Conduction of Heat in Solids*. London: Oxford University Press, 1959.

3. I. G. Petrovsky, *Lectures on Partial Differential Equations* (trans. from the Russian by A. Shenitzer). New York: Interscience (a division of John Wiley & Sons), 1954.

4. J. W. Daily and D. R. F. Harleman, *Fluid Dynamics*. Reading, Mass.: Addison-Wesley, 1966.

5. I. H. Shames, *Mechanics of Fluids*. New York: McGraw-Hill, 1962.

6. R. Courant and D. Hilbert, *Methods of Mathematical Physics*, Vol. II. New York: Interscience (a division of John Wiley & Sons), 1962.

7. W. F. Ames, *Nonlinear Partial Differential Equations in Engineering*. New York: Academic Press, 1965.

8. P. R. Garabedian, *Partial Differential Equations*. New York: John Wiley & Sons, 1964.

9. S. G. Mikhlin (Ed.), *Linear Equations of Mathematical Physics* (trans. from the Russian by Scripta Technica, Inc.). New York: Holt, Rinehart and Winston, 1967.

PROBLEMS

Note: Wherever your results depend on particular assumptions, you must state the assumptions clearly.

2.1 Derive the partial differential equation for heat conduction in a sphere, in which K, c, and ρ are assumed to be known and constant. Present your result in spherical coordinates.

2.2 Starting from basic principles and using polar coordinates, derive the partial differential equation for the small vibrations of a circular membrane.

2.3 Utilize a formal change of variables to transform Eq. (2.19) into

(a) spherical coordinates.   (b) cylindrical coordinates.

2.4 Construct a mathematical model for the longitudinal vibrations of a thin, round, uniform rod that is hung by one end from the ceiling (see Fig. 2.4P). All motions are directed along the rod; the longitudinal displacement of any cross section of the rod from its original (unstretched or uncompressed) position is called $z(x, t)$. In the undisturbed or neutral state, the rod has a length l, a cross-sectional area A, a modulus of elasticity E, and a density

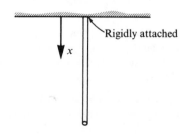

Rigidly attached

x

FIGURE 2.4P

ρ = mass/unit length. Within the limits of small amplitude vibrations, the force f needed to cause an extension Δz of a segment of rod of original length Δx is governed by Hooke's law; that is,

$$f(x, t) = AE\frac{\Delta z(x, t)}{\Delta x}$$

or, in the limit,

$$f = AE\frac{\partial z}{\partial x}$$

Assume a suitable set of nonzero initial conditions for your model.

2.5   Under the assumption that all variations with respect to time are zero (steady-state conditions), find the time-independent distortion of the rod of Fig. 2.4P—that is, the $z(x)$ caused by gravity alone.

2.6   Suppose that as a class demonstration project, a string is attached in a small tank filled with clear, viscous liquid as shown in Fig. 2.6P. The hook is used to displace the end of the string upward by a small initial distance Δ. When released from this static position, the string begins to vibrate in some manner; the vibration is sustained by a forced sinusoidal oscillation of the other end of the string with an amplitude ε and period of 4 sec (i.e., 1 cycle per 4 sec) that begins when the string is released.

The string has a length l and a mass per unit length ρ. The viscosity of the fluid is μ; the fluid exerts a drag force per unit length on each element of the moving string. If $z(y, t)$ is the displacement of the string due to small transverse vibrations, the fluid drag per unit length is given by

$$D = \rho C_D z_t$$

in which C_D is proportional to μ. Assuming that ε and Δ are small and positive and that $c^2 = T/\rho$, where T is the string tension, begin with first principles and construct a mathematical model of the preceding physical process.

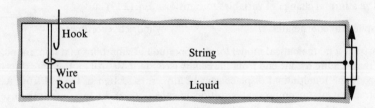

FIGURE 2.6P

2.7   Formulate an initial-boundary-value problem for the temperature distribution caused by heat conduction in a thin, laterally insulated rod that is equipped with a pair of feedback devices—one at each end. These devices relate the temperature at one end of the rod to the flux at the other. The rod is of length l and has constant properties.

2.8   Formulate an initial-boundary-value problem for the temperature distribution caused by radial heat flow in a sphere. Let the outer surface of the sphere be at a temperature $u(R, t) = T_0$ and the initial temperature distribution be $u(r, 0) = T(r)$. What condition, if any, is apparently required or satisfied at $r = 0$? (*Hint:* See Probs. 2.1 and 2.3.)

2.9 Give a physical interpretation, in terms of heat conduction where $u(x, t)$ is temperature, for the following mathematical model:

$$u_t = ku_{xx} - q(x + 1)u, \qquad 0 < x < 1, \quad t > 0$$
$$u_x(0, t) = u(0, t),$$
$$u_x(1, t) = 0, \qquad t > 0$$
$$u(x, 0) = 1 \,°C, \qquad 0 \le x \le 1$$

Assume that $k = K/\rho c$ and q are constants.

2.10 Give a physical interpretation, in terms of heat conduction where $u(x, t)$ is temperature, for the following mathematical model:

$$u_t = ku_{xx} + Ae^{-t}, \qquad 0 < x < L, \quad t > 0$$

$$u_x(0, t) = -\frac{F_0}{K},$$
$$u(L, t) = T, \qquad t > 0$$

$$u(x, 0) = f(x), \qquad 0 \le x \le L$$

Assume that K, k, A, F_0, and T are constants.

2.11 For the mathematical model of Prob. 2.10, find the solution as $t \to \infty$—that is, the steady-state solution.

2.12 Formulate a mathematical model for heat conduction in a hollow sphere with uniform, constant composition and properties K, ρ, and c between the bounding radii $R_1 < R_2$. Use the results of Prob. 2.1 or 2.3 (or work one) to obtain the partial differential equation. The temperature of the outer surface of the sphere is $T_2 = $ constant; the inner surface temperature is $T_1 = $ constant. The initial temperature is some given function $U(r, \theta, \phi)$.

2.13 Discuss the case $R_1 = 0$ as applied to Prob. 2.12. Can we specify T_1? What happens to the partial differential equation? Do you end up with enough auxiliary conditions?

2.14 Find the temperature distribution in the sphere of Prob. 2.12 as $t \to \infty$—that is, the steady-state distribution.

2.15 Construct a mathematical model for the transverse vibrations of a thin, circular membrane of radius R if the membrane is fixed at elevation $z = 0$ around its outer edge, has a hole of radius R_H in the center, and has

(a) no initial velocity, but an initial displacement $= z_0(r, \theta, 0)$, $R_H \le r \le R$.

(b) no initial velocity, but an initial displacement $= z_0(r, 0)$, $R_H \le r \le R$.

Assume that lateral, but no vertical, restraint is present on the edge of the hole.

2.16 For the model of Prob. 2.15(b), assume that damping reduces the vibrations to zero as $t \to \infty$. Find the ultimate steady-state solution if gravity is the only external force acting on the membrane.

2.17 Consider the case $R_H \to 0$ in Prob. 2.15(b). How does the model obtained differ from the model (2.63)? Can you give a physical interpretation of your result?

2.18 Solve the mathematical model given by Eqs. (2.63) for steady-state conditions (no t-variations). Demonstrate that the requirement $z_r(0) = 0$ is precisely equivalent to the requirement $z(0) < \infty$; that is, z is bounded at $r = 0$. Let F be constant.

2.19   The ends of two thin and laterally insulated bars of equal cross-sectional area are brought together. Establish the conditions on the heat flux and temperature that must exist across the joint when the contact between the bar ends is clean and flush (the ends are in good mechanical and thermal contact and there is no insulating air gap or film present). Let one bar have the properties K_1, ρ_1, and c_1 and the other the properties K_2, ρ_2, and c_2.

2.20   Frequently, in heat conduction systems, we find that the bounding surface of a body is covered by a thin skin of scale, grease, or oxide, etc. This skin may be a poor conductor of heat and thus may materially affect our surface boundary conditions. Consider a body with properties K, ρ, and c; the body is covered by a skin of thickness Δ_s, conductivity K_s, and *negligible* heat capacity. Derive an appropriate boundary condition for the body temperature $u(0, t)$ for the case shown in Fig. 2.20P. [*Hint:* See Prob. 2.19 and note that $u_{RES} = u(-\Delta_s, t)$.]

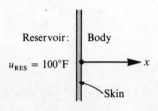

FIGURE 2.20P

2.21   Consider the two thin, round rods shown in Fig. 2.21P, together with their properties and lengths. At $x = 0$, we attach a spring of strength K that always opposes any displacement with a force equal to K times the displacement. At $x = l_1 + l_2$, we attach a dashpot (shock absorber) that uses viscous action to oppose motion with a force equal to the velocity of the bar end times a constant C_D. Construct a mathematical model for the longitudinal vibrations in the pair of rods. Assume some appropriate general initial conditions. Be sure to list any other assumptions inherent in your model—for example, Hooke's law applies, displacements are small, etc. (*Hint:* See the text of Prob. 2.4 for a discussion of forces in a longitudinally vibrating bar. Be careful to define fully all coordinates in this problem; recall the correct definition of Newton's Second Law with regard to coordinate systems.)

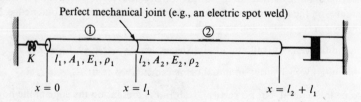

FIGURE 2.21P

2.22   A thin, square plate of small, uniform thickness δ is perfectly insulated over its two large faces. If an x, y coordinate system is attached to the plate so that the plate lies in $0 \le x \le l_1$ and $0 \le y \le l_2$, the plate's edges at $y = 0$ and $y = l_2$ are also found to be insulated, while the edges at $x = 0$ and $x = l_1$ are kept at temperatures T_0 and T_1, respectively. For this problem, state a complete initial-boundary-value problem for the temperature $u(x, y, t)$ in the plate if the thermal diffusivity k is a function of u alone and if initially the temperature is $T(x, y)$.

2.23 Show that the linear model for small-amplitude water waves on the surface of a tank (Fig. 2.23P) is

$$\nabla^2\phi = 0, \quad\quad 0 < x < l, \quad\quad -d < y < 0, \quad\quad 0 < t$$
$$\phi_x(0, y, t) = \phi_x(l, y, t) = 0, \quad\quad -d < y < 0, \quad\quad 0 < t$$
$$\phi_y(x, -d, t) = 0, \quad\quad 0 \le x \le l, \quad\quad 0 < t$$
$$\eta_t(x, t) = \phi_y(x, 0, t),$$
$$\phi_t(x, 0, t) + g\eta(x, t) = 0, \quad\quad 0 < x < l \quad\quad 0 < t$$
$$\eta(x, 0) = \eta_0(x),$$
$$\eta_t(x, 0) = V_0(x), \quad\quad 0 \le x \le l$$

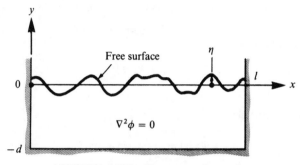

y

Free surface η

0 l

$\nabla^2\phi = 0$ x

$-d$

FIGURE 2.23P   Water waves in a tank.

where $\eta(x, t)$ is the unknown displacement of the free surface of the water from the mean level where $y = 0$. [*Hint:* At the free surface the pressure $p(x, \eta, t)$ is zero and the water particles follow the surface, so that $v(x, \eta, t) = d\eta(x, t)/dt = \eta_t(x, t) + \eta_x(x, t)\,dx/dt = \eta_t + \eta_x u(x, \eta, t)$. According to the small amplitude assumption (see Sec. 2.2.2), the squares and products of dependent variables and their derivatives are negligible—for example, $\phi_x^2, \eta_x u$, etc., compared to ϕ_x, u, η, etc. For boundary conditions prescribed on the unknown free surface, expand dependent variables about $y = 0$ in a Taylor's series and neglect higher-order terms to remove η as the location of the boundary condition—that is, transfer the boundary condition to $y = 0$.]

2.24 Consider the string stretching from $0 \le y \le l$ shown in Fig. 2.24P. The end at $y = 0$ is attached to a small lead ball of weight W, which in turn is attached to a leaf spring with an

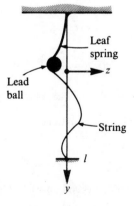

Leaf
spring
z

Lead
ball

String

l

y

FIGURE 2.24P

effective spring constant K. The spring is undisturbed when $z = 0$ but otherwise exerts a restoring force proportional to the displacement. The end of the string at $y = l$ is fixed. If the string has a mass per unit length ρ and is under a tension T, formulate an appropriate mathematical model for the small transverse vibrations of this system. Assume an appropriate nonzero set of initial conditions. Is the mathematical model composed of linear, homogeneous equations?

2.25 Consider the case of a string when (2.78) is the equation in the region $0 < y < l/2$. Find the solution for the shape of the string if $z(0) = z_y(l/2) = 0$. Compare this result with (2.81) and discuss.

2.26 Rework Prob. 1.11 using the properties of linear operators introduced in Sec. 2.4 as criteria. In addition, specify whether each equation is homogeneous or inhomogeneous.

2.27 If u_1 and u_2 are solutions of $L[u_i] = f_i$, where $i = 1$ and 2 and the f_i are constants, find C_1 and C_2 such that

$$L[v] = 0$$

when $v = C_1 u_1 + C_2 u_2$.

2.28 Refer to Prob. 1.10. Show that

$$u(x, y) = \sum_{n=1}^{\infty} A_n \sin \lambda_n x \cosh \lambda_n y$$

also satisfies

$$u_{xx} + u_{yy} = 0$$

for all A_n and λ_n. For what values of λ_n is

(a) $u(\pi, y) = 0$?   (b) $u_y(x, 0) = 0$?

(c) $u_x(0, y) = 0$?   (d) $u(\pi, y) = u_y(x, 0) = u(0, y) = 0$?

2.29 Functions of the form

$$u(x, t) = e^{-\lambda^2 kt} \sin \lambda x$$

satisfy

$$u_t = k u_{xx}, \qquad 0 < x, \quad 0 < t$$

and

$$u(0, t) = 0, \qquad t \geq 0$$

Show that the integral form

$$u(x, t) = \int_0^{\infty} e^{-\lambda^2 kt} \sin \lambda x \, d\lambda$$

also satisfies these equations for finite values of t.

2.30 Determine the type of the following equations:

(a) $u_{xx} + 2u_{xy} + u_{yy} + u_x + u_y = 0$

(b) $x^2 u_{xx} + u_{yy} = xy$

Does the type of this equation depend on x or y? If so, how?

(c) $u_{xx} + u_{xy} + 4u_{yy} + 5xu_x = 3$

2.31   How does the type of the equation

$$u_{xx} - yu_{yy} = 0$$

depend on x and y if $u = u(x, y)$?

2.32   What is the type of

$$u_{xx} + (x^2 - y^2)u_{yy} = u_y$$

in the x–y plane if $u = u(x, y)$?

2.33   What is the type of

$$u_{xx} + (1 - x^2 - y^2)u_{yy} = 0$$

in the x–y plane if $u = u(x, y)$?

2.34   The type of an equation may depend on the solution as well as on the domain of the independent variables when the equation is quasi-linear. What is the type of $u_{xx} + uu_{yy} = 0$ in the x–y plane?

2.35   A partial differential equation involving derivatives with respect to one variable only may be solved as an ordinary differential equation by treating the other independent variables as parameters. Find general solutions to the following equations, in which $u = u(x, y)$:

(a) $u_{yy} + xy = 0$ (*Hint:* Try direct integration.)

(b) $u_{yy} + u = 0$ (*Hint:* Try exponentials.)

(c) $u_{xx} = 5u_x$ (*Hint:* Let $\Phi = u_x$; then integrate.)

(d) $u_{xx} + u_x + u = 0$

(e) $u_{xy} = 0$ (*Hint:* Try direct integration of $\partial^2 u/\partial x\, \partial y = 0$.)

2.36   Transform the hyperbolic equation

$$u_{xx} - u_{yy} = 0$$

for $u = u(x, y)$ into the alternate canonical form

$$u_{\xi\eta} = 0$$

and find ξ and η as functions of x and y. [*Hint:* Integrate (2.106) to find the level curves $\Phi_1(x, y) = c_1$ and $\Phi_2(x, y) = c_2$. If $y = +x + c_1$, then $\Phi_1(x, y) = y - x = c_1$ and $\xi(x, y) = \Phi_1(x, y) = y - x$, etc.]

2.37   Transform the parabolic equation
$$u_{xx} + 2u_{xy} + u_{yy} + u_y = 0$$

for $u = u(x, y)$, into its canonical form. [*Hint:* See the hint for Prob. 2.36; recall that $\eta = \eta(x, y)$ can be freely chosen as long as it is independent of $\xi = \xi(x, y)$.]

2.38   Transform the equation

$$u_{xx} + 2u_{xy} - u_{yy} = 0$$

for $u = u(x, y)$, into its canonical form. (*Hint:* The hint for Prob. 2.36 still applies.)

2.39   The transformation of elliptic equations is generally a complex process; however, in simple cases, simple methods may work. Transform the equation

$$u_{xx} + 2u_{xy} + 2u_{yy} = 0$$

for $u = u(x, y)$, into its canonical form. [*Hint*: First, introduce a new set of coordinates r and s by rotation of axes so that the second of (2.109) is satisfied; that is, eliminate the mixed second derivative. Second, introduce another new set of coordinates ξ and η by stretching r and s so that $A = C$; that is, the first of (2.109) is satisfied. Note that stretching—that is, letting $\xi = kr$ and $\eta = ls$—does not affect the second equation and the resulting ξ and η will also satisfy it.]

2.40 Transform the equation of Prob. 2.39 into its canonical form by solving (2.106) and then using (2.111) and the ideas following.

2.41 Transform the equation

$$u_{xx} + yu_{yy} = 0$$

for $u = u(x, y)$, into its canonical form for

(a) $y > 0$ \hspace{3cm} (b) $y < 0$

[*Hint*: Show that $(\xi, \eta) = (x \pm 2\sqrt{-y})$ for $y < 0$, while $(\xi, \eta) = (x, 2\sqrt{y})$ for $y > 0$.]

2.42 Transform the "Tricomi" equation [5, p. 162]

$$u_{xx} + xu_{yy} = 0$$

for $u = u(x, y)$, into its canonical form for

(a) $x > 0$ \hspace{3cm} (b) $x < 0$

[*Hint*: Show that $(\xi, \eta) = (\tfrac{3}{2}y \pm (-x)^{3/2})$ for $x < 0$, while $(\xi, \eta) = (\tfrac{3}{2}y, -x^{3/2})$ for $x > 0$.]

2.43 The following equations are typical of some canonical forms achieved for hyperbolic equations, in which $u = u(x, y)$:

(a) $u_{xy} = u_y$ \hspace{3cm} (b) $u_{xy} = \dfrac{1}{2x}u_y$

(c) $u_{xy} = x^{-1}u_y$ \hspace{3cm} (d) $u_{xy} = f(x)u_y$

Find general solutions to each equation by letting $\phi(x, y) = u_y$ and then performing the necessary direct integrations to find $u(x, y)$.

CHAPTER 3

SEPARATION OF VARIABLES— SOLUTION OF SIMPLE PROBLEMS

3.1 THE METHOD

Separation of variables is a frequently used method for solving the initial-boundary-value problems posed in Chap. 2. By application of the method, a problem involving, say, an unknown function $u(x, t)$ of two independent variables is reduced to a *pair* of problems, each of which is concerned with an unknown function of a single independent variable. To accomplish this reduction for the homogeneous equation

$$u_t = ku_{xx} \tag{3.1}$$

for heat flow in a rod [see (2.20)], we seek $u(x, t)$ as a *product of functions of the separate independent variables* and let

$$u(x, t) = X(x)T(t) \tag{3.2}$$

Thus the *method of separation of variables* is to seek solutions to partial differential equations in the form of products of functions, each of which depends only on one independent variable.

To illustrate the method, let us consider the partial differential equation (2.76a) governing the model of steady-state heat conduction in a sphere. This equation

53

is most conveniently described in terms of spherical coordinates (r, θ, ϕ) in this case, where [1, 2]

$$x = r \sin \phi \cos \theta$$

$$y = r \sin \phi \sin \theta \qquad r^2 = x^2 + y^2 + z^2$$

$$z = r \cos \phi$$

Equation (2.76a) is

$$\nabla^2 u = (r^2 u_r)_r + \frac{1}{\sin \phi}(\sin \phi u_\phi)_\phi + \frac{1}{\sin^2 \phi} u_{\theta\theta} = 0 \qquad (3.3)$$

in spherical coordinates (see Probs. 2.1 and 2.2).

Now, we assume a product solution of the form

$$u(r, \theta, \phi) = R(r)\Theta(\theta)\Phi(\phi) \qquad (3.4)$$

and introduce (3.4) into (3.3) to achieve

$$(r^2 R' \Theta \Phi)_r + \frac{1}{\sin \phi}(\sin \phi R \Theta \Phi')_\phi + \frac{1}{\sin^2 \phi} R \Theta'' \Phi = 0 \qquad (3.5)$$

If (3.5) is divided by $R\Theta\Phi$ and rearranged, it becomes

$$\frac{(r^2 R')_r}{R} + \frac{1}{\Phi \sin \phi}(\sin \phi \Phi')_\phi + \frac{\Theta''}{\Theta \sin^2 \phi} = 0$$

or

$$\frac{r^2 R'' + 2rR'}{R} = -\frac{1}{\Phi \sin \phi}(\sin \phi \Phi'' + \cos \phi \Phi') - \frac{\Theta''}{\Theta \sin^2 \phi} \qquad (3.6)$$

The left side of (3.6) is a function of r alone, but the right side is a function of θ and ϕ only. Clearly, the functions of r have been separated from the functions of (θ, ϕ). If the equality in (3.6) is to hold for all (r, θ, ϕ) in the sphere, *both sides* of the equation must equal the *same constant*. Thus we may set each side equal to a constant, which it is convenient to choose as $n(n + 1)$, so that, first,

$$\frac{r^2 R'' + 2rR'}{R} = n(n + 1)$$

and, second,

$$-\frac{1}{\Phi \sin \phi}(\sin \phi \Phi'' + \cos \phi \Phi') - \frac{\Theta''}{\Theta \sin^2 \phi} = n(n + 1)$$

The constant $n(n + 1)$ is the *separation constant* and is presently of unknown magnitude. The foregoing equations can be rewritten as

$$r^2 R'' + 2rR' - n(n + 1)R = 0 \qquad (3.7)$$

and

$$\frac{\Theta''}{\Theta} = -\frac{[\sin^2 \phi \Phi'' + \sin \phi \cos \phi \Phi' + n(n + 1)\sin^2 \phi \Phi]}{\Phi} \qquad (3.8)$$

We are ready to repeat the preceding argument for (3.8). Thus by writing

$$\frac{\Theta''}{\Theta} = -\lambda^2 \qquad (3.9)$$

and consequently

$$\sin^2 \phi \Phi'' + \sin \phi \cos \phi \Phi' + [n(n + 1) \sin^2 \phi - \lambda^2]\Phi = 0 \qquad (3.10)$$

we acknowledge that the left and right sides of (3.8) depend on different independent variables and must be equal to the same separation constant $-\lambda^2$.

From (3.7), (3.9), and (3.10), we see that the proposal of a product-form solution (3.4) has led to the separation of (3.3) into the three ordinary differential equations

$$r^2 R'' + 2rR' - n(n + 1)R = 0$$

$$\Theta'' + \lambda^2 \Theta = 0 \qquad (3.11)$$

$$\sin^2 \phi \Phi'' + \sin \phi \cos \phi \Phi' + [n(n + 1) \sin^2 \phi - \lambda^2]\Phi = 0$$

where $n(n + 1)$ and $-\lambda^2$ are the successively obtained separation constants. When we have fewer or greater numbers of independent variables, the process of separation is shorter or longer, respectively, but not different in principle. If the preceding process is possible—that is, if the partial differential equation (3.3) can be reduced to a set of ordinary differential equations—the original partial differential equation is said to be *separable*.

The separation constants $n(n + 1)$ and $-\lambda^2$ were chosen in their particular forms because doing so led to ordinary differential equations whose solutions are well known. For example, the first of Eqs. (3.11) is an *Euler*- or *Cauchy*-type equation whose general solution is

$$R = C_n r^n + D_n r^{-1-n}$$

where C_n and D_n are arbitrary constants. The second equation in (3.11) is a common equation of vibrations with the general solution

$$\Theta = c_{0\lambda} \cos \lambda\theta + \frac{c_{1\lambda}}{\lambda} \sin \lambda\theta$$

(see Sec. A.2.2, Example A.1), where $c_{0\lambda}$ and $c_{1\lambda}$ are arbitrary constants. The last equation in (3.11) can be transformed (see the Problems) by setting

$$x = \cos \phi \quad \text{and} \quad X(x) = \Phi(\phi)$$

to the *Associated Legendre Equation*

$$(1 - x^2)X'' - 2xX' + \left[n(n + 1) - \frac{\lambda^2}{1 - x^2}\right]X = 0$$

whose solutions are the *Associated Legendre Functions* (see Appendix 3) [1]. The case $\lambda^2 = 0$ is treated in Sec. A.2.2, Example A.2.

Thus we know how to obtain solutions for Eqs. (3.11). In fact, because they are ordinary differential equations of simple types, there are closed-form general solutions for each equation. Furthermore, each general solution has an arbitrary constant for each order of the equation, *and* since each equation contains unspecified separation constants—namely, $n(n + 1)$ and $-\lambda^2$—there are a different set of arbitrary constants for each value of the separation constants. For example, given n and λ^2, we can form a solution to (3.3), using subscripts to indicate dependence on n and λ^2,

$$u(r, \theta, \phi; n, \lambda) = R_n(r)\Theta_\lambda(\theta)\Phi_{n\lambda}(\phi) \tag{3.12}$$

But (3.3) is linear. Thus, by superposition,

$$u(r, \theta, \phi) = \sum_\lambda \sum_n R_n(r)\Theta_\lambda(\theta)\Phi_{n\lambda}(\phi) \tag{3.13}$$

is also a solution. Here we have simply added up all the individual solutions (3.12) that are available for each value of n, λ^2. Recall that there are many, many arbitrary constants in (3.13). We have thus generated a solution to (3.4), and the solution has arbitrary constants that should be valuable in satisfying auxiliary conditions. The remaining sections of this chapter are concerned with specific applications and justification of the separation method and the series solutions thereby generated in the case of a simple vibration-type equation with constant coefficients. The properties and applications of equations with variable coefficients, such as the Cauchy and Legendre equations, are treated under their general title, Sturm-Liouville equations, in Chap. 4.

Because of its simplicity, separation of variables is one of the most frequently used methods in applied mathematics. For this reason, we shall study the method and its applications extensively. On the other hand, the method has significant limitations that must be recognized. For example, nonlinear and inhomogeneous equations may not be separable. The Problems are designed to provide the experience necessary for the reader to learn when an equation can be fruitfully separated. Finally, the auxiliary conditions of a particular model may prevent separation of variables in the model as a whole; however, let us postpone discussion of this point until the end of the chapter, when we have the background afforded by experience with the method.

3.2   FORMAL SOLUTIONS

The method of separation of variables is now applied to the initial-boundary-value problem for heat conduction in a thin rod (see Table 2.1). From Table 2.1, for $l_1 = 1$,

$$u_t = ku_{xx}, \qquad 0 < t, \quad 0 < x < 1 \tag{3.14a}$$

$$u(0, t) = 0, \qquad 0 < t \tag{3.14b}$$

$$u(1, t) = 0, \qquad 0 < t \tag{3.14c}$$

$$u(x, 0) = u_0(x), \qquad 0 < x < 1 \tag{3.14d}$$

Because we believe that (3.14) represents a well-posed problem, we expect the existence of a unique solution that depends continuously on the prescribed data. If we find only one solution, we will be satisfied for now that existence and uniqueness hold; however, we shall test any solution for continuous dependence on the initial data. A function $u(x, t)$ is a solution of (3.14) if each of the equations becomes an identity in the independent variables (x, t) upon substitution of u and its appropriate derivatives in the equation. In our present formulation, the solution is not defined at $(0, 0)$ and $(1, 0)$. However, if $u_0(x)$ is zero at $x = 0$ and $x = 1$, then we may replace (3.14d) by $u(x, 0) = u_0(x)$, $0 \leq x \leq 1$, and a solution valid for $0 \leq x \leq 1$, $0 \leq t$ can be found (see Chap. 6 for a detailed consideration of this point).

The governing equation of (3.14) is identical to (3.1), so let's use (3.2), $u(x, t) = X(x)T(t)$, to separate variables so that

$$XT' = kX''T$$

Logically, then,

$$\frac{T'}{kT} = \frac{X''}{X} = -\lambda^2$$

and

$$
\begin{aligned}
T' + \lambda^2 kT &= 0 \\
X'' + \lambda^2 X &= 0
\end{aligned}
\tag{3.15}
$$

From the auxiliary conditions of (3.14), we get

$$X(0)T(t) = 0 \tag{3.16}$$

$$X(1)T(t) = 0 \tag{3.17}$$

$$X(x)T(0) = u_0(x) \tag{3.18}$$

Clearly, (3.16) and (3.17) are meaningfully satisfied if $X(0) = X(1) = 0$. But $X(x)$ must then satisfy the ordinary-differential-equation, boundary-value problem:

$$
\begin{aligned}
X'' + \lambda^2 X &= 0 \\
X(0) &= 0 \\
X(1) &= 0
\end{aligned}
\tag{3.19}
$$

Interestingly, (3.19) is not well posed; that is, a second-order equation with only two boundary conditions *and* a free parameter λ^2 does not have a unique solution. Since the general solution of the equation has two arbitrary constants, the outcome of solving (3.19) should yield either a determination of the constants as functions of λ^2 or perhaps elimination of one constant and a determination of λ^2.

Equation (3.18) cannot be satisfied because $X(x)$ is the solution of (3.19) and $u_0(x)$ is arbitrary. Thus the solutions $X(x)$ cannot be matched to the arbitrary *function* $u_0(x)$ by use of a multiplying *constant* $T(0)$. We shall not try to satisfy (3.18); rather, we shall work directly to satisfy (3.14d) after solving (3.19).

Returning to (3.19), we recall that the general solution to the governing equation is

$$X(x) = c_0 \cos \lambda x + c_1 \frac{\sin \lambda x}{\lambda} \tag{3.20}$$

(see, e.g., [3] or Example A.1, Sec. A.2.2). We must distinguish three cases—$\lambda^2 > 0$, $\lambda^2 < 0$, and $\lambda^2 = 0$. When $\lambda^2 > 0$, (3.20) remains as is. When $\lambda^2 < 0$, $\lambda = i\Lambda$, so that

$\Lambda^2 > 0$. Then (3.20) becomes

$$X(x) = c_0 \cosh \Lambda x + c_1 \frac{\sinh \Lambda x}{\Lambda}, \qquad \Lambda^2 > 0 \qquad (3.21)$$

Finally, as $\lambda^2 \to 0$ (or $\Lambda^2 \to 0$), (3.20) becomes

$$X(x) = c_0 + c_1 x, \qquad \lambda^2 = \Lambda^2 = 0 \qquad (3.22)$$

since

$$\lim_{\lambda \to 0} \frac{\sin \lambda x}{\lambda} = \lim_{\Lambda \to 0} \frac{\sinh \Lambda x}{\Lambda} = x$$

We seek to delineate solutions to (3.19) in the foregoing three cases; we consider them in inverse order.

Upon introduction into the first boundary condition of (3.19), (3.22) yields

$$c_0 = 0 \qquad (3.23)$$

Then $X(1) = 0$ produces

$$c_1 = 0 \qquad (3.24)$$

From (3.23) and (3.24), we conclude that $X(x) \equiv 0$ when $\lambda^2 = 0$; therefore only a trivial solution exists for $\lambda^2 = 0$.

Upon introduction into the first boundary condition of (3.19), (3.21) yields

$$c_0 = 0$$

Then $X(1) = 0$ produces

$$c_1 \frac{\sinh \Lambda}{\Lambda} = 0$$

Since $\sinh \Lambda \neq 0$ for any $\Lambda^2 > 0$, only $c_1 = 0$ is possible. Thus again we conclude that $X(x) \equiv 0$ when $\lambda^2 < 0$ ($\Lambda^2 > 0$), and only a trivial solution exists for $\lambda^2 < 0$ *in this case*.

Finally, introduction of (3.20) into the first boundary condition of (3.19) yields

$$c_0 = 0 \qquad (3.25)$$

whence introduction of (3.20) into the second boundary condition produces

$$c_1 \frac{\sin \lambda}{\lambda} = 0, \qquad \lambda^2 > 0 \qquad (3.26)$$

Now either $c_1 = 0$, which clearly is of no value, or since $\lambda^2 \neq 0$,

$$\sin \lambda = 0 \qquad (3.27)$$

But the sine function is periodic with period 2π and is oscillatory; therefore the values

$$\lambda^2 = (n\pi)^2, \qquad n = 1, 2, 3, \ldots$$

satisfy (3.27). In summary, noting that there is a distinct arbitrary constant c_1 for each value of λ^2 and incorporating the λ in the denominator of (3.20) into c_1, we now write the solution to (3.19)

$$X(x) = c_{1n} \sin \lambda_n x \tag{3.28}$$

where

$$\lambda_n^2 = (n\pi)^2, \qquad n = 1, 2, 3, \ldots$$

and the c_{1n} are arbitrary constants. Note that only particular $\lambda^2 = \lambda_n^2$ satisfy (3.19); these λ_n^2 are the values belonging to the problem (3.19) or, from the German *eigenwerte*, the *eigenvalues*. Accordingly, the functions $\sin \lambda_n x$ are the functions belonging to the problem (3.19) or the *eigenfunctions*, and problem (3.19) is the *eigenvalue problem* for the initial-boundary-value problem (3.14).

The reader should convince himself that because $\sin(-x) = -\sin x$ and the c_{1n} are arbitrary, values of $\lambda_n < 0$ make no new contribution and thus can be ignored. Similar remarks can be made in regard to the cosine function when it appears in eigenvalue problems. Also, although we have yet to prove it (see Sec. 4.3), the eigenvalues and eigenfunctions that we encounter here and later are all real.

The solution to the T-equation in (3.15) is known to be (see Sec. A.2.1)

$$T(t) = e^{-\lambda^2 kt} \tag{3.29}$$

Our solution $u(x, t) = XT$ for (3.14a) to (3.14c) can then be written for each λ_n^2 as

$$u_n(x, t; \lambda_n^2) = c_{1n} e^{-\lambda_n^2 kt} \sin \lambda_n x \tag{3.30}$$

In view of the linearity and homogeneity of (3.14a) to (3.14c), the sum

$$u(x, t) = \sum_{n=1}^{\infty} u_n(x, t; \lambda_n^2) = \sum_{n=1}^{\infty} c_{1n} e^{-\lambda_n^2 kt} \sin \lambda_n x \tag{3.31}$$

is also a solution to (3.14a) to (3.14c) according to the principle of superposition. From (3.14d) and (3.31), we have

$$u(x, 0) = u_0(x) = \sum_{n=1}^{\infty} c_{1n} \sin \lambda_n x \tag{3.32}$$

This is a purely formal relationship, for we have demonstrated neither that the c_{1n} can be found so that (3.32) is true nor that such a series is convergent. In fact, however, the c_{1n} can be found through use of a valuable property of eigenfunctions called *orthogonality*.

The functions $\sin \lambda_n x$ and $\sin \lambda_m x$, where $m \neq n$ and $\lambda_m^2 = (m\pi)^2$, are called *orthogonal* on the interval $0 \leq x \leq 1$ because

$$\int_0^1 \sin \lambda_n x \sin \lambda_m x \, dx = 0, \qquad m \neq n \tag{3.33}$$

as may be seen by direct integration in this simple case. When $m = n$,

$$\int_0^1 \sin^2 \lambda_n x \, dx = \tfrac{1}{2} \tag{3.34}$$

Because of (3.33) and (3.34), we may multiply (3.32) by $\sin \lambda_m x$ and integrate over $0 \leq x \leq 1$ to obtain

$$\int_0^1 u_0(x) \sin \lambda_m x \, dx = \tfrac{1}{2} c_{1m} \qquad (3.35)$$

since only one term survives on the right-hand side of (3.32).

Thus, for the initial-boundary-value problem (3.14), we have obtained

1. Eigenvalues: $\qquad \lambda_n^2 = (n\pi)^2, \qquad n = 1, 2, 3, \ldots$ $\qquad\qquad$ (3.36a)

2. Eigenfunctions: $\qquad\qquad\qquad \sin \lambda_n x$ $\qquad\qquad\qquad\qquad$ (3.36b)

3. The formal solution:

$$u(x, t) = \sum_{n=1}^{\infty} c_{1n} e^{-n^2 \pi^2 k t} \sin n\pi x \qquad (3.36c)$$

where

$$c_{1n} = 2 \int_0^1 u_0(x) \sin n\pi x \, dx \qquad (3.36d)$$

The formal solution is also called an *eigenfunction expansion* for obvious reasons.

In summary, Eqs. (3.36) give a solution for the mathematical model (3.14) under the implied assumption that the series converges suitably. It seems plausible that the solution (3.36c) both exists and is unique in view of (3.36d)—that is, only a single set of coefficients was found. Furthermore, let us introduce a small error term $\Delta(x)$ into the initial data and employ a shorthand Δ-notation to denote terms involving the small error. We can see then that (3.36d) becomes

$$c_{1n}^{\Delta} = 2 \int_0^1 [u_0(x) + \Delta(x)] \sin n\pi x \, dx \qquad (3.37a)$$

$$c_{1n}^{\Delta} = c_{1n} + 2 \int_0^1 \Delta(x) \sin n\pi x \, dx \qquad (3.37b)$$

$$c_{1n}^{\Delta} = c_{1n} + \Delta c_{1n} \qquad (3.37c)$$

so

$$u^{\Delta}(x, t) = u(x, t) + \sum_{n=1}^{\infty} \Delta c_{1n} e^{-n^2 \pi^2 k t} \sin n\pi x \qquad (3.38)$$

for $t > 0$. Now, from (3.37b) and (3.37c), we find that if $\max [\Delta(x)]$ is the largest absolute value of $\Delta(x)$ on the interval, then

$$|\Delta c_{1n}| \leq 2 \max [\Delta(x)] = 2\Delta_m \qquad (3.39)$$

because

$$\Delta_m = \max [\Delta(x)] \int_0^1 dx \geq \int_0^1 \Delta(x) \sin n\pi x \, dx, \qquad |\sin n\pi x| \leq 1$$

Therefore, in (3.38),

$$|u^{\Delta}(x, t) - u(x, t)| \leq 2\Delta_m \left| \sum_{n=1}^{\infty} e^{-n^2\pi^2kt} \sin n\pi x \right| \tag{3.40}$$

when we remove the constant term $2\Delta_m$ from each term of the series. Next, by virtue of the ratio test [2] for infinite series, the series

$$S_c(t) = \sum_{n=1}^{\infty} |e^{-n^2\pi^2kt}|$$

is absolutely convergent *for any fixed* $t > 0$. Accordingly, the Wierstrass M-test [2] shows that the series

$$S_f(x, t) = \sum_{n=1}^{\infty} |e^{-n^2\pi^2kt} \sin n\pi x| \leq S_c \tag{3.41}$$

is uniformly convergent. Clearly,

$$\left| \sum_{n=1}^{\infty} e^{-n^2\pi^2kt} \sin n\pi x \right| \leq S_f$$

is always less than some finite number M because the convergent series S_c is bounded from above, whence

$$|u^{\Delta}(x, t) - u(x, t)| \leq 2M \max [\Delta(x)] \tag{3.42}$$

Thus the solution (3.36c) is continuous with respect to small changes in the initial data, since small data changes lead to small solution changes—namely, the change in u is of the order of the maximum data change.

Finally, we make use of (3.41) to show that the series (3.36c) is also uniformly convergent for $t > 0$. From (3.36d),

$$|c_{1n}| \leq 2|u_0|_{\max}$$

Accordingly, (3.36c) can be written as

$$\frac{u(x, t)}{2|u_0|_{\max}} = \sum_{n=1}^{\infty} \alpha_n e^{-n^2\pi^2kt} \sin n\pi x$$

where

$$|\alpha_n| = \frac{|c_{1n}|}{2|u_0|_{\max}} \leq 1$$

However, the absolute value of each term in this series is less than or equal to the corresponding term of the uniformly convergent series $S_f(x, t)$ [see (3.41)]. It follows that (3.36c) is also a uniformly convergent series for $t > 0$.

3.3   THE FOURIER SERIES

In the previous section the formal solution to a mathematical model was obtained, in part, by representing the known initial-value function by an infinite trigonometric series. The series was composed of sine terms and constant coefficients that could be explicitly evaluated. As an example, a representative series for a known function $S(x)$ in $0 \leq x \leq \pi$ is [see (3.32)]

$$S(x) = \sum_{n=1}^{\infty} s_n \sin nx, \qquad 0 \leq x \leq \pi \tag{3.43}$$

We are able to determine the s_n because

$$\int_0^\pi \sin nx \sin mx \, dx = 0, \qquad m \neq n$$

while

$$\int_0^\pi \sin^2 mx \, dx = \frac{\pi}{2}$$

That is, the $\sin mx$ are orthogonal on $0 \leq x \leq \pi$. Multiplying (3.43) by $\sin mx$ and integrating over $(0, \pi)$ yield directly

$$s_m = \frac{2}{\pi} \int_0^\pi S(x) \sin mx \, dx \tag{3.43a}$$

It is easy to show (see the Problems) that a cosine series can be written as

$$C(x) = \tfrac{1}{2}c_0 + \sum_{n=1}^{\infty} c_n \cos nx, \qquad 0 \leq x \leq \pi \tag{3.44}$$

and that via orthogonality

$$c_m = \frac{2}{\pi} \int_0^\pi C(x) \cos mx \, dx \tag{3.44a}$$

As a logical extension of (3.43) and (3.44) and their coefficient expressions, the more general expression for a function $F(x)$ in $-\pi \leq x \leq \pi$ is

$$F(x) = \tfrac{1}{2}c_0 + \sum_{n=1}^{\infty} c_n \cos nx + s_n \sin nx \tag{3.45}$$

Direct integration confirms that

$$\int_{-\pi}^\pi \sin mx \sin nx \, dx = \int_{-\pi}^\pi \cos mx \cos nx \, dx = 0, \qquad m \neq n$$

$$\int_{-\pi}^\pi \cos px \sin qx \, dx = 0 \qquad \text{for all } p \text{ and } q$$

and

$$\int_{-\pi}^\pi \cos^2 mx \, dx = \int_{-\pi}^\pi \sin^2 mx \, dx = \pi, \qquad m \geq 1$$

Hence multiplying (3.45) by $\sin mx$ and integrating over $(-\pi, \pi)$ give

$$s_m = \frac{1}{\pi} \int_{-\pi}^\pi F(x) \sin mx \, dx, \qquad m \geq 1 \tag{3.45a}$$

whereas multiplying (3.45) by $\cos mx$ and integrating over $(-\pi, \pi)$ give

$$c_m = \frac{1}{\pi} \int_{-\pi}^{\pi} F(x) \cos mx \, dx, \qquad m \geq 0 \qquad (3.45b)$$

The series given by (3.43) to (3.45) are called *Fourier Series* after their developer, Jean Baptiste Joseph Fourier. He developed these series while solving a problem in heat flow and published his results in 1822 in his now classic *Theorie analytique de la chaleur*. Usually the series (3.43) to (3.44) are called the sine and cosine series, respectively, or the half-range expansions, while (3.45) is the full-range expansion. Our concern with Fourier series is twofold. First, we need to understand their character. Second, we need to prove that they converge so that we may use them with confidence when they arise in our analyses.

A most important characteristic of Fourier series, as must be clear from the nature of their component terms, is that the series are periodic. Thus once the coefficients are determined in (3.45), for example, the series gives for all x a representation that is periodic with period 2π. Only in the region $-\pi \leq x \leq \pi$ does the series represent $F(x)$, which may or may not be periodic. Because we need only represent arbitrary functions in fixed intervals, the periodic nature of the series is not of interest except as it affects convergence. Typical plots of Fourier series are shown in Fig. 3.1. In each case, the period is 2π.

When $F(x) = -F(-x)$—that is, $F(x)$ is odd—the full-range expansion (3.45) degenerates to a form equivalent to (3.43). When $F(x) = F(-x)$—that is, $F(x)$ is even—the full-range expansion (3.45) degenerates to a form equivalent to (3.44). In both cases, it is then necessary to specify the known function only on $(0, \pi)$. This point is explored further in the Problems.

3.3.1 The Convergence of the Series

The application of Fourier series in the solution of partial differential equations depends on two factors. First, the proper type of series must be selected; as we saw earlier, this step is accomplished when the eigenfunctions are determined. Second, the selected series must converge suitably so that a valid representation of the problem's solution function is obtained. In Sec. 3.2 the uniform convergence of the solution series (3.36c) within the x-t domain was demonstrated. It remains then to show that series of the type (3.32), postulated for the initial condition, do in fact converge to the given initial value. We shall give a convergence proof for (3.45). The reader should be able to discern the few minor modifications needed to extend the results to (3.43) and (3.44).

For our proof we require that a function $f(x)$ be known such that

(a) $f(x)$ is periodic with period 2π.
(b) $f'(x)$ exists and is continuous in $-\pi \leq x \leq \pi$; accordingly, $f(x)$ is continuous also.
(c) $f(x) = F(x), \qquad -\pi \leq x \leq \pi.$

$$(3.46)$$

More general developments can be found in Refs. [2, 3, 4, 5, 6] and the Problems.

THEOREM 3.1   If a function $f(x)$ satisfies conditions (3.46) in $-\pi \leq x \leq \pi$, then the Fourier series (3.45) with coefficients given by (3.45a and b) converges for $-\pi < x < \pi$ to $f(x)$.

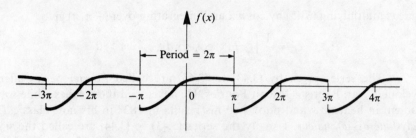

Typical representation by full-range Fourier series with
basic interval $-\pi \leq x \leq \pi$.

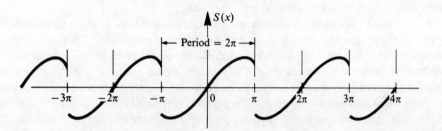

Typical representation by half-range Fourier sine series
with basic interval $0 \leq x \leq \pi$.

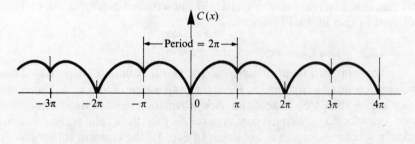

Typical representation by half-range Fourier cosine series
with basic interval $0 \leq x \leq \pi$.

FIGURE 3.1

Proof: Convergence of the series is established through the use of partial
sums and a limit process.

Let

$$PS_k = \tfrac{1}{2}c_0 + \sum_{n=1}^{k} c_n \cos nx + s_n \sin nx$$

Using the coefficient equations (3.45a and b) in the partial sum produces [recall that
$f(x) = F(x)$ here]

$$PS_k = \frac{1}{2\pi} \int_{-\pi}^{\pi} f(\xi)\, d\xi + \frac{1}{\pi} \sum_{n=1}^{k} \int_{-\pi}^{\pi} f(\xi)(\cos n\xi \cos nx + \sin n\xi \sin nx)\, d\xi$$

The order of integration and summation may be interchanged freely in the case of finite sums; hence

$$PS_k = \frac{1}{\pi} \int_{-\pi}^{\pi} f(\xi) \left[\frac{1}{2} + \sum_{n=1}^{k} (\cos n\xi \cos nx + \sin n\xi \sin nx) \right] d\xi \qquad (3.47)$$

Now let

$$I = \frac{1}{2} + \sum_{n=1}^{k} (\cos n\xi \cos nx + \sin n\xi \sin nx) = \frac{1}{2} + \sum_{n=1}^{k} \cos n(\xi - x) \qquad (3.48)$$

and $t = \xi - x$, whence*

$$I = \frac{1}{2} + \sum_{n=1}^{k} \cos nt = \frac{1}{2} \left[1 + \frac{2 \cos \left[\frac{1}{2}(k + 1)t \right] \sin kt/2}{\sin t/2} \right]$$

$$= \frac{1}{2} \frac{\sin \left[(k + \frac{1}{2})t \right]}{\sin t/2}$$

Thus, in (3.47),

$$PS_k = \frac{1}{\pi} \int_{-\pi}^{\pi} f(t + x) \frac{\sin \left[(k + \frac{1}{2})t \right]}{2 \sin t/2} \, dt$$

Because of the periodicity of our functions, it was not necessary to shift the limits of integration in the foregoing equation. In addition, direct integration of (3.48) shows that

$$\int_{-\pi}^{\pi} I(t) \, dt = \int_{-\pi}^{\pi} \frac{\sin \left[(k + \frac{1}{2})t \right]}{2 \sin t/2} \, dt = \pi$$

We wish to show that $PS_k - f(x)$ is zero as $k \to \infty$—that is, that the series converges. Using the preceding results gives

$$PS_k - f(x) = \frac{1}{\pi} \int_{-\pi}^{\pi} \frac{f(t + x) - f(x)}{2 \sin t/2} \sin \left[\left(k + \frac{1}{2} \right) t \right] dt \qquad (3.49)$$

and we can investigate the limit of the right-hand side of (3.49) as $k \to \infty$ to complete our proof. Let

$$\alpha(t) = \frac{f(t + x) - f(x)}{2 \sin t/2}$$

Clearly, $\alpha(t)$ is bounded and continuous, except perhaps where $t = 0$. Near $t = 0$, we have, from a series expansion (see Example A.1, Sec. A.2.2),

$$\sin \frac{t}{2} = \frac{1}{2}t + O(t^3) \quad \text{or} \quad \lim_{t \to 0} \left(\frac{\sin t/2}{\frac{1}{2}t} \right) = 1$$

while because $f(x)$ has a derivative everywhere in the interval $-\pi \le x \le \pi$,

$$\lim_{t \to 0} \frac{f(x + t) - f(x)}{t} = f'(x)$$

* See L. B. W. Jolley, *Summation of Series*, 2nd ed., revised. New York: Dover, 1961.

[The order notation $O(t)$ is defined in Appendix 1.] Therefore

$$\lim_{t \to 0} \alpha(t) = \lim_{t \to 0} \left\{ \frac{f(t + x) - f(x)}{t} \cdot \frac{t/2}{\sin t/2} \right\}$$

$$= \lim_{t \to 0} \left\{ \frac{f(t + x) - f(x)}{t} \right\} \cdot \lim_{t \to 0} \left\{ \frac{t/2}{\sin t/2} \right\} = f'(x)$$

whence $\alpha(t)$ is seen to be bounded at $t = 0$ because $f'(x)$ exists and is continuous in $-\pi \le x \le \pi$ according to assumptions (3.46). From the definition of $\alpha(t)$ above and the continuity of $f(x)$ and $\sin t/2$, it follows now that $\alpha(t)$ is bounded everywhere in $-\pi \le t \le \pi$ if $\alpha(0)$ is taken as

$$\alpha(0) = \lim_{t \to 0} \alpha(t)$$

Otherwise $\alpha(t)$ is not defined at $t = 0$.

Then we seek

$$\lim_{k \to \infty} \int_{-\pi}^{\pi} \alpha(t) \sin (k + \tfrac{1}{2})t \, dt = 0 \tag{3.50}$$

This result can be established by use of the Riemann-Lebesgue lemma (the proof follows that by Sagan [5]*):

LEMMA: If a function $\alpha(t)$ is bounded and continuous on $a \le x \le b$, then

$$\lim_{\beta \to \infty} \int_{a}^{b} \alpha(t) \sin \beta t \, dt = 0$$

Proof: Let $t = \tau + \pi\beta^{-1}$, where β is sufficiently large, so that $b - \pi\beta^{-1} > a$. Then $\sin \beta t = \sin \beta(\tau + \pi\beta^{-1}) = -\sin \beta\tau$ and

$$L = \int_{a}^{b} \alpha(t) \sin \beta t \, dt = -\int_{a - \pi\beta^{-1}}^{b - \pi\beta^{-1}} \alpha(\tau + \pi\beta^{-1}) \sin \beta\tau \, d\tau$$

Clearly,

$$2L = \int_{a}^{b} \alpha(t) \sin \beta t \, dt - \int_{a - \pi\beta^{-1}}^{b - \pi\beta^{-1}} \alpha(\tau + \pi\beta^{-1}) \sin \beta\tau \, d\tau$$

Changing the dummy variable of integration in the second integral to t again and grouping terms produce

$$2L = \int_{a}^{b - \pi\beta^{-1}} [\alpha(t) - \alpha(t + \pi\beta^{-1})] \sin \beta t \, dt$$

$$+ \int_{b - \pi\beta^{-1}}^{b} \alpha(t) \sin \beta t \, dt - \int_{a - \pi\beta^{-1}}^{a} \alpha(t + \pi\beta^{-1}) \sin \beta t \, dt$$

Now α is bounded so $|\alpha(t)| \leq M$, and $|\sin \beta t| \leq 1$. Thus

$$\left| \int_{b-\pi\beta^{-1}}^{b} \alpha(t) \sin \beta t \, dt \right| \leq \frac{\pi M}{\beta},$$

$$\left| \int_{a-\pi\beta^{-1}}^{a} \alpha(t + \pi\beta^{-1}) \sin \beta t \, dt \right| \leq \frac{\pi M}{\beta},$$

$$\left| \int_{a}^{b-\pi\beta^{-1}} [\alpha(t) - \alpha(t + \pi\beta^{-1})] \sin \beta t \, dt \right| \leq \int_{a}^{b-\pi\beta^{-1}} |\alpha(t) - \alpha(t + \pi\beta^{-1})| \, dt,$$

and

$$2|L| \leq \frac{2\pi M}{\beta} + \int_{a}^{b-\pi\beta^{-1}} |\alpha(t) - \alpha(t + \pi\beta^{-1})| \, dt$$

Now, because $\alpha(t)$ is continuous, there exists a $\pi\beta^{-1} < \delta$ such that

$$|\alpha(t) - \alpha(t + \pi\beta^{-1})| \leq |\alpha(t) - \alpha(t + \delta)| \leq \frac{\varepsilon}{b - a - \pi\beta^{-1}}$$

for $a \leq t \leq b - \pi\beta^{-1}$ and ε arbitrarily small. Let β be so large that $2\pi M/\beta < \varepsilon$ and $\pi/\beta < \delta$; then

$$2|L| \leq 2\varepsilon \rightarrow |L| < \varepsilon$$

for sufficiently large β. Clearly,

$$\lim_{\beta \to \infty} L = 0 \qquad\qquad \text{Q.E.D.}$$

Because $k = \beta - \frac{1}{2}$ and $\alpha(t)$ is continuous, (3.50) must be satisfied in accordance with the lemma. But from (3.49), then,

$$\lim_{k \to \infty} [\text{PS}_k - f(x)] = 0$$

and the partial sums of the Fourier series converge to $f(x)$ for any x in $-\pi < x < \pi$.

$$\text{Q.E.D.}$$

3.3.2   Uniform Convergence; Mean-Square Approximation; Completeness

The pointwise convergence of Fourier series has been demonstrated in Sec. 3.3.1. To establish a base for further applications, we discuss now some additional properties of the Fourier series.

In establishing pointwise convergence, we have shown that $\text{PS}_k \to f(x)$ as $k \to \infty$. Thus, in fact, PS_N approximates $f(x)$ because, according to the properties of sequences and our proofs in Sec. 3.3.1, we can always set N large enough so that, for a given x,

$$|\text{PS}_N - f(x)| < \varepsilon \qquad\qquad (3.51)$$

for any arbitrary small $\varepsilon > 0$. However, is the convergence of the Fourier series uniform; that is, does an N exist so that (3.51) holds for all x? Also, are there other useful definitions of convergence that can be employed in our applications or theoretical developments? We shall touch on these questions here; more extensive remarks are to be found in the references [2–6].

First, the question of uniform convergence is answered by the following theorem for a useful, but special, case:

THEOREM 3.2   If a function $f(x)$ satisfies conditions (3.46) *and* has a continuous second derivative, then the Fourier series (3.45), with coefficients given by (3.45a and b), converges uniformly for all x.

Proof: The coefficients of our series are

$$s_m = \frac{1}{\pi} \int_{-\pi}^{\pi} f(x) \sin mx \, dx, \qquad m \geq 1 \tag{3.52}$$

and

$$c_m = \frac{1}{\pi} \int_{-\pi}^{\pi} f(x) \cos mx \, dx, \qquad m \geq 0 \tag{3.53}$$

while

$$f(x) = \tfrac{1}{2} c_0 + \sum_{n=1}^{\infty} (s_n \sin nx + c_n \cos nx), \qquad -\pi < x < \pi \tag{3.54}$$

Consider the s_m. We integrate by parts twice to achieve

$$s_m = \frac{1}{\pi} \int_{-\pi}^{\pi} f(x) \sin mx \, dx$$

$$= \frac{1}{\pi} \left[\frac{-f(x) \cos mx}{m} \Big|_{-\pi}^{\pi} + \frac{1}{m} \int_{-\pi}^{\pi} f'(x) \cos mx \, dx \right]$$

0 due to the continuity and periodicity of $f(x)$

$$= \frac{1}{m\pi} \left[\frac{f'(x) \sin mx}{m} \Big|_{-\pi}^{\pi} - \frac{1}{m} \int_{-\pi}^{\pi} f''(x) \sin mx \, dx \right]$$

0 due to the continuity of $f'(x)$

$$= -\frac{1}{m^2 \pi} \int_{-\pi}^{\pi} f''(x) \sin mx \, dx$$

Since $f''(x)$ is continuous, $|f''(x)| < K$ for some real number K. Because $|\sin mx| \leq 1$, it follows that

$$|s_m| \leq \frac{1}{m^2 \pi} \int_{-\pi}^{\pi} K \, dx = \frac{2K}{m^2}, \qquad m \geq 1$$

Similarly, from (3.53),

$$|c_m| \leq \frac{2K}{m^2}, \qquad m \geq 1$$

The series of constants

$$\frac{1}{2}|c_0| + \sum_{n=1}^{\infty} \left(\frac{2K}{n^2} + \frac{2K}{n^2}\right)$$

is convergent [1]. But then each term of the Fourier series (3.54) is less than or equal to the corresponding term of this convergent series of constants. According to the Wierstrass M-test [2], the series (3.54) is then uniformly convergent.   Q.E.D.

Now, in lieu of pointwise convergence, suppose that we study the approximation of $f(x)$ by PS_k in the sense of *least squares* or in the *mean*; that is, we examine

$$\int_{-\pi}^{\pi} [PS_k - f(x)]^2 \, dx \geq 0 \tag{3.55}$$

First, because $\lim_{k \to \infty} [PS_k - f(x)] = 0$ for all x in $-\pi < x < \pi$,

$$\lim_{k \to \infty} \int_{-\pi}^{\pi} [PS_k - f(x)]^2 \, dx = 0 \tag{3.56}$$

Second, when the Fourier series converges uniformly, there exists an N such that

$$|PS_N - f(x)| < \left(\frac{\varepsilon}{2\pi}\right)^{1/2}$$

Hence

$$\int_{-\pi}^{\pi} |PS_N - f(x)|^2 \, dx < \varepsilon \tag{3.57}$$

That is, the Fourier series (3.45) then also converges in the sense of least squares or in the mean.

Now introduce the Fourier series (3.45) into (3.55) to achieve

$$\int_{-\pi}^{\pi} \left[\frac{1}{2}c_0 + \sum_{n=1}^{k} (c_n \cos nx + s_n \sin nx) - f(x)\right]^2 dx \geq 0 \tag{3.58}$$

In view of (3.45a and b) and the orthogonality relations for $\sin nx$ and $\cos nx$, we can formally expand this result to the ultimate form

$$\int_{-\pi}^{\pi} f^2(x) \, dx - \pi \left[\frac{c_0^2}{2} + \sum_{n=1}^{k} (c_n^2 + s_n^2)\right] \geq 0$$

or

$$\frac{c_0^2}{2} + \sum_{n=1}^{k} (c_n^2 + s_n^2) \leq \frac{1}{\pi} \int_{-\pi}^{\pi} f^2(x) \, dx \tag{3.59}$$

for all k. Because the right-hand side of (3.59) is finite in view of conditions (3.46) on $f(x)$ and is independent of k, it follows immediately that we may let $k \to \infty$ and obtain the so-called *Bessel inequality*

$$\frac{c_0^2}{2} + \sum_{n=1}^{\infty} (c_n^2 + s_n^2) \leq \frac{1}{\pi} \int_{-\pi}^{\pi} f^2(x) \, dx \tag{3.60}$$

But from Eqs. (3.56) through (3.59), equality must hold in (3.60) for our special case of the Fourier series and coefficients; that is,

$$\frac{c_0^2}{2} + \sum_{n=1}^{\infty} (c_n^2 + s_n^2) = \frac{1}{\pi} \int_{-\pi}^{\pi} f^2(x)\,dx \tag{3.61}$$

This is called *Parseval's equation*, and it holds only if (3.56) holds.

Finally, we are led to define a *completeness* concept.

DEFINITION   If for a class of functions $f(x)$ satisfying certain conditions—for example, conditions (3.46)—it is possible to find for any arbitrary small $\varepsilon > 0$ an N such that, for $-\pi \le x \le \pi$,

$$\int_{-\pi}^{\pi} \left[\frac{c_0}{2} + \sum_{n=1}^{k} (c_n \cos nx + s_n \sin nx) - f(x) \right]^2 dx < \varepsilon \tag{3.62}$$

for all $k > N$, then the set of orthogonal trigonometric functions—1, $\cos nx$, $\sin nx$—is *complete* with respect to the class of functions $f(x)$. Clearly, our set of trigonometric functions is complete with respect to functions satisfying (3.46) [see (3.57)]. Also, the validity of Parseval's equation (3.61) implies completeness, and vice versa. Accordingly, the validity of Parseval's equation is equivalent to completeness.

In conclusion, we remark without proof that every continuous function can be approximated in the mean by trigonometric polynomials (the partial sums PS_k). Again, this means that the trigonometric functions are a complete set and the approximation can be carried to any desired degree of accuracy by choosing k large enough in (3.62).

3.4 APPLICATIONS AND EXAMPLES

The following examples serve to illustrate the power and range of our method and to point out special features of certain classes of problem.

EXAMPLE 3.1   *Steady-State Heat Conduction in a Thin Plate*. Consider the mathematical model from Table 2.1, where Group 1 boundary conditions are used with $T_3 = T_4 = 0$; that is, find $u(x, y)$ such that

$$u_{xx} + u_{yy} = 0, \qquad 0 < x < l_1, \quad 0 < y < l_2$$

$$\begin{aligned} u(x, 0) &= T_1(x), \\ &\qquad\qquad\qquad\qquad 0 < x < l_1 \\ u(x, l_2) &= T_2(x), \end{aligned} \tag{3.63}$$

$$\begin{aligned} u(0, y) &= 0, \\ &\qquad\qquad\qquad\qquad 0 \le y \le l_2 \\ u(l_1, y) &= 0, \end{aligned}$$

In order to separate variables, let $u(x, y) = X(x)Y(y)$, so that

$$X''Y + XY'' = 0 \quad \text{or} \quad \frac{X''}{X} + \frac{Y''}{Y} = 0$$

Since the homogeneous boundary conditions in (3.63) have x-limits, we introduce the separation constant λ^2 so that

$$\frac{X''}{X} = -\frac{Y''}{Y} = -\lambda^2$$

The eigenvalue problem becomes

$$X'' + \lambda^2 X = 0$$
$$X(0) = X(l_1) = 0 \tag{3.64a}$$

Also,

$$Y'' - \lambda^2 Y = 0 \tag{3.64b}$$

From Sec. 3.2 we deduce that the eigenvalues and eigenfunctions for (3.64a) are [see (3.36a and b)]

$$\lambda_n^2 = \left(\frac{n\pi}{l_1}\right)^2 > 0, \qquad X_n(x) = \sin \lambda_n x \qquad (n = 1, 2, 3, \ldots) \tag{3.65}$$

Also from (3.21) and the discussion preceding it,

$$Y(y) = c_0 \cosh \lambda y + \frac{c_1}{\lambda} \sinh \lambda y$$

In view of these results, we propose

$$u(x, y) = \sum_n X_n(x) Y_n(y) = \sum_{n=1}^{\infty} \left(c_{0n} \cosh \lambda_n y + \frac{c_{1n}}{\lambda_n} \sinh \lambda_n y\right) \sin \lambda_n x \tag{3.66}$$

At $y = 0$, we need

$$u(x, 0) = T_1(x) = \sum_{n=1}^{\infty} c_{0n} \sin \lambda_n x \tag{3.67}$$

The eigenfunctions X_n are orthogonal on the interval $(0 - l_1)$, since

$$\int_0^{l_1} X_n X_m \, dx = \int_0^{l_1} \sin \lambda_n x \sin \lambda_m x \, dx = 0, \qquad m \neq n$$

Furthermore, the so-called *normalizing constants* * N_n are

$$N_n = \int_0^{l_1} X_n^2 \, dx = \int_0^{l_1} \sin^2 \lambda_n x \, dx = \frac{l_1}{2}$$

Thus we multiply (3.67) by $\sin \lambda_m x$ and integrate over $0 \leq x \leq l_1$ to obtain

$$c_{0m} = \frac{2}{l_1} \int_0^{l_1} T_1(x) \sin \lambda_m x \, dx \tag{3.68}$$

At $y = l_2$, we require

$$u(x, l_2) = T_2(x) = \sum_{n=1}^{\infty} \left(c_{0n} \cosh \lambda_n l_2 + \frac{c_{1n}}{\lambda_n} \sinh \lambda_n l_2\right) \sin \lambda_n x$$

---

* If $\phi_n = X_n/N_n, \int_0^{l_1} \phi_n^2 \, dx = 1$; that is, the "new" eigenfunctions ϕ_n are normalized on the value unity. The collection or set of ϕ_n is called *orthonormal*, for it is both orthogonal and normalized.

Another application of the orthogonality relations as above yields

$$c_{0m} \cosh \lambda_m l_2 + \frac{c_{1m}}{\lambda_m} \sinh \lambda_m l_2 = \frac{2}{l_1} \int_0^{l_1} T_2(x) \sin \lambda_m x \, dx$$

and then rearrangement produces

$$c_{1m} = \frac{2\lambda_m}{l_1 \sinh \lambda_m l_2} \int_0^{l_1} T_2(x) \sin \lambda_m x \, dx - \lambda_m \coth \lambda_m l_2 c_{0m} \tag{3.69}$$

By using (3.65) and (3.66), plus (3.68) and (3.69), we assemble the final solution to (3.63) as

$$u(x, y) = \frac{2}{l_1} \sum_{n=1}^{\infty} \left[\left(\cosh \frac{n\pi}{l_1} y - \coth n\pi \frac{l_2}{l_1} \sinh \frac{n\pi}{l_1} y \right) \int_0^{l_1} T_1(\xi) \sin \frac{n\pi}{l_1} \xi \, d\xi \right.$$

$$\left. + \frac{\sinh (n\pi/l_1)y}{\sinh n\pi(l_2/l_1)} \int_0^{l_1} T_2(\xi) \sin \frac{n\pi}{l_1} \xi \, d\xi \right] \sin \frac{n\pi}{l_1} x \tag{3.70}$$

Note that we obtained the solution to this entirely space-dependent problem in a manner completely analogous to that used for the unsteady-state problem in Sec. 3.2.

EXAMPLE 3.2   *A Negative Eigenvalue.* Suppose that we consider again heat conduction in a thin, round, laterally insulated rod equipped with a pair of special feedback devices that relate the temperature u at one end of the rod to the heat flux at the other end. An appropriate mathematical model is

$$u_t = ku_{xx}, \quad 0 < x < 1, \quad 0 < t$$

$$u(0, t) = u_x(1, t),$$
$$\qquad\qquad\qquad\qquad 0 < t \tag{3.71}$$
$$u(1, t) = -u_x(0, t),$$

$$u(x, 0) = u_0(x), \quad 0 \le x \le 1$$

The boundary conditions in (3.71) arise from considering the flux *out* of the rod ends (see Sec. 2.2.1), namely,

$$f_x(1, t) = -Ku_x(1, t) = -\alpha K u(0, t)$$
$$f_{-x}(0, t) = Ku_x(0, t) = -\alpha K u(1, t)$$

where α is representative of the feedback control. Let $\alpha = 1$ for this analysis.

For $\alpha = 1$, $f_x(1, t)$ and $f_{-x}(0, t)$ are negative if we assume $u \ge 0$. Heat flows *into* the otherwise insulated rod at both ends. Clearly, as $t \to \infty$, $u \to \infty$ also because heat accumulates in the rod. The solution to the model (3.71) should give the same result. In practice, it might be useful to set α to zero when some desired temperature level had been reached in the rod, which, being then completely insulated, would hold its heat. Therefore it will be helpful if an estimate of the time required to reach a given high temperature can be made.

To solve (3.71), we propose a product-form solution $u(x, t) = X(x)T(t)$ and separate variables. This gives, from the differential equation,

$$XT' = kX''T \quad \text{or} \quad \frac{T'}{kT} = \frac{X''}{X} = -\lambda^2$$

and from the boundary conditions,

$$X(0)T(t) = X'(1)T(t) \quad \text{or} \quad X(0) = X'(1)$$

$$X(1)T(t) = -X'(0)T(t) \quad \text{or} \quad X(1) = -X'(0)$$

Thus the eigenvalue problem is

$$X'' + \lambda^2 X = 0, \qquad 0 < x < 1$$

$$X'(1) - X(0) = 0 \tag{3.72a}$$

$$X'(0) + X(1) = 0$$

and T must satisfy

$$T' + k\lambda^2 T = 0 \tag{3.72b}$$

From (3.20), the solution to the differential equation of the eigenvalue problem (3.72a) is

$$X(x) = c_0 \cos \lambda x + c_1 \frac{\sin \lambda x}{\lambda}$$

so

$$X'(x) = -c_0 \lambda \sin \lambda x + c_1 \cos \lambda x$$

Substitution of this solution and its derivative in the boundary conditions of (3.72a) produces

$$-c_0 \lambda \sin \lambda + c_1 \cos \lambda - c_0 = 0$$

$$c_1 + c_0 \cos \lambda + c_1 \frac{\sin \lambda}{\lambda} = 0$$

or

$$(1 + \lambda \sin \lambda)c_0 - \cos \lambda c_1 = 0$$

$$\cos \lambda c_0 + \left(1 + \frac{\sin \lambda}{\lambda}\right) c_1 = 0 \tag{3.73}$$

Equations (3.73) are a pair of homogeneous, linear, algebraic, simultaneous equations for the unknowns c_0 and c_1. We must determine λ in order to obtain the eigenvalues and a relation between c_0 and c_1 so as to establish the precise form of the eigenfunctions. Here neither c_0 nor c_1 will be zero, so this case differs from those treated so far.

A necessary and sufficient condition [2] for (3.73) to have a nontrivial solution for c_0 and c_1 is that the determinant D of the coefficients be zero; that is,

$$D = \begin{vmatrix} 1 + \lambda \sin \lambda & -\cos \lambda \\ \cos \lambda & 1 + \frac{\sin \lambda}{\lambda} \end{vmatrix} = 0$$

Indeed, if $D \neq 0, c_1 = c_0 = 0$; when $D = 0$, there are an infinite number of solutions (as we expect for an eigenvalue problem; i.e., any constant times the eigenfunction is still a solution).

From $D = 0$, we have

$$0 = (1 + \lambda \sin \lambda)\left(1 + \frac{\sin \lambda}{\lambda}\right) - (\cos \lambda)(-\cos \lambda)$$

$$= 1 + (\lambda^2 + 1)\frac{\sin \lambda}{\lambda} + \sin^2 \lambda + \cos^2 \lambda$$

or

$$(\lambda^2 + 1)\frac{\sin \lambda}{\lambda} = -2$$

This equation can be manipulated to a more convenient form after we check if $\lambda^2 = 0$ or $\lambda^2 = -1$ are solutions. If $\lambda^2 \to 0, \lambda^2 + 1 \to 1$ and $\lambda^{-1} \sin \lambda \to 1$; thus $\lambda^2 = 0$ is not a solution. If $\lambda^2 = -1$, the equation cannot be satisfied; $\lambda^2 \neq -1$ and $\lambda^2 + 1 \neq 0$. Accordingly, we may multiply the equation by $\lambda(\lambda^2 + 1)^{-1}$ to achieve

$$\sin \lambda = \frac{-2\lambda}{\lambda^2 + 1} \tag{3.74}$$

Note that (3.74) has the root $\lambda^2 = 0$, which we shall ignore because it was introduced by the transformation $\lambda(\lambda^2 + 1)^{-1}$.

When λ^2 satisfies (3.74), the determinant D of the equation set (3.73) is zero. A solution exists for each λ^2 value satisfying (3.74); these solutions are the eigenfunctions, and the λ^2 are the corresponding eigenvalues of our original eigenvalue problem. If we plot $\sin \lambda$ and $-2\lambda/(\lambda^2 + 1)$, the eigenvalues λ^2 are found at the intersections of the curves where (3.74) is satisfied. Even for this relatively simple problem, the eigenvalues are no longer explicitly known, and a graph, a calculator, or a computer is needed to find λ^2. For illustration, a graphical procedure suits our needs. We must consider the two possibilities $\lambda^2 < 0$ and $\lambda^2 > 0$.

Let $\lambda^2 = -\Lambda^2 < 0$ so $\Lambda^2 > 0$ and $\lambda = i\Lambda$. Now, (3.74) becomes

$$\sinh \Lambda = \frac{2\Lambda}{\Lambda^2 - 1}$$

because $\sin i\Lambda = i \sinh \Lambda$. Figure 3.2 shows a plot of $\sinh \Lambda$ and $2\Lambda/\Lambda^2 - 1$. Clearly, there is a single negative eigenvalue $\lambda_0^2 = -\Lambda_0^2 \cong -2.37$.

For $\lambda^2 > 0$, a typical plot is given in Fig. 3.3. At the boxed intersections (3.74) is satisfied (we ignore $\lambda^2 = 0$ as planned). Thus the eigenvalues we seek are given by $\lambda_n^2, n = 1, 2, 3, \ldots$, and now

$$\lambda_0^2 < 0 < \lambda_1^2 < \lambda_2^2 < \lambda_3^2 < \cdots < \lambda_n^2 < \cdots$$

The eigenvalues are an ordered, discrete, infinite set of values as we have had before (except one value is now negative). See the Problems for a further discussion of these λ_n^2.

For each λ_n^2 we have, from (3.74), $\sin \lambda_n = -2\lambda_n/(\lambda_n^2 + 1)$. These λ_n^2 make $D = 0$, so (3.73) must have nontrivial solutions. The λ_n^2 make the two equations of (3.73) identical, as you can see by using (3.74) to replace the trigonometric functions

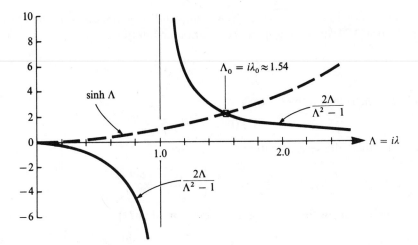

FIGURE 3.2

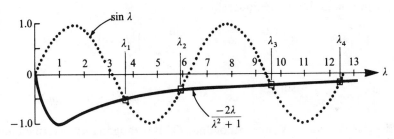

FIGURE 3.3

in (3.73). Thus either equation can be used to find c_1 as a function of c_0, for example, and c_0 is then arbitrary. From the first of (3.73),

$$c_{1n} = \frac{c_{0n}(1 + \lambda_n \sin \lambda_n)}{\cos \lambda_n}$$

Now

$$\cos^2 \lambda_n + \sin^2 \lambda_n = 1$$

or

$$\cos \lambda_n = (1 - \sin^2 \lambda_n)^{1/2} = \frac{\lambda_n^2 - 1}{\lambda_n^2 + 1}$$

if (3.74) is used. Therefore

$$c_{1n} = -c_{0n}$$

because

$$1 + \lambda_n \sin \lambda_n = \frac{1 - \lambda_n^2}{\lambda_n^2 + 1}$$

according to (3.74).

It follows that for (3.72a) the eigenvalues and eigenfunctions are the λ_n^2 values obtained from (3.74) (from a graphical or computer solution) and

$$X_n = c_{0n}\left(\cos \lambda_n x - \frac{\sin \lambda_n x}{\lambda_n}\right), \qquad n \geq 0$$

From (3.29), the solution to (3.72b) is

$$T(t) = e^{-\lambda_n^2 kt}$$

We propose, then, the series solution

$$u(x, t) = \sum_{n=1}^{\infty} c_{0n} e^{-\lambda_n^2 kt}\left(\cos \lambda_n x - \frac{\sin \lambda_n x}{\lambda_n}\right) \tag{3.75}$$

At $t = 0$ according to the initial condition of (3.71),

$$u(x, 0) = u_0(x) = \sum_{n=1}^{\infty} c_{0n}\left(\cos \lambda_n x - \frac{\sin \lambda_n x}{\lambda_n}\right) \tag{3.76}$$

Direct integration (although tedious) shows

$$\int_0^1 \left(\cos \lambda_n x - \frac{\sin \lambda_n x}{\lambda_n}\right)\left(\cos \lambda_m x - \frac{\sin \lambda_m x}{\lambda_m}\right) dx = 0, \qquad m \neq n$$

and

$$\int_0^1 \left(\cos \lambda_m x - \frac{\sin \lambda_m x}{\lambda_m}\right)^2 dx = N_m = \frac{1}{2}(1 - \lambda_m^{-2}) > 0, \qquad m \geq 0 \tag{3.77}$$

that is, the eigenfunctions X_n are orthogonal. (This orthogonality is verified formally in the Problems of Chap. 4.) We multiply (3.76) by

$$X_m(x) = \cos \lambda_m x - \frac{\sin \lambda_m x}{\lambda_m}$$

and integrate over $0 \leq x \leq 1$ to obtain

$$c_{0m} = \frac{1}{N_m} \int_0^1 u_0(x) X_m(x)\, dx = \frac{1}{N_m} \int_0^1 u_0(x)\left(\cos \lambda_m x - \frac{\sin \lambda_m x}{\lambda_m}\right) dx$$

The complete solution to (3.71) is then

$$u(x, t) = \sum_{n=0}^{\infty} \left[\frac{2}{1 - \lambda_m^{-2}} \int_0^1 u_0(\xi)\left(\cos \lambda_n \xi - \frac{\sin \lambda_n \xi}{\lambda_n}\right) d\xi\right]$$

$$\times e^{-\lambda_n^2 kt}\left(\cos \lambda_n x - \frac{\sin \lambda_n x}{\lambda_n}\right) \tag{3.78}$$

where the λ_n^2 are given by (3.74) and Figs. 3.2 and 3.3.

Now, $\lambda_n^2 > 0$ for $n \geq 1$. In this case, $e^{-\lambda_n^2 kt} \to 0$ very rapidly as t increases for $n \geq 1$. For large t, only the first term of (3.78) is important because $\lambda_0^2 < 0$ and $e^{-\lambda_0^2 kt} = e^{\Lambda_0^2 kt} \gg 1$ for large t. For large t, a good approximation to the solution is

$$u(x, t) \approx \left[\frac{1}{1 - \lambda_0^{-2}} \int_0^1 u_0(\xi)\left(\cos \lambda_0 \xi - \frac{\sin \lambda_0 \xi}{\lambda_0}\right) d\xi\right] e^{-\lambda_0^2 kt}\left(\cos \lambda_0 x - \frac{\sin \lambda_0 x}{\lambda_0}\right) \tag{3.79}$$

Replacing λ_0^2 by $-\Lambda_0^2$ and cosine and sine by the appropriate cosh and sinh, we have from (3.79)

$$u(x, t) \approx \left[\frac{2}{1 + \Lambda_0^{-2}} \int_0^1 u_0(\xi) \left(\cosh \Lambda_0 \xi - \frac{\sinh \Lambda_0 \xi}{\Lambda_0} \right) d\xi \right] e^{\Lambda_0^2 kt} \left(\cosh \Lambda_0 x - \frac{\sinh \Lambda_0 x}{\Lambda_0} \right)$$

$$\approx c_{00} e^{\Lambda_0^2 kt} \left(\cosh \Lambda_0 x - \frac{\sinh \Lambda_0 x}{\Lambda_0} \right) \tag{3.80}$$

In (3.80), $u_0(\xi) \geq 0$ on physical grounds and $\cosh \Lambda_0 x > \Lambda_0^{-1} \sinh \Lambda_0 x$; therefore $c_{00} > 0$ and

$$\lim_{t \to \infty} u(x, t) = \infty$$

as we deduced in the introductory discussion. Given $u_0(\xi)$, we determine $c_{00} > 0$. The minimum value of $u(x, t)$ in (3.80) occurs where $u_x(x, t) = 0$; that is, at x_0 given by $\tanh \Lambda_0 x_0 = \Lambda_0^{-1}$. ($x_0 = 0.5$. Why?) If k is known for the rod, the minimum value $u(x_0, t)$ can be predicted by (3.80) as a function of t quite accurately for fairly large t.

EXAMPLE 3.3   *Zero as an Eigenvalue.* The following model has a zero eigenvalue:

$$z_{tt} = c^2 z_{yy}, \qquad 0 < y < l, \quad 0 < t$$

$$z_y(0, t) 0, \qquad z_y(l, t) = 0, \qquad 0 < t \tag{3.81}$$

$$z(y, 0) = z_0(y), \qquad z_t(y, 0) = 0, \qquad 0 \leq y \leq l$$

If $z = z(y, t)$ is a displacement, this model describes the vibration of a flexible string of length l. The string supports are of the free-boundary type (lateral, but no vertical restraint), and no external forces are acting.

The solution to the model (3.81) is to be found by separation of variables and eigenfunction expansion. Introduction of the product form $z(y, t) = Y(y)T(t)$ in the governing equation and boundary conditions of (3.81) produces

$$\frac{T''}{c^2 T} = \frac{Y''}{Y} = -\lambda^2$$

$$Y'(0)T(t) = 0$$

$$Y'(l)T(t) = 0$$

Accordingly, the eigenvalue problem is

$$Y'' + \lambda^2 Y = 0$$
$$Y'(0) = Y'(l) = 0 \tag{3.82}$$

and T must satisfy

$$T'' + c^2 \lambda^2 T = 0 \tag{3.83}$$

The general solutions to the differential equations for T and Y in (3.83) and (3.82) are, from (3.20),

$$T(t) = A_0 \cos c\lambda t + \frac{A_1}{c\lambda} \sin c\lambda t \tag{3.84}$$

and

$$Y(y) = c_0 \cos \lambda y + \frac{c_1}{\lambda} \sin \lambda y \tag{3.85}$$

If $Y'(0) = 0, c_1 = 0$ for all $\lambda^2 \gtrless 0$. Hence

$$Y'(l) = -c_0 \lambda \sin \lambda l = 0 \tag{3.86}$$

according to the second condition of (3.82). For $c_0 = 0$, the result is trivial; therefore (3.86) is meaningfully satisfied when either $\lambda = 0$ or $\sin \lambda l = 0$. The eigenvalues for (3.82) are then

$$\lambda_n^2 = \left(\frac{n\pi}{l}\right)^2, \qquad n = 0, 1, 2, 3, \ldots \tag{3.87}$$

and the corresponding eigenfunctions are

$$Y_n(y) = c_{0n} \cos \lambda_n y \tag{3.88}$$

Note that to $\lambda_0 = 0$ there corresponds the *constant* eigenfunction $Y_0(y) = c_{00}$. The reader can easily verify that there are no negative eigenvalues for the eigenvalue problem (3.82).

Now (3.88) and (3.84) are combined to produce the series solutions

$$z(y, t) = \sum_{n=0}^{\infty} \left(\tilde{A}_{0n} \cos c\lambda_n t + \frac{\tilde{A}_{1n}}{c\lambda_n} \sin c\lambda_n t \right) \cos \lambda_n y \tag{3.89}$$

in which $\tilde{A}_{0n} = A_{0n}c_{0n}$, $\tilde{A}_{1n} = A_1 c_{0n}$, and the term $(\sin c\lambda_n t)/c\lambda_n \to t$ when $\lambda_0 = 0$. At $t = 0$, (3.89) becomes

$$z(y, 0) = \sum_{n=0}^{\infty} \tilde{A}_{0n} \cos \lambda_n y = z_0(y) \tag{3.90}$$

according to (3.81), while

$$z_t(y, 0) = \sum_{n=0}^{\infty} \tilde{A}_{1n} \cos \lambda_n y = 0$$

according to (3.81) and (3.89). Clearly, $\tilde{A}_{1n} = 0$ for all $n \geq 0$. Furthermore, direct integration shows that

$$\int_0^l \cos \lambda_m y \cos \lambda_n y \, dy = 0, \qquad m \neq n$$

and the normalizing constants

$$N_m = \int_0^l \cos^2 \lambda_m y \, dy = \frac{l}{2}, \qquad m \geq 1 \tag{3.91}$$

but

$$N_0 = \int_0^l 1^2 \, dy = l \tag{3.92}$$

Thus the eigenfunctions are orthogonal, whereas the normalizing constant corresponding to $\lambda_0 = 0$ requires special treatment. To complete the determination of $\tilde{A}_{0n}$, we multiply (3.90) by $\cos \lambda_m y$, integrate over $0 \le y \le l$ to utilize the orthogonality property, and obtain

$$\tilde{A}_{0m} = \frac{1}{N_m} \int_0^l z_0(y) \cos \lambda_m y \, dy, \qquad m \ge 0 \tag{3.93}$$

The complete solution to (3.81) is constructed from (3.87), (3.89), and (3.91) to (3.93):

$$z(y, t) = \sum_{n=0}^{\infty} \left[\frac{1}{N_m} \int_0^l z_0(\xi) \cos \frac{n\pi}{l} \xi \, d\xi \right] \cos c \frac{n\pi}{l} t \cos \frac{n\pi}{l} y$$

or

$$z(y, t) = \frac{1}{l} \int_0^l z_0(\xi) \, d\xi + \frac{2}{l} \sum_{n=1}^{\infty} \left[\int_0^l z_0(\xi) \cos \frac{n\pi}{l} \xi \, d\xi \right] \cos c \frac{n\pi}{l} t \cos \frac{n\pi}{l} y \tag{3.94}$$

Equation (3.94) effectively displays the lead term produced by the zero eigenvalue. Because the terms in the infinite series for $n \ge 1$ oscillate in time with a zero mean value, the lead term

$$\frac{1}{l} \int_0^l z_0(\xi) \, d\xi$$

represents the average displacement of the string initially and for all time.

The special features of the zero eigenvalues—the constant or perhaps linearly varying eigenfunction and unusual normalizing constant—demand that care be exercised in treating problems where a zero eigenvalue is possible. Remember that Fourier series converge only when complete sets of functions are employed; the eigenfunction set can only be complete if all the eigenfunctions are found.

3.5 SUMMARY

The methods of separation of variables and eigenfunction expansions provide the tools necessary for solution of a large class of initial-boundary-value problems. The mathematical models represented by these problems were solved in a systematic way as follows:

1. Separation of the variables in the governing equation and boundary conditions was achieved by postulating that the problem solution could be obtained as a product of functions of the separate independent variables. The governing partial differential equation was reduced to a set of ordinary differential equations.

2. An eigenvalue problem was formed through use of a pair of boundary conditions and one of the ordinary differential equations obtained in the separation process.

3. The eigenfunctions found as the solution to the eigenvalue problem were employed as terms in a convergent infinite series that represented the solution to the original problem.

As an adjunct to the preceding process, we were able to demonstrate that the infinite trigonometric series used possessed the necessary convergence properties and thus that our results gave a valid representation of the solution to the initial-boundary-value problem.

Several key points were raised in our development. First, step 1, above—that is, separation of variables in the governing equation—*cannot* be carried out unless the governing equation is *homogeneous*. Second, step 2, above—that is, formulation of a proper eigenvalue problem—*cannot* be carried out unless the requisite pair of boundary conditions are *homogeneous*. Third, whereas in general the eigenvalues in our problems are positive and infinite in number, a finite number of negative eigenvalues may occur as a result of special physical circumstances associated with our mathematical models. Fourth, the infinite series used cannot converge to the functions that they are supposed to represent unless *all* the eigenvalues and corresponding eigenfunctions are determined and used. For example, consider the significance of failing to find the zero eigenvalue in Example 3.3.

Building on the methods of this chapter, we shall develop additional techniques in later chapters to:

1. Cope with inhomogeneous problems (Chap. 5).
2. Establish the properties of eigenvalues without specifically solving the eigenvalue problem (Chap. 4). For example, we shall show that in most cases the eigenvalues are real and the eigenfunctions are orthogonal.
3. Generalize the Fourier series so that we may attack a much wider range of problems (Chaps. 4 and 5 and Appendix 3).

In closing, note that it is important, in applying separation of variables and eigenfunction expansion, to get the appropriate auxiliary conditions for the resulting ordinary differential equation problems. After some study, we can draw the following conclusions (whose relevance is tested in the Problems) with regard to separation and expansion for the total set of equations of a model. Separation of variables and eigenfunction expansions can only be applied to a mathematical model if the following points are true (compare Weinberger[6]):

1. The governing equation of the model is separable and linear. (Because superposition of solutions to nonlinear equations is not possible, separation of variables is not usually practicable for nonlinear equations.)
2. All auxiliary conditions of the model are applied on level curves of *an independent variable*—for example, initial conditions along $t = 0$ and boundary conditions along $x = $ constant if the independent variables are (x, t).
3. All auxiliary conditions are linear combinations of the dependent variable and its normal derivative with respect to the level curve on which the condition is applied.

Although we usually treat only models satisfying the foregoing conditions, the Problems show that a change of variables may bring other models to a form amenable to separation of variables.

REFERENCES

1. M. Abramowitz and I. A. Stegun, *Handbook of Mathematical Functions*. New York: Dover, 1965.

2. W. Kaplan, *Advanced Calculus*. Reading, Mass.: Addison-Wesley, 1952.

3. P. W. Berg and J. L. McGregor, *Elementary Partial Differential Equations*. San Francisco: Holden-Day, 1966.

4. R. V. Churchill, *Fourier Series and Boundary Value Problems*, 2nd ed. New York: McGraw-Hill, 1963.

5. H. Sagan, *Boundary and Eigenvalue Problems in Mathematical Physics*. New York: John Wiley & Sons, 1961.

6. H. F. Weinberger, *Partial Differential Equations*. New York: Blaisdell, 1965.

PROBLEMS

3.1 Reduce the following equations to pairs of ordinary differential equations by the method of separation of variables:

(a) $u_{xx} + xu_y = 0$, where $u = u(x, y)$

(b) $u_{xy} + u_y = 0$, where $u = u(x, y)$

(c) $u_{yy} + xyu_x = 0$, where $u = u(x, y)$

(d) $u_{tt} - u_{xx} - u = 0$, where $u = u(x, t)$

(e) $u_{tt} - x^2 u_{xx} = 0$, where $u = u(x, t)$

(f) $u_{xy} = f(x)g(y)$, where $u = u(x, y)$

(g) $u_{xx} = f(x)g(y)$, where $u = u(x, y)$

(h) $u_{rr} + \dfrac{1}{r}u_r + \dfrac{1}{r^2}u_{\theta\theta} + u_{zz} = 0$, where $u = u(r, \theta, z)$

3.2 Find product-form solutions to the equations of parts (f) and (g) in Prob. 3.1.

3.3 Show that

$$\sin^2 \phi \Phi'' + \sin \phi \cos \phi \Phi' + [n(n + 1) \sin^2 \phi - \lambda^2]\Phi = 0$$

can be transformed to

$$(1 - x^2)X'' - 2xX' + \left[n(n + 1) - \frac{\lambda^2}{1 - x^2} \right]X = 0$$

by a simple change of variables.

3.4 Determine in which of the following equations the method of separation of variables *cannot* be meaningfully carried out:

(a) $u_{tt} - u_{xt} + u_{xx} = 0$, where $u = u(x, t)$

(b) $u_{xx} + u_{yy} = xy$, where $u(x, y)$

(c) $u_{xx} + u_t^2 = 0$, where $u = u(x, t)$

(d) $u_{xy} + xyu = 0$, where $u = u(x, y)$

(e) $u_{xx} + u_{xy} + u_y = 0$, where $u = u(x, y)$

(f) $u_t + uu_x + uu_y = 0$, where $u = u(x, y, t)$

(g) $u_{xy}^2 = u$, where $u = u(x, y)$

(h) $u_{xx} - 2u_{xy} + u_{yy} = 0$, where $u = u(x, y)$

3.5   Each of the following sets of equations is a mathematical model of some physical process. Determine the appropriate eigenvalue problem in each case by the method of separation of variables. (Do not attempt to solve the problem.)

(a) $z_{tt} = z_{yy} - z_t,$ $0 < y < 1,$ $t > 0$
$z_y(0, t) = 0,$
$z(1, t) = 0,$ $t > 0$
$z(y, 0) = 1 - y,$ $0 \le y \le 1$
$z_t(y, 0) = 0,$
in which $z = z(y, t)$.

(b) $z_{tt} = z_{yy} - z,$ $0 < y < l,$ $t > 0$
$z(0, t) = 0,$
$z_y(l, t) = 0,$ $t > 0$
$z(y, 0) = 0,$
$z_t(y, 0) = y(l - y),$ $0 \le y \le l$
in which $z = z(y, t)$.

(c) $u_t = ku_{xx},$ $0 < x < l,$ $t > 0$
$u_x(0, t) + u(0, t) = 0,$
$u(l, t) = 0,$ $t > 0$
$u(x, 0) = u_0(x),$ $0 \le x \le l$
in which $u = u(x, t)$.

(d) $u_t = ku_{xx},$ $0 < x < 1,$ $t > 0$
$u(0, t) = u(1, t),$
$u_x(0, t) = u_x(1, t),$ $t > 0$
$u(x, 0) = u_0(x),$ $0 \le x \le 1$
in which $u = u(x, t)$.

(e) $u_t = k\left(u_{rr} + \dfrac{1}{r}u_r\right),$ $0 < a < r < 1,$ $t > 0$

$u_r(1, t) = 0,$
$u_r(a, t) = 0,$ $t > 0$
$u(r, 0) = Tr^2,$ $a \le r \le 1$
in which $u = u(r, t)$.

In Probs. 3.6 through 3.10, a formal solution should be obtained by separating variables, solving the resulting eigenvalue problem, demonstrating the orthogonality of the eigenfunctions, stating the formal eigenfunction expansion, and, finally, evaluating the expressions for the unknown constants.

3.6   Find a formal solution to the following mathematical model, in which $z = z(y, t)$:

$z_{tt} = c^2 z_{yy},$ $0 < y < l,$ $t > 0$
$z(0, t) = 0$
$z_y(l, t) = 0,$ $t > 0$
$z(y, 0) = 0,$
$z_t(y, 0) = y,$ $0 \le y \le l$

3.7   Find a formal solution to the following mathematical model, in which $u = u(x, t)$:

$u_t = ku_{xx}, \quad 0 < x < l, \quad t > 0$
$u_x(0, t) = 0,$
$u(l, t) = 0, \quad t > 0$
$u(x, 0) = U_0 \cos x, \quad 0 \le x \le l$

3.8   Find formal solutions to the mathematical models of Prob. 3.3, parts (a) and (b). Give a physical interpretation of the model in each case. (*Note:* It is not necessary to evaluate the integrals in the expressions for the series coefficients.)

3.9   Find a formal solution to the following mathematical model, in which $u = u(x, t)$:

$u_t = ku_{xx}, \quad 0 < x < l, \quad t > 0,$
$u_x(0, t) = 0,$
$u(l, t) + u(0, t) = 0, \quad t > 0$
$u(x, 0) = u_0(x), \quad \le x \le l$

3.10   Calculate the displacement $z(1, t)$ of the right-hand end of a string whose transverse motion is described by the mathematical model

$z_{tt} = z_{yy}, \quad 0 < y < 1, \quad t > 0$
$z(0, t) = 0,$
$z_y(1, t) = 0, \quad t > 0$
$z(y, 0) = 0, \quad 0 \le y \le 1$
$z_t(y, 0) = Vy,$
in which $z = z(y, t)$.

3.11   Verify that the c_n in Eq. (3.44) are, in fact, given by Eq. (3.44a) by
(a) direct substitution.
(b) employing the orthogonality of $\cos nx$ on $0 \le x \le \pi$.

3.12   By introduction of a change of variables, find expressions equivalent to Eqs. (3.43) through (3.45b) for the more general interval $0 \le x \le l$ or $-l \le x \le l$ as may be appropriate.

3.13   Find the Fourier series and coefficient expressions for a function $g(x)$ in $0 \le x \le L$ if $g(x)$ is periodic with period L.

3.14   Use Eqs. (3.45) to find the Fourier series and coefficient expressions for the function

$$F(x) = \begin{cases} C(-x), & -\pi \le x < 0 \\ C(x), & 0 \le x \le \pi \end{cases}$$

Compare your results to Eqs. (3.44), and state the conclusions that you draw from the comparison.

3.15   Use Eq. (3.45) to find the Fourier series and coefficient expressions for the function

$$F(x) = \begin{cases} -S(-x), & -\pi \le x < 0 \\ S(x), & 0 \le x \le \pi \end{cases}$$

Compare your results to Eq. (3.43), and state the conclusions that you draw from the comparison.

3.16   Expand $C(x) = \sin x$ on $0 \le x \le \pi$ in a Fourier cosine series according to Eqs. (3.44). Plot $C(x)$ and the first three partial sums of your series (i.e., PS_0, PS_2, and PS_4) on an appropriately sealed graph. Study the graph carefully to verify that $C(x)$ is being approached as a limit; discuss the significance of the first or lead term in your expansion.

3.17   Expand $S(x) = \cos x$ on $0 \le x \le \pi$ in a Fourier sine series according to Eq. (3.43).

3.18   Expand the function

$$F(x) = \begin{cases} \frac{1}{2}\pi + x, & -\pi \le x < 0 \\ \frac{1}{2}\pi - x, & 0 \le x \le \pi \end{cases}$$

in a Fourier series. Plot the first two partial sums of your series and $F(x)$ in the interval $-\pi \le x \le \pi$ on an appropriately scaled graph.

3.19   Construct a Fourier series for the "square wave" represented by

$$F(x) = \begin{cases} -1, & -1 \le x < 0 \\ 1, & 0 \le x \le 1 \end{cases}$$

Discuss the behavior of the series at $x = 0, \pm 1, \pm 2, \dots \pm n$, etc. Plot $F(x)$ and the three partial sums PS_1, PS_3, and PS_5 on an appropriately scaled graph. Would it be correct to say, "At a point x_i of discontinuity of the function $f(x)$, the Fourier series for $f(x)$ converges to the average of the left- and right-hand limits—that is, to $\frac{1}{2}[f(x_i - 0) + f(x_i + 0)]$?" Discuss. Note that $x_i - 0$ implies the limit as x approaches x_i from the left, etc. (*Hint*: Let $y = x/\pi$ in Fourier series for $-\pi < x < \pi$.)

Note: Problems 3.20 through 3.23 lead to a generalization of the Fourier series convergence proof given in Sec. 3.3.1 for continuous functions.

Definition: A function $F(x)$ is called *piecewise continuous* in an interval $a \le x \le b$ if there are only a finite number of discontinuities of $F(x)$ at $x_1, x_2, \dots, x_n$ for $a \le x_i \le b$ and if $F(x)$ has finite limits from the left and from the right at each discontinuity.

3.20   Verify that Eq. (3.47) is valid for a piecewise-continuous function $f(x)$ that is also periodic with period 2π. (*Hint:* Postulate the existence of a finite number of discontinuities, and then perform the necessary integrations over a series of subintervals bounded by the discontinuities.)

3.21   Prove the extended Riemann–Lebesgue Lemma : If a function $\alpha(t)$ is bounded and piecewise continuous on $a \le t \le b$, then

$$\lim_{\beta \to \infty} \int_a^b \alpha(t) \sin \beta t \, dt = 0$$

[*Hint:* Can the original lemma be applied sequentially in each subinterval bounded by the discontinuities of $\alpha(t)$?]

3.22   Consider a function $f(x)$ that is periodic with period 2π, is piecewise continuous, and has a piecewise-continuous first derivative. By dealing first with the interval $-\pi \le t \le 0$ and, second, with $0 \le t \le \pi$, show that
(a) from (3.47), one has

$$PS_k = \frac{1}{\pi}\left[\int_{-\pi}^0 f(t + x)\frac{\sin\left[(k + \frac{1}{2})t\right] dt}{2 \sin t/2} \right.$$

$$\left. + \int_0^\pi f(t + x)\frac{\sin\left[(k + \frac{1}{2})t\right]}{2 \sin t/2}\, dt \right]$$

(b) Subsequently, by direct integration of (3.48), one can obtain

$$PS_k - \frac{1}{2}[f(x - 0) + f(x + 0)] = \frac{1}{\pi}\left[\int_{-\pi}^0 \frac{f(t + x) - f(x - 0)}{2 \sin t/2} \sin\left[\left(k + \frac{1}{2}\right)t\right] dt \right.$$

$$\left. + \int_0^\pi \frac{f(t + x) - f(x + 0)}{2 \sin t/2} \sin\left[\left(k + \frac{1}{2}\right)t\right] dt \right]$$

3.23 Use the procedure outlined in Sec. 3.3.1 above, the extended Riemann–Lebesgue lemma proved in Prob. 3.21, and the second result of Prob. 3.22 to show that

$$\lim_{k \to \infty} \{PS_k - \tfrac{1}{2}[f(x - 0) + f(x + 0)]\} = 0$$

and hence that the Fourier series convergence theorem can be extended to read:

Theorem: If a function $f(x)$ is periodic with period 2π, is piecewise continuous, has a piecewise-continuous first derivative, and equals $F(x)$ in $-\pi \le x \le \pi$, then the Fourier series (3.45) with coefficients given by (3.45a and b) converges to

(a) $\tfrac{1}{2}[f(x - 0) + f(x + 0)]$ in $-\pi < x < \pi$

and

(b) $\tfrac{1}{2}[f(\pi - 0) + f(-\pi + 0)]$ at $x = \pm\pi$

3.24 Expand the function

$$F(x) = \begin{cases} -1, & -\pi \le x \le -\dfrac{\pi}{2} \\[2mm] 0, & -\dfrac{\pi}{2} < x < \dfrac{\pi}{2} \\[2mm] 1, & \dfrac{\pi}{2} \le x \le \pi \end{cases}$$

in a Fourier series in $-\pi \le x \le \pi$. Plot $F(x)$ and the third partial sum of your series on a suitably scaled graph. Discuss your results in the light of the theorem proved in Prob. 3.23.

3.25 Consider a continuous function $f(x)$ that is periodic with period $2L$ and has piecewise-continuous first and second derivatives. Prove that the Fourier series representation of $f(x)$ is uniformly convergent for all x. [*Hint:* Divide the interval of integration into sub-intervals bounded by the points of discontinuity in $f''(x)$; then follow the general pattern given in Sec. 3.3.2 above.] [*Note:* If $f(x)$ is also piecewise continuous, the preceding convergence theorem can be shown to hold in every closed interval where there is no discontinuity of $f(x)$[2,4].]

3.26 The uniform convergence of the Fourier series (3.45) has been proved in Sec. 3.3.2. Use this proof and theorem statement as a guide to construct a theorem statement and proof for the uniform convergence of the sine series (3.43).

3.27 Consider a continuous function $F(x)$ that is represented by a uniformly convergent series of partial sums PS_k on $-\pi \le x \le \pi$. If $G(x)$ is a piecewise-continuous function on $-\pi < x < \pi$, prove that

$$\int_{-\pi}^{\pi} F(x)G(x)\, dx = \sum_{n=1}^{\infty} \int_{-\pi}^{\pi} f_n(x)G(x)\, dx$$

where

$$PS_k = \sum_{n=1}^{k} f_n(x)$$

(*Hint:* Use the properties implied by uniform convergence and an inequality constructed from

$$\int_{-\pi}^{\pi} [F(x)G(x) - PS_k G(x)]\, dx)$$

3.28   Construct an appropriate theorem and proof for the situation of Prob. 3.27 on the interval $a \leq x \leq b$.

3.29   Demonstrate that the theorems of Prob. 3.27 or 3.28 can be used to justify the validity of term-by-term integration of a Fourier series. Under what conditions is term-by-term integration possible? [*Hint:* Try $G(x) = 1$.]

3.30   Prove the following proposition: Term-by-term differentiation of a convergent series is permissible provided that the functions $f_n(x)$ of the series have continuous derivatives and that the series of derivatives is uniformly convergent; then, if $F(x) = \sum_{n=1}^{\infty} f_n(x)$,

$$F'(x) = \sum_{n=1}^{\infty} f'_n(x)$$

on a given interval $a \leq x \leq b$. [*Hint:* Define $D(x) = \sum_{n=1}^{\infty} f'_n(x)$; use the result of Prob. 3.28 (or 3.27) by integrating $D(x)$ from, say, a to x_1, evaluating the definite integrals of the series terms, and, finally, differentiating the result with respect to x_1.]

3.31   Demonstrate that the uniformly convergent Fourier series

$$\sum_{n=1}^{\infty} \frac{\sin nx}{n} = \frac{1}{2}(\pi - x)$$

cannot be differentiated term by term. (*Hint:* Apply the result of Prob. 3.30.)

3.32   Find the conditions required on the function $F(x)$ in Eq. (3.45) to ensure that the series formed by twice differentiating the Fourier series term by term is uniformly convergent on $-\pi < x < \pi$. Note that this bears some relation to our needs in obtaining series solutions to second-order partial differential equations.

3.33   Give the conditions that must be satisfied by z_0 and V_0 so that the formal solution to the following mathematical model is continuous with respect to small changes in the initial data:

$z_{tt} = z_{yy}, \qquad 0 < y < \pi, \quad t > 0$
$z(0, t) = 0,$
$z(\pi, t) = 0, \qquad t > 0$
$z(y, 0) = z_0(y),$
$z_t(y, 0) = V_0(y), \qquad 0 \leq y \leq \pi$

in which $z = z(y, t)$. (*Hint:* Consider an extension of the method used in Sec. 3.2.)

3.34   Under what conditions on z_0 and V_0 is the formal solution to Prob. 3.33 uniformly convergent in $0 < y < \pi$, $t > 0$?

In Probs. 3.35 through 3.46, if a formal solution is required, follow the instructions given before Prob. 3.6. Where eigenvalues are given as the solution of complicated transcendental equations, a sketch of the plots required to determine the answers graphically will suffice. The intrepid may care to write a computer program to obtain these answers.

3.35   Find a formal solution to the following mathematical model, in which $u = u(x, y)$:

$u_{xx} + u_{yy} = 0, \qquad 0 < x < l_1, \quad 0 < y < l_2$
$u(x, 0) = 100\left(1 - \dfrac{x}{l_1}\right),$
$\qquad\qquad\qquad\qquad 0 < x < l_1$
$u_y(x, l_2) = 0,$
$u_x(0, y) = 0,$
$u(l_1, y) = 0, \qquad 0 < y < l_2$

Set $l_2/l_1 = 2$ for the following computations. Use the third partial sum of the series for $u(x, y)$ to determine approximately the lines of constant u in the (x, y) domain of the problem. Sketch these lines on an appropriately scaled graph, and give a physical interpretation of the model in terms of heat conduction.

3.36 Find a formal solution to the following mathematical model, in which $u = u(x, y)$:

$$u_{xx} + u_{yy} = 0, \quad 0 < x < l_1, \quad 0 < y < l_2$$
$$u_y(x, 0) = 0,$$
$$u_y(x, l_2) = 0, \quad 0 < x < l_1$$
$$u(0, y) = T(y),$$
$$u(l_1, y) = S(y), \quad 0 < y < l_2$$

3.37 Find a formal solution to the following mathematical model, in which $u = u(x, y)$:

$$u_{xx} + u_{yy} = 0, \quad 0 < x < l_1, \quad 0 < y < l_2$$
$$u_y(x, 0) = 0,$$
$$u(x, l_2) = 0, \quad 0 < x < l_1$$
$$u(0, y) = 100\left(1 - \frac{y}{l_2}\right),$$
$$\qquad\qquad\qquad\qquad 0 < y < l_2$$
$$u_x(l_1, y) = 30\left(\frac{y}{l_2^2}\right),$$

Give a physical interpretation of this model. (*Hint:* This problem requires a logical extension of the pattern that you have been developing for obtaining formal solutions.)

3.38 Find a formal solution to and give a physical interpretation in terms of fluid flow for the following mathematical model, in which $\phi = \phi(x, y)$:

$$\phi_{xx} + \phi_{yy} = 0, \quad 0 < x < \pi, \quad 0 < y < \pi$$
$$\phi_y(x, 0) = 0,$$
$$\phi(x, \pi) = 5, \quad 0 < x < \pi$$
$$\phi_x(0, y) = 0,$$
$$\phi(\pi, y) = 0, \quad 0 \le y \le \pi$$

3.39 In Sec. 3.4, Example 3.2, the positive eigenvalues λ_n^2 are given by Eq. (3.74). Find approximate values of λ_n^2 for large n. [*Hint:* Consider the behavior of the left- and right-hand sides of Eq. (3.74) for large λ or look at Fig. 3.3.]

3.40 For Example 3.2, verify that $N_m = \frac{1}{2}(1 - \lambda_m^{-2})$ by direct integration. (*Hint:* First, do the indicated integration formally. Second, replace all trigonometric functions by the equivalent λ_n^2 expression.)

Note: You may need to use the techniques for obtaining nontrivial solutions to a pair of homogeneous, simultaneous, algebraic equations in order to find an equation for the eigenvalues in some of the following problems.

3.41 Find a formal solution to the following mathematical model, in which $u = u(x, t)$:

$$u_t = ku_{xx}, \quad 0 < x < 1, \quad t > 0$$
$$u_x(0, t) + u(0, t) = 0,$$
$$u(1, t) = 0, \quad t > 0$$
$$u(x, 0) = 1 - x, \quad 0 \le x \le 1$$

3.42 Find a formal solution to and give a physical interpretation of the following mathematical model, in which $Z = Z(y, t)$:

$$Z_{tt} - Z_{yy} = 0, \quad 0 < y < 1, \quad t > 0$$

$$Z(0, t) = 0,$$
$$Z_y(1, t) + Z(1, t) = 0, \qquad t > 0$$
$$Z(y, 0) = 0,$$
$$Z_t(y, 0) = 1 - y, \qquad 0 \le y \le 1$$

3.43 Find a formal solution to, and give a physical interpretation in terms of, heat conduction for the following mathematical model, in which $u = u(x, y)$ and H and K are positive:

$$u_{xx} + u_{yy} = 0, \qquad 0 < x < 1, \quad 0 < y < 2$$
$$Ku_x(0, y) - Hu(0, y) = 0,$$
$$Ku_x(1, y) + Hu(1, y) = 0, \qquad 0 < y < 2$$
$$u(x, 0) = 100x(1 - x),$$
$$u_y(x, 2) = 0, \qquad 0 < x < 1$$

3.44 Construct a mathematical model for heat conduction in the following physical situation, and obtain a formal solution to the model: A thin cylindrical bar, made from a material with constant k, ρ, and c, is 1 ft long and has its surface insulated. The ends of the bar are exposed to streams of moving fluid of temperature 0; the initial temperature of the bar is 100 °C. [*Hint:* See Eq. (2.25); note K and $H > 0$ on physical grounds and n is the outward normal unit vector.]

3.45 A thin plate is equipped with special feedback devices along the edges at $x = 0$ and $x = 1$. The mathematical model for heat conduction is, in this case,

$$u_{xx} + u_{yy} = 0, \qquad 0 < x < 1, \quad 0 < y < \tfrac{1}{2}$$
$$u_x(0, y) + \alpha u(0, y) = 0,$$
$$u_x(1, y) - \alpha u(1, y) = 0, \qquad 0 < y < \tfrac{1}{2}$$
$$u(x, 0) = 100(1 - x),$$
$$u_y(x, \tfrac{1}{2}) = 0, \qquad 0 < x < 1$$

The feedback control is represented by the constant α in the model. Find formal solutions to the above for $u = u(x, y)$ when

(a) $\alpha = +1$

(b) $\alpha = +2$

(c) $\alpha = +3$ (How many negative eigenvalues did you find?)

3.46 Consider heat conduction in a laterally insulated rod equipped with a pair of feedback devices that relate the flux at the rod end to the temperature there. The mathematical model is

$$u_t = ku_{xx}, \qquad 0 < x < l, \quad t > 0$$
$$u_x(0, t) + \alpha u(0, t) = 0,$$
$$u_x(l, t) + \alpha u(l, t) = 0, \qquad t > 0$$
$$u(x, 0) = 100\left(1 - \frac{x}{l}\right) \text{ °C}, \qquad 0 \le x \le l$$

Feedback control is represented by the constant α. Find a formal solution to this model for $u = u(x, t)$. Discuss the behavior of the solution as related to the sign and magnitude of α and time t.

3.47 Obtain a formal solution to the following mathematical model of a rod fitted with a device that maintains a heat flux f_x out through the end in direct proportion to the temperature $u(l, t)$ there:

$$u_t = ku_{xx}, \qquad 0 < x < l, \quad t > 0$$

$$u_x(0, t) = 0,$$
$$Ku_x(l, t) = -Hu(l, t), \qquad t > 0$$
$$u(x, 0) = u_0(x), \qquad 0 \le x \le l$$

Give a physical interpretation of the situation for large t; does the result depend on the sign or size of H/K? [*Hint*: Select $H/K = \pm 1$, and plot the curves of the relation establishing the eigenvalues for each case (see Example 3.2).]

3.48   Find a formal solution to each of the following models, and give a physical interpretation of the model and the solution:

(a) $z = z(y, t)$, with k and c constant
$$z_{tt} + kz_t - c^2 z_{yy} = 0, \qquad 0 < y < l, \quad t > 0$$
$$z(0, t) = z(l, t) = 0, \qquad t > 0$$
$$z(y, 0) = \sin\frac{3\pi y}{l},$$
$$\qquad\qquad\qquad\qquad 0 \le y \le l$$
$$z_t(y, 0) = \sin\frac{\pi y}{l},$$

(b) $u = u(x, t)$, with k and a constant
$$u_t - ku_{xx} + au = 0, \qquad 0 < x < \pi, \quad t > 0$$
$$u(0, t) = u_x(\pi, t) = 0, \qquad t > 0$$
$$u(x, 0) = \left(\pi - \frac{x}{2}\right)x, \qquad 0 \le x \le \pi$$

(c) $u = u(x, y)$
$$u_{xx} + u_{yy} = u, \qquad 0 < x < 1, \quad 0 < y < 1$$
$$u_x(0, y) = u(1, y) = 0, \qquad 0 < y < 1$$
$$u_y(x, 0) = u_y(x, 1) = \frac{100}{K}, \qquad 0 < x < 1$$

(d) $z = z(y, t)$
$$z_{tt} = z_{yy} - z, \qquad 0 < y < l, \quad t > 0$$
$$z_y(0, t) = 0,$$
$$z_y(l, t) = 0, \qquad t > 0$$
$$z(y, 0) = 0,$$
$$z_t(y, 0) = y(l - y), \qquad 0 \le y \le l$$

3.49   Consider the following model in which $u = u(x, t)$:

$$u_t = ku_{xx}, \qquad 0 < x < 1, \quad t > 0$$
$$u_x(0, t) = 0,$$
$$u(1, t) - u(0, t) = 0, \qquad t > 0$$
$$u(x, 0) = 1414 \sin \pi x, \qquad 0 \le x \le 1$$

For this model,

(a) determine and state the eigenvalue problem.

(b) solve the eigenvalue problem—that is, find the eigenvalues and eigenfunctions.

(c) find an approximation (an actual number) to $u(x, t)$ for large t.

3.50   Find formal solutions (if possible) for the following models by separation of variables (explain any failures):

(a) for $u = u(x, y)$

$$\nabla^2 u = 0, \qquad 0 < x < 1, \quad 0 < y < 1$$

$$u(0, y) = 0 \qquad u_x(1, y) = 5, \qquad 0 < y < 1$$
$$u(x, 0) = 0, \qquad 0 < x < 1$$
$$u(x, 1) + u_x(x, 1) = 0, \qquad 0 < x < 1$$

(b) for $u = u(x, y)$, solve part (a) with the last condition replaced by

$$u_x(x, 1) = 0, \qquad 0 < x < 1$$

(*Hint:* This can be changed to a more reasonable problem by integration of the above condition, but an assumption is required.)

(c) for $u = u(x, y)$, solve part (a) with the last condition replaced by
$$u^2(x, 1) + u_y(x, 1) = 0, \qquad 0 < x < 1$$

(d) for $u = u(x, y)$, solve without changing variables:

$$\nabla^2 u = 0, \qquad x^2 + y^2 < 1$$
$$u(x, y) = y^2 \qquad \text{on} \quad x^2 + y^2 = 1$$

3.51 Repeat Prob. 3.50, parts (a) to (c), with $u_x(1, y) = 0$ and $u(x, 0) = 10$.

3.52 Apply the suggested change of variables, and then show that the resulting model is separable (i.e., give the ordinary differential equations and their auxiliary conditions):

(a) $x = r \cos \theta$, $y = r \sin \theta$ to the model of Prob. 3.50, part (d); (r, θ) are polar coordinates.

(b) $x = \cosh \phi \cos \psi$
$y = \sinh \phi \sin \psi$ to
$$\nabla^2 u = 0, \frac{4x^2}{3} - 4y^2 < 1$$

$u(x, y) = y^2$ on $\dfrac{4x^2}{3} - 4y^2 = 1$;

(ϕ, ψ) are elliptic coordinates.

3.53 In Example 3.3, Sec. 3.4, replace the initial conditions by $z(y, 0) = 0$ and $z_t(y, 0) = V_0 \sin (\pi/l)x$. Find a formal solution, plot some typical results, and give an interpretation of the physical meaning of the results.

3.54 Solve the model in Prob. 2.23 if

(a) $\eta(x, 0) = a \sin wx$
$\eta_t(x, 0) = 0$

(b) η and η_t are prescribed in a manner to achieve the simplest nontrivial form of solution. What is the resulting wave pattern? (*Hint:* Eliminate η to get complete model for ϕ alone; determine η after ϕ is known.)

CHAPTER 4

STURM–LIOUVILLE THEORY
AND ORTHOGONAL FUNCTIONS

If the equations of a mathematical model are separable, one or more eigenvalue problems—that is, boundary-value problems for ordinary differential equations—are obtained in the separation process. Because the equations obtained in Chap. 3 were both simple and familiar, we easily solved the necessary problems. More complex models will lead to more complex sets of ordinary differential equations (see Sec. 3.1). In Appendix 2 a brief review is given of those concepts and methods that are of immediate use in this book.

This chapter is concerned with a general theory for second-order eigenvalue problems. Results are derived to establish that the solutions to very general eigenvalue problems possess the characteristics required for application of the technique of eigenfunction expansions. In addition, the Galerkin method is presented for the approximate determination of eigenvalues and eigenfunctions in cases where the complexities of the problem make power series methods impractical.

It is important to reemphasize that the power series (see Appendix 2) is the natural or basic form of solution for ordinary differential equations. We are very familiar with the $\sin(x)$, $\cos(x)$, and $\exp(x)$ functions and operations with them, but at times we tend to forget that sin, cos, and exp are merely symbols for tabulated functions whose values are determined by the summation of power series. When new functional symbols are introduced for Bessel functions and Legendre polynomials, etc., many books treat these new objects as special functions. Here, however, they are regarded simply as symbols for new power series, and it is established in this chapter that all such functions that are solutions to eigenvalue problems possess the necessary properties for use in eigenfunction expansions. Thus no special treatment is given to special functions, and the reader is urged to think, as he progresses through this chapter, in terms of eigenvalues and eigenfunctions rather than in terms of their particular forms, such as sin and cos. Appendix 3 gives a summary of the properties of some Bessel functions and the Legendre polynomials for use in the Problems. Appendix 2 contains brief derivations of the representative series for all the functions mentioned above as part of the review of ordinary differential equations.

4.1   INTRODUCTION

The eigenvalue problems of Chap. 3 required solution of a simple, second-order, linear ordinary differential equation, and in most cases both eigenvalues and eigenfunctions had explicit analytic forms. However, separation of the variables in the mathematical models of many physical systems leads to ordinary differential equations of much greater complexity. The complexity can arise, for example, from use of the polar coordinate system to describe a circular membrane [see (2.61)], from the lengthwise variation of the density of a vibrating string, or from the lengthwise variation of thermal conductivity and density along a heated rod [see (2.16)].

EXAMPLE 4.1   *The Effect of Coordinates.* The symmetric vibrations of a circular membrane are governed by [see (2.63a)]

$$z_{tt} = c^2\left(z_{rr} + \frac{1}{r}z_r\right), \qquad 0 < r < R, \quad 0 < t \tag{4.1}$$

in the absence of external forces.

Separation of variables through the use of the product form $z = \phi(r)T(t)$ yields an equation for $T(t)$ and

$$\phi'' + \frac{1}{r}\phi' + \lambda^2\phi = 0, \qquad 0 < r < R \tag{4.2}$$

where λ^2 is the separation constant. This equation is a form of the Bessel's equation of zero order [(A.2.31)]. Both (4.2) and (A.2.31) have singular points at $r = 0$, which corresponds to the center of the membrane. This feature requires special treatment, as we shall see later in this section. However, the solutions to (A.2.31) are tabulated, and although not precisely periodic, their properties are well known [1].

EXAMPLE 4.2   *Heat Conduction in a Variable Material.* When the temperature u in a solid varies only in the x direction and with time, the equation for heat conduction (2.16) becomes

$$\rho c u_t = (K u_x)_x + A \tag{4.3}$$

Suppose that the material of the solid varies with x—that is, $\rho = \rho(x)$, $c = c(x)$, and $K = K(x)$—while the heat sources are controlled by their position in the solid and the local temperature—that is, $A = a(x)u$. Equation (4.3) remains linear under these conditions, and separation of variables is possible.

Letting $u = X(x)T(t)$ leads to an equation for $T(t)$, and

$$[K(x)X'(x)]' + [a(x) + \lambda^2\rho(x)c(x)]X(x) = 0 \qquad (4.4)$$

In its most general form, (4.4) can only be solved by numerical integration or through the use of a complicated power series expansion whose summations and properties most assuredly are not tabulated.

The methods of Chap. 3 are very useful when we can separate variables, solve the resulting eigenvalue problem, and superpose the results to form a complete solution. The methods summarized in Appendix 2 will produce solutions to many ordinary differential equations. However, solutions to even relatively simple equations [e.g., (A.2.9), (A.2.13), and (A.2.25)] are only found in terms of power series. The solution of the general linear equation of second order (4.4) [see (A.2.5)] by the power series method is, while possible, at best a tedious process. The additional task of using the power series to solve the eigenvalue problem and then determine the necessary properties of the solution remains.

It would be useful to know *in advance*, before we obtain a series solution, that it will have all the characteristics required by the methods of Chap. 3. For example, do eigenvalues exist? Are they real? Are the eigenfunctions orthogonal? In what sense? Can a series expansion be used? In Secs. 4.2 to 4.5 it is shown that, for a very large class of second-order eigenvalue problems, the existence and character of both the eigenvalues and the eigenfunctions can be established *on the basis of the problem form* without explicit knowledge of either eigenvalues or eigenfunctions.

4.2   THE GENERALIZED EIGENVALUE PROBLEM

From the foregoing examples and the problems of earlier chapters, we can induce a general, second-order, linear eigenvalue problem of the form

$$X''(x) + P_1(x)X'(x) + [P_{21}(x) + \lambda^2 P_{22}(x)]X(x) = 0, \qquad a < x < b: \qquad (4.5)$$

$$\alpha X(a) + \beta X'(a) = 0$$
$$\gamma X(b) + \delta X'(b) = 0 \qquad (4.6)$$

The governing equation (4.5) is drawn from (A.2.5) and (4.4), while the boundary conditions (4.6) represent the first, second, or third types according to the choice of the real constants α, β, γ, and δ (neither α, β nor γ, δ are simultaneously zero). The functions P_1, P_{21}, and P_{22} are taken to be real and analytic in $a \leq x \leq b$; thus they are bounded and all x in the interval are ordinary points (see Sec. A.2.2). Later, equations for which the endpoints $x = a$ or $x = b$ are singular points are discussed, as is a type of boundary condition not included in (4.6). The constants α, β, γ, and δ, and the functions P_1, P_{21}, and P_{22} are assumed to be independent of λ^2.

Because we shall construct a pair of general integral relations based on (4.5) and (4.6), it is useful now to form the derivative terms in (4.5) into an exact differential. This manipulation also coalesces all second-order equations of the type of (4.5) to a single standard form. As in Sec. A.2.1, where a first-order equation is treated, the integrating factor, a standard tool in ordinary differential equation analysis [2], can be used.

Comparison of (A.2.1) and (4.5) indicates that the integrating factor $I(x)$, with β_1 replaced by P_1 in (A.2.2), will make $X'' + P_1 X'$ an exact differential; that is,

$$I(x) = \exp\left[\int^x P_1(\eta)\,d\eta\right]$$

Multiplying (4.5) by I produces

$$IX'' + IP_1 X' + I(P_{21} + \lambda^2 P_{22})X = 0, \qquad a < x < b$$

or since $IX'' + IP_1 X'$ is a perfect differential,

$$\frac{d}{dx}(IX') + (IP_{21} + \lambda^2 IP_{22})X = 0, \qquad a < x < b \tag{4.7}$$

Commonly, this equation is written in the standard form

$$\frac{d}{dx}\left(r\frac{dX}{dx}\right) + (q + \lambda^2 p)X = 0, \qquad a < x < b \tag{4.8}$$

where

$$r = r(x) = I = \exp\left[\int^x P_1(\eta)\,d\eta\right] \tag{4.8a}$$

$$q = q(x) = IP_{21} = rP_{21} \tag{4.8b}$$

$$p = p(x) = IP_{22} = rP_{22} \tag{4.8c}$$

Because of the assumed analyticity of P_1, $r > 0$.

It is important to remember that *every* second-order, linear ordinary differential equation of the general form (4.5) can be reduced to the standard form (4.8). The function p that multiplies the product $\lambda^2 X$ is called the *weight function*. In the eigenvalue problems of Chap. 3, $r = 1$, $p = 1$, and $q = 0$ in each case.

EXAMPLE 4.3   Reduce the following equations to the standard form (4.8):
(a) Bessel's equation of order n, similar to (A.2.25), on $1 < x < b$:

$$X'' + \frac{1}{x}X' + \left(\lambda^2 - \frac{n^2}{x^2}\right)X = 0$$

Here

$$P_1 = \frac{1}{x}, \quad P_{21} = -\frac{n^2}{x^2}, \quad P_{22} = 1$$

Accordingly,

$$r = I = \exp\left[\int^x \eta^{-1}\, d\eta\right] = x, \quad q = -\frac{n^2}{x}, \quad p = x$$

and the standard form is

$$\frac{d}{dx}\left(x\frac{dX}{dx}\right) + \left(\frac{-n^2}{x} + \lambda^2 x\right)X = 0$$

(b) Legendre's equation (A.2.13) on $-\frac{1}{2} < x < -\frac{1}{2}$:

$$(1 - x^2)X'' - 2xX' + \lambda(\lambda + 1)X = 0$$

By observation,

$$P_1 = -\frac{2x}{(1 - x^2)}, \quad P_{21} = 0, \quad P_{22} = (1 - x^2)^{-1}$$

if we identify λ^2 with $\lambda(\lambda + 1)$. Therefore

$$r = I = \exp\left(\int^x \frac{-2\eta}{1 - \eta^2}\, d\eta\right) = 1 - x^2, \quad q = 0, \quad p = 1$$

and the standard form is

$$\frac{d}{dx}\left[(1 - x^2)\frac{dX}{dx}\right] + \lambda(\lambda + 1)X = 0$$

(c) The equation:

$$X'' + X' + \lambda^2 X = 0, \quad 0 < x < l$$

Now, $P_1 = 1$, $P_{21} = 0$, and $P_{22} = 1$, whence

$$r = I = \exp\left(\int^x d\eta\right) = e^x, \quad q = 0, \quad p = e^x$$

and

$$\frac{d}{dx}\left(e^x\frac{dX}{dx}\right) + \lambda^2 e^x X = 0$$

is the standard form.

If (4.5) is replaced by its equivalent standard form (4.8), the general eigenvalue problem (4.5) and (4.6) becomes the *Sturm–Liouville* system* on $a \le x \le b$:

$$\frac{d}{dx}\left[r(x)\frac{dX}{dx}\right] + [q(x) + \lambda^2 p(x)]X = 0, \quad a < x < b$$

$$\alpha X(a) + \beta X'(a) = 0 \tag{4.9}$$

$$\gamma X(b) + \delta X'(b) = 0$$

* After J. C. F. Sturm (1803–1855), a Swiss mathematician, and J. Liouville (1809–1882), a French mathematician. See, for example, *J. de Mathématique*, 1836–1838.

In practical problems derived from physical models, it is usually true that p, q, and r are real and continuous, but not necessarily analytic, functions of x on the *finite* interval $a \le x \le b$. Under this assumption of continuity and reality, we shall examine the character of the Sturm–Liouville system (4.9) on a finite interval and establish that character in the form of a set of theorems. Because of the generality of (4.9), these theorems are, of course, applicable to any second-order, linear eigenvalue problem with boundary conditions of the first, second, or third types, and thus they provide the general framework for analysis that we seek.

4.3   CHARACTERIZATION OF EIGENVALUES AND EIGENFUNCTIONS

In the simple eigenvalue problems in Chap. 3, there always existed an infinite set of eigenvalues that could be ordered by increasing size so that $\lambda_n^2 \to \infty$ as $n \to \infty$. The eigenvalues were discrete, and to each eigenvalue there corresponded one eigenfunction that was obtained from the two linearly independent solutions to the governing homogeneous equation. These results extend to the Sturm–Liouville system in accordance with the following theorem:

THEOREM 4.1   If $p > 0$ and $r > 0$ on $a < x < b$, there exists for the system (4.9) an infinite set of eigenvalues $\lambda_0^2, \lambda_1^2, \lambda_2^2, \ldots$ such that

$$\lambda_0^2 < \lambda_1^2 < \lambda_2^2 < \lambda_3^2 < \cdots \qquad \lambda_n^2 \to \infty \text{ as } n \to \infty$$

and there exists an infinite set of corresponding eigenfunctions $X_0, X_1, X_2, \ldots$, on $a \le x \le b$ such that X_n has exactly n zeros on $a < x < b$. Except for an unessential multiplying constant, to each eigenvalue λ_n^2 there corresponds one and only one eigenfunction X_n.

Discussion. The preceding theorem is presented without proof, which can be found in Ince [3] and Leighton [2]. (The problems contain an exercise leading to a proof of the uniqueness of the eigenfunctions.) However, let's consider the assumptions and results of the theorem further.

First, $r > 0$ whenever P_1 is bounded. However, the requirement $p > 0$ is an essential assumption leading to proof of the theorem. In any case, for most physically-based mathematical models, *both* p and r are greater than zero, except perhaps at the interval endpoints. We shall extend the results of Theorem 4.1 to these exceptional cases later. Ince [3] states a similar theorem for the case in which p changes sign in the interval $a < x < b$.

The eigenvalues λ_n^2 for the system (4.9) form a set of discrete numbers. In particular, $|\lambda_m^2 - \lambda_n^2| > 0$ unless $m = n$. If S is the set $\{1, 2, \ldots\}$ of positive integers, the set $\{\lambda_n^2\}$ of eigenvalues is equivalent to S; that is, there is a one-to-one relationship between S and λ_n^2, ordered as we have them in a sequence of increasing numerical value. Accordingly, the set $\{\lambda_n^2\}$ is said to be *countable* [4]; this countable set of eigenvalues for an eigenvalue problem constitutes the *spectrum* of the given problem.

EXAMPLE 4.4

(a) Describe the spectrum of the eigenvalue problem (3.82).

The eigenvalues are $\lambda_n^2 = (n\pi/l)^2, n = 0, 1, 2, \ldots$, according to (3.87). There-fore the spectrum is the ordered set $\{0, \pi^2/l^2, 4\pi^2/l^2, 9\pi^2/l^2, \ldots\}$ of real numbers.

(b) Demonstrate Theorem 4.1 for the eigenvalue problem (3.72a)

$$X'' + \lambda^2 X = 0, \qquad 0 < x < 1$$

$$X'(1) - X(0) = 0$$
$$X'(0) + X(1) = 0$$

The variables in (4.9) have the values $r = 1, p = 1, q = 0, a = 0$, and $b = 1$ for this problem. However, the boundary conditions are of a new type. In view of the results of Example 3.2, it is clear that eigenvalues and eigenfunctions exist. We shall see if the theorem remains valid. In Fig. 3.2 $\Lambda = i\lambda$ and $\Lambda_0 \approx 1.54$, so $\lambda_0^2 = -\Lambda_0^2 \approx -2.37$. In Fig. 3.3 $\lambda_1 \approx 3.68$ and $\lambda_2 \approx 5.92$, so $\lambda_1^2 \approx 13.6, \lambda_2^2 \approx 35.0$. We also observe in Fig. 3.3 that $\lambda_n \approx n\pi$, when $n > 4$, so $\lambda_n^2 \approx n^2\pi^2$ then. Therefore we have

$$\lambda_0^2 < \lambda_1^2 < \lambda_2^2 \ldots \qquad \lim_{n \to \infty} \lambda_n^2 = \infty$$

Corresponding to λ_n^2 there are the eigenfunctions (see Example 3.2, Sec. 3.4)

$$X_n(x) = c_{0n}\left(\cos \lambda_n x - \frac{\sin \lambda_n x}{\lambda_n}\right), \qquad n = 0, 1, 2, \ldots$$

In particular,

$$X_0 = c_{00}\left(\cosh 1.54x - \frac{\sinh 1.54x}{1.54}\right)$$

$$X_1 = c_{01}\left(\cos 3.68x - \frac{\sin 3.68x}{3.68}\right)$$

$$X_2 = c_{02}\left(\cos 5.92x - \frac{\sin 5.92x}{5.92}\right)$$

In the interval $0 < x < 1$, X_0 has no zeros because the positive function $\cosh 1.54x > \sinh 1.54x/1.54$. However, X_1 has one zero (at $x = 0.36$) and X_2 has two zeros (at $x = 0.24$ and $x = 0.77$) on $0 < x < 1$.   Q.E.D.

Further examples are contained in the Problems.

Additional properties of the eigenvalues λ_n^2 and eigenfunctions X_n of the general system (4.9) are derived by integral methods. By integrating certain variations of the governing equation of (4.9) over the interval $a \le x \le b$, we are able to utilize the known boundary conditions of the problem to ascertain the properties of λ_n^2 and X_n^2. Be sure to note as we proceed that the development depends crucially on the form of the governing equation, thus justifying our efforts to put (4.5) into an exact-differential standard form. Two general one-dimensional relations are developed; they are called Green's Identities in analogy to their two-dimensional counterparts (see the Gauss theorem and Green's identitities in Appendix 1).

Green's Identities

To begin, write the Sturm–Liouville equation from (4.9) in the form

$$(rX_n')' = -\lambda_n^2 pX_n - qX_n \tag{4.10}$$

Now multiply both sides of (4.10) by X_n and integrate over $a \le x \le b$. First,

$$(rX_n')'X_n = -\lambda_n^2 pX_n^2 - qX_n^2 \tag{4.11}$$

Then

$$\int_a^b (rX_n')'X_n\,dx = -\lambda_n^2 \int_a^b pX_n^2\,dx - \int_a^b qX_n^2\,dx \tag{4.12}$$

The left-hand side of (4.12) can be integrated by parts to yield

$$\int_a^b (rX_n')'X_n\,dx = [rX_n'X_n]_a^b - \int_a^b r(X_n')^2\,dx \tag{4.13}$$

Combining (4.12) and (4.13), plus some rearrangement, produces *Green's First Identity*

$$\lambda_n^2 \int_a^b pX_n^2\,dx = -[rX_n'X_n]_a^b + \int_a^b r(X_n')^2\,dx - \int_a^b qX_n^2\,dx \tag{4.14}$$

for the Sturm–Liouville equation (4.10).

Next we let λ_m^2 and X_m be a distinct eigenvalue and eigenfunction for the same eigenvalue problem as λ_n^2 and X_n—that is, $m \ne n$ and $\lambda_m^2 \ne \lambda_n^2$. Then, in lieu of (4.11), we may write

$$(rX_n')'X_m = -\lambda_n^2 pX_nX_m - qX_nX_m \tag{4.15}$$

and

$$(rX_m')'X_n = -\lambda_m^2 pX_mX_n - qX_mX_n \tag{4.16}$$

Take the difference of (4.15) and (4.16) and integrate over $a \le x \le b$ to achieve first

$$(rX_n')'X_m - X_n(rX_m')' = (-\lambda_n^2 + \lambda_m^2)pX_mX_n$$

and second

$$\int_a^b [(rX_n')'X_m - X_n(rX_m')']\,dx = (-\lambda_n^2 + \lambda_m^2)\int_a^b pX_mX_n\,dx \tag{4.17}$$

Because of the form of (4.10), the term in brackets on the left in (4.17) is an exact differential. Therefore (4.17) becomes after the integration

$$(\lambda_m^2 - \lambda_n^2)\int_a^b pX_mX_n\,dx = [r(X_n'X_m - X_nX_m')]_a^b \tag{4.18}$$

which is *Green's Second Identity* for (4.10).

Application of Green's Identities

THEOREM 4.2 If the eigenfunctions X_m and X_n corresponding to the distinct eigenvalues λ_m^2 and λ_n^2 of the system (4.9) exist, they are orthogonal with respect to the weight function p.

Proof: Because the eigenvalues λ_m^2 and λ_n^2 are distinct $(m \neq n)$, $\lambda_m^2 - \lambda_n^2 \neq 0$. Call the term on the right side of (4.18)

$$\Delta = [r(X_n' X_m - X_n X_m')]_a^b$$
$$= r(b)[X_n'(b)X_m(b) - X_n(b)X_m'(b)]$$
$$- r(a)[X_n'(a)X_m(a) - X_n(a)X_m'(a)] \tag{4.19}$$

Now, introduction of the boundary conditions from (4.9) gives

$$\Delta = r(b)\left[-\frac{\gamma}{\delta}X_n(b)X_m(b) + \frac{\gamma}{\delta}X_n(b)X_m(b) \right]$$

$$- r(a)\left[-\frac{\alpha}{\beta}X_n(a)X_m(a) + \frac{\alpha}{\beta}X_n(a)X_m(a) \right] = 0$$

Thus from (4.18) we have

$$(\lambda_m^2 - \lambda_n^2)\int_a^b pX_m X_n \, dx = 0 \tag{4.20}$$

Because $\lambda_m^2 - \lambda_n^2 \neq 0$, it follows that

$$\int_a^b pX_m X_n \, dx = 0, \qquad m \neq n \tag{4.21}$$

That is, the eigenfunctions are orthogonal *with respect to* $p = p(x)$.   Q.E.D.

Discussion. The role of the weight function p in the generalized orthogonality condition (4.21) is an essential feature of the preceding theorem and proof. Furthermore, Theorem 4.2 is valid whenever $\Delta = 0$; this suggests possible generalization of the results (see below, Sec. 4.4).

THEOREM 4.3   If $p \neq 0$ in $a < x < b$, the eigenvalues λ_n^2 of the system (4.9) are real.

Proof: Suppose that $\lambda_n^2 = v + i\eta$, where v and η are real constants, is a complex eigenvalue of (4.9) with corresponding (possibly complex) eigenfunction X_n. Then

$$(rX_n')' + (q + \lambda_n^2 p)X_n = 0$$

If $X_n = N + iH$, the following equations must hold:

$$(rN')' + (q + vp)N - \eta pH + i[(rH')' + (q + vp)H + \eta pN] = 0$$

or

$$(rN')' + (q + vp)N - \eta pH = 0$$

$$(rH')' + (q + vp)H + \eta pN = 0$$

The complex conjugates $\lambda_m^2 = \overline{\lambda_n^2} = v - i\eta$ and $X_m = \overline{X}_n = N - iH$ are also a distinct eigenvalue and corresponding eigenfunction for (4.9), as direct substitution and comparison with the above equations show. The relation (4.20) is used to obtain

$$(\overline{\lambda_n^2} - \lambda_n^2) \int_a^b p\overline{X}_n X_n \, dx = 0$$

or

$$-2i\eta \int_a^b p(N - iH)(N + iH) \, dx = 0$$

As $(N - iH)(N + iH) = N^2 + H^2$, we have

$$-2i\eta \int_a^b p(N^2 + H^2) \, dx = 0$$

Because p does not change sign in $a < x < b$ and neither p nor $N^2 + H^2$ is identically zero on the interval, we have

$$\int_a^b p(N^2 + H^2) \, dx \neq 0$$

Therefore, $\eta = 0$ and the λ_n^2 must be real; that is, $\lambda_n^2 = v$ alone. For $\eta = 0$, N and H satisfy the same eigenvalue problem and so differ by at most an arbitrary constant. Accordingly, X_n is real, except for an arbitrary, perhaps complex, multiplying constant, which we neglect in applications in any case.   Q.E.D.

THEOREM 4.4   If $p > 0$ and $q \leq M$, where M is a constant, a lower bound on λ_n^2 is given by

$$\lambda_n^2 \geq -M \frac{\int_a^b X_n^2 \, dx}{\int_a^b p X_n^2 \, dx}$$

for boundary conditions of the first and second type.

Proof: Consider the terms in Green's First Identity (4.14):
(a) $\int_a^b p X_n^2 \, dx = A_1 > 0$ because $p > 0$.
(b) $\int_a^b q X_n^2 \, dx \leq M \int_a^b X_n^2 \, dx = MA_2$ because $q \leq M$.
(c) $\int_a^b (rX_m')^2 \, dx = A_3 \geq 0$ because $r > 0$ for the regular system [see (4.8a)], while $(X_n')^2 \geq 0$ [note $X_n'(x)$ may be zero in some cases].
(d) $[rX_n'X_n]_a^b = 0$ for boundary conditions of the first or second type; for example, $X_n(a) = 0$ or $X_n'(a) = 0$.

Therefore (4.14) becomes $\lambda_n^2 A_1 \geq A_3 - MA_2$. As $A_3 \geq 0$ and $A_1 > 0$, $\lambda_n^2 \geq -MA_2/A_1$ or

$$\lambda_n^2 \geq -M \frac{\int_a^b X_n^2 \, dx}{\int_a^b p X_n^2 \, dx} \qquad\qquad \text{Q.E.D.}$$

Discussion. If $M = 0$—that is, $q(x) \leq 0$ on $a \leq x \leq b$—$\lambda_n^2 \geq 0$; the eigenvalues of *all* problems with boundary conditions of the first or second type are non-negative when $q \leq 0$. If $q(x) < 0$ strictly,

$$\int_a^b q X_m^2 \, dx < 0 \quad \text{and} \quad \lambda_n^2 > 0$$

EXAMPLE 4.5   Characterize the eigenvalues and eigenfunctions of the following problem (based on a fluid flow model):

$$x^2 X'' + x X' + \lambda^2 X = 0, \qquad 0 < a < x < 1$$

$$X(a) = 0$$

$$X'(1) + X(1) = 0$$

Step 1. Reduce the equation to standard form. Division by x^2 produces

$$X'' + \frac{1}{x} X' + \frac{\lambda^2}{x^2} X = 0$$

Therefore, from (4.8a),

$$r = \exp \left[\int^x \eta^{-1} \, d\eta \right] = x$$

and, consequently, $q = rP_{21} = 0$; $p = rP_{22} = 1/x$. The standard-form eigenvalue problem is

$$\frac{d}{dx} \left(x \frac{dX}{dx} \right) + \lambda^2 \left(\frac{1}{x} \right) X = 0, \qquad 0 < a < x < 1$$

$$X(a) = 0$$

$$X'(1) + X(1) = 0$$

Step 2. Apply theorems. Both $r = x$ and $p = 1/x$ are real, continuous, positive functions on $a \le x \le 1$, while $q = 0$. Therefore Theorem 4.1 holds, so an infinite set of eigenvalues λ_n^2 and corresponding eigenfunctions X_n exist. Similarly, Theorem 4.2 holds and the X_n are orthogonal with respect to the weight function p; that is,

$$\int_a^1 \frac{1}{x} X_m X_n \, dx = 0, \qquad m \ne n$$

As $p \ne 0$ in the problem interval, Theorem 4.3 holds and the λ_n^2 are all real.

Finally, consider Theorem 4.4. It is clear that $\lambda_n^2 \ge 0$ in this case because $q = 0 = M$ and $-[rX_n'X_n]_a^1 = X_n^2(1) \ge 0$, depending on the value of $X_n(1)$. It is not possible for both $X_n(1)$ and $X_n'(1)$ to be zero, for then $X_n(x) \equiv 0$ for all λ^2; thus $\lambda^2 > 0$ (see Prob. 4.16).

4.4   EXTENSIONS TO SPECIAL CASES

The four theorems of the previous section apply to cases in which the general equation (4.5) is regular on $a \le x \le b$—that is, $P_1(x)$, $P_{21}(x)$, and $P_{22}(x)$ are bounded there—and in which the boundary conditions were of limited types. However, some of the theorems have possible application for the case of singular equations—for example, where $P_1(a) = \infty$ so $r(a) = 0$—or more general boundary condition types. In this section we extend the theorems of Sec. 4.3 to two special cases of some practical significance.

The Periodic Boundary Conditions; Multiple Eigenvalues

A physical problem of great classical interest is the problem of a ring-shaped heat conductor [5]. Physically the conductor is a slender, uniform rod that has been laterally insulated and formed into a continuous ring; heat conduction is assumed to occur only along the circumference of the ring (one-dimensional transfer; see Chap. 2). Accordingly, if we arbitrarily select a coordinate origin on the ring, a mathematical model for the temperature u in the ring might be

$$u_t = ku_{xx}, \qquad -1 < x < 1, \quad t > 0 \tag{4.22a}$$

$$\left.\begin{aligned} u(1, t) &= u(-1, t), \\ u_x(1, t) &= u_x(-1, t), \end{aligned}\right\} \quad t > 0 \tag{4.22b}$$

$$u(x, 0) = u_0(x), \qquad -1 \le x \le 1 \tag{4.22c}$$

where the thermal diffusivity k is a constant.

Physically this model implies that the circumference of the ring is two units and that because the ring is continuous, the temperature u and heat flux Ku_x must be continuous across any plane section that we choose as a matter of convenience to divide our problem mathematically. The conditions (4.22b) are called the *periodic* or *compatibility boundary conditions*.

Separation of variables in (4.22) leads to an eigenvalue problem (see the Problems) that we generalize, in the spirit of our earlier discussion in Sec. 4.3, to the form

$$\frac{d}{dx}\left[r(x)\frac{dX}{dx} \right] + [q(x) + \lambda^2 p(x)]X = 0, \qquad a < x < b \tag{4.23a}$$

$$\left.\begin{aligned} X(a) &= X(b) \\ X'(a) &= X'(b) \end{aligned}\right. \tag{4.23b}$$

$$r(a) = r(b) \tag{4.23c}$$

Physically we identify $r = K > 0$ and $p = K/k > 0$. Because the flux at $x = a$ must equal the flux at $x = b$, the condition $r(a) = r(b)$ is a necessary addition to the second boundary condition. It also follows physically that $p(a) = p(b)$. (Why?)

Equation (4.23a) is formally the same as the governing equation of the Sturm–Liouville system (4.9); also, p, q, and r still are real, continuous functions on the finite interval $a \le x \le b$. Consequently, Green's identities (4.14) and (4.18) apply here also. Let us now consider a set of appropriate theorems for the present case.

THEOREM 4.1'   If $p > 0$ and $r > 0$ on $a \le x \le b$, there exists for the system (4.121) a spectrum of eigenvalues λ_n^2 such that

$$\lambda_0^2 < \lambda_1^2 < \lambda_2^2 < \lambda_3^2 < \cdots \qquad \lambda_n^2 \to \infty \text{ as } n \to \infty$$

and there exists an infinite set of corresponding eigenfunctions $X_{01}, X_{02}, X_{11}, X_{12}, \ldots$, on $a \le x \le b$ such that there is at least one and perhaps two linearly independent eigenfunctions X_{ni}, $i = 1$ or 2, for each λ_n^2.

Discussion. The Sturm–Liouville system (4.9) had (as given in Theorem 4.1 and demonstrated in the Problems) only one eigenfunction X_n for each eigenvalue λ_n^2. These eigenvalues have a *multiplicity* of one. A general, second-order, linear ordinary differential equation has two and only two linearly independent solutions (see Sec. A.2.1 or [2]). Therefore, in the case of Theorem 4.1', the λ_n^2 can have a multiplicity of two at most; that is, to each λ_n^2 there may correspond two linearly independent eigenfunctions. The following partial proof illustrates that two independent eigenfunctions may exist; the subsequent example illustrates their existence for a simple case.

Proof: Assume that λ_n^2 is an eigenvalue of (4.23) and X_{n1} and X_{n2} are two eigenfunctions for that λ_n^2. Consider the *wronskian* [2] of the two solutions

$$W_n(x) = X'_{2n}(x)X_{1n}(x) - X'_{1n}(x)X_{2n}(x) = \begin{vmatrix} X_{1n} & X_{2n} \\ X'_{1n} & X'_{2n} \end{vmatrix}$$

Leighton [2] shows that the two solutions X_{1n} and X_{2n} to (4.23) are linearly dependent if and only if $W_n(x)$ is zero on $a \leq x \leq b$ and that $W_n(x)$ is either never zero or always zero on $a \leq x \leq b$. In general,

$$W_n(a) = X'_{2n}(a)X_{1n}(a) - X'_{1n}(a)X_{2n}(a) = f_n$$

$$W_n(b) = X'_{2n}(b)X_{1n}(b) - X'_{1n}(b)X_{2n}(b) = g_n$$

For boundary conditions of the first, second, or third type, we see that both f_n and g_n are always zero and $W_n = 0$. It follows that X_{1n} and X_{2n} are linearly dependent for boundary conditions of the first three types and only one independent eigenfunction exists (see Example 3.2).

However, the periodic boundary conditions yield no information on the values of f_n or g_n. If $f_n \neq 0$ and $g_n \neq 0$, X_{1n} and X_{2n} exist and are linearly independent.   Q.E.D.

The following example illustrates that in a given problem some, but not necessarily all, λ_n^2 have a multiplicity of two; this is in accord with the lack of specific knowledge available to determine f_n and g_n in the general case above.

EXAMPLE 4.6   The eigenvalue problem for the ring-shaped heat conductor is (see the Problems)

$$X'' + \lambda^2 X = 0, \quad -1 < x < 1 \tag{4.24}$$

$$X(-1) = X(1)$$
$$X'(-1) = X'(1) \tag{4.25}$$

Find the eigenvalues and eigenfunctions.

From (A.2.9) and (A.2.12), the general solution to (4.24) is

$$X(x) = c_0 \cos \lambda x + c_1 \frac{\sin \lambda x}{\lambda}$$

Introduction of this solution in (4.25) leads to the conditions

$$2c_1 \frac{\sin \lambda}{\lambda} = 0$$

$$-2c_0 \lambda \sin \lambda = 0$$

For $\lambda^2 \to 0$, we find, first, that $2c_1 = 0$, because

$$\lim_{\lambda^2 \to 0} \frac{\sin \lambda}{\lambda} = 1$$

and, second, that c_0 can be arbitrary. Therefore $X_0 = 1$ is the *only* eigenfunction corresponding to $\lambda_0^2 = 0$ (we discard the unessential constant c_0).

However, for $\lambda^2 > 0$, $\sin \lambda = 0$ when $\lambda^2 = (n\pi)^2$ for $n \geq 1$; accordingly, both c_0 and c_1 can be arbitrary. To each $\lambda_n^2 = n^2\pi^2$, $n \geq 1$, there correspond the two linearly independent eigenfunctions

$$X_{n1} = \cos \lambda_n x$$

$$X_{n2} = \sin \lambda_n x$$

THEOREM 4.2′ The eigenvalues X_{mi} and X_{nj} corresponding to the distinct eigenvalues λ_m^2 and λ_n^2 of the system (4.23) are orthogonal with respect to the weight function p. In addition, a linear combination $\tilde{X}_{n2}$ of the two linearly independent eigenfunctions X_{n1} and X_{n2} corresponding to the same λ_n^2 can be constructed so that the linearly independent eigenfunctions X_{n1} and $\tilde{X}_{n2}$ are orthogonal with respect to p also.

Proof: From (4.19), $\Delta = 0$ for the conditions (4.23b) and (4.23c). It follows from (4.18) that

$$(\lambda_m^2 - \lambda_n^2) \int_a^b p X_{mi} X_{nj} \ dx = 0$$

for $i = 1, 2$, $j = 1, 2$, and $m \neq n$. As $\lambda_m^2 \neq \lambda_n^2$, $m \neq n$,

$$\int_a^b p X_{ni} X_{mj} \ dx = 0$$

That is, the eigenfunctions are orthogonal.

The proof that a linear combination $\tilde{X}_{n2} = X_{n2} + AX_{n1}$ exists so that

$$\int_a^b p X_{n1} \tilde{X}_{n2} \, dx = 0$$

is left to the Problems. Note that $\tilde{X}_{n2}$ is linearly independent of X_{n1} (Why?).   Q.E.D.

THEOREM 4.3′ If $p \neq 0$ in $a < x < b$, the eigenvalues λ_n^2 of the system (4.23) are real.

Proof: The proof follows that of Theorem 4.3 and is left to the Problems.

THEOREM 4.4′ If $p > 0$ and $q \leq M$ on $a \leq x \leq b$, where M is a constant, then

$$\lambda_n^2 \geq \max\left[-M \left\{ \frac{\int_a^b X_{n1}^2 \, dx}{\int_a^b p X_{n1}^2 \, dx} ; \frac{\int_a^b X_{n2}^2 \, dx}{\int_a^b p X_{n2}^2 \, dx} \right\} \right]$$

for boundary conditions of the first and second kind.

Proof: From Green's First Identity (4.14),

(a) $\int_a^b p X_{ni}^2 \, dx = A_{1i} > 0$ because $p > 0$.
(b) $\int_a^b q X_{ni}^2 \, dx \leq M \int_a^b X_{ni}^2 \, dx = M A_{2i}$ because $q \leq M$.
(c) $\int_a^b r(X_{ni}')^2 \, dx \geq 0$ because $r > 0$.
(d) $[r X_{ni}' X_{ni}]_a^b = 0$ according to (4.23b) and (4.23c).
Therefore $\lambda_n^2 A_{1i} \geq -M A_{2i}$ or

$$\lambda_n^2 \geq -M \frac{A_{2i}}{A_{1i}}$$

Because λ_n^2 is a single number, it must be greater than or equal to the larger of $-M(A_{21}/A_{11})$ and $-M(A_{22}/A_{12})$.   Q.E.D.

Singular Cases

Many physical problems lead via their mathematical models to eigenvalue problems of the Sturm–Liouville type in which r is zero at one or both of the interval endpoints. In this chapter we have already considered two important equations with singular endpoints (recall that $r = 0$ when $P_1 \to \infty$ and such a point is called a singular point).

Bessel's Equation of Order n. From Example 4.3, Sec. 4.2,

$$\frac{d}{dx}\left(x \frac{dX}{dx} \right) + \left(-\frac{n^2}{x} + \lambda^2 x \right) X = 0$$

on the interval $0 \leq x \leq 1$ (which corresponds to that for the membrane, Sec. 4.1, Example 4.1, where $n = 0$), we have $r(0) = 0$ so that $x = 0$ is a singular point.

Legendre's Equation (A.2.13). From Example 4.3, Sec. 4.2,

$$\frac{d}{dx}\left[(1 - x^2) \frac{dX}{dx} \right] + \lambda(\lambda + 1) X = 0$$

On the interval $-1 \leq x \leq 1$ (which corresponds to the interval found for the eigenvalue problem for heat conduction in a sphere), we have $r(-1) = r(1) = 0$, so that $x = -1$ and $x = 1$ are singular points.

Let us examine the effect of singular endpoints on Theorems 4.1 through 4.4.

THEOREM 4.1 The existence and uniqueness of eigenvalues and eigenfunctions.

Provided $r > 0$, except possibly for $r = 0$ at $x = a$ or $x = b$, and provided p does not change sign on $a \leq x \leq b$, the conclusions of this theorem are not changed.

THEOREM 4.2   The orthogonality of eigenfunctions.

Examination of the proof of this theorem shows that if p is not identically zero and does not change sign in $a < x < b$, then the eigenfunctions are orthogonal as stated whenever $\Delta = 0$. Clearly, $\Delta = 0$ for r bounded on $a \leq x \leq b$ and boundary conditions of the first three types. If $r(a) = 0$ and a boundary condition of the first three types is satisfied at $x = b$, then $\Delta = 0$ provided

$$\lim_{x \to a} r(X_n' X_m - X_n X_m') = 0 \tag{4.26}$$

No specific boundary conditions need be specified at $x = a$. A similar result holds if $x = b$ is the singular point while $x = a$ is not or if both are singular points.

EXAMPLE 4.7   *Vibration of a Circular Membrane with Fixed Circumference.* From (2.63) and Example 4.1, Sec. 4.1, the complete eigenvalue problem is

$$\phi'' + \frac{1}{r}\phi' + \lambda^2\phi = 0, \qquad 0 < r < R \tag{4.27}$$

$$\phi'(0) = \phi(R) = 0 \tag{4.28}$$

where r is the radial polar coordinate here.

For eigenfunctions ϕ_n and ϕ_m to be orthogonal, condition (4.26)—that is,

$$\lim_{r \to 0} r(\phi_n'\phi_m - \phi_n\phi_m') = 0 \tag{4.29}$$

must be satisfied because the standard form of (4.27) is

$$\frac{d}{dr}\left(r\frac{d\phi}{dr}\right) + \lambda^2 r\phi = 0 \tag{4.30}$$

$\phi_m'(0) = \phi_n'(0) = 0$ and $\phi_m(r) = \phi_n(r) = 0$. The general solution to (4.27) or (4.30) is obtained from (A.2.36) by replacing x by λr there; then

$$\phi(r) = AJ_0(\lambda r) + BN_0(\lambda r) \tag{4.31}$$

Near $r = 0$,

$$J_0(\lambda r) \sim 1 - \frac{\lambda^2 r^2}{2} + O(r^4)$$

$$N_0(\lambda r) \sim J_0(\lambda r)\ln \lambda r + \frac{\lambda^2 r^2}{2} + O(r^4)$$

Thus

$$\frac{dJ_0}{dr} \sim -\lambda^2 r + O(r^3)$$

$$\frac{dN_0}{dr} \sim -\lambda^2 r \ln \lambda r + \frac{1}{r}J_0(\lambda r) + O(r)$$

For $\phi'(0) = 0$ it follows that, in (4.31), $B = 0$ because

$$\lim_{r \to 0} \frac{dN_0}{dr} \to \infty$$

But then

$$\lim_{r \to 0} \phi(r) = A \lim_{r \to 0} J_0(\lambda r) = A < \infty$$

and (4.29) is satisfied. We see that, in this case, the boundary conditions of the problem are sufficient to eliminate the Bessel function of the second kind whose behavior near the origin is also not acceptable on physical grounds [$\lim_{r \to 0} N_0(\lambda r) \to -\infty$]. The eigenfunctions are thus of the form

$$\phi_n(r) = A_n J_0(\lambda_n r)$$

and the λ_n^2 are found from (4.28) as the roots of $\phi_n(R) = 0$ or $J_0(\lambda_n R) = 0$ (see [1]). In fact, $\lambda_0^2 = 5.78/R^2$, $\lambda_1^2 = 30.5/R^2$, etc.

THEOREM 4.3   The reality of eigenvalues.

This theorem holds whenever Theorem 4.2 above holds—that is, when $\Delta = 0$.

THEOREM 4.4   A lower bound on λ_n^2.

This theorem holds as originally given and extends to cases in which one or both of the endpoints are singular points. For example, from (4.14),

$$\lambda_n^2 \int_a^b p X_n^2 \, dx = -[r X_n' X_n]_a^b + \int_a^b r(X_n')^2 \, dx - \int_a^b q X_n^2 \, dx$$

If $r(a) = r(b) = 0$ and $r > 0$ otherwise, then

$$\lambda_n^2 \geq -\frac{\int_a^b q X_n^2 \, dx}{\int_a^b p X_n^2 \, dx} \geq -M \frac{\int_a^b X_n^2 \, dx}{\int_a^b p X_n^2 \, dx}$$

as before because $\int_a^b r(X_n')^2 \, dx \geq 0$ and $q \leq M$. When $r(a) = 0$ and boundary conditions of the first and second types are satisfied at $x = b$, the same result is found, and so on.

4.5   THE GENERALIZED EXPANSION

The methods of separation of variables and eigenfunction expansions require that the eigenfunctions be employed as terms in a convergent infinite series that represents the solution to the original problem (check Sec. 3.5). In particular, the series of eigenfunctions must be able to represent an arbitrary, but reasonable, function $f(x)$ over the problem interval $a \leq x \leq b$.

For a given eigenvalue problem (4.9), suppose that the spectrum $\{\lambda_n^2\}$ and corresponding X_n are known and that the arbitrary initial condition $f(x)$ of the original problem is to be represented. Can such a function be expanded in terms of the eigenfunctions X_n in the manner of the Fourier series (see Sec. 3.3)? To find out, we propose the series representation

$$f(x) = \sum_{n=0}^{\infty} c_n X_n, \qquad a \leq x \leq b \tag{4.32}$$

composed of the set of known eigenfunctions and the unknown constant coefficients c_n. The X_n are orthogonal on the interval with respect to a known weight function p. Accordingly, if (4.32) is multiplied by pX_m and integrated over the interval (see Sec. 3.3 again), we have first

$$\int_a^b pfX_m\,dx = \int_a^b \left\{ \sum_{n=0}^{\infty} c_n pX_m X_n \right\} dx$$

and second

$$\int_a^b pfX_m\,dx = \sum_{n=0}^{\infty} c_n \int_a^b pX_m X_n\,dx$$

provided that the series converges suitably—for example, uniformly to $f(x)$ on $a \leq x \leq b$. But

$$\int_a^b pX_m X_n\,dx = 0, \qquad m \neq n$$

Therefore

$$c_m = \frac{1}{N_m} \int_a^b pfX_m\,dx \tag{4.33}$$

where

$$N_m = \int_a^b pX_m^2\,dx > 0 \tag{4.34}$$

The N_m are the *normalizing constants* (see below).

The question now arises, "Under what conditions does the series expansion (4.32) of a function $f(x)$ in terms of the orthogonal functions X_n converge to $f(x)$?" At present, we know only that if (4.32) exists, the coefficients c_n are uniquely determined by (4.33) and (4.34). On the basis of our experience with Fourier series (Sec. 3.3.1 and 3.3.2), we can be confident that if $f(x)$ satisfies certain conditions of smoothness on $a \leq x \leq b$, the series (4.32) will converge to $f(x)$ in some sense. The series (4.32) can be called a *Generalized Fourier Series*.

The convergence and representation character of the series (4.32) with coefficients (4.33) is established by the following theorems. No proofs are offered in the text; these proofs [3, 6, 7] are somewhat beyond our scope although they deal, in principle, with the same type of concepts used to prove convergence of the Fourier series in Chap. 3. The theorems are given here formally only for the case of the system (4.9) under the conditions of Theorem 4.1, Sec. 4.3, but they are applicable to the other cases that we have examined.

THEOREM 4.5 [3]   If λ_n^2 and $X_n(x)$ are the solutions to (4.9) and $f(x)$ is of class C^2 on the finite interval $a \leq x \leq b$, the series

$$\sum_{n=0}^{\infty} X_n \left\{ \frac{\int_a^b p(\xi)f(\xi)X_n(\xi)\,d\xi}{\int_a^b p(\xi)X_n^2(\xi)\,d\xi} \right\} \tag{4.35}$$

converges absolutely and uniformly to $f(x)$ in the interval.

THEOREM 4.6 [7, 8]   If the function $f(x)$ in Theorem 4.5 is piecewise continuous on $a \leq x \leq b$ and has a square-integrable first derivative there [$\int_a^b pf'^2 \, dx < \infty$; see Appendix 1], the series (4.35) converges absolutely and uniformly to $f(x)$, where $f(x)$ is continuous in $a < x < b$, and (like the Fourier series) to

$$\tfrac{1}{2}[f(x - 0) + f(x + 0)]$$

at points of discontinuity (see Prob. 3.23). [Courant and Hilbert [7] point out that $f(x)$ does *not* need to satisfy the boundary conditions of (4.9), a point with physical significance (see Sec. 2.2.1) and noted for simpler cases in Chap. 3.]

THEOREM 4.7 [6]   If $f(x)$ in Theorem 4.5 is square integrable on $a \leq x \leq b$—that is, if

$$\int_a^b pf^2 \, dx < \infty$$

the series (4.35) [or (4.32) with (4.33)] converges to $f(x)$ in the interval in the sense of least squares or in the mean. Thus there exists an N such that

$$\int_a^b p\left[f - \sum_{n=0}^k c_n X_n \right]^2 dx < \varepsilon \tag{4.36}$$

where $\varepsilon > 0$ and $k > N$, and in the limit as $N \to \infty$,

$$\int_a^b p\left[f - \sum_{n=0}^\infty c_n X_n \right]^2 dx = 0 \tag{4.37}$$

Discussion. Because $p \geq 0$ in $a \leq x \leq b$, it follows that if we expand (4.36), use the appropriate orthogonality relationships, and then pass to the limit $N \to \infty$, we obtain the Parseval equation

$$\int_a^b pf^2 \, dx = \sum_{n=0}^\infty c_n^2 \int_a^b pX_n^2 \, dx \tag{4.38}$$

In view of (4.36) and (4.38), we have

THEOREM 4.8 [6]   The eigenfunctions X_n of the Sturm–Liouville system (4.9) are complete under the conditions of Theorem 4.1.

Discussion. Recall (Sec. 3.3.2) that a set of orthogonal functions X_n is said to be *complete* with respect to a class of functions $f(x)$ if (a) a condition such as (4.36) holds—that is, $f(x)$ can be approximated in the mean with arbitrary accuracy by the series—or (b) Parseval's equation (4.36) holds.

Finally, it is often convenient to normalize the eigenfunctions $X_n(x)$ as follows: Let $\tilde{X}_n(x) = N_n^{-1/2} X_n(x)$, where N_n is given by (4.34). The functions $\tilde{X}_n$

remain eigenfunctions (recall that eigenfunctions are only unique up to a multiplicative constant) and

$$\int_a^b p\tilde{X}_m\tilde{X}_n\,dx = \delta_{mn}$$

where the "Kronecker delta"

$$\delta_{mn} = \begin{cases} 0, & m \neq n \\ 1, & m = n \end{cases}$$

Thus the $\tilde{X}_n$ are a set of *orthonormal* functions, being both orthogonal and normalized. It follows from (4.32) and (4.33) that the generalized Fourier series becomes

$$f(x) = \sum_{n=0}^{\infty} \tilde{c}_n\tilde{X}_n$$

with

$$\tilde{c}_n = \int_a^b pf\tilde{X}_n\,dx$$

The foregoing analysis has demonstrated that the eigenvalues and eigenfunctions of both the regular and singular Sturm–Liouville systems have the necessary character for use in the method of eigenfunction expansions. The methods of Chap. 3 extend directly to mathematical models in which separation of variables leads to a Sturm–Liouville system. It is important then to reread the Summary, Sec. 3.5, to refresh our memory as to the systematic procedure leading to formal series solutions.

Be forewarned, however, that finding solutions to a Sturm–Liouville system is not a trivial task. In fact, the next section is devoted to the task of obtaining approximations for eigenvalues and eigenfunctions that cannot be determined in usable explicit forms.

4.6   APPROXIMATION OF EIGENVALUES AND EIGENFUNCTIONS: THE GALERKIN METHOD

Often eigenfunctions are expressible only as power series that are not tabulated, and the eigenvalues are obtainable only through extensive numerical computations using power series whose character is not well known. An alternative is to deal directly with the equations of the original model through the numerical method of finite differences (see Chap. 10). However, a finite-difference solution to a problem is obtained as a discrete function defined only at the intersection or node points of a grid covering the problem domain and is subject to the errors introduced by the difference approximations to differentials.

If the need in a given complex case is for prediction of the behavior of a physical system in terms of continuous functions or is for accurate determination of eigenvalues (e.g., in a vibration problem), the *Galerkin Method* is very useful. In this method, one utilizes orthogonality and a set of complete functions to generate an approximate solution to a given mathematical model or eigenvalue problem. Although the method is equally applicable to the entire model or an eigenvalue problem derived from the model [9], only the latter application is considered here.

4.6.1   The Rationale and Principle

Suppose that an eigenvalue problem is given in the form of the Sturm–Liouville system (4.9). In operator notation, the problem is

$$L[X;\lambda^2] = 0, \qquad a_1 < x < a_2$$
$$B_i[a_i] = 0, \qquad i = 1, 2 \tag{4.39}$$

where the linear operator L is continuous and given by

$$L[X;\lambda^2] = \frac{d}{dx}\left[r(x)\frac{dX}{dx}\right] + [q(x) + \lambda^2 p(x)]X \tag{4.40}$$

and, for example, the first of the linear boundary conditions B_1 is

$$B_1[a_1] = \alpha X(a_1) + \beta X'(a_1) = 0 \tag{4.41}$$

In general, the solution to problem (4.39) is not easily found by direct methods. However, it is easy to generate a complete set of linearly independent functions $\{X_{Rn}\}$ that satisfy the boundary conditions $B_i[a_i]$ of the problem (4.39) for which $L[X;\lambda^2] = 0$ is the governing equation.

EXAMPLE 4.8   If
$$B_1[a_1] = X(a_1) = 0$$
$$B_2[a_2] = X(a_2) = 0$$

then from (3.28) a complete set of linearly independent functions is

$$X_{Rn} = \sin n\pi x, \qquad n = 1, 2, 3, \ldots$$

Note that $L[X_{Rn}; n^2\pi^2] \neq 0$ unless $r = p = 1$ and $q = 0$ in (4.40); therefore the X_{Rn} are not, in general, a solution to $L[X;\lambda^2] = 0$.

The Galerkin method is based on two key principles developed earlier—namely, the ability of a complete set of functions to represent any arbitrary, but reasonable, function and the orthogonality concept. Before developing the Galerkin method, it is convenient to state the definition of completeness from a new point of view. A restatement in general terms of our definition in Sec. 3.3.2 is: If for a class of functions $f(x)$ it is possible to find for any arbitrary small $\varepsilon > 0$ a positive integer N and a set of coefficients $\{c_n\}$ such that, for $a_1 \leq x \leq a_2$,

$$\int_{a_1}^{a_2} \left[\sum_{n=1}^{n=k} c_n X_{Rn} - f(x)\right]^2 dx < \varepsilon$$

for all $k > N$, then the set of linearly independent functions $\{X_{Rn}\}$ is complete with respect to the class of functions $f(x)$—for example, the class $f(x) \in C^2$ (see Appendix 1). Now, the negative alternative is: For a class of functions $f(x) \in C^i$ on the interval $a_1 \leq x \leq a_2$, a complete set $\{X_{Rn}\}$ is defined as a set such that no particular function $F(x) \in C^i$ exists that cannot be expanded in terms of $\{X_{Rn}\}$. As an example, if $F(x) \in C^2$, then

$$F(x) = \sum_n c_n X_{Rn}, \qquad a_1 \leq x \leq a_2$$

implies *either* that some $c_n \neq 0$ and $F(x)$ is expandable in terms of $\{X_{Rn}\}$ *or* that all $c_n \equiv 0$—that is, $F(x)$ is orthogonal to all (not representable in terms of) $\{X_{Rn}\}$—and we must conclude that $F(x) \equiv 0$ because $\{X_{Rn}\}$ is complete.

Based on the preceding discussion, the Galerkin method for problem (4.39) consists of two steps:

1. Represent the actual eigenfunction X in a series

$$X = \sum_n c_n X_{Rn} \tag{4.42}$$

where $\{X_{Rn}\}$ is any complete set of continuous and linearly independent functions that satisfy the boundary conditions B_i of (4.39).

2. Require that the "function" $L[X; \lambda^2]$ be orthogonal to *every* X_{Rn}—that is, that

$$\int_{a_1}^{a_2} X_{Rj} L[X; \lambda^2] \, dx = 0 \tag{4.43}$$

for all j.

If (4.43) is satisfied, it follows from the completeness of $\{X_{Rn}\}$ and the foregoing discussion that

$$L[X; \lambda^2] \equiv 0$$

which is precisely the condition needed to ensure that $X = \sum_n c_n X_{Rn}$ is a solution of the original eigenvalue problem. We can now show that (4.42) and (4.43) are sufficient to determine the c_n and λ^2, and we will develop the requisite mechanics for obtaining numerical answers.

4.6.2 Approximate Solution of the Eigenvalue Problem

Introduction of (4.42) into (4.43) yields

$$\int_{a_1}^{a_2} X_{Rj} L\left[\sum_n c_n X_{Rn}; \lambda^2\right] dx = \sum_n c_n \int_{a_1}^{a_2} X_{Rj} L[X_{Rn}; \lambda^2] \, dx = 0, \qquad j = 1, 2, 3, \ldots \tag{4.44}$$

because of the linearity of L. Equation (4.44) represents a series of equations (one for each value of j) and is compactly written in the form

$$\sum_n A_{jn} c_n = 0, \qquad j = 1, 2, 3, \ldots \tag{4.45}$$

where

$$A_{jn} = \int_{a_1}^{a_2} X_{Rj} L[X_{Rn}; \lambda^2] \, dx$$

$$= \int_{a_1}^{a_2} X_{Rj}[r X'_{Rn}]' \, dx + \int_{a_1}^{a_2} q X_{Rn} X_{Rj} \, dx + \lambda^2 \int_{a_1}^{a_2} p X_{Rn} X_{Rj} \, dx \tag{4.46}$$

Equations (4.45) represent a set of homogeneous, linear, algebraic, simultaneous equations for the unknowns c_n with coefficients A_{jn}. The indices j and n range over the positive integers, so the number of unknowns is equal to the number of equations.

A necessary and sufficient condition for (4.45) to have a nontrivial solution for the c_n is that the determinant of the coefficients equals zero [10]. Thus we require

$$\det A_{jn} = |A_{jn}| = 0$$

or

$$\begin{vmatrix} A_{11} & A_{12} & A_{13}\cdots \\ A_{21} & A_{22} & \\ A_{31} & & \\ \vdots & & \end{vmatrix} = 0 \qquad (4.47)$$

As $A_{jn} = A_{jn}(\lambda^2)$ because all other parameters are prescribed, (4.47) is an equation for λ^2 and yields an infinite set $\{\lambda_s^2\}$ of λ^2 values. Each value from the set $\{\lambda_s^2\}$ makes $\det A_{jn} = 0$; hence for each λ_s^2 the equations (4.45) have a nontrivial solution; that is, to λ_s^2 there corresponds a set of values $\{c_n^{(s)}\}$.

In summary, when the proposed series (4.42) converges, the solution of (4.45) under the restraint (4.47) produces an infinite set of eigenvalues λ_s^2 and the corresponding eigenfunctions

$$X_s = \sum_n c_n^{(s)} X_{Rn} \qquad (4.48)$$

as the solutions to the original problem (4.39).

We cannot deal effectively with an infinite set of equations; however, we can consider the first N functions of the complete set $\{X_{Rn}\}$, $n = 1, 2, 3, \ldots, N, \ldots$. For X_s to be an exact solution of (4.39), $L[X_s; \lambda_s^2]$ must be identically zero, this requirement being equivalent to the requirement that $L[X_s; \lambda_s^2]$ be orthogonal to each member of the complete set $\{X_{Rn}\}$. When there are only N functions in the proposed series (4.42)— that is,

$$X = \sum_{n=1}^{N} c_n X_{Rn} \qquad (4.49)$$

only N orthogonality conditions (4.43) can be satisfied. As a result, (4.45) becomes

$$\sum_{n=1}^{N} A_{jn} c_n = 0, \qquad j = 1, 2, 3, \ldots, N \qquad (4.50)$$

and $\det A_{jn}$ is an $N \times N$ determinant. Equation (4.50) and the ancillary requirement

$$\det A_{jn} = 0 \qquad (4.51)$$

lead to determination of the unknown coefficients c_n and establishment of an approximate eigenfunction

$$X_s = \sum_{n=1}^{N} c_n^{(s)} X_{Rn}$$

In the simplest case, $N = 1$ and the approximation becomes $X = c_1 X_{R1}$— that is, a one-term series. Equation (4.50) becomes

$$A_{11} c_1 = 0 \qquad (4.52)$$

(4.51) yields

$$A_{11} = 0$$

and from (4.46)

$$\int_{a_1}^{a_2} X_{R1}[rX'_{R1}]' \, dx + \int_{a_1}^{a_2} qX_R^2 \, dx + \lambda^2 \int_{a_1}^{a_2} pX_R^2 \, dx = 0 \qquad (4.53)$$

From (4.53), λ^2 is found by evaluating the integrals; hence (4.52) is satisfied for arbitrary c_1. This latter result is appropriate because eigenfunctions are determined only up to an arbitrary multiplying constant (see Chap. 3). The one-term approximation produces an approximate value for the smallest eigenvalue λ^2 and an approximate function for the first eigenfunction X_1. Furthermore, if the operator L is in Sturm–Liouville form, the approximate eigenvalue is always greater than or equal to the true eigenvalue (see Sec. 4.6.3 below).

The vibration of a circular membrane with fixed circumference is commonly used to illustrate the Galerkin method because the related eigenvalue problem is more complex than that of a simple string vibration, yet the solution is known. From Sec. 4.4 (and Chap. 2), the complete eigenvalue problem is

$$L[\phi; \lambda^2] = (r\phi')' + \lambda^2 r\phi = 0$$
$$\phi(1) = \phi'(0) = 0 \qquad (4.54)$$

where L is in Sturm–Liouville form and the radius of the membrane $R = 1$. Recall from Sec. 4.4 that the preceding equation is a Bessel equation of zeroth order and the eigenfunctions are

$$\phi_s = A_s J_0(\lambda_s r) \qquad (4.55)$$

where $\lambda_1^2 = 5.78$, $\lambda_2^2 = 30.5$, and $\lambda_3^2 = 74.9$ (see [1] and Appendix 3). Approximate solutions are found by the Galerkin method in the following three examples.

EXAMPLE 4.9   *The One-Term Approximation.* To obtain a one-term approximation to (4.54), take the first function from a complete set of continuous and linearly-independent functions that satisfy the boundary conditions of (4.54). Based on our experience in Chap. 3, we know that

$$\phi_{Rn}(r) = \cos(n - \tfrac{1}{2})\pi r, \qquad n \geq 1 \qquad (4.56)$$

is such a set (we follow Kantorovich and Krylov [9] here). In this example,

$$\phi(r) = c_1 \phi_{R1}$$

where

$$\phi_{R1}(r) = \cos\frac{\pi}{2}r \qquad (4.57)$$

Then (4.53) holds for the present approximation, and because $r(x) = r$, $p(x) = r$, and $q(x) = 0$, here

$$\int_0^1 \phi_{R1}[r\phi'_{R1}]' \, dr + \lambda^2 \int_0^1 r\phi_{R1}^2 \, dr = 0$$

Introduction of (4.57) in the preceding equation yields

$$\int_0^1 \cos\frac{\pi}{2}r \left[-\frac{\pi}{2}\sin\frac{\pi r}{2} - \frac{\pi^2}{4}r\cos\frac{\pi r}{2} \right] dr + \lambda^2 \int_0^1 r\cos^2\frac{\pi r}{2}\,dr = 0$$

Evaluation of the integrals produces

$$-0.86685 + 0.14868\lambda^2 = 0$$

or

$$\lambda^2 = 5.83$$

Thus we obtain an approximate eigenvalue

$$\lambda_1^2 = 5.83$$

and an approximate eigenfunction

$$\phi_1 = c_1^{(1)} \cos\frac{\pi}{2}r$$

whereas the true eigenvalue is 5.78 to three significant figures and the first eigenfunction is $J_0(2.405r)$. The one-term approximation produced an estimate of the first eigenvalue within one percent of the true value. Figure 4.1 gives a comparison of $J_0(2.405r)$ and the approximate eigenfunction $\phi_1(r)$.

EXAMPLE 4.10   *The Two-Term Approximation.* We take from (4.56)

$$\phi(r) = c_1\phi_{R1} + c_2\phi_{R2}$$

$$= c_1\cos\frac{\pi r}{2} + c_2\cos\frac{3\pi}{2}r \qquad (4.58)$$

as the two-term approximation. For this approximation, we use the general formulation given by (4.45) to (4.47). In particular, now

$$\sum_{n=1}^{2} A_{jn}c_n = 0, \qquad j = 1, 2 \qquad (4.59)$$

and

$$\det A_{jn} = \begin{vmatrix} A_{11} & A_{12} \\ A_{21} & A_{22} \end{vmatrix} = 0 \qquad (4.60)$$

Introduction of (4.58) into (4.46) produces, for the coefficients in (4.60),

$$A_{11} = -0.86685 + 0.14868\lambda^2$$

$$A_{12} = 0.75000 - 0.10132\lambda^2$$

$$A_{21} = A_{12} = 0.75000 - 0.10132\lambda^2 \qquad (4.61)$$

$$A_{22} = -5.8015 + 0.23874\lambda^2$$

so that (4.60) becomes

$$\begin{vmatrix} -0.86685 + 0.14868\lambda^2 & 0.75000 - 0.10132\lambda^2 \\ 0.75000 - 0.10132\lambda^2 & -5.8015 + 0.23874\lambda^2 \end{vmatrix} = 0$$

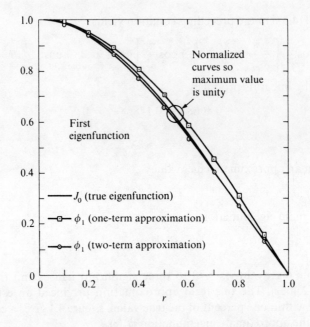

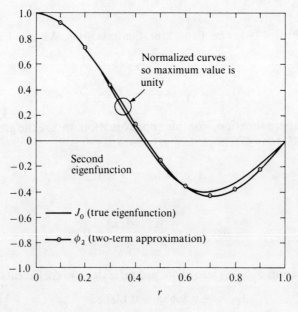

FIGURE 4.1

Expansion of this determinant produces a quadratic equation for λ^2

$$\alpha\lambda^4 + \beta\lambda^2 + \gamma = 0 \tag{4.62}$$

where $\alpha = 0.02523$, $\beta = -0.91754$, and $\gamma = 4.4665$. The discriminant $\beta^2 - 4\alpha\gamma = 0.39112 > 0$ so that there are two real solutions for λ^2. Thus the two-term approximation yields two roots that are approximations to the first two eigenvalues λ_1^2 and

λ_2^2. The roots of (4.62) are

$$\lambda_1^2 = 5.79 \qquad \text{(the true eigenvalue is 5.78)}$$

$$\lambda_2^2 = 30.6 \qquad \text{(the true eigenvalue is 30.5)}$$

The two-term approximation produces an estimate of the first eigenvalue within 0.2 percent of the true value and an estimate of the second eigenvalue within 0.4 percent of the true value.

To conclude the solution, we use the approximate values λ_1^2 and λ_2^2 successively in (4.59) to obtain the coefficients c_1 and c_2 for each eigenfunction. Equations (4.59) are

$$\begin{aligned} A_{11}c_1 + A_{12}c_2 = 0 \\ A_{21}c_1 + A_{22}c_2 = 0 \end{aligned} \tag{4.63}$$

As (4.60) is satisfied, these equations are dependent in that the solution of the first satisfies the second identically. Accordingly, we cannot find both c_1 and c_2, but only c_2 in terms of c_1, or vice versa.

For the first value $\lambda_1^2 = 5.79$, the first of (4.63) becomes [see (4.61)]

$$0.00599c_1^{(1)} - 0.16336c_2^{(1)} = 0$$

Hence $c_2^{(1)} = 0.0370c_1^{(1)}$, and the approximation to the first eigenfunction is

$$\phi_1 = c_1^{(1)}\left(\cos\frac{\pi}{2}r + 0.0370\cos\frac{3\pi}{2}r\right) \tag{4.64}$$

For the second value $\lambda_2^2 = 30.6$, the first of (4.63) is

$$3.6828c_1^{(2)} - 2.3504c_2^{(2)} = 0$$

Hence $c_2^{(2)} = 1.565c_1^{(2)}$, and the approximation to the second eigenfunction is

$$\phi_2 = c_1^{(2)}\left(\cos\frac{\pi}{2}r + 1.565\cos\frac{3\pi}{2}r\right) \tag{4.65}$$

For comparison, Fig. 4.1 shows the approximate eigenfunctions obtained in the preceding two examples and the true eigenfunctions, $J_0(2.405r)$ and $J_0(5.52r)$.

EXAMPLE 4.11   *The Three-Term Approximation.* The three-term approximation is

$$\phi(r) = \sum_{n=1}^{3} c_n\phi_{Rn} = c_1\cos\frac{\pi r}{2} + c_2\cos\frac{3\pi r}{2} + c_3\cos\frac{5\pi r}{2}$$

Equations (4.45) and (4.46) become

$$\begin{aligned} A_{11}c_1 + A_{12}c_2 + A_{13}c_3 = 0 \\ A_{21}c_1 + A_{22}c_2 + A_{23}c_3 = 0 \\ A_{31}c_1 + A_{32}c_2 + A_{33}c_3 = 0 \end{aligned} \tag{4.66}$$

and

$$\begin{vmatrix} A_{11} & A_{12} & A_{13} \\ A_{21} & A_{22} & A_{23} \\ A_{31} & A_{32} & A_{33} \end{vmatrix} = 0 \tag{4.67}$$

respectively. Expansion of this determinant produces a cubic equation for λ^2 of the form

$$\alpha\lambda^6 + \beta\lambda^4 + \gamma\lambda^2 + \delta = 0$$

with three positive real roots: λ_1^2, λ_2^2, and λ_3^2. These are approximations to the first three eigenvalues of the original problem. Successive introduction of these approximate values into any two of (4.66) [the third equation is dependent in view of (4.67)] produces the coefficients $c_n^{(i)}$ in $\phi_1(c_n^{(1)})$ for λ_1^2, $\phi_2(c_n^{(2)})$ for λ_2^2, and $\phi_3(c_n^{(3)})$ for λ_3^2. The details and comparisons are left to the Problems.

From the foregoing examples and Fig. 4.1, we can now draw several conclusions and considerably generalize the results obtained. First, an N-term approximation produces an Nth-degree polynomial equation for λ^2. The polynomial has N positive real roots, each of which yields a particular set of coefficients for the N-term approximate series. When the roots of the λ^2 polynomial are written in ascending order,

$$\lambda_1^2 \le \lambda_2^2 \le \lambda_3^2 \le \cdots \le \lambda_N^2$$

each root is an approximation to the corresponding true eigenvalue of the original problem and, in fact, is an upper bound on the true value (see Sec. 4.6.3). Therefore, if $\lambda_s^{2(N)}$ is an approximation to the sth eigenvalue from an N-term approximation,

$$\lambda_s^{2(N)} \ge \lambda_s^2 \quad \text{and} \quad \lim_{N \to \infty} \lambda_s^{2(N)} = \lambda_s^2$$

In general, for fixed N, as s increases the accuracy of the approximation decreases, while for fixed s, as N increases the accuracy of the approximation to both λ_s^2 and ϕ_s increases. Finally, if the mean error in the approximation to ϕ_s is of the order of ε, the error in the approximation to λ_s^2 is of the order ε^2 (this proof is left to the Problems).

4.6.3   Comments on the Rigor and Convergence of the Galerkin Method

The Galerkin method has received considerable attention in the Russian literature [9, 11, 12], and, in fact, it is in these references that the validity and convergence of the method are demonstrated rigorously. It is not worthwhile to reproduce the lengthy proofs here, and the reader is urged to consult the references for details. However, Keldych [11] has established the convergence (in the mean square) of solutions and the convergence to the true eigenvalues of values obtained by the Galerkin method as outlined in the previous sections. In particular, if we are

1. given the problem (4.39) with continuous, linear operator L and linear boundary conditions B_i,
2. given that the solution is represented in terms of a complete and linearly-independent set $\{X_{Rn}\}$, then

THEOREM 4.9   The set of approximate eigenvalues $\{\lambda_i^{2(N)}\}$ obtained by the Galerkin method converges to the corresponding true eigenvalues λ_i^2 as $N \to \infty$.

THEOREM 4.10   If $\lambda_i^{2(N)}$ is known, the Galerkin method produces an approximate solution of the eigenvalue problem (4.39) that converges to the true corresponding eigenfunction ϕ_i in the mean square as $N \to \infty$.

The validity of these theorems is suggested by the excellent accuracy obtained in the examples given above.

Another approach to the questions of rigor and convergence is equally convincing. The problem (4.39) is called *self-adjoint* [2, 6, 13]. This means that, for the linear system (4.39), any two sufficiently differentiable functions f and g that satisfy the homogeneous boundary conditions $B_i[a_i] = 0$ always satisfy the condition

$$\int_{a_1}^{a_2} fL[g; \lambda^2]\,dx = \int_{a_1}^{a_2} gL[f; \lambda^2]\,dx$$

This result is derived in the same manner used in Sec. 4.3 to obtain Green's Second Identity. For the Sturm–Liouville operator L,

$$\int_{a_1}^{a_2} \{fL[g; \lambda^2] - gL[f; \lambda^2]\}\,dx = [r(g'f - gf')]_{a_1}^{a_2}$$

but the right-hand side of this equation is always zero if f and g satisfy $B_i[a_i] = 0$; that is,

$$B_1[a_1] = \alpha f(a_1) + \beta f'(a_1) = 0$$
$$B_2[a_2] = \gamma f(a_2) + \delta f'(a_2) = 0$$

etc. Therefore

$$\int_{a_1}^{a_2} fL[g; \lambda^2]\,dx = \int_{a_1}^{a_2} gL[f; \lambda^2]\,dx$$

as stated.

Two interesting results flow from the self-adjoint property of (4.39). First, a practical result is, from (4.46),

$$A_{jn} = \int_{a_1}^{a_2} X_{Rj}L[X_{Rm}; \lambda^2]\,dx = \int_{a_1}^{a_2} X_{Rm}L[X_{Rj}; \lambda^2]\,dx = A_{nj}$$

so that the chore of evaluating coefficients is considerably reduced and the coefficient matrix $\{A_{nj}\}$ is symmetric. Second, when the operator L is self-adjoint (as in the case we have studied here), the Galerkin method is exactly the same as the method of Rayleigh and Ritz [12, 13], in which the solutions and eigenvalues of a homogeneous, self-adjoint, boundary-value problem [i.e., system (4.39)] are found by solving a variational problem.

Although an understanding of the variational bases of the Rayleigh–Ritz method requires mastery of the rudiments of the variational calculus, it is worthwhile to note one key conclusion drawn from the method and applicable to the preceding Galerkin method results. The approximate values $\lambda_i^{2(N)}$ obtained by either method from an N-term approximation form a monotonically decreasing sequence of upper bounds for the ith eigenvalue λ_i^2 such that

$$\lambda_i^{2(i)} \geq \lambda_i^{2(i+1)} \geq \lambda_i^{2(i+2)} \geq \cdots \geq \lambda_i^2$$

Note that $N \geq i$ is required to get an approximation for the ith eigenvalue.

In closing, it is important to remember that the Galerkin method does not rely on variational theory or the presence of an operator L in Sturm–Liouville form. Although the latter condition is convenient, it is not necessary, and, as mentioned in the beginning of Sec. 4.6, the Galerkin method is applicable to a wide range of problems. For example, Keldych [11] considers applications for boundary-value problems with ordinary differential equations of order $2n$ and with partial differential equations (the Dirichlet problem). Miklin and Smolitsky [12] consider applications in ordinary differential and integral equations. Indeed, Ames [14] shows that the Galerkin method is also applicable for nonlinear operators L and for nonlinear problems of partial differential equations. If we return to the original problem (4.39) and the Galerkin steps (4.42) and (4.43), it is possible to retrace the development of the computations and find that the only major change is that the equations for the c_n are nonlinear and must (most probably) be solved on an analog or digital computer.

REFERENCES

1. F. Bowman, *Introduction to Bessel Functions*. New York: Dover, 1958.

2. W. Leighton, *Ordinary Differential Equations*. Belmont, Calif.: Wadsworth, 1963.

3. E. L. Ince, *Ordinary Differential Equations*. New York: Dover, 1956.

4. E. Gaughan, *Introduction to Analysis*. Belmont, Calif.: Brooks/Cole, 1968.

5. A. Sommerfeld, *Partial Differential Equations in Physics* (trans. by E. G. Straus). New York: Academic Press, 1964.

6. H. F. Weinberger, *Partial Differential Equations*. New York: Blaisdell, 1965.

7. R. Courant and D. Hilbert, *Methods of Mathematical Physics*, Vol. I. New York: Interscience (a division of John Wiley & Sons), 1953.

8. E. C. Titchmarsh, *Eigenfunction Expansions*, Part I, 2nd ed. London: Oxford University Press, 1962.

9. L. V. Kantorovich and V. I. Krylov, *Approximate Methods of Higher Analysis* (trans. by C. D. Benster). New York: Interscience (a division of John Wiley & Sons), 1958.

10. F. E. Hohn, *Elementary Matrix Algebra*. New York: Macmillan, 1958.

11. M. V. Keldych, "On Galerkin's Method of Solution of Boundary Problems" (in Russian), Akademiia Nauk SSSR, Izvestia, Seriia Matematicheskaia, V. 6, 1942, pp. 309–330.

12. S. G. Mikhlin and K. L. Smolitskiy, *Approximate Methods of Solution of Differential and Integral Equations* (trans. by Scripta Technica, Inc.). New York: American Elsevier, 1967.

13. H. Sagan, *Boundary and Eigenvalue Problems in Mathematical Physics*. New York: John Wiley & Sons, 1961.

14. W. F. Ames, *Nonlinear Partial Differential Equations in Engineering*. New York: Academic Press, 1965.

PROBLEMS

4.1 Determine the eigenvalue problem corresponding to the mathematical model of Prob. 2.8.

4.2 Determine the eigenvalue problem corresponding to the mathematical model of Prob. 2.9.

4.3 Reduce the following equations to the standard form (4.8)—that is, the Sturm–Liouville form:

(a) $X'' - 2xX' + \lambda^2 X = 0, \qquad 0 < x < 1$

(b) $(1 - x^2)X'' - xX' + \lambda^2 X = 0, \qquad 0 < x < 1$

(c) $xX'' + 2X' + \left(x + \dfrac{1}{x} + 2\lambda^2\right)X = 0, \qquad 0 < a < x < b$

(d) $\dfrac{1}{1 + x^2}X'' + [\lambda^2 - q(x + 1)]X = 0, \qquad 0 < x < \dfrac{1}{2}$ for $q = $ constant

(e) $xX'' + (1 - x)X' + \lambda^2 X = 0, \qquad 0 < x$

4.4 Prove that the eigenfunctions X_n in Theorem 4.1 are unique except for an unessential multiplying constant. Then show that the eigenfunctions must be real except possibly for a complex multiplying constant. [*Hint:* Assume that two eigenfunctions X and $\tilde{X}$ exist. Define the wronskian

$$W(x) = \tilde{X}'(x)X(x) - X'(x)\tilde{X}(x)$$

Use the theory of the wronskian for ordinary differential equations [2] to show that because $W(a)$ and $W(b) = 0$, $W = 0$ and X and $\tilde{X}$ are linearly dependent. Finally, refer to the proof of Theorem 4.3 to deal with the real and imaginary parts of the eigenfunction, again using the wronskian concept.]

Note: In Probs. 4.5 through 4.8, renumber eigenvalues and eigenfunctions when necessary so that the first one has zero index.

4.5 For the eigenvalue problem (3.19) [with eigenfunctions (3.36b) and eigenvalues (3.36a)], show that the number of zeros in the eigenfunctions is in accord with Theorem 4.1 by plotting the first, third, and fifth eigenfunctions on $0 \le x \le 1$. Note the movement of the first zero in each eigenfunction as λ^2 increases.

4.6 The eigenvalue problem

$$X'' + X' + \lambda^2 X = 0$$

$$X(0) = X(1) = 0$$

has eigenfunctions

$$X_n = e^{-x/2} \sin \tfrac{1}{2}(4\lambda_n^2 - 1)^{1/2}x$$

with eigenvalues

$$\lambda_n^2 = \frac{4n^2\pi^2 + 1}{4}, \qquad n \ge 1$$

Show that Theorem 4.1 holds with respect to the character of λ_n^2 and the number of zeros for X_n.

4.7 Repeat Prob. 4.5 for the eigenvalue problem (3.82). Use the first four *even* Y_n, $n \ge 0$, and let $l = 1$.

4.8 Show that the eigenfunctions of the eigenvalue problem (3.72a) are orthogonal.

4.9 Derive the general Green's identities

$$\int_a^b \{(rf')'g - f(rg')'\} \, dx = [r(f'g - fg')]_a^b$$

$$\int_a^b (rf')'g \, dx = [rf'g]_a^b - \int_a^b rf'g' \, dx$$

for any two functions f and g that are C^2 on $a \leq x \leq b$—that is, are continuous and have two continuous derivatives.

4.10 For the equations and intervals given in parts (a) and (c) of Prob. 4.3, describe the form of the orthogonality condition and the possible combinations of boundary conditions for which eigenfunctions corresponding to different eigenvalues will be orthogonal.

4.11 Given the eigenvalue problem

$$e^{-x}X'' + \lambda^2 X = 0, \qquad 0 < x < 1$$

$$X(0) + X'(1) = 0$$

$$X(1) - X'(0) = 0$$

prove that each eigenvalue λ_n^2 is real and that eigenfunctions corresponding to different eigenvalues are orthogonal with respect to some weight function.

4.12 Given the eigenvalue problem

$$X'' + \lambda^2 X = 0, \qquad 0 < x < 1$$

$$X'(0) + \alpha X(0) = 0$$

$$X'(1) - \alpha X(1) = 0$$

find a lower bound on the eigenvalues λ_n^2 in terms of the constant α. Then give a physical interpretation of the problem on the assumption that it was derived from a heat-conduction model for a uniform rod.

4.13 Given the eigenvalue problem

$$Y'' + Y' + (Q + \lambda^2)Y = 0, \qquad 0 < y < l$$

$$Y'(0) = Y'(l) = 0$$

prove that $\lambda^2 \geq -Q$ if Q is a constant.

4.14 Rework Prob. 4.13 for the boundary conditions

$$Y'(0) - Y(0) = 0$$

$$Y'(l) + Y(l) = 0$$

4.15 For the mathematical model given in Prob. 2.9,

(a) find the eigenvalue problem (see Prob. 4.2).

(b) prove that each eigenvalue λ_n^2 is real and the eigenfunctions corresponding to different eigenvalues are orthogonal.

(c) prove that $\lambda_n^2 \geq 2q/k$ when $q \leq 0$, while $\lambda_n^2 > q/k$ when $q > 0$.

4.16 Find the eigenvalues and eigenfunctions for Example 4.5 following Theorem 4.4. Use these results to verify the conclusions reached in the example.

4.17   Find the eigenvalue problem for the model (4.22).

4.18   Show that a constant A can be determined such that

$$\tilde{X}_{n2} = X_{n2} + A X_{n1}$$

is linearly independent of and orthogonal to X_{m1} in the case of the system (4.23) and Theorem 4.2′.

4.19   Prove Theorem 4.3′.

4.20   Find the eigenfunctions and an equation for the eigenvalues for

$$\phi'' + \frac{1}{r}\phi' + \lambda^2\phi = 0, \qquad 0 < r < R$$

$$\phi'(0) = 0$$

and

(a) $\phi'(R) = 0$

(b) $\phi'(R) + \alpha\phi(R) = 0$

4.21   Supply a complete proof of Theorem 4.3 for a Sturm–Liouville system with singular endpoints.

4.22   Prove Theorem 4.4 for boundary conditions of the third type. Determine if this is a general result or if it depends on some restriction on the boundary conditions.

4.23   Derive the Parseval equation (4.38) from (4.36).

4.24   The eigenfunctions for (4.24) and (4.25) are

$$X_{n1} = \cos \lambda_n x, \qquad n \geq 0$$

$$X_{n2} = \sin \lambda_n x, \qquad n \geq 1$$

with $\lambda_n^2 = n^2\pi^2$, $n \geq 0$. Construct an equivalent set of orthonormal eigenfunctions.

4.25   Find a formal solution for the mathematical model

$$u_{xx} + \frac{1}{x}u_x + \frac{1}{x^2}u_{yy} = 0, \qquad 0 < a < x < 1, \; 0 < y < \frac{\pi}{2}$$

$$u(a, y) = 0 \qquad u(1, y) = 0, \qquad 0 < y < \frac{\pi}{2}$$

$$u(x, 0) = 0 \qquad u\left(x, \frac{\pi}{2}\right) = U(y), \qquad a < x < 1$$

Use the necessary theorems to establish the character of the eigenvalues and eigenfunctions. (*Hint*: Seek eigenfunctions in the form $Ax^{i\lambda} + Bx^{-i\lambda}$ initially; then put them in a form utilizing sine and cosine.)

4.26   Consider a thin, circular membrane of radius 1, whose initial shape is $z(r, 0) = 1 - r^2$ and whose initial transverse velocity is zero.

(a) Derive a mathematical model for the small transverse vibrations of the membrane if the outer boundary is attached to a rubber sheet such that

$$z_r(1, t) = -z(1, t)$$

that is, $k/T = 1$.

(b) Find a formal solution to the mathematical model of part (a). (This means separate variables, prove that the eigenfunctions are orthogonal and that the eigenvalues are real and positive, solve the eigenvalue problem, propose a series solution, and give the coefficient expressions obtained by use of orthogonality, etc.) (*Note:* Do not evaluate the integrals unless you have a table of integrals of Bessel functions.)

4.27   Find $z(0, t)$ for representative t (a set of values as a plot) for Prob. 4.26.

4.28   Find a formal solution for the mathematical model

$$z_{tt} + z_t = c^2(z_{yy} + z_y), \qquad 0 < y < 1, \quad 0 < t$$
$$z(0, t) = z(1, t) = 0, \qquad t > 0$$
$$z(y, 0) = \sin y, \qquad 0 \le y \le 1$$

4.29   Find a formal solution for the model (4.22). [*Hint:* Be sure to postulate a series that includes *all* the eigenfunctions—for example, in analogy with the Fourier series (3.45),

$$u(x, t) = \sum_n T_n(c_{1n}x_{n1} + c_{2n}x_{n2}).]$$

4.30   Plot $u(x, t)$ for various t for $u_0(x) = 1 - x^2$ in Prob. 4.29. Use as many terms as you deem necessary to achieve an accuracy of ± 5 percent of the maximum value of $u_0(x)$. How many more terms are required to get ± 1 percent accuracy?

Special Problems: The following are designed to lead advanced readers to the referenced literature in search of the required techniques of proof. It is not sufficient to copy the proofs from the listed source; each step must be fully justified.

4.31   To establish the effect of the functions p, q, and r on solutions $X(x; \lambda)$ of the Sturm–Liouville system

$$\frac{d}{dx}\left[r(x)\frac{dX}{dx}\right] + [q(x) + \lambda^2 p(x)]X = 0, \qquad a < x < b$$

$$X(a; \lambda) = X(b; \lambda) = 0$$

show that the solution $X(x; \lambda)$ oscillates more rapidly than the solution $Y(x; \lambda)$ of the system

$$\frac{d}{dx}\left(R\frac{dY}{dx}\right) + (q + \lambda^2 p)Y = 0, \qquad a < x < b$$

$$Y(a; \lambda) = Y(b; \lambda) = 0$$

and less rapidly than the solution $Z(x; \lambda)$ of the system

$$\frac{d}{dx}\left(r\frac{dZ}{dx}\right) + (Q + \lambda^2 P)Z = 0, \qquad a < x < b$$

$$Z(a; \lambda) = Z(b; \lambda) = 0$$

if $0 < r \le r(x) \le R$; $0 < p \le p(x) \le P$; $0 < q \le q(x) \le Q$; and r, R, p, P, and q, Q are constants. Ref. [2, p. 201].

4.32   Prove an existence theorem analogous to Theorem 4.1 for the case in which p changes sign in $a < x < b$. See Ref. [3, pp. 235 ff].

4.33   Prove Theorem 4.5. Ref. [3, pp. 275–276].

4.34   Prove Theorem 4.6. Ref. [7, pp. 427–429].

4.35   Prove Theorem 4.7. Ref. [6, pp. 165–166].

Galerkin Method Problems: Unless otherwise specified, use either sine or cosine functions in the set $\{X_{Rn}\}$.

4.36 Obtain a two-term approximation to the first two eigenvalues and eigenfunctions for the problem

$$r\phi'' + \phi' + \lambda^2 r\phi = 0$$

$$\phi'(1) = \phi'(0) = 0$$

4.37 Using $X_{R1} = 1 - x^2$, find an approximation to the first eigenvalue of

$$xX'' + X' + \lambda^2 xX = 0$$

$$X(1) = X'(0) = 0$$

4.38 Obtain a one-term approximation to the first eigenvalue and eigenfunction of

$$X'' + X' + \lambda^2 X = 0$$

$$X(0) = X(1) = 0$$

Find the true eigenvalues and eigenfunctions and compare to your approximate result. (See Prob. 4.6.)

4.39 Repeat Prob. 4.38, using a two-term approximation.

4.40 Apply the Galerkin method to get first a one-, then a two-term approximation for eigenvalues and eigenfunctions of

$$X'' + (1 + x)\lambda^2 X = 0$$

$$X'(0) = X(1) = 0$$

4.41 Find a one-term approximation to the first eigenvalue and eigenfunction of

$$X'' + \frac{1}{x}X' + \left(\lambda^2 - \frac{1}{x^2}\right)X = 0$$

$$X'(0) = X(1) = 0$$

4.42 Repeat Prob. 4.41, using a two-term approximation.

4.43 Find an approximation to the first eigenvalue of

$$Y'' + Y' + (4 + \lambda^2)Y = 0$$

$$Y'(0) = Y'(1)$$

4.44 Find an approximation to the first two eigenvalues and eigenfunctions of

$$(1 - x^2)X'' - 2xX' + \lambda(\lambda + 1)X = 0$$

$$X(-1) = X(1) = 0$$

4.45 Complete Example 4.11, Sec. 4.6.2. Compare the results for a three-term series with those for Examples 4.9 and 4.10; see Fig. 4.1.

4.46 For our eigenvalue problems we can write, if ϕ_s and λ_s^2 are a corresponding eigenfunction and eigenvalue,

$$L[\phi_s, \lambda_s^2] = 0$$

or

$$L_s[\phi_s] + \lambda_s^2 p\phi_s = 0$$

where

$$L_s[\phi_s] = [r\phi_s']' + q\phi_s$$

In general, when X is not an eigenfunction, the ratio

$$\lambda^2 = \frac{\displaystyle\int_a^b XL[X]\,dx}{-\displaystyle\int_a^b pX^2\,dx}$$

gives the value λ^2 necessary to make $L[X, \lambda^2] = 0$, which is precisely what the Galerkin method attempts.

If $X = \phi_s + \varepsilon u$ is close to ϕ_s—for example, if ε is small and $u \in C^2$ satisfies the problem boundary conditions—show that $\lambda^2 = \lambda_s^2 + O(\varepsilon^2)$. Does this result agree with the numerical results obtained in the text? That is, does a rough approximation to ϕ_s give a good approximation to λ_s^2?

CHAPTER 5

GENERALIZATIONS
AND ADDITIONAL METHODS

In Chap. 2 types of partial differential equations and mathematical models for a number of physical systems were described. The methods of separation of variables and eigenfunction expansions were developed in Chap. 3. The role of ordinary differential equations in the solution process was also delineated there, while in Chap. 4 some aspects of ordinary differential equation theory were reviewed.

In the present chapter we shall build on previous results. First, techniques are given that transform inhomogeneous problems (in two independent variables) so that they can be treated by extending the method of eigenfunction expansions. Second, separation of variables and two-dimensional eigenfunction expansions in the form of a double Fourier series are used in the treatment of problems with three independent variables. Finally, mathematical models with linear, fourth-order governing equations are developed and treated through use of familiar methods.

5.1   INHOMOGENEOUS EQUATIONS

So that we may develop our concepts with definite goals in mind, suppose that we consider a mathematical model for the vibration of a flexible string. From

Table 2.1 and Eq. (2.46), where now the general force per unit mass $F = F(y, t)$ alone,

$$z_{tt} = c^2 z_{yy} + F(y, t), \qquad 0 < y < l, \quad t > 0 \tag{5.1}$$

$$\begin{aligned} z(0, t) &= f_1(t), \\ z(l, t) &= f_2(t), \end{aligned} \qquad t > 0 \tag{5.2}$$

$$\begin{aligned} z(y, 0) &= z_0(y), \\ z_t(y, 0) &= V_0(y), \end{aligned} \qquad 0 \le y \le l \tag{5.3}$$

The objective is to find a solution $z = z(y, t)$ for this mathematica! model, which is composed of linear equations and conditions. On the basis of our current knowledge, we would first try to separate variables and establish an eigenvalue problem. Next, we would solve the eigenvalue problem to obtain eigenvalues and eigenfunctions. Finally, we would expand the solution z in terms of the eigenfunctions to obtain an explicit solution. Unfortunately, such a direct approach is not possible. First, the boundary conditions (5.2) are inhomogeneous. Thus we cannot obtain an eigenvalue problem with the homogeneous boundary conditions that are necessary to our method (see Sec. 3.5). In addition, the governing equation (5.1) is inhomogeneous; this means that we cannot linearly superpose solutions to (5.1) to achieve our solution (see Sec. 2.4).

As a result, we must treat problems like (5.1) to (5.3) in two distinct parts. First, we remove the inhomogeneous boundary conditions. Second, we use a method based on an expansion of the solution z in terms of the eigenfunctions of a related, but purely homogeneous, problem.

5.1.1   Removal of Inhomogeneous Boundary Conditions

We being by reducing the model (5.1) to (5.3) to a "standard form" with homogeneous boundary conditions—that is, to

$$Z_{tt} = c^2 Z_{yy} + \tilde{F}(y, t), \qquad 0 < y < l, \quad t > 0 \tag{5.4}$$

$$\begin{aligned} Z(0, t) &= 0, \\ Z(l, t) &= 0, \end{aligned} \qquad t > 0 \tag{5.5}$$

$$\begin{aligned} Z(y, 0) &= Z_0(y), \\ Z_t(y, 0) &= \tilde{V}_0(y), \end{aligned} \qquad 0 \le y \le l \tag{5.6}$$

Later we shall learn to solve standard-form problems.

Since the mathematical model (5.1) to (5.3) is linear, we employ linearity to reduce the boundary conditions.

Case 1. Suppose that in (5.2)

$$\begin{aligned} z(0, t) &= A \\ z(l, t) &= B \end{aligned} \tag{5.7}$$

That is, f_1 and f_2 are constant. We let

$$z(y, t) = Z(y, t) + s(y) \tag{5.8}$$

and require, *in this case*,

$$s_{yy} = 0$$
$$s(0) = A$$
$$s(l) = B$$

(5.9)

Here (5.9) is a time-independent problem. It follows that, by virtue of linearity, (5.1) to (5.3) become

$$Z_{tt} = c^2 Z_{yy} + F(y, t), \qquad 0 < y < l, \quad t > 0$$
$$Z(0, t) = 0$$
$$Z(l, t) = 0$$
$$Z(y, 0) = z_0(y) - s(y) = Z_0(y)$$
$$Z_t(y, 0) = V_0(y) = \tilde{V}_0(y)$$

(5.10)

This is the standard form sought; it remains only to solve (5.9).

The general solution to $s_{yy} = 0$ is

$$s(y) = \alpha y + \beta$$

where α and β are arbitrary constants. By using the boundary conditions in (5.9), we have

$$s(0) = \beta = A$$
$$s(l) = \alpha l + \beta = \alpha l + A = B$$

so that

$$\alpha = \frac{B - A}{l}$$

In summary, when $f_1(t) = A$ and $f_2(t) = B$, the model (5.1) to (5.3) can be reduced to a standard form (5.10) *and* a time-independent solution

$$s(y) = \frac{B - A}{l} y + A$$

(5.11)

Because $s = s(y)$ alone *and* because $s_{yy} = 0$, s does not enter the governing equation of (5.10) but *does* appear explicitly in the initial conditions. We must sometimes choose $s_{yy} = c$ or $s_{yy} = f(y)$ in order to satisfy the inhomogeneous boundary conditions (see the Problems).

Case 2. We return now to the original model given by (5.1) to (5.3). We let

$$z(y, t) = Z(y, t) + S(y, t)$$

(5.12)

and now require only

$$S(0, t) = f_1(t)$$
$$S(l, t) = f_2(t)$$

(5.13)

Next we select some (at least) continuous function $S = S(y, t)$ that satisfies (5.13). In most cases, a function of the type

$$S(y, t) = A_0(t)\left(1 - \frac{y}{l}\right)^n + A_1(t)\left(\frac{y}{l}\right)^m \tag{5.14}$$

will suffice; here n and m are positive integers. Our only objective is to remove the inhomogeneous boundary conditions. In doing so, we probably will make the governing equation for $Z(y, t)$ inhomogeneous (or at least introduce another inhomogeneous term). Introducing (5.14) into (5.13) produces

$$A_0(t) = f_1(t)$$

$$A_1(t) = f_2(t)$$

for $m, n \geq 1$. We take $m = n = 1$ and thus obtain

$$S(y, t) = f_1(t)\left(1 - \frac{y}{l}\right) + f_2(t)\frac{y}{l} \tag{5.15}$$

It remains now to introduce (5.12) and (5.15) into (5.1) to (5.3) in order to obtain the new "standard form." From (5.1),

$$Z_{tt} + S_{tt} = c^2(Z_{yy} + S_{yy}) + F(y, t)$$

or

$$Z_{tt} = c^2 Z_{yy} + F(y, t) - \left[f_{1tt}\left(1 - \frac{y}{l}\right) + f_{2tt}\frac{y}{l}\right] \tag{5.15a}$$

From (5.2),

$$Z(0, t) = 0$$

$$Z(l, t) = 0$$

and from (5.3),

$$Z(y, 0) = z_0(y) - S(y, 0)$$

or

$$Z(y, 0) = z_0(y) - f_1(0)\left(1 - \frac{y}{l}\right) - f_2(0)\left(\frac{y}{l}\right) \tag{5.15b}$$

and

$$Z_t(y, 0) = V_0(y) - S_t(y, 0)$$

or

$$Z_t(y, 0) = V_0(y) - f_{1t}(0)\left(1 - \frac{y}{l}\right) - f_{2t}(0)\left(\frac{y}{l}\right) \tag{5.15c}$$

In summary, the mathematical model (5.1) to (5.3) is reduced, in this case, to

$$Z_{tt} = c^2 Z_{yy} + Q(y, t)$$

$$Z(0, t) = 0$$

$$Z(l, t) = 0 \tag{5.16}$$

$$Z(y, 0) = Z_0(y)$$

$$Z_t(y, 0) = \tilde{V}_0(y)$$

where

$$Q(y, t) = F(y, t) - (S_{tt} - c^2 S_{yy})$$

$$Z_0(y) = z_0(y) - S(y, 0)$$

$$\tilde{V}_0(y) = V_0(y) - S_t(y, 0)$$

and $S = S(y, t)$ is given by the known relation (5.15). Note from (5.15a to c) that f_1 and f_2 must necessarily be continuous and differentiable up to second order (you may wish to consider this point in relation to the analyses of Sec. 3.3 and Probs. 3.20 to 3.23 and 3.33 to 3.34).

5.1.2 Expansion in Terms of Eigenfunctions of the Homogeneous Problem

In the previous section a method was given for reducing linear mathematical models to a standard form. That form contains homogeneous boundary conditions, but it may also contain an inhomogeneous partial differential equation. In the following discussion it is assumed that the reduction has been accomplished and that it is necessary to solve only the standard-form problem. Therefore consider the following problem: Find $Z = Z(y, t)$ such that

$$Z_{tt} = c^2 Z_{yy} + Q(y, t), \qquad 0 < y < l, \quad t > 0 \tag{5.17}$$

$$\begin{aligned} Z(0, t) &= 0, \\ Z(l, t) &= 0, \end{aligned} \qquad t > 0 \tag{5.18}$$

$$\begin{aligned} Z(y, 0) &= Z_0(y), \\ Z_t(y, 0) &= \tilde{V}_0(y), \end{aligned} \qquad 0 \le y \le l \tag{5.19}$$

where Q, Z_0, and $\tilde{V}_0$ are known.

If $Q \equiv 0$, (5.17) to (5.19) can be solved with the methods of Chap. 3. In particular, after separation of variables, an eigenvalue problem can be formulated and solved. The eigenfunctions, together with the appropriate time-dependent functions and some free constants, can then be combined in an infinite series. This series will represent the reasonable, but arbitrary, functions in the initial conditions and hence will represent the actual solution. Thus, for $Q \equiv 0$,

$$Z(y, t) = \sum_n T_n(t) Y_n(y) \tag{5.20}$$

where

$$T_n(t) = A_{0n} \cos c\lambda_n t + \frac{A_{1n}}{c\lambda_n} \sin c\lambda_n t$$

and the eigenvalues and eigenfunctions are

$$\lambda_n^2 = \left(\frac{n^2 \pi^2}{l^2}\right) \qquad Y_n(y) = \sin \lambda_n y, \qquad n = 1, 2, 3, \ldots \tag{5.21}$$

Because $Q \equiv 0$, the solution (5.20) is called the solution to the *related homogeneous problem* [related to (5.17) to (5.19)], which in this case is the free vibration of a fixed-end string. The Y_n are then the eigenfunctions of the related homogeneous problem.

We seek now to extend the expansion-in-terms-of-eigenfunctions concept. The Y_n are capable of representing, through an infinite series, an arbitrary function of y; were the coefficients properly chosen, the series (5.20) could actually represent an "arbitrary" solution function $Z(y, t)$. Finally, in Sec. A.2.2 we show that solutions to ordinary differential equations can be represented by a power series under very general conditions and that the coefficients of the power series can be evaluated.

In view of the preceding points we assert now

PROPOSITION   The solution $Z(y, t)$ to (5.17) to (5.19) can be expanded as an infinite series in terms of the eigenfunctions $Y_n(y)$ of the related homogeneous problem, *and* the unknown time-dependent coefficients $T_n(t)$ in the series can be evaluated by introducing the proposed series into the governing partial differential equation of the *original* inhomogeneous problem.

The Method: We consider the initial-boundary-value problem (5.17) to (5.19). We set $Q(y, t) \equiv 0$ and, via separation of variables, find the eigenvalue problem for the related homogeneous problem:

$$Y'' + \lambda^2 Y = 0$$

$$Y(0) = 0 \tag{5.22}$$

$$Y(l) = 0$$

The eigenfunctions $Y_n(y)$ for (5.22) are given by (5.21).

We propose

$$Z(y, t) = \sum_n T_n(t) Y_n(y) \tag{5.23}$$

where the $T_n(t)$ are unknown. Now $p(y) = 1$ is the weight function associated with $Y_n(y)$ (see Sec. 4.2); therefore, via the orthogonality of the Y_n, we have from (5.23)

$$T_m(t) = \frac{1}{N_m} \int_0^l p(y) Z(y, t) Y_m(y) \, dy = \frac{1}{N_m} \int_0^l Z(y, t) Y_m(y) \, dy \tag{5.24}$$

where the normalizing constants N_m are given by

$$N_m = \int_0^l p(y) Y_m^2(y) \, dy = \int_0^l Y_m^2(y) \, dy \tag{5.25}$$

The initial conditions (5.19) become initial conditions on T_n; that is, from (5.24)

$$T_m(0) = \frac{1}{N_m} \int_0^l Z_0 Y_m \, dy \tag{5.26}$$

and

$$T'_m(0) = \frac{1}{N_m} \int_0^l \tilde{V}_0 Y_m \, dy \tag{5.27}$$

Now, we introduce (5.23) into (5.17) and achieve

$$\sum_n T_n'' Y_n = c^2 \sum_n T_n Y_n'' + Q(y, t) \tag{5.28}$$

In accordance with the ability of eigenfunction expansions to represent reasonable functions, we further assume that the known function $Q(y, t)$ can be expanded in a convergent series:

$$Q(y, t) = \sum_n q_n(t) Y_n(y) \tag{5.29}$$

so that, via the orthogonality of $Y_n(y)$ and the definition (5.25),

$$q_m(t) = \frac{1}{N_m} \int_0^l Q(y, t) Y_m(y) \, dy \tag{5.30}$$

Introduction of (5.29) into (5.28) gives

$$\sum_n Y_n(T_n'' + c^2 \lambda_n^2 T_n - q_n) = 0 \tag{5.31}$$

in which we have also used

$$Y_n'' = -\lambda_n^2 Y_n$$

obtained from (5.22).

For (5.31) to be satisfied for all y in $0 < y < l$, the coefficient of each $Y_n(y)$ must be zero; accordingly,

$$T_n''(t) + c^2 \lambda_n^2 T_n(t) = q_n(t) \tag{5.32}$$

for all $n \geq 1$; λ_n^2 and $q_n(t)$ *are known*. Note that (5.26) and (5.27) provide just the proper initial conditions for (5.32); that is, the ordinary differential equation (5.32) with conditions (5.26) and (5.27) has a unique solution for each $n \geq 1$.

From Sec. A.2.1 we know that the solution to (5.32) is given by a linear combination of a complementary solution T_c [the solution for $q_n(t) \equiv 0$] and a particular solution T_p. From (A.2.9) and (A.2.12),

$$T_{cn} = A_{0n} \cos c\lambda_n t + \frac{A_{1n}}{c\lambda_n} \sin c\lambda_n t \tag{5.33}$$

while

$$T_{pn} = \frac{1}{c\lambda_n} \sin c\lambda_n t \int_0^t q_n(\tau) \cos c\lambda_n \tau \, d\tau - \frac{1}{c\lambda_n} \cos c\lambda_n t \int_0^t q_n(\tau) \sin c\lambda_n \tau \, d\tau \tag{5.34}$$

from (A.2.55) in Example A.4. Thus

$$T_n(t) = T_{cn} + T_{pn} \tag{5.35}$$

After using (5.26) and (5.27) to evaluate A_{0n} and A_{1n}, we may write the complete solution to (5.17) to (5.19) as an appropriate combination of results from Eqs. (5.21), (5.23), (5.25), (5.30), and (5.35). A complete example is treated in the next section.

5.1.3   Applications and Examples

In this section the methods outlined above are applied to several illustrative problems.

EXAMPLE 5.1   *Heat Conduction in a Thin, Round, Insulated Rod with Heat Sources Present.* Consider the mathematical model from Table 2.1, where a heat source term $A = A(x, t)$ is added [see (2.15)] and the Group 1 boundary conditions with $T_1 = T_2 = 0$ are used; that is, find $u = u(x, t)$ such that

$$u_t - ku_{xx} = \frac{A}{\rho c}, \qquad 0 < x < l, \quad 0 < t$$

$$u(0, t) = 0,$$
$$\qquad\qquad\qquad 0 < t \tag{5.36}$$
$$u(l, t) = 0,$$

$$u(x, 0) = u_0(x), \qquad 0 \le x \le l$$

in which ρ and c are constants and A is at least a continuous function of x and t.

The boundary conditions are already homogeneous; hence our first step is to set $A/\rho c = 0$ and separate variables in

$$u_t - ku_{xx} = 0 \tag{5.37}$$

to find the eigenvalues and eigenfunctions of the related homogeneous problem. Setting $u = X(x)T(t)$ gives (see Sec. 3.2)

$$\frac{T'}{kT} = \frac{X''}{X} = -\lambda^2$$

It follows that

$$X'' + \lambda^2 X = 0$$
$$\qquad\qquad\qquad\qquad \tag{5.38}$$
$$X(0) = X(l) = 0$$

The desired eigenfunctions and eigenvalues are

$$X_n(x) = \sin \lambda_n x \qquad \lambda_n^2 = \left(\frac{n\pi}{l}\right)^2 \qquad \text{for } n \ge 1 \tag{5.39}$$

A quick check using the methods of Sec. 4.3 for Sturm–Liouville problems shows that there are no negative or zero $\lambda_n^2 (\lambda_n^2 > 0)$, that the λ_n^2 are real, and that the X_n are orthogonal on $0 < x < l$ with respect to the weight function $p = 1$. In fact, the normalizing constants

$$N_n = \int_0^l pX_n^2 \, dx = \int_0^l \sin^2 \frac{n\pi}{l} x \, dx = \frac{l}{2} \tag{5.40}$$

Now, for the inhomogeneous problem (5.36), we propose

$$u(x, t) = \sum_{n=1}^{\infty} T_n(t)X_n(x) \tag{5.41}$$

Clearly, (5.41) satisfies the boundary conditions of (5.36) and, via orthogonality,

$$\int_0^l puX_m \, dx = \sum_{n=1}^{\infty} T_n(t) \int_0^l pX_nX_m \, dx$$

or from (5.40), with $p = 1$,

$$T_m(t) = \frac{2}{l} \int_0^l u(x, t) X_m(x) \, dx$$

But then

$$T_m(0) = \frac{2}{l} \int_0^l u_0(x) \sin \frac{m\pi}{l} x \, dx \tag{5.42}$$

which is an initial condition for $T_m(t)$.

Introduction of (5.41) into the governing equation of (5.36) gives

$$\sum_{n=1}^{\infty} T_n' X_n - k \sum_{n=1}^{\infty} T_n X_n'' = \frac{A}{\rho c} \tag{5.43}$$

If we expand $A/\rho c$ so that it is represented by a convergent series on $0 < x < l$, $0 < t$, as

$$\frac{A}{\rho c} = \sum_{n=1}^{\infty} q_n(t) X_n(x) \tag{5.43a}$$

then, via orthogonality and (5.40),

$$q_m(t) = \frac{2}{l} \int_0^l \frac{A(x, t)}{\rho c} \sin \frac{m\pi}{l} x \, dx \tag{5.44}$$

that is, the $q_m(t)$ are known. Now, (5.43) becomes

$$\sum_{n=1}^{\infty} X_n(T_n' + \lambda_n^2 k T_n - q_n) = 0$$

since $X_n'' = -\lambda_n^2 X_n$ from (5.38). It follows that

$$T_n'(t) + \lambda_n^2 k T_n(t) = q_n(t) \tag{5.45}$$

for each $n \geq 1$. The unique solution to (5.45) with its initial condition (5.42) is

$$T_n(t) = T_n(0)e^{-\lambda_n^2 kt} + \int_0^t e^{\lambda_n^2 k(\tau - t)} q_n(\tau) \, d\tau \tag{5.46}$$

according to Sec. A.2.1.

Therefore, from (5.41) and (5.46), the full solution is

$$u(x, t) = \sum_{n=1}^{\infty} \left[T_n(0)e^{-\lambda_n^2 kt} + \int_0^t e^{\lambda_n^2 k(\tau - t)} q_n(\tau) \, d\tau \right] X_n(x) \tag{5.47}$$

where X_n, λ_n^2, $T_n(0)$, and $q_n(t)$ are given by (5.39), (5.42), and (5.44).

The solution (5.47) is supposed to satisfy the inhomogeneous partial differential equation, the homogeneous boundary conditions, and the inhomogeneous initial conditions of (5.36). Let us examine this supposition.

First, in the limit as $t \to 0$ and at $t = 0$,

$$\int_0^t e^{\lambda_n^2 k(\tau - t)} q_n(\tau) \, d\tau = 0$$

because the q_n are bounded for all t; thus, from (5.47),

$$u(x, 0) = \sum_{n=1}^{\infty} T_n(0) X_n(x) \qquad (5.48)$$

But by using (5.39) and (5.42), we can write (5.48) as

$$u(x, 0) = \sum_{n=1}^{\infty} \left[\frac{2}{l} \int_0^l u_0(x) \sin \frac{n\pi}{l} x \, dx \right] \sin \frac{n\pi}{l} x$$

whence, via the formal definitions of the Fourier sine series, it follows that

$$u(x, 0) = u_0(x) \qquad \text{Q.E.D.}$$

Therefore (5.47) satisfies the problem's initial conditions.

Second, at $x = 0$ and $x = l$ (and in the limits as $x \to 0$ and $x \to l$), we have from (5.39)

$$X_n(0) = X_n(l) = 0$$

and then from (5.47), as the series converges for $t > 0$ (Sec. 3.2 or 6.4),

$$u(0, t) = u(l, t) = 0 \qquad \text{Q.E.D.}$$

Therefore (5.47) satisfies the problem's boundary conditions.

Third, we introduce (5.47) into the governing partial differential equation of (5.36). We find, through differentiation and use of Leibnitz's rule,

$$\sum_{n=1}^{\infty} \left[-T_n(0)\lambda_n^2 k e^{-\lambda_n^2 kt} + q_n(t) - \lambda_n^2 k \int_0^t e^{\lambda_n^2 k(\tau - t)} q_n(\tau) \, d\tau \right] X_n(x)$$

$$- k \sum_{n=1}^{\infty} \left[+T_n(0) e^{-\lambda_n^2 kt} + \int_0^t e^{\lambda_n^2 k(\tau - t)} q_n(\tau) \, d\tau \right] X_n''(x) = \frac{A}{\rho c}$$

By using (5.38) and several stages of rearrangement in this equation, we obtain

$$\sum_{n=1}^{\infty} T_n(0)\lambda_n^2 k e^{-\lambda_n^2 kt}[X_n(x) - X_n(x)] + \sum_{n=1}^{\infty} q_n(t) X_n(x)$$

$$+ \sum_{n=1}^{\infty} \lambda_n^2 k \int_0^t e^{\lambda_n^2 k(\tau - t)} q_n(\tau) \, d\tau [-X_n(x) + X_n(x)] = \frac{A}{\rho c}$$

Clearly, then,

$$\sum_{n=1}^{\infty} q_n(t) X_n(x) = \frac{A}{\rho c}$$

which is an identity according to (5.43a). Therefore (5.47) is a solution to the governing equation in accordance with our definition in Sec. 1.1.

In view of the preceding discussion (5.47), which was generated by the method of Sec. 5.1.2, is a solution to the mathematical model (5.36) under the presumption that all indicated series converge appropriately (see Sec. 3.3).

EXAMPLE 5.2 *Heat Conduction in a Thin, Round, Insulated Rod with Inhomogeneous Boundary Conditions.* Consider the mathematical model from Table

2.1, where Group 2 and 3 boundary conditions are used (see Example 3.2, Sec. 3.4). We seek to reduce the following to a standard form:

$$u_t - ku_{xx} = 0, \qquad 0 < x < l, \quad 0 < t$$

$$u_x(0, t) = f_0(t),$$

$$Ku_x(l, t) + Hu(l, t) = Hu_s(t), \qquad 0 < t \tag{5.49}$$

$$u(x, 0) = u_0(x), \qquad 0 \le x \le l$$

Let

$$u(x, t) = U(x, t) + S(x, t) \tag{5.50}$$

where, according to (5.14),

$$S(x, t) = A_0(t)\left(1 - \frac{x}{l}\right)^n + A_1(t)\left(\frac{x}{l}\right)^m \tag{5.51}$$

We require

$$S_x(0, t) = f_0(t)$$

$$KS_x(l, t) + HS(l, t) = Hu_s(t)$$

and introduce (5.51) into these equations to find (let $m = n = 1$ for a first trial)

$$-\frac{A_0(t)}{l} + \frac{A_1(t)}{l} = f_0(t) \tag{5.52a}$$

$$K\left[-\frac{A_0(t)}{l} + \frac{A_1(t)}{l}\right] + HA_1(t) = Hu_s(t) \tag{5.52b}$$

Introducing (5.52a) into (5.52b) yields

$$A_1(t) = u_s(t) - \frac{K}{H}f_0(t)$$

whence from (5.52a)

$$A_0(t) = u_s(t) - f_0(t)\left(l + \frac{K}{H}\right)$$

Therefore

$$S(x, t) = \left[u_s(t) - f_0(t)\left(l + \frac{K}{H}\right)\right]\left(1 - \frac{x}{l}\right) + \left[u_s(t) - \frac{K}{H}f_0(t)\right]\left(\frac{x}{l}\right) \tag{5.53}$$

Now, $S_{xx} = 0$ but $S_t \neq 0$. Therefore the introduction of (5.50) into (5.49) produces the standard form

$$U_t - kU_{xx} = -S_t, \qquad 0 < x < l, \quad 0 < t$$

$$U_x(0, t) = 0,$$

$$KU_x(l, t) + HU(l, t) = 0, \qquad 0 < t \tag{5.54}$$

$$U(x, 0) = u_0(x) - S(x, 0), \qquad 0 < x < l$$

where S is given by (5.53).

Note that we could have used $m = 0, n = 1$ in (5.51). Then, as is easily verified,

$$S(x, t) = u_s(t) + f_0(t)\left(l - x - \frac{K}{H}\right) \tag{5.55}$$

and (5.54) is unchanged.

EXAMPLE 5.3   *Steady, Two-Dimensional, Irrotational Flow of an Ideal Fluid in a Corner* (Fig. 5.1). The mathematical model for this flow in a limited region of a corner can be derived from the discussion of Sec. 2.2.3. A velocity potential $\phi(x, y)$ exists. The governing equation is $\phi_{xx} + \phi_{yy} = 0$. The condition that no flow pass through a wall is $\phi_n = 0$, where n is in a direction perpendicular to the wall. The condition that the flow be perpendicular to a given line—for example, $y = y_0$ = constant—is $\phi(x, y_0) = c_2$ because then $\phi_x(x, y_0) = 0$; that is, $u(x, y_0) = 0$. It follows that the conditions shown in Fig. 5.1 are appropriate and that a mathematical model is

$$\nabla^2\phi = \phi_{xx} + \phi_{yy} = 0, \qquad 0 < x < \pi, \;\; 0 < y < \pi$$

$$\phi_x(0, y) = 0, \qquad 0 < y < \pi$$

$$\phi(\pi, y) = c_1, \qquad 0 < y \leq \pi \tag{5.56}$$

$$\phi_y(x, 0) = 0, \qquad 0 < x < \pi$$

$$\phi(x, \pi) = c_2, \qquad 0 < x < \pi$$

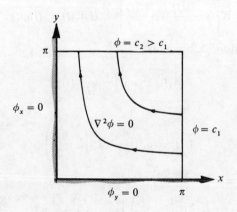

FIGURE 5.1

The conditions in (5.56) are all boundary conditions; hence it is necessary to find only one matched pair (e.g., at $x = 0$ and $x = \pi$) of homogeneous conditions to use for an eigenvalue problem. Let

$$\phi(x, y) = \Phi(x, y) + S(x, y) \tag{5.57}$$

and require

$$S_x(0, y) = 0$$

$$S(\pi, y) = c_1$$

Almost obviously, we choose

$$S(x, y) = c_1 \tag{5.58}$$

In terms of Φ, (5.56) becomes

$$\nabla^2 \Phi = 0, \quad 0 < x < \pi, \quad 0 < y < \pi$$

$$\Phi_x(0, y) = 0,$$
$$\qquad\qquad\qquad 0 < y < \pi$$
$$\Phi(\pi, y) = 0, \tag{5.59}$$

$$\Phi_y(x, 0) = 0,$$
$$\qquad\qquad\qquad\qquad 0 < x < \pi$$
$$\Phi(x, \pi) = c_2 - S(x, \pi) = c_2 - c_1,$$

But (5.59) can be solved by the methods of Chap. 3 with the following results:

1. If $\Phi(x, y) = X(x)Y(y)$,

$$X'' + \lambda^2 X = 0 \qquad Y'' - \lambda^2 Y = 0$$
$$X'(0) = X(\pi) = 0 \qquad Y'(0) = 0$$

and then

$$X_n(x) = \cos(n - \tfrac{1}{2})x,$$
$$\qquad\qquad\qquad\qquad n \geq 1$$
$$Y_n(y) = A_n \cosh(n - \tfrac{1}{2})y,$$

2. Since $\int_0^\pi X_n^2(x)\, dx = \pi/2$ and the $X_n(x)$ are orthogonal, the solution to (5.59) is

$$\Phi(x, y) = \sum_{n=1}^{\infty} A_n \cosh(n - \tfrac{1}{2})y \cos(n - \tfrac{1}{2})x$$

with

$$A_n = \frac{4(c_2 - c_1)(-1)^{n+1}}{(2n - 1)\pi \cosh(n - \tfrac{1}{2})\pi}$$

3. Then, from (5.57) and (5.58),

$$\phi(x, y) = c_1 + \frac{4(c_2 - c_1)}{\pi} \sum_{n=1}^{\infty} \frac{(-1)^{n+1} \cosh(n - \tfrac{1}{2})y \cos(n - \tfrac{1}{2})x}{(2n - 1) \cosh(n - \tfrac{1}{2})\pi}$$

5.2 DOUBLE FOURIER SERIES

Separation of variables in a linear, governing equation with two independent variables leads to an eigenvalue problem governed by an ordinary differential equation. When three independent variables are present, separation of variables leads to an eigenvalue problem governed by a partial differential equation in two dimensions. Use of the solution to a two-dimensional eigenvalue problem in an eigenfunction expansion requires a double Fourier series. We shall explore these new concepts through a pair of examples.

5.2.1   Separation of Variables and the Eigenfunction Expansion: Heat Conduction in a Plate

What is the mathematical model for heat conduction in a thin, completely insulated, flat place of uniform composition? If an initial temperature distribution $U_0(x, y)$ is known, we deduce from Sec. 2.2.1 that, in terms of a temperature $u = u(x, y, t)$, the appropriate model is

$$\nabla^2 u = \frac{1}{k} u_t, \qquad 0 < x < l_1, \quad 0 < y < l_2, \quad 0 < t \tag{5.60}$$

$$u_x(0, y, t) = u_x(l_1, y, t) = 0, \qquad 0 \le y \le l_2, \quad 0 < t$$
$$u_y(x, 0, t) = u_y(x, l_2, t) = 0, \qquad 0 \le x \le l_1, \quad 0 < t \tag{5.61}$$

$$u(x, y, 0) = U_0(x, y), \qquad 0 \le x \le l_1, \quad 0 \le y \le l_2 \tag{5.62}$$

This model is interesting because the temperature distribution as $t \to \infty$ can be deduced on physical grounds alone; this result can then be compared to the limit value found as $t \to \infty$ in our series solution.

From (2.4), the heat stored in the plate per unit of thickness (in the z direction) is initially

$$\int_0^{l_2} \int_0^{l_1} \rho c U_0(x, y) \, dx \, dy$$

No heat can escape because of the insulation, and according to the law of heat conduction (2.1), heat will flow to areas of lower temperature as long as a temperature gradient exists. Therefore, as $t \to \infty$, the plate temperature must assume some uniform value; that is, $\lim_{t \to \infty} u(x, y, t) = U_\infty = $ constant. The heat stored in the plate is then $\rho c U_\infty l_1 l_2$. Consequently, for ρ and c constant,

$$U_\infty = \frac{1}{l_1 l_2} \int_0^{l_2} \int_0^{l_1} U_0(x, y) \, dx \, dy \tag{5.63}$$

because the initial and final heat contents are equal.

Following the methods outlined in Secs. 3.1 and 3.2, we shall now separate variables in (5.60) and formulate an eigenvalue problem by using the boundary conditions (5.61). Let us seek product solutions in the form

$$u(x, y, t) = T(t)\Omega(x, y) \tag{5.64}$$

Then, from (5.60),

$$\frac{\nabla^2 \Omega}{\Omega} = \frac{\Omega_{xx} + \Omega_{yy}}{\Omega} = \frac{T'}{kT} = -\lambda^2 \tag{5.65}$$

As before, λ^2 must be a constant because $\Omega = \Omega(x, y)$ alone, while $T = T(t)$. Now, from (5.65), we obtain the ordinary differential equation

$$T' + \lambda^2 kT = 0 \tag{5.66}$$

and the partial differential equation

$$\nabla^2 \Omega + \lambda^2 \Omega = 0 \tag{5.67}$$

which is called the *Helmholtz Equation*.

Insertion of (5.64) into the homogeneous boundary conditions (5.61) demonstrates that Ω must satisfy the following conditions if (5.61) are to be satisfied for all t:

$$\Omega_x(0, y) = \Omega_x(l_1, y) = \Omega_y(x, 0) = \Omega_y(x, l_2) = 0,$$

$$0 \le x \le l_1, \quad 0 \le y \le l_2 \tag{5.68}$$

The combination (5.67) and (5.68) is an eigenvalue problem; that is, the homogeneous boundary-value problem

$$\nabla^2\Omega + \lambda^2\Omega = 0, \qquad 0 < x < l_1, \quad 0 < y < l_2$$

$$\begin{aligned}\Omega_x(0, y) &= 0, \\ \Omega_x(l_1, y) &= 0,\end{aligned} \qquad 0 \le y \le l_2$$

$$\begin{aligned}\Omega_y(x, 0) &= 0, \\ \Omega_y(x, l_2) &= 0,\end{aligned} \qquad 0 \le x \le l_1 \tag{5.69}$$

is not well posed (the solution is not unique), because of the presence of the "free" parameter λ^2 (see Sec. 3.2).

We seek eigenfunctions Ω_v that are solutions to (5.69) for particular λ_v and are not identically zero; the subscript v is taken now to be indicative of some appropriate index system as yet unknown. The Ω_v are to be continuous functions with continuous first and second derivatives on the domain of interest $R + C$ in analogy to their one-dimensional counterparts. Here $R: 0 < x < l_1, 0 < y < l_2$; and C is the boundary of R such that $R + C: 0 \le x \le l_1, 0 \le y \le l_2$.

Before solving (5.69) we can employ extensions of the methods of Sec. 4.3 to gain some advance knowledge of the λ_v^2 and Ω_v. From Appendix 1 (Sec. A.1.4), we have Green's First Identity in two dimensions for two functions f and g

$$\int_C f\frac{\partial g}{\partial n}\,ds = \iint_R f\,\nabla^2 g\,dx\,dy + \iint_R (\nabla f \cdot \nabla g)\,dx\,dy \tag{5.70}$$

while the Second Identity is

$$\int_C \left(f\frac{\partial g}{\partial n} - g\frac{\partial f}{\partial n}\right)ds = \iint_R (f\,\nabla^2 g - g\,\nabla^2 f)\,dx\,dy \tag{5.71}$$

Next, suppose that Ω_μ and Ω_v are two solutions to (5.69) corresponding to two distinct values λ_μ^2 and λ_v^2.

First, in (5.70) we identify f and g as $f = g = \Omega_\mu$. Then, everywhere on C,

$$\frac{\partial g}{\partial n} = \frac{\partial \Omega_\mu}{\partial n} = 0$$

according to (5.69), while

$$\nabla f \cdot \nabla g = \nabla \Omega_\mu \cdot \nabla \Omega_\mu = \Omega_{\mu x}^2 + \Omega_{\mu y}^2$$

and

$$f\,\nabla^2 g = \Omega_\mu \nabla^2 \Omega_\mu = -\lambda_\mu^2 \Omega_\mu^2$$

Accordingly, (5.70) reduces to

$$\lambda_\mu^2 \int\int_R \Omega_\mu^2 \, dx \, dy = \int\int_R (\Omega_{\mu x}^2 + \Omega_{\mu y}^2) \, dx \, dy$$

Because the integrands in this equation are everywhere nonnegative and Ω_μ^2 is not identically zero, the eigenvalues λ_μ^2 must all be positive: $\lambda_\mu^2 \geq 0$ for all μ. It is possible that $\Omega_\mu(x, y) = $ constant, whence $\Omega_{\mu x} = \Omega_{\mu y} = 0$ and $\lambda_\mu^2 = 0$. One must always check for this possibility in any eigenvalue problem.

Now, in (5.71), set $f = \Omega_\mu$ and $g = \Omega_\nu$. Then, according to (5.69), everywhere on C,

$$\frac{\partial f}{\partial n} = \frac{\partial \Omega_\mu}{\partial n} = 0 \quad \text{and} \quad \frac{\partial g}{\partial n} = \frac{\partial \Omega_\nu}{\partial n} = 0$$

Also

$$\nabla^2 f = \nabla^2 \Omega_\mu = -\lambda_\mu^2 \Omega_\mu$$

$$\nabla^2 g = \nabla^2 \Omega_\nu = -\lambda_\nu^2 \Omega_\nu$$

Thus (5.71) becomes

$$-\int\int_R (\lambda_\nu^2 \Omega_\mu \Omega_\nu - \lambda_\mu^2 \Omega_\nu \Omega_\mu) \, dx \, dy = 0$$

or

$$(\lambda_\mu^2 - \lambda_\nu^2) \int\int_R \Omega_\mu \Omega_\nu \, dx \, dy = 0$$

This relation demonstrates the orthogonality property: Any two eigenfunctions Ω_μ and Ω_ν, corresponding to two distinct eigenvalues λ_μ^2 and λ_ν^2, are orthogonal; that is,

$$\int\int_R \Omega_\mu \Omega_\nu \, dx \, dy = 0 \tag{5.72}$$

Additional properties (the λ_ν^2 are real, for example) and generalizations of these results are treated in the problem exercises.

Having demonstrated that the eigenvalues are nonnegative and that the eigenfunctions are orthogonal in the two-dimensional problem (5.69) just as in the equivalent one-dimensional case, we return to the job of producing an explicit set of λ_ν^2 and Ω_ν. As (5.69) is a homogeneous and linear boundary-value problem governed by a partial differential equation, the methods of Chap. 3 are appropriate.

Let $\Omega(x, y) = X(x)Y(y)$; then, from (5.69), we can obtain in the usual manner

$$\frac{X''}{X} + \frac{Y''}{Y} + \lambda^2 = 0$$

or

$$\frac{X''}{X} = -\lambda^2 - \frac{Y''}{Y} = -\beta^2 = \text{constant} \tag{5.73}$$

and the boundary conditions

$$X'(0) = X'(l_1) = 0$$
$$Y'(0) = Y'(l_2) = 0$$
(5.74)

Combining (5.73) and (5.74) produces *two* one-dimensional eigenvalue problems

$$X'' + \beta^2 X = 0, \qquad 0 < x < l_1$$
$$X'(0) = X'(l_1) = 0$$
(5.75)

and

$$Y'' + (\lambda^2 - \beta^2)Y = 0, \qquad 0 < y < l_2$$
$$Y'(0) = Y'(l_2) = 0$$
(5.76)

whose solutions are well known to us. In fact, for (5.75) we have

$$X_m = c_{0m} \cos \beta_m x \qquad \beta_m^2 = \frac{m^2 \pi^2}{l_1^2}, \qquad m \geq 0$$
(5.77)

while for (5.76)

$$Y_n = C_{0n} \cos \kappa_n y \qquad \kappa_n^2 = \frac{n^2 \pi^2}{l_2^2}, \qquad n \geq 0$$
(5.78)

in which κ^2 has replaced $\lambda^2 - \beta^2$. Thus $\lambda^2 = \beta^2 + \kappa^2$, and accordingly the eigenvalues λ^2 must be given by a *double* sequence

$$\lambda_{mn}^2 = \beta_m^2 + \kappa_n^2 = \pi^2 \left(\frac{m^2}{l_1^2} + \frac{n^2}{l_2^2} \right), \qquad m, n \geq 0$$
(5.79)

Using the results (5.77) and (5.78) in the definition $\Omega(x, y) = X(x)Y(y)$ produces the eigenfunctions

$$\Omega_{mn} = \cos \frac{m\pi x}{l_1} \cos \frac{n\pi y}{l_2}$$
(5.80)

from which the product of arbitrary constants $c_{0m}C_{0n}$ has been discarded.

The solutions to the two-dimensional problem (5.69) are then the double sequence of eigenvalues λ_{mn}^2 in (5.79) and the double sequence of corresponding eigenfunctions Ω_{mn} in (5.80). There exists a "double" infinity of eigenvalues. Although we shall not do it here, we could prove [1] that the foregoing method yields all the eigenvalues—that is, that every eigenvalue of (5.69) is given by the double sequence (5.79). Furthermore, Petrovsky [2] shows that the system of eigenfunctions $\Omega_{mn}(x, y)$ is a complete system (see Sec. 3.3.2) for all continuous, square-integrable functions* $f(x, y)$ on the region R. Petrovsky's proof, which is left to the Problems, demonstrates the very plausible concept: The system of functions $\Omega_{mn}(x, y) = X_m(x)Y_n(y)$, formed from the functions X_m and Y_n of two complete systems of continuous functions that are orthogonal, respectively, with respect to weight functions $p(x)$ and $\tilde{p}(y)$, is also a complete system of functions that are orthogonal with respect to the weight function $\bar{p}(x, y) = p(x)\tilde{p}(y)$.

* The integral $\iint\limits_{R} f^2 \, dx \, dy$ is finite.

Consequently, the square-integrable function $f(x, y)$ may be represented on R in the present case by a *double Fourier series expansion*

$$f(x, y) = \sum_{m=0}^{\infty} \sum_{n=0}^{\infty} A_{mn} \Omega_{mn}(x, y) \tag{5.81}$$

in which (as we can easily deduce through use of the orthogonality of the Ω_{mn})

$$A_{mn} = \frac{1}{N_{mn}} \int \int_R f(x, y) \Omega_{mn}(x, y) \, dx \, dy \tag{5.82}$$

and the normalizing constants

$$N_{mn} = \int \int_R \Omega_{mn}^2(x, y) \, dx \, dy \tag{5.83}$$

Here $p = \tilde{p} = \bar{p} = 1$. The properties of the series (5.81) are established in the same manner as that used in Sec. 3.3, but the bounded interval and the line integrals of Sec. 3.3 are replaced in the present case by the rectangular region R and the integrals over R. The details of the necessary derivations are left to the problem exercises. The results can be summarized as follows:

1. Parseval's equality

$$\int \int_R \bar{p}(x, y) f^2(x, y) \, dx \, dy = \sum_{m=1}^{\infty} \sum_{n=1}^{\infty} A_{mn}^2 \tag{5.84}$$

holds for every continuous, square-integrable function $f(x, y)$ [2].

2. If $f(x, y)$ and its first partial derivatives are continuous and its second partial derivatives are square integrable, then the double Fourier series (5.81) converges absolutely and uniformly to $f(x, y)$ on R.

3. If $f(x, y)$ is only continuous on $R + C$, then the partial sums of the series (5.81) converge to $f(x, y)$ in the mean square on R.

Now, given that the solution to (5.66) is [see (3.29) or Sec. A.2.1]

$$T_{mn}(t) = e^{-\lambda_{mn}^2 kt}$$

the product-form solution to Eqs. (5.60) and (5.61) can be written [see also (5.79) and (5.80)]

$$u_{mn}(x, y, t) = T_{mn}(t) \Omega_{mn}(x, y)$$

$$= e^{-\lambda_{mn}^2 kt} \cos \frac{m\pi x}{l_1} \cos \frac{n\pi y}{l_2}$$

But the problem (5.60) to (5.62) is linear, the governing equation and boundary conditions are homogeneous, and the Ω_{mn} are a complete system. Therefore the formal solution can be found by linear superposition and expansion in a convergent double series, provided only that the initial temperature distribution U_0 is square integrable. In particular, on introduction of the undetermined free constants A_{mn},

$$u(x, y, t) = \sum_{m=0}^{\infty} \sum_{n=0}^{\infty} A_{mn} u_{mn}(x, y, t) = \sum_{m=0}^{\infty} \sum_{n=0}^{\infty} A_{mn} T_{mn}(t) \Omega_{mn}(x, y)$$

$$= \sum_{m=0}^{\infty} \sum_{n=0}^{\infty} A_{mn} e^{-\lambda_{mn}^2 kt} \cos \frac{m\pi x}{l_1} \cos \frac{n\pi y}{l_2} \tag{5.85}$$

where the λ_{mn}^2 are given by (5.79). At $t = 0$,

$$u(x, y, 0) = U_0(x, y) = \sum_{m=0}^{\infty} \sum_{n=0}^{\infty} A_{mn} \cos \frac{m\pi x}{l_1} \cos \frac{n\pi y}{l_2}$$

$$= \sum_{m=0}^{\infty} \sum_{n=0}^{\infty} A_{mn} \Omega_{mn}(x, y) \tag{5.86}$$

It follows from (5.81) to (5.83) that

$$A_{mn} = \frac{1}{N_{mn}} \int \int_R U_0(x, y)\Omega_{mn}(x, y) \, dx \, dy \tag{5.87}$$

and

$$N_{mn} = \int \int_R \Omega_{mn}^2(x, y) \, dx \, dy = \int_0^{l_2} \int_0^{l_1} \cos^2 \frac{m\pi x}{l_1} \cos^2 \frac{n\pi y}{l_2} \, dx \, dy$$

$$= \begin{cases} l_1 l_2, & n = m = 0 \\[2mm] \dfrac{l_1 l_2}{2}, & n = 0 \quad or \quad m = 0 \\[2mm] \dfrac{l_1 l_2}{4}, & m, n > 0 \end{cases} \tag{5.88}$$

Accordingly, (5.85) to (5.88), plus (5.79) and (5.80), give the complete formal solution to (5.60) to (5.62). This solution is in the form of a double eigenfunction expansion employing the trigonometric functions (a double Fourier series). The problem and solution are summarized in Table 5.1. From this table we see that

$$\lim_{t \to \infty} u(x, y, t) = A_{00}$$

and that

$$A_{00} = \frac{1}{l_1 l_2} \int_0^{l_2} \int_0^{l_1} U_0(x, y) \, dx \, dy$$

Thus as $t \to \infty$, the limit given by the formal series solution is precisely that predicted on physical grounds and given in (5.63). Finally, the effect of the negative exponential factor in each term of (5.85) is so strong that, where the series converges, an accurate representation of the solution in R for $t > 0$ may be obtained with a partial sum containing only a very few of the lowest-order nonzero terms in the double expansion.

The treatment of inhomogeneous problems in three independent variables is not different in principle from that used in Sec. 5.1 for two-dimensional problems. However, attempts to separate steady-state or equilibrium solutions from the basic problem as a means of removing inhomogeneous boundary conditions usually lead to two-dimensional boundary-value problems whose solution can only be given as an infinite series. Thus, while the concepts of reduction to standard form and expansion in terms of the eigenfunctions of the related homogeneous problem are the same in two and three dimensions, the complexities in the latter case are formidable.

TABLE 5.1

Problem	Region
$u_t = k \nabla^2 u$ $u_x(0, y, t) = u_x(l_1, y, t) = u_y(x, 0, t)$ $\quad = u_y(x, l_2, t) = 0$ $u(x, y, 0) = U_0(x, y)$	$R: 0 < x < l_1, \quad 0 < y < l_2$ C: boundary so $R + C: 0 \le x \le l_1,$ $\qquad\qquad\qquad\qquad\quad 0 \le y \le l_2$ Time: $0 < t$

Eigenvalues	Eigenfunctions
$\lambda_{mn}^2 = \pi^2\left(\dfrac{m^2}{l_1^2} + \dfrac{n^2}{l_2^2}\right), \qquad m, n \ge 0$	$\Omega_{mn} = \cos\dfrac{m\pi x}{l_1}\cos\dfrac{n\pi y}{l_2}, \qquad m, n \ge 0$

Normalizing Constants

$$N_{mn} = \iint\limits_R \Omega_{mn}^2 \, dx \, dy = \begin{cases} l_1 l_2, & n = m = 0 \\[2mm] \dfrac{l_1 l_2}{2}, & n = 0 \quad or \quad m = 0 \\[2mm] \dfrac{l_1 l_2}{4}, & n, m > 0 \end{cases}$$

Formal Expansion	Coefficients
$u(x, y, t) = \displaystyle\sum_{m=0}^{\infty} \sum_{n=0}^{\infty} A_{mn} e^{-\lambda_{mn}^2 kt} \Omega_{mn}$	$A_{mn} = \dfrac{1}{N_{mn}} \displaystyle\iint\limits_R U_0(x, y)\Omega_{mn}(x, y) \, dx \, dy$

Solution

$$u(x, y, t) = A_{00} + \sum_{n=1}^{\infty} A_{0n}\, e^{-\pi^2 n^2 kt/l_2^2} \cos\frac{n\pi y}{l_2} + \sum_{m=1}^{\infty} A_{m0}\, e^{-\pi^2 m^2 kt/l_1^2}\cos\frac{m\pi x}{l_1}$$

$$+ \sum_{m=1}^{\infty} \sum_{n=1}^{\infty} A_{mn} \exp\left[-\pi^2\left(\frac{m^2}{l_1^2} + \frac{n^2}{l_2^2}\right)kt\right] \cos\frac{m\pi x}{l_1}\cos\frac{n\pi y}{l_2}$$

with

$$A_{00} = \frac{1}{l_1 l_2} \int_0^{l_2}\int_0^{l_1} U_0(x, y)\, dx\, dy$$

$$A_{0n} = \frac{2}{l_1 l_2} \int_0^{l_2}\int_0^{l_1} U_0(x, y)\cos\frac{n\pi y}{l_2}\, dx\, dy, \qquad n \ge 1$$

$$A_{m0} = \frac{2}{l_1 l_2} \int_0^{l_2}\int_0^{l_1} U_0(x, y)\cos\frac{m\pi x}{l_1}\, dx\, dy, \qquad m \ge 1$$

$$A_{mn} = \frac{4}{l_1 l_2} \int_0^{l_2}\int_0^{l_1} U_0(x, y)\cos\frac{m\pi x}{l_1}\cos\frac{n\pi y}{l_2}\, dx\, dy, \qquad m, n \ge 1$$

Accordingly, as the numerical finite-difference methods of Chap. 10 appear to offer a more practical means of achieving numerical results in such cases, the inhomogeneous three-dimensional problem is not treated here. It is essential to remember, however, that the eigenvalues and eigenfunctions appropriate to the inhomogeneous problem are always those of the related homogeneous problem and are therefore known to us. In many cases, it is sufficient to know these eigencharacteristics—for example, in vibration problems where the natural frequencies of vibration are needed to study the response to a forcing function.

5.2.2   Vibration of a Membrane

The second example for our double-series development is the vibration of a uniform, flexible membrane with a plane, fixed boundary. If the membrane is square with unit dimensions and no external forces acting, then the appropriate model according to Sec. 2.2.2, in terms of the transverse displacement $z = z(x, y, t)$, is

$$z_{tt} = c^2(z_{xx} + z_{yy}), \qquad 0 < x, y < 1, \quad 0 < t \tag{5.89}$$

$$z(0, y, t) = z(1, y, t) = z(x, 0, t) = z(x, 1, t) = 0,$$
$$0 \le x, y \le 1, \quad 0 < t \tag{5.90}$$

$$z(x, y, 0) = z_0(x, y),$$
$$z_t(x, y, 0) = V_0(x, y), \qquad 0 \le x, y \le 1 \tag{5.91}$$

We may proceed as before; let $z(x, y, t) = T(t)\Omega(x, y)$. From (5.89) and (5.90), we obtain

$$T'' + \lambda^2 c^2 T = 0 \tag{5.92}$$

and the eigenvalue problem

$$\nabla^2\Omega + \lambda^2\Omega = \Omega_{xx} + \Omega_{yy} + \lambda^2\Omega = 0$$
$$\Omega(0, y) = \Omega(1, y) = \Omega(x, 0) = \Omega(x, 1) = 0 \tag{5.93}$$

in which $-\lambda^2$ is the separation constant.

The solution to (5.92) is [see Example A.2, (A.2.12)]

$$T = A_0 \cos c\lambda t + \frac{A_1}{c\lambda} \sin c\lambda t \tag{5.94}$$

in which we retain the arbitrary constants A_0 and A_1. The Green's identities (5.70) and (5.71) can be used again to show that the eigenfunction solutions to (5.93) are orthogonal and the corresponding eigenvalues are nonnegative ($\lambda^2 \ge 0$). Similarly, separation of variables in (5.93) leads again to two eigenvalue problems whose solutions are well known to us. In fact, by following precisely the same steps used in the preceding section, one can easily show [see (3.36)] that the desired results are (note $\lambda_{mn}^2 > 0$)

$$\Omega_{mn} = \sin m\pi x \sin n\pi y$$
$$\lambda_{mn}^2 = \pi^2(m^2 + n^2), \qquad m, n \ge 1 \tag{5.95}$$

The combination of (5.94) and (5.95) produces a system of functions

$$z_{mn}(x, y, t) = \left(A_{0mn} \cos c\lambda_{mn}t + \frac{A_{1mn}}{c\lambda_{mn}} \sin c\lambda_{mn}t\right) \sin m\pi x \sin n\pi y$$

$$= A_{mn} \sin m\pi x \sin n\pi y \cos(\lambda_{mn}ct + \varepsilon_{mn}) \tag{5.96}$$

each of which is a solution to the fundamental problem (5.89) and (5.90). Each z_{mn} is an *eigenvibration* or (m, n) *normal mode* of vibration of the membrane corresponding to the eigenvalues λ_{mn}^2. The second form of z_{mn}, in which

$$A_{mn}^2 = A_{0mn}^2 + \frac{A_{1mn}^2}{c^2 \lambda_{mn}^2}$$

and

$$\varepsilon_{mn} = \tan^{-1} \left(\frac{A_{1mn}}{c \lambda_{mn} A_{0mn}} \right)$$

was obtained through the use of trigonometric identities; clearly, the frequency of an eigenvibration does not depend on the values of A_{0mn} or A_{1mn}, but the phase relationship between eigenvibrations, $\varepsilon_{mn} - \varepsilon_{pq}$, does.

The vibrations governed by the initial conditions (5.91) can be represented by a superposition of the z_{mn}. Thus

$$z(x, y, t) = \sum_{m=1}^{\infty} \sum_{n=1}^{\infty} \left(A_{0mn} \cos c\lambda_{mn} t + \frac{A_{1mn}}{c\lambda_{mn}} \sin c\lambda_{mn} t \right) \sin m\pi x \sin n\pi y \quad (5.97)$$

At $t = 0$,

$$z(x, y, 0) = z_0(x, y) = \sum_{m=1}^{\infty} \sum_{n=1}^{\infty} A_{0mn} \sin m\pi x \sin n\pi y$$

and

$$z_t(x, y, 0) = V_0(x, y) = \sum_{m=1}^{\infty} \sum_{n=1}^{\infty} A_{1mn} \sin m\pi x \sin n\pi y$$

Thus because the Ω_{mn} are orthogonal on $0 \leq x, y \leq 1$ with a weight function $p(x, y) = 1$ [see (3.36) and the previous section], we have directly

$$A_{0mn} = 4 \int_0^1 \int_0^1 z_0(x, y) \sin m\pi x \sin n\pi y \, dx \, dy \quad (5.98)$$

and

$$A_{1mn} = 4 \int_0^1 \int_0^1 V_0(x, y) \sin m\pi x \sin n\pi y \, dx \, dy \quad (5.99)$$

because

$$\int_0^1 \int_0^1 \sin^2 m\pi x \sin^2 n\pi y \, dx \, dy = \tfrac{1}{4}$$

The formal solution to problem (5.89) through (5.91) is given by (5.97) to (5.99). Because the time-dependent portion of the expansion is oscillatory, the convergence of the series in (5.97) depends at any point only on the rates of change of the coefficients A_{0mn} and A_{1mn} with increasing m and n. These rates depend, in turn, on the continuity and differentiability of z_0 and V_0 (see Probs. 3.33 and 3.34 for the one-dimensional analog and a basis for analysis of the present case). Unfortunately, the size of the terms in (5.97) decreases with despairing slowness as m and n increase, even in the best cases. Hence numerical representation of the surface of the membrane by (5.97) is usually not practical. However, the frequencies of the eigenvibrations z_{mn} that make up the solution are of great interest, and they are known explicitly.

If the time-dependent portion of an eigenvibration has the form $\cos(c\lambda t + \varepsilon)$, the frequency of vibration in Hertz is $f = c\lambda/2\pi$ because the argument of the cosine is given in radians. In the case of a string with fixed ends, the eigenvibrations (for free vibrations without a forcing function) were found in Sec. 5.1.2 to be [see (5.20) and (5.21)]

$$z_n(y, t) = \left(A_{0n} \cos c\lambda_n t + \frac{A_{1n}}{c\lambda_n} \sin c\lambda_n t \right) \sin \lambda_n y$$

or

$$z_n(y, t) = A_n \sin \lambda_n y \cos(c\lambda_n t + \varepsilon_n)$$

where for a unit-length string $\lambda_n^2 = n^2\pi^2$, $n \geq 1$. For a string of length l, $\lambda_n^2 = (n\pi/l)^2$, $n \geq 1$. Thus the normal modes of vibration have frequencies

$$f_n = \frac{nc}{2l} \tag{5.100}$$

Recall that $c = \sqrt{T/\rho}$, in which T is the string tension and ρ is the mass per unit length (the density). The lowest frequency $f_1 = c/2l$ is the *fundamental* frequency or *pitch*; the remaining f_n, $n \geq 2$, are called *overtones* (or *harmonics* because they are simple numerical multiples of the pitch). From (5.100) and the definition of c, we deduce [3] *Mersenne's Law* for a string: The fundamental frequency varies directly as the square root of the tension and inversely as the length and the square root of the density. The *tone* or the quality of vibration is governed by the proportion of energy in each of the overtones (see the problem exercises). Each musical instrument is characterized by its tone—that is, the lower the proportion of energy in the harmonics, the purer the musical note of the instrument.

On the other hand, for the vibrating rectangular membrane, the eigenvibrations are given by (5.96). For the unit-square membrane, $\lambda_{mn}^2 = \pi^2(m^2 + n^2)$; $m, n \geq 1$; for the rectangular membrane with sides l_1 and l_2, $\lambda_{mn}^2 = \pi^2(m^2/l_1^2 + n^2/l_2^2)$, $m, n \geq 1$ (see Sec. 5.2.1). Thus, in the general case, the frequencies of vibration of the (m, n) normal modes are

$$f_{mn} = \frac{c}{2}\left(\frac{m^2}{l_1^2} + \frac{n^2}{l_2^2} \right)^{1/2}$$

$$= \left[\left(\frac{m^2}{l_1^2} + \frac{n^2}{l_2^2} \right) \frac{T}{4\rho} \right]^{1/2}, \qquad m, n \geq 1 \tag{5.101}$$

where T is the tension and ρ is the density (mass per unit area of membrane surface). (For a square membrane $l_1 = l_2 = l$ and Mersenne's law holds as before.) The fundamental frequency is

$$f_{11} = \left[\left(\frac{1}{l_1^2} + \frac{1}{l_2^2} \right) \frac{T}{4\rho} \right]^{1/2}$$

The overtones $(f_{mn}; m, n > 1)$ are no longer simple numerical multiples of the fundamental frequency. Accordingly, although the sound of a vibrating string in which several modes are excited together is pleasing because of the simple relation of overtones to fundamental, the sound of a vibrating rectangular membrane in which several modes are present is much less musical to the ear. Similarly, the overtones for circular membranes also are not simply related to the fundamental, explaining thereby the lack of musical quality of drums [4]. (Coulson [3] notes that [fortunately for us] bells are a special case in which certain key overtones are harmonics—that is, have frequencies that are simple multiples of the fundamental.)

To examine a final point, we return to the eigenvibrations for the membrane (5.96) and the corresponding eigenvalues λ_{mn}^2 given by (5.95). For the specific case considered (the unit-square membrane), $\lambda_{mn}^2 = \lambda_{nm}^2 = \lambda_e^2$, but

$$z_{mn} = A_{mn} \sin m\pi x \sin n\pi y \cos (\lambda_e ct + \varepsilon_{mn})$$

while

$$z_{nm} = A_{nm} \sin n\pi x \sin m\pi y \cos (\lambda_e ct + \varepsilon_{nm})$$

Thus the eigenvalue λ_e^2 is a *multiple* eigenvalue with at least two* corresponding eigenfunctions that are functionally different—for example, if $m = 2$ and $n = 1$, $\lambda_{21} = \lambda_{12} = \lambda_e^2 = 5\pi^2$, and

$$\Omega_{21} = \sin 2\pi x \sin \pi y$$

$$\Omega_{12} = \sin \pi x \sin 2\pi y$$

Thus, for the multiple eigenvalue, there may exist eigenvibrations of the same frequency but having different displacement characteristics. These characteristics are best studied by examination of the *nodal lines*, the curves along which the membrane is at rest during a given eigenvibration. Here they are curves where $\Omega_{mn} = 0$. For each multiple eigenvalue, the corresponding eigenvibrations have the same frequency but entirely different nodal lines (see the problem exercises).

In the case of the vibration of the general rectangular membrane of dimensions (l_1, l_2) or the case of heat conduction examined in Sec. 5.2.1 above, multiple eigenvalues always occur if the ratio l_1/l_2 of the body dimensions is rational [4], because then the equation

$$\left(\frac{m^2}{l_1^2} + \frac{n^2}{l_2^2}\right) = \left(\frac{\mu^2}{l_1^2} + \frac{v^2}{l_2^2}\right)$$

always has some nontrivial integral solutions (μ^2, v^2) for $0 \leq m^2, n^2 < \infty$. The presence of multiple eigenvalues and eigenfunctions causes no great difficulty, for, as shown in the problem exercises, the eigenfunctions corresponding to the same eigenvalue are still orthogonal.

5.3   FOURTH-ORDER EQUATIONS

5.3.1   A Mathematical Model

The mathematical model for the transverse vibration of a perfectly flexible string was derived in Sec. 2.2.2. The string offered no resistance to bending; the governing equation for the model was the second-order wave equation. Now the

---

* Courant and Hilbert [5] pose the problem as follows: "The question of the multiplicity of an eigenvalue in the case of the square domain is thus reduced to the number-theoretic problem: in how many ways can a number $\pi^{-2}\lambda_e^2$ be represented as the sum $\pi^{-2}\lambda_e^2 = m^2 + n^2$ of two squares?"

mathematical model for the transverse vibrations of an elastic beam is derived. The beam offers great resistance to bending; as we shall see, the governing equation is now a fourth-order equation.

For simplicity, consider an elastic beam with uniform rectangular cross section and density ρ (mass per unit length). The beam lies along a y axis between $0 \leq y \leq l$. The transverse motions are assumed to occur in the z-y plane (Fig. 5.2a).

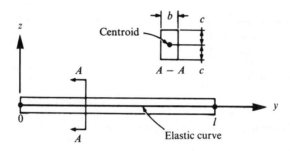

(a) Undeflected position.

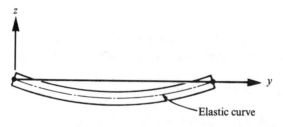

(b) Deflected position.

FIGURE 5.2   Elastic beam.

The deflection z of the beam is the vertical distance from the undeflected or straight position to the corresponding point on the *elastic curve* of the deflected beam. For purely elastic motions (governed by Hooke's law), the elastic curve passes through the geometric centroid of each cross section of the uniform beam. The elastic curve is also the curve along which no extension or compression of the beam takes place during vibration.

The change in the slope across a small isolated section of a beam (Fig. 5.3) can be related to the bending moments M acting about an axis perpendicular to the z-y plane and through the elastic curve. The beam is assumed to be composed of laminas of thickness dh and width b, each of which responds elastically to the compression or extension induced by the bending, and hence deflection, caused by the applied moments. According to Hooke's law (see Prob. 2.4), the force required to compress a lamina at level h an amount $h\, d\phi$ (see Fig. 5.3) is

$$f_h = AE \frac{h\, d\phi}{ds}$$

in which $A = b\, dh$ and E is the Young's modulus of elasticity of the material. Note that f_h changes sign and represents tension when $h < 0$. The moments acting at each

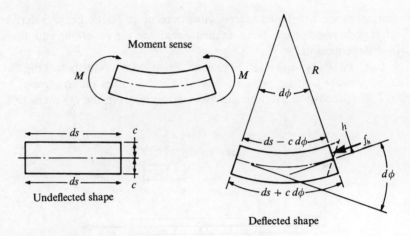

Moment sense

M M R

$d\phi$

$ds - c\,d\phi$ h f_h

ds c

$ds - c\,d\phi$ $d\phi$

ds c

Undeflected shape $ds + c\,d\phi$

Deflected shape

Assumptions: Deflection causes only elastic deformations.
Ends of section remain plane during deformation.

FIGURE 5.3   Differential change in slope under action of a moment M.

end of the segment ds must be equal to the sum of the products of the force f_h acting on each lamina times the lever arm h. Thus at the right end of the small section,

$$M = \int_{-c}^{c} hb(dh)E\frac{h\,d\phi}{ds} = \frac{d\phi}{ds}E\int_{-c}^{c} bh^2\,dh$$

The integral is equal to $I = 2bh^3/3$, which is the plane moment of inertia of the beam cross section about an axis perpendicular to the z–y plane at the elastic curve. Thus we have

$$\frac{d\phi}{ds} = \frac{M}{EI} \tag{5.102}$$

From purely geometric considerations, $d\phi/ds$ is seen to be the curvature of the elastic curve $z = z(y, t)$ [6], and, in particular,

$$\frac{d\phi}{ds} = \frac{z_{yy}}{(1 + z_y^2)^{3/2}} \tag{5.103}$$

We see that a nonlinear relationship for the unknown z is developing. If we restrict our attention to small motions (as usual), z_y^2 is negligible compared to unity. Accordingly, for small motions, the combination of (5.102) and (5.103) gives

$$EIz_{yy} = M \tag{5.104}$$

where EI is called the *flexural rigidity* and M is the bending moment at any cross section.

Figure 5.4 shows an equilibrium or free-body diagram of the forces and moments that may act on a segment of beam under conditions of varying loads. Here Q is the shearing force acting between adjacent cross sections of the beam; q is a continuous load (force per unit length along the beam) that is applied externally. For example, when gravity acts in the negative z direction, $q = -W$, where W is the

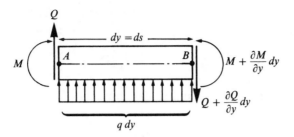

FIGURE 5.4   The loaded element.

weight per unit length of the beam itself. If we take counterclockwise moments about point A in Fig. 5.4, we obtain for equilibrium

$$-M + \left(M + \frac{\partial M}{\partial y} dy\right) - \left(Q + \frac{\partial Q}{\partial y} dy\right) dy + (q\, dy)\frac{dy}{2} = 0$$

On dividing by dy in this equation and letting $dy \to 0$, we next find

$$\frac{\partial M}{\partial y} = Q \qquad (5.105)$$

A summation of forces in the z direction in Fig. 5.4 gives

$$Q - \left(Q + \frac{\partial Q}{\partial y} dy\right) + q\, dy = 0$$

or, after division by dy, in the limit as $dy \to 0$

$$\frac{\partial Q}{\partial y} = q \qquad (5.106)$$

Accordingly, from (5.104) to (5.106),

$$\frac{\partial}{\partial y}(EIz_{yy}) = \frac{\partial M}{\partial y} = Q \qquad (5.107)$$

and

$$\frac{\partial^2}{\partial y^2}(EIz_{yy}) = \frac{\partial Q}{\partial y} = q \qquad (5.108)$$

Equation (5.108) can be used [7] to obtain the equation for lateral vibration of the beam. The force per unit length

$$F_R = \frac{\partial^2}{\partial y^2}(EIz_{yy})$$

is the restoring force provided by the resistance of the beam to deflection. Thus F_R is directed downward for upward deflection. Writing Newton's Second Law (1.13) for the plane motion of the element AB in Fig. 5.4, we equate the acceleration-mass product for the section to the force F_R and the external forces:

$$ma = \rho\, dy\, z_{tt} = \left[-\frac{\partial^2}{\partial y^2}(EIz_{yy}) + q\right] dy$$

Consequently, the governing equation for the small, lateral or transverse vibration of a uniform beam is

$$\rho z_{tt} = -\frac{\partial^2}{\partial y^2}(EIz_{yy}) + q \tag{5.109}$$

For the uniform beam EI is constant; (5.109) becomes

$$z_{tt} + c^2 z_{yyyy} = \frac{q}{\rho} \tag{5.110}$$

where

$$c^2 = \frac{EI}{\rho}$$

Interestingly, (5.104), (5.107), and (5.108) also yield the necessary boundary conditions. At a point- or simply-supported end of the beam, the deflection is zero and no moment acts. Thus $z = 0$ and $z_{yy} = 0$ from (5.104). The shearing force is not zero because it is equal to the support reaction force. At a free end of a beam, the shearing force and bending moments are zero. Thus, from (5.107), $z_{yyy} = 0$ and, from (5.104), $z_{yy} = 0$. At a clamped or rigidly fixed end, the beam deflection and local slope are zero. Hence $z = 0$ and $z_y = 0$.

From earlier considerations it is clear that four boundary conditions (two at each end of the beam) are needed. They are available in this case. Additionally, two initial conditions are required: the initial position $z(y, 0)$ and the initial velocity $z_t(y, 0)$ of the elastic curve. Table 5.2 presents a pair of complete mathematical models. The effect of gravity and/or distributed loads on the beam has been neglected so that the given models have a homogeneous governing equation.

5.3.2   A Method of Solution

The mathematical models shown in Table 5.2 will yield to the methods of separation of variables and eigenfunction expansions. Let us consider the case of the simply-supported beam. The mathematical model is

$$z_{tt} + c^2 z_{yyyy} = 0, \qquad 0 < y < l, \quad 0 < t \tag{5.111}$$

$$z(0, t) = z_{yy}(0, t) = z(l, t) = z_{yy}(l, t) = 0, \qquad 0 < t \tag{5.112}$$

$$\begin{matrix} z(y, 0) = z_0(y), \\ z_t(y, 0) = V_0(y), \end{matrix} \qquad 0 \le y \le l \tag{5.113}$$

Let $z(y, t) = Y(y)T(t)$ and introduce this in (5.111) and (5.112) to separate the variables. First, we find from (5.111)

$$\frac{T''}{c^2 T} = -\frac{Y''''}{Y} = -\lambda^4$$

in which λ^4 is the separation constant. Using this result and those obtained from (5.112), we next find

$$T'' + c^2\lambda^4 T = 0 \tag{5.114}$$

TABLE 5.2   Two Mathematical Models for Vibrating Beams

Type of Supports	Simply Supported Beam	Cantilevered Beam
Picture of uniform beam configuration		
Governing equation (neglecting gravity and loads)	$z_{tt} + c^2 z_{yyyy} = 0, \quad 0 < y < l, \ 0 < t$	$z_{tt} + c^2 z_{yyyy} = 0, \quad 0 < y < l, \ 0 < t$
Boundary conditions	$z(0, t) = 0 \quad z(l, t) = 0$ $z_{yy}(0, t) = 0 \quad z_{yy}(l, t) = 0$	$z(0, t) = 0 \quad z_{yy}(l, t) = 0$ $z_y(0, t) = 0 \quad z_{yyy}(l, t) = 0$
Initial conditions	$z(y, 0) = z_0(y),$ $z_t(y, 0) = V_0(y),$ $\quad 0 \le y \le l$	$z(y, 0) = z_0(y),$ $z_t(y, 0) = V_0(y),$ $\quad 0 \le y \le l$

and the eigenvalue problem

$$Y'''' - \lambda^4 Y = 0$$
$$Y(0) = Y''(0) = Y(l) = Y''(l) = 0 \tag{5.115}$$

Application of the power series method (Sec. A.2.2) to the governing equation in (5.115) would show that the general solution, valid for all λ^4, is

$$Y(y) = c_1[\cos \lambda y + \cosh \lambda y] + \frac{c_2}{\lambda}[\sin \lambda y + \sinh \lambda y]$$

$$+ \frac{c_3}{\lambda^2}[\cos \lambda y - \cosh \lambda y] + \frac{c_4}{\lambda^3}[\sin \lambda y - \sinh \lambda y] \tag{5.116}$$

Before proceeding to find the eigenvalues and eigenfunctions for (5.115), it is wise to determine their general character through the use of appropriate formal identities, as we have done before.

Rather than use a generalization of Green's identities (see Secs. 4.3 and 5.2.1), it is simpler here to construct the necessary relations by recalling the pattern of Green's identities and manipulating (5.115) accordingly. Thus if λ_m^4 and λ_n^4 are two distinct eigenvalues to (5.115) with corresponding eigenfunctions Y_m and Y_n, then we write

$$Y_m'''' = \lambda_m^4 Y_m \tag{5.117a}$$

$$Y_n'''' = \lambda_n^4 Y_n \tag{5.117b}$$

Now, multiply (5.117a) by Y_m and integrate over the problem interval; the result is

$$\int_0^l Y_m Y_m'''' \, dy = \lambda_m^4 \int_0^l Y_m^2 \, dy$$

The left-hand side of this relation may be integrated by parts twice to achieve

$$\int_0^l Y_m Y_m'''' \, dy = Y_m Y_m''' \Big|_0^l - \int_0^l Y_m' Y_m''' \, dy$$

$$= - Y_m' Y_m'' \Big|_0^l + \int_0^l (Y_m'')^2 \, dy$$

The indicated terms go to zero when the boundary conditions satisfied by the eigenfunctions are introduced. Therefore

$$\lambda_m^4 \int_0^l Y_m^2 \, dy = \int_0^l (Y_m'')^2 \, dy \tag{5.118}$$

Except for the trivial case, Y_m can never be identically zero on $(0 - l)$ for a given λ_m^4. It follows from (5.118) that $\lambda_m^4 > 0$ for all m unless $Y_m'' \equiv 0$ for some value of m. If $Y_m'' \equiv 0$, then $\lambda_m = 0$. Using (5.116) with $\lambda_0 = 0$ gives

$$Y_0(y) = 2c_1 + 2c_2 y - c_3 y^2 - \tfrac{1}{3} c_4 y^3$$

From (5.115),

$$Y_0(0) = 0 = 2c_1 \quad \text{produces} \quad c_1 = 0$$

$$Y_0''(0) = 0 = -2c_3 \quad \text{produces} \quad c_3 = 0$$

$$Y_0''(l) = 0 = -2c_4 l \quad \text{produces} \quad c_4 = 0$$

and

$$Y_0(l) = 0 = 2c_2 l \quad \text{produces} \quad c_2 = 0$$

Therefore $Y_0 \equiv 0$ and $\lambda_0 = 0$ is not an eigenvalue. Consequently,

$$\lambda_m^4 > 0$$

that is, the eigenvalues are positive. Their existence and reality, and so forth, can also be proved.

Next, multiplying (5.117a) by Y_n and (5.117b) by Y_m, subtracting the results, and then integrating over $(0, l)$ produce first

$$\int_0^l (Y_n Y_m'''' - Y_m Y_n'''') \, dy = (\lambda_m^4 - \lambda_n^4) \int_0^l Y_m Y_n \, dy$$

and, second, after the left-hand side of this relation is integrated by parts twice,

$$(\lambda_m^4 - \lambda_n^4) \int_0^l Y_m Y_n \, dy = [Y_n Y_m''' - Y_m Y_n''' - Y_n' Y_m'' + Y_m' Y_n'']_0^l$$

But the right-hand side of this relation is identically zero because of the boundary conditions satisfied by the eigenfunctions. Therefore

$$\int_0^l Y_m Y_n \, dy = 0 \tag{5.119}$$

that is, the eigenfunctions corresponding to distinct eigenvalues of the fourth-order eigenvalue problem (5.115) are orthogonal.

Having established that our methods and concepts carry over to this fourth-order problem, we can now use (5.116) in the boundary conditions of (5.115) to find λ_n^4 and Y_n explicitly. Because $\lambda^4 > 0$, we obtain

$$Y(0) = 2c_1 = 0 \quad \text{or} \quad c_1 = 0$$

$$Y''(0) = -2c_3 = 0 \quad \text{or} \quad c_3 = 0$$

and

$$Y(l) = \frac{c_2}{\lambda}(\sin \lambda l + \sinh \lambda l) + \frac{c_4}{\lambda^3}(\sin \lambda l - \sinh \lambda l) = 0$$

$$\tag{5.120}$$

$$Y''(l) = \lambda c_2(-\sin \lambda l + \sinh \lambda l) + \frac{c_4}{\lambda}(-\sin \lambda l - \sinh \lambda l) = 0$$

The relations (5.120) are a pair of homogeneous, simultaneous equations for the unknowns c_2 and c_4. Because the equations are homogeneous, we can only find one unknown as a function of the other; that is, our eigenfunction will retain its multiplicative free constant as we hoped and expected. Furthermore, we must set the determinant of the coefficients in (5.120) to zero to ensure that a nontrivial solution exists [5]. As a result, we have

$$
\begin{vmatrix}
\dfrac{1}{\lambda}\ (\sin \lambda l + \sinh \lambda l) & \dfrac{1}{\lambda^3}\ (\sin \lambda l - \sinh \lambda l) \\[3mm]
\lambda(-\sin \lambda l + \sinh \lambda l) & \dfrac{1}{\lambda}\ (-\sin \lambda l - \sinh \lambda l)
\end{vmatrix} = 0
\tag{5.121}
$$

which is the equation for the eigenvalues λ^4.

Expansion of the determinant (5.121) yields

$$
-\frac{4}{\lambda^2} \sin \lambda l \sinh \lambda l = 0
$$

from which we conclude that, as $\lambda^4 > 0$ and $\sinh \lambda l \neq 0$ for any real λ,

$$
\sin \lambda l = 0
$$

Accordingly, the eigenvalues are

$$
\lambda_n^4 = \left(\frac{\pi n}{l}\right)^4, \qquad n \geq 1
\tag{5.122}
$$

By introducing the values (5.122) in (5.120), we achieve

$$
\frac{c_{2n}}{\lambda_n} \sinh \lambda_n l - \frac{c_{4n}}{\lambda_n^3} \sinh \lambda_n l = 0
$$

$$
\lambda_n c_{2n} \sinh \lambda_n l - \frac{c_{4n}}{\lambda_n} \sinh \lambda_n l = 0
$$

Clearly, the solution that we seek is

$$
c_{4n} = \lambda_n^2 c_{2n}
$$

Returning to (5.116) with these results and the fact that $c_1 = c_3 = 0$, we find the eigenfunctions

$$
Y_n = \frac{2c_{2n}}{\lambda_n} \sin \lambda_n y
\tag{5.123}
$$

which are particularly simple for this case (see the more complex case of a cantilever beam in the Problems).

Now, given that the solution to (5.114) is

$$
T_n(t) = A_{0n} \cos c\lambda_n^2 t + \frac{A_{1n}}{c\lambda_n^2} \sin c\lambda_n^2 t
$$

we can write the product-form solution to (5.111) and (5.112)

$$
z_n(y, t) = \left(\tilde{A}_{0n} \cos c\lambda_n^2 t + \frac{\tilde{A}_{1n}}{c\lambda_n^2} \sin c\lambda_n^2 t \right) \sin \lambda_n y
$$

in which the arbitrary term $2c_{2n}/\lambda_n$ has been absorbed in $\tilde{A}_{0n}$ and $\tilde{A}_{1n}$. Because the problem (5.111) to (5.113) is linear, whereas (5.111) and (5.112) are homogeneous and the $\sin \lambda_n y$ are a complete orthogonal system, the formal solution is

$$z(y, t) = \sum_{n=1}^{\infty} z_n(y, t)$$

$$= \sum_{n=1}^{\infty} \left(\tilde{A}_{0n} \cos c\lambda_n^2 t + \frac{\tilde{A}_{1n}}{c\lambda_n^2} \sin c\lambda_n^2 t \right) \sin \lambda_n y \qquad (5.124)$$

The $\tilde{A}_{0n}$ and $\tilde{A}_{1n}$ are found in the usual manner through the use of the orthogonality of the eigenfunctions $\sin \lambda_n y$. In particular, because

$$z(y, 0) = z_0(y)$$

$$\tilde{A}_{0n} = \frac{2}{l} \int_0^l z_0(y) \sin \lambda_n y \, dy \qquad (5.125)$$

while because

$$z_t(y, 0) = V_0(y)$$

$$\tilde{A}_{1n} = \frac{2}{l} \int_0^l V_0(y) \sin \lambda_n y \, dy \qquad (5.126)$$

The complete eigenfunction-expansion solution to (5.111) through (5.113) is given by (5.124) to (5.126). As in other vibration problems, the convergence of the series (5.124) and those used to derive (5.125) and (5.126) depends on the character of z_0 and V_0 (see Probs. 3.33 and 3.34, as well as the Problems for this chapter).

The method of treatment of inhomogeneous problems involving fourth-order equations is, in principle, precisely the same as that used in Sec. 5.1 for second-order equations. A different homogenizing function $S(x, t)$ [see (5.14)] is required for fourth-order equations because there are four boundary conditions; however, the remainder of the method is the same in detail and in general. Several examples are treated in the Problems to illustrate this point.

REFERENCES

1. P. W. Berg and J. L. McGregor, *Elementary Partial Differential Equations*. San Francisco: Holden-Day, 1966.

2. I. G. Petrovsky, *Lectures on Partial Differential Equations* (trans. from the Russian by A. Shenitzer). New York: Interscience (a division of John Wiley & Sons), 1954.

3. C. A. Coulson, *Waves*, 7th ed. Edinburgh: Oliver and Boyd Ltd. (New York: Interscience), 1958.

4. M. Kac, "Can One Hear the Shape of a Drum?," *American Mathematics Monthly*, Vol. 73, No. 4, April 1966.

5. R. Courant and D. Hilbert, *Methods of Mathematical Physics*, Vol. 1. New York: Interscience (a division of John Wiley & Sons), 1953.

6. A. E. Taylor, *Calculus*. Englewood Cliffs, N.J.: Prentice-Hall, 1959.

7. S. Timoshenko, *Vibration Problems in Engineering*. New York: D. Van Nostrand, 1928.

PROBLEMS

5.1   For each of the following mathematical models with inhomogeneous boundary conditions, find a function that transforms the model into an equivalent standard-form model
with a matched pair of homogeneous boundary conditions: see Sec. 5.1.1 (give the standard-
form model also):

(a) $u = u(x, t)$
$$u_t = ku_{xx}, \qquad 0 < x < l, \quad t > 0$$
$$u_x(0, t) = A,$$
$$u_x(l, t) = B, \qquad t > 0$$
$$u(x, 0) = x(l - x), \qquad 0 \leq x \leq l$$

(b) $z = z(y, t)$
$$z_{tt} - c^2 z_{yy} = -g, \qquad 0 < y < 1, \quad t > 0$$
$$z(0, t) = c_1,$$
$$z_y(1, t) = c_2, \qquad t > 0$$
$$z(y, 0) = 3 \sin \frac{5\pi y}{2},$$
$$\qquad\qquad\qquad\qquad 0 \leq y \leq 1$$
$$z_t(y, 0) = 5 \cos \frac{9\pi y}{2},$$

(c) $u = u(x, t)$
$$u_t = ku_{xx}, \quad 0 < x < l, \quad t > 0$$
$$u(0, t) = A,$$
$$Ku_x(l, t) + Hu(l, t) = B, \qquad t > 0$$
$$u(x, 0) = 0, \qquad 0 \leq x \leq l$$

(d) $u = u(x, t)$
$$u_t = ku_{xx}, \qquad 0 < x < 2\pi, \quad t > 0$$
$$u(0, t) - u(2\pi, t) = A,$$
$$u_x(0, t) - u_x(2\pi, t) = B, \qquad t > 0$$
$$u(x, 0) = U_0(x), \qquad 0 \leq x \leq 2\pi$$

(e) $u = u(x, y)$
$$u_{xx} + u_{yy} = 0, \qquad 0 < x < l_1, \quad 0 < y < l_2$$
$$u_x(0, y) = 0,$$
$$u_x(l_1, y) = A, \qquad 0 \leq y \leq l_2$$
$$u(x, 0) = U_0,$$
$$Ku_y(x, l_2) + Hu(x, l_2) = 0, \qquad 0 < x < l_1$$

(f) The model derived in Prob. 2.6.

5.2   Find a function that transforms the following models into standard form according to the
method of Sec. 5.1.1:

(a) $z = z(y, t)$
$$z_{tt} - c^2 z_{yy} = 0, \qquad 0 < y < l, \qquad t > 0$$
$$z_y(0, t) = A \sin t,$$
$$z(l, t) = \delta, \qquad t > 0$$
$$z(y, 0) = \delta y^2 / l^2,$$
$$z_t(y, 0) = 0, \qquad 0 \leq y \leq l$$

(b) $u = u(x, t)$
$$u_t = ku_{xx}, \qquad 0 < x < 1, \quad t > 0$$

$u(0, t) = a \sin \pi t,$
$Ku_x(1, t) + Hu(1, t) = b \cos \pi t,$ $\quad t > 0$
$u(x, 0) = 0, \quad 0 \le x \le 1$

(c) $u = u(x, y)$
   $u_{xx} + u_{yy} = 0, \quad 0 < x < \pi, \quad 0 < y < \pi$

$u_x(0, y) = -\dfrac{F_0}{K},$ $\quad 0 \le y \le \pi$
$u_x(\pi, y) = y(\pi - y),$

$u_y(x, 0) = x(\pi - x),$ $\quad 0 < x < \pi$
$u(x, \pi) = 100,$

5.3   Solution of the model (5.1) to (5.3) by the method of eigenfunction expansions requires that, after reduction of (5.1) to (5.3) to the standard form (5.16), the inhomogeneous term $Q(y, t)$ be representable in terms of a convergent Fourier series. Accordingly, $Q(y, t)$ must be at least piecewise continuous. Using the analyses of Sec. 3.3 and Probs. 3.20 to 3.23, establish the necessary conditions of continuity and differentiability for the functions $f_1(t)$ and $f_2(t)$.

5.4   Find formal solutions to the following mathematical models:

(a) $u = u(x, t)$
   $u_t = ku_{xx}, \quad 0 < x < l, \quad t > 0$

$u_x(0, t) = -\dfrac{F_0}{K},$ $\quad t > 0$
$u(l, t) = T,$

$u(x, 0) = \dfrac{Tx}{l}, \quad 0 \le x \le l$

(b) $z = z(y, t)$
   $z_{tt} - c^2 z_{yy} = 0, \quad 0 < y < l, \quad t > 0$

$z(0, t) = a,$
$z_y(l, t) + \dfrac{k}{T} z(l, t) = b,$ $\quad t > 0$

$z(y, 0) = 0,$ $\quad 0 \le y \le l$
$z_t(y, 0) = 0,$

[*Hint for parts (a) and (b):* Try to remove the inhomogeneous boundary conditions without introducing inhomogeneous terms into the governing differential equation.]

5.5   Use the solution to part (a), Prob. 5.4, to find the value of u as $t \to \infty$ for that model. In this case, the $\lim_{t \to \infty} u(y, t)$ is called the *steady-state solution*. Is it easily identifiable in retrospect?

5.6   Find formal solutions to the following mathematical models by using the method described in Sec. 5.1.2:

(a) $z = z(y, t)$
   $z_{tt} - z_{yy} = \cos \dfrac{\pi}{l} t \sin \dfrac{\pi}{l} y, \quad 0 < y < l, \quad t > 0$
   $z(0, t) = z(l, t) = 0, \quad t > 0$
   $z(y, 0) = z_t(y, 0) = 0, \quad 0 \le y \le l$

(b) $u = u(x, t)$ and $A = $ constant
$$u_t = ku_{xx} + Ae^{-t}, \qquad 0 < x < l, \quad t > 0$$
$$u(0, t) = u_x(l, t) = 0, \qquad t > 0$$
$$u(x, 0) = U_0(x), \qquad 0 \leq x \leq l$$

(c) $z = z(y, t)$ and $A = $ constant
$$z_{tt} - c^2 z_{yy} = A, \qquad 0 < y < l, \quad t > 0$$
$$z(0, t) = z_y(l, t) = 0, \qquad t > 0$$
$$z(y, 0) = f(y),$$
$$z_t(y, 0) = 0, \qquad 0 \leq y \leq l$$

(d) $u = u(x, y)$ and $q = $ constant
$$u_{xx} + u_{yy} = q \cosh \pi y \cos \pi x, \qquad 0 < x < 1, \quad 0 < y < 1$$
$$u_x(0, y) = u_x(1, y) = 0, \qquad 0 \leq y \leq 1$$
$$u_y(x, 0) = 0,$$
$$u(x, 1) = 100x(1 - x), \qquad 0 < x < 1$$

(e) Part (b), Prob. 5.1.
(f) Part (c), Prob. 5.1.
(g) Part (d), Prob. 5.1.
(h) Part (e), Prob. 5.1.

5.7   Complete the formal solution of Example 5.2, Sec. 5.1.3, if

$$f_0(t) = 10 \sin 2\pi t$$

$$u_s(t) = 100$$

5.8   Find a formal solution to, give a physical interpretation in terms of heat conduction for, and find the $\lim_{t \to \infty} u(x, t)$ of the following mathematical model, in which $u = u(x, t)$:

$$u_t = u_{xx} + e^{-t} \sin 2\pi t, \qquad 0 < x < l, \quad t > 0$$
$$u_x(0, t) = 0,$$
$$u_x(l, t) = 100 - u(l, t), \qquad t > 0$$
$$u(x, 0) = 0, \qquad 0 \leq x \leq l$$

5.9   Find a formal solution to the following, in which $z = z(y, t)$:
$$z_{tt} + kz_t - c^2 z_{yy} = Hz + G(y, t), \qquad 0 < y < 1, \quad t > 0$$
$$z(0, t) + z_y(1, t) = 0,$$
$$z(1, t) - z_y(0, t) = 0, \qquad t > 0$$
$$z(y, 0) = 0,$$
$$z_t(y, 0) = \sin \pi y, \qquad 0 \leq y \leq 1$$

5.10   The following mathematical model arises from a fluid mechanics research problem. Find a formal solution for $\psi = \psi(r, \theta)$ in the region $R : \frac{1}{2} \leq r \leq 1, 0 \leq \theta \leq \pi/3$ (segment of an annulus):

$$\nabla^2 \psi = \psi_{rr} + \frac{1}{r} \psi_r + \frac{1}{r^2} \psi_{\theta\theta} = D, \qquad \frac{1}{2} < r < 1, \quad 0 < \theta < \frac{\pi}{3}$$

$$\psi(1, \theta) = \psi\left(\frac{1}{2}, \theta\right) = 0, \qquad 0 \leq \theta \leq \frac{\pi}{3}$$

$$\psi(r, 0) = 0,$$
$$\psi\left(r, \frac{\pi}{3}\right) = f(r), \qquad \frac{1}{2} < r < 1$$

[*Hint:* The eigenfunctions can be found by using $Ar^{i\lambda} + Br^{-i\lambda}$ and then writing the result in terms of $\sin(\lambda \ln r)$ and $\cos(\lambda \ln r)$, where λ^2 is the separation constant. The change of variables $\rho = \ln r$ may be useful.]

5.11 Given the mathematical model

$$z_{tt} = c^2(z_{yy} + z_y) + F(y, t), \qquad 0 < y < 1, \quad 0 < t$$
$$z(0, t) = 0,$$
$$z_y(1, t) = 0, \qquad 0 < t$$
$$z(y, 0) = z_0(y),$$
$$z_t(y, 0) = V_0(y), \qquad 0 \le y \le 1$$

find

(a) the eigenvalue problem required to yield eigenvalues and eigenfunctions for expansion of the solution in a series. *Do not attempt to solve the eigenvalue problem*, but explain how it can be solved.

(b) proof that the eigenvalues are nonnegative and the eigenfunctions are orthogonal.

(c) a formal solution under the assumption that an appropriate set of λ_n^2 and $Y_n(y)$ are known, as is $F(y, t)$. Give integral expressions for all coefficients.

5.12 Find the motion induced on the surface of a tank of water (Fig. 2.23P) by the periodic pulsing of the air pressure according to

(a) $p(x, t) = a \sin \omega t \sin \dfrac{\pi}{l} x$

(b) $p(x, t) = a \sin \omega(x + ct)$

Are there any values of ω and c for which unusual results occur? Plot the free surface shape $\eta(x, t)$ as a function of time, and determine the fluid velocities $u(x, y, t)$ and $v(x, y, t)$. [*Hint:* Assume that the constant a is small and that viscosity is negligible. Then you can use the small amplitude theory and assume that a velocity potential $\phi(x, y, t)$ exists. Assume, also, that the water is initially completely at rest, so $\eta(x, 0) = \eta_t(x, 0) = 0$.]

5.13 Equation (5.47) is apparently the solution to the mathematical model (5.36) under the presumption that all indicated series converge appropriately (see Sec. 3.3). What should we mean by appropriate here? Establish the conditions that must be satisfied by the functions $A = A(x, t)$ and $u_0(x)$ in this case if appropriate convergence is to be achieved.

5.14 Find a formal solution to the mathematical model of part (a), Prob. 5.1. Assume that $B > A$. Give a physical interpretation of the model and your result in terms of heat conduction. Are they valid for all time? [*Hint:* On physical grounds, the solution $u(x, t)$ must have a form $u(x, t) = Pt + U(x, t)$.]

5.15 Consider the following inhomogeneous model for heat conduction in a rod with heat sources present:

$$u_t = ku_{xx} + e^{(1-k)t} \sin x, \qquad 0 < x < \pi, \quad t > 0$$
$$u(0, t) = u(\pi, t) = 0, \qquad t > 0$$
$$u(x, 0) = 0, \qquad 0 \le x \le \pi$$

Accomplish the following:

(a) Find a formal solution by the method of Sec. 5.1.2.
(b) Let $u(x, t) = v(x, t) + U(x, t)$, where v is chosen as a particular solution of the governing equation—for example, $v(x, t) = e^{(1-k)t} \sin x$. Solve the resulting problem for $U(x, t)$.
(c) Compare the results of parts (a) and (b). In what cases would the "superposition" method of part (b) be most effective?

5.16   Find a formal solution to the following, in which $u = u(x, t)$:

$$u_t = ku_{xx} + q(x), \qquad 0 < x < 1, \quad t > 0$$
$$u(0, t) = K_1,$$
$$u_x(1, t) = K_2, \qquad t > 0$$
$$u(x, 0) = U_0(x), \qquad 0 \le x \le 1$$

[*Hint:* Let $u(x, t) = w(x) + U(x, t)$, where $w'' = -q(x)/k$.]

5.17   Use the method of Sec. 5.1 to solve Prob. 3.48. (*Hint:* Treat the terms, such as kz_t, au, and u, as inhomogeneous terms.)

5.18   In the case of pure boundary-value problems, one technique for handling inhomogeneous boundary conditions that interfere with the formulation of eigenvalue problems is to use the linearity of the model and to decompose the problem into several parts. Each part is made to have the necessary matched pair of homogeneous boundary conditions, while the sum of the parts satisfies the original problem. Use this idea in Prob. 5.2(c) to obtain two standard-form models for unknowns $U(x, y)$ and $V(x, y)$ such that

$$u(x, y) = U(x, y) + V(x, y)$$

and

$$U_x(0, y) = 0$$
$$U_x(\pi, y) = 0$$

while

$$V_y(x, 0) = 0$$
$$V(x, \pi) = 0$$

Now, obtain a solution for $u(x, y)$ by finding formal solutions for $U(x, y)$ and $V(x, y)$.

5.19   Use the idea from Prob. 5.18 and find a formal solution to the model of Prob. 5.1(e).

5.20   Solve Example 5.3, Sec. 5.1.3, by the method suggested in Prob. 5.18. Prove that the result you obtain is equivalent to that given in Example 5.3.

5.21   In the creep testing of certain alloys at low stresses and high temperatures, it appears that the concentration gradient of atomic vacancies in the crystal lattice of the alloy is related to the primary creep. A research problem to determine the vacancy concentration $C(x, t)$ in a solid as a function of time yielded the following mathematical model:

$$C_t = DC_{xx}, \qquad 0 < x < l, \quad 0 < t$$
$$C(0, t) = C_0,$$
$$C(l, t) = C^*, \qquad 0 < t$$
$$C(x, 0) = 0, \qquad 0 \le x \le l$$

in which D equals the diffusivity of vacancies (assumed independent of C) and C^* and C_0 are the fixed concentrations at the bounding planes of the solid slab of material. Find $C(x, t)$.

5.22   Each of the following sets of equations is a mathematical model of some physical process. Determine the appropriate eigenvalue problem in each case by the method of separation of variables.

(a) $z_{tt} = z_{xx} + z_{yy} - z_t, \qquad 0 < x, y < 1, \quad 0 < t$
$z_x(0, y, t) = 0,$
$z(1, y, t) = 0, \qquad 0 < y < 1, \quad 0 < t$

$$z_y(x, 0, t) = 0,$$
$$z(x, 1, t) = 0, \qquad 0 < x < 1, \quad 0 < t$$
$$z(x, y, 0) = (1 - x)(1 - y),$$
$$z_t(x, y, 0) = 0, \qquad 0 \le x, y \le 1$$
in which $z = z(x, y, t)$.

(b) $z_{tt} = z_{xx} + z_{yy} - z, \qquad 0 < x, y < l, \quad 0 < t$
$$z_x(0, y, t) = 0,$$
$$z_x(l, y, t) = 0, \qquad 0 \le y \le l, \quad 0 < t$$
$$z_y(x, 0, t) = 0,$$
$$z_y(x, l, t) = 0, \qquad 0 < x < l, \quad 0 < t$$
$$z(x, y, 0) = 0,$$
$$z_t(x, y, 0) = xy(l - y)(l - x), \qquad 0 \le x, y \le l$$
in which $z = z(x, y, t)$.

(c) $u_t = k(u_{xx} + u_{yy}), \qquad 0 < x, y < l, \quad 0 < t$
$$u_x(0, y, t) + u(0, y, t) = 0, \qquad 0 < y < l, \quad 0 < t$$
$$u(l, y, t) = 0,$$
$$u_y(x, 0, t) = 0, \qquad 0 < x < l, \quad 0 < t$$
$$u_y(x, l, t) + u(x, l, t) = 0,$$
$$u(x, y, 0) = U_0(x, y), \qquad 0 \le x, y \le l$$
in which $u = u(x, y, t)$.

(d) $u_t = k(r_0^{-2} u_{\theta\theta} + u_{zz}), \qquad 0 < \theta < 2\pi, \quad 0 < z < 1, \quad 0 < t$
$$u(0, z, t) = u(2\pi, z, t), \qquad 0 < z < 1, \quad 0 < t$$
$$u_\theta(0, z, t) = u_\theta(2\pi, z, t),$$
$$u(\theta, 0, t) = 0, \qquad 0 < \theta < 2\pi, \quad 0 < t$$
$$u(\theta, 1, t) = 0,$$
$$u(\theta, z, 0) = U_0(\theta, z), \qquad 0 \le \theta < 2\pi, \quad 0 < z < 1$$
in which r_0 is a constant, θ is an angle in radians, and $u = u(\theta, z, t)$. This is a model of heat conduction in the wall of a thin tube; draw a sketch and give a detailed physical interpretation of the model.

(e) $u_t = k\left(u_{rr} + \dfrac{1}{r}u_r + \dfrac{1}{r^2}u_{\theta\theta}\right), \qquad r_0 < r < R, \quad 0 < \theta < 2\pi, \quad 0 < t$
$$u_r(r_0, \theta, t) = 0, \qquad 0 < \theta < 2\pi, \quad 0 < t$$
$$u(R, \theta, t) = 0,$$
$$u(r, 0, t) = u(r, 2\pi, t), \qquad r_0 < r < R, \quad 0 < t$$
$$u_\theta(r, 0, t) = u_\theta(r, 2\pi, t),$$
$$u(r, \theta, 0) = U_0(r, \theta), \qquad r_0 \le r \le R, \quad 0 \le \theta < 2\pi$$
in which $r_0 < R$ and $u = u(r, \theta, t)$.

5.23   Use Green's Second Identity (5.71) to prove that the eigenfunctions for the following eigenvalue problems are orthogonal with respect to a nonnegative weight function in the prescribed region R with boundary C:

$$\nabla^2 \Omega + \lambda^2 p \Omega = 0 \quad \text{in } R, \quad p \ge 0$$

with $\Omega = \Omega(x, y)$ and

(a) $\Omega = 0$ on C.

(b) $\Omega_n = 0$ on C.

(c) $\Omega_n + k\Omega = 0$ on C for $k = k(x, y)$.

5.24   Use Green's First Identity (5.70) to prove that the eigenvalues λ^2 in Prob. 5.23 are at least nonnegative for parts (a) and (b) and to explain how the lowest value of λ^2 depends on k in part (c).

5.25   Prove that the eigenvalues λ^2 in Prob. 5.23 are real in each case.

5.26   If $l_1 = l_2$ in (5.79), $\lambda_{mn}^2 = \lambda_{nm}^2$. Use the properties of X_m and Y_n to prove that the eigenfunctions Ω_{mn} and Ω_{nm} of (5.69) are orthogonal.

5.27   For the eigenvalue problem defined by (5.69), prove that any pair of distinct eigenfunctions Ω_{mn} and $\Omega_{\mu\nu}$, whose corresponding eigenvalues λ_{mn}^2 and $\lambda_{\mu\nu}^2$ are equal, are orthogonal. Thus conclude that all eigenfunctions corresponding to the same multiple eigenvalue are orthogonal. (*Hint*: See Prob. 5.26.)

5.28   Find the solutions to the following eigenvalue problem:

$$\nabla^2\Omega + \lambda^2\Omega = 0, \qquad 0 < x < l_1, \ \ 0 < y < l_2$$
$$\Omega_x - h_1\Omega = 0 \quad \text{on } x = 0$$
$$\Omega_x + h_2\Omega = 0 \quad \text{on } x = l_1$$
$$\Omega_y - h_3\Omega = 0 \quad \text{on } y = 0$$
$$\Omega_y + h_4\Omega = 0 \quad \text{on } y = l_2$$

in which $\Omega = \Omega(x, y)$ and the constants $h_i > 0$. A careful sketch of the plots required to evaluate the eigenvalues will suffice in lieu of explicit values for them.

5.29   Determine the relations between the h_i and the smallest eigenvalue in Prob. 5.28 if $l_1 = 2l_2 = 2$. Consider both positive and negative h_i in some systematic manner.

5.30   Find the solutions to the following eigenvalue problem, in which $\Omega = \Omega(x, y)$:

$$\nabla^2\Omega + \lambda^2\Omega = 0, \qquad 0 < x < l_1, \ \ 0 < y < l_2$$
$$\Omega_x = 0 \quad \text{on } x = 0$$
$$\Omega = 0 \quad \text{on } x = l_1$$
$$\Omega_y = 0 \quad \text{on } y = 0$$
$$\Omega = 0 \quad \text{on } y = l_2$$

5.31   Find the four smallest, nonzero values of D for which Φ_n is identically zero on the boundary C of a region $R: 0 < x < 3\pi, 0 < y < 2\pi$, if

$$\nabla^2\Phi + D\Phi = 0 \quad \text{in } R, \quad \Phi = \Phi(x, y)$$

and n is the outward normal to C.

5.32   For the largest value D_4 of D in Prob. 5.31, find Φ_4, such that

$$\iint\limits_R \Phi_4^2 \, dx \, dy = 1$$

Plot the lines in R along which $\Phi_4 = 0$.

Note: Problems 5.33 and 5.34 lead to a proof of the following lemma, due to Petrovsky [2]:

Lemma: Let $X_m(x)$, $m = 1, 2, \ldots$, be a complete system of functions orthogonal and normalized with respect to the weight function $p(x)$ on $0 \le x \le l_1$. Furthermore, let there be given for every m a complete system of functions $Y_n(y)$, $n = 1, 2, \ldots$, orthogonal and normalized with respect to the weight function $\tilde{p}(y)$ on $0 \le y \le l_2$. Assume that p and $\tilde{p}$ are bounded and positive. Then the functions

$$\Omega_{mn}(x, y) = X_m(x)Y_n(y)$$

form a complete system of orthogonal and normalized functions with respect to the weight function $\bar{p} = p(x)\tilde{p}(y)$ in the rectangular region $R: 0 \leq x \leq l_1, 0 \leq y \leq l_2$.

5.33   Prove that

$$\int_0^{l_2} \int_0^{l_1} \bar{p}(x, y)\Omega_{mn}\Omega_{\mu\nu}\, dx\, dy = \begin{cases} 1 & \text{for } m = \mu, \quad n = \nu \\ 0 & \text{otherwise} \end{cases}$$

that is, the Ω_{mn} are orthonormal.

5.34   Prove that Parseval's equality

$$\int_0^{l_2} \int_0^{l_1} \bar{p}(x, y)[f(x, y)]^2\, dx\, dy = \sum_{n=1}^{\infty} \sum_{m=1}^{\infty} A_{mn}^2$$

holds for every continuous, square-integrable function $f(x, y)$, where

$$A_{mn} = \int_0^{l_1} \int_0^{l_2} \bar{p}(x, y)f(x, y)\Omega_{mn}(x, y)\, dx\, dy$$

Recall that the validity of Parseval's equation is equivalent to completeness (see Sec. 3.3.2). [*Hints:* Define

$$g_m(y) = \int_0^{l_1} p(x)f(x, y)X_m(x)\, dx$$

Then

$$\int_0^{l_2} \tilde{p}(y)g_m(y)Y_n(y)\, dy = A_{mn}$$

and application of Parseval's equality for $Y_n(y)$ produces

$$\int_0^{l_2} \tilde{p}(y)g_m^2(y)\, dy = \sum_{n=1}^{\infty} A_{mn}^2$$

Finally, expanding the right-hand side of the proposed Parseval equation, and using the Parseval equality for X_m, leads to the necessary identity.]

5.35   Derive (5.82) and (5.83).

5.36   Prove that if $f(x, y)$ is only continuous on $R + C$, then the partial sums of the series (5.81) converge to $f(x, y)$ in the mean square on R. [*Hint:* See Sec. 3.3.2 for the definition of completeness; generalize this definition to the present case. A heuristic proof follows directly from the equivalence of completeness and Parseval's equality (5.84). See Probs. 5.33 and 5.34. Recall that a continuous function on the finite region R is clearly square integrable.]

5.37   Prove that if $f(x, y)$ and its first partial derivatives are continuous and its second partial derivatives are square integrable, then the double Fourier series (5.81) converges absolutely and uniformly to $f(x, y)$ on R. [*Hint:* The integral

$$\int_0^{l_2} \int_0^{l_1} (f_{xx}^2 + 2f_{xy}^2 + f_{yy}^2)\, dx\, dy$$

is finite and thus possesses a Parseval equality in terms of the coefficients A_{mn}. Using the convergent series from this equality and the Schwarz inequality, the absolute difference of two partial sums P_{MN} and P_{RS} of the series (5.81) can be shown to approach zero, independently of x and y as M, N and R, S approach infinity. See H. F. Weinberger, *Partial Differential Equations*, Blaisdell, New York, 1965, for the complete proof.]

5.38   Plot the exponential decay factor [from (5.85)]

$$D = e^{-\lambda_{mn}^2 kt}$$

as a function of λ_{mn}^2 with $kt = 1$. Locate the points corresponding to $\lambda_{00}^2, \lambda_{01}^2 = \lambda_{10}^2, \lambda_{11}^2$, and λ_{12}^2 on the plot for $l_1 = l_2 = 1$. What is the effect of D on the higher-order terms in the expansion (5.85)?

5.39   Use the results of Table 5.1 with $l_1 = 1$, $l_2 = 2$, $k = \pi^{-2}$, and $U_0(x, y) = x^2 y^2$. Evaluate $u(x, y, 1)$ and $u(x, y, 2)$. Plot $u(x, y, 0)$, $u(x, y, 1)$, and $u(x, y, 2)$ for $x = 0.2$, 0.5, and 0.8 as functions of y to see changes with time as a function of position in the plate. (*Hint:* This problem should be carried out on a computer. Set up your computer program to cut off evaluation of higher-numbered terms at some predetermined level where they are no longer significant. Can the lead term be used as a size reference here?)

5.40   Find $u = u(x, y, t)$, and give a physical interpretation of the following model:

$$u_t = \nabla^2 u, \quad 0 < x < \pi, \quad 0 < y < 2\pi, \quad 0 < t$$

$$\begin{aligned} u(0, y, t) &= 0, \\ u_x(\pi, y, t) &= 0, \end{aligned} \quad 0 < y < 2\pi, \quad 0 < t$$

$$\begin{aligned} u(x, 0, t) &= 0, \\ u_y(x, 2\pi, t) &= 0, \end{aligned} \quad 0 \le x \le \pi, \quad 0 < t$$

$$u(x, y, 0) = 10(x - \pi)(y - 2\pi), \quad 0 \le x \le \pi, \ 0 \le y \le 2\pi$$

5.41   Obtain a formal solution to the model of Prob. 5.22(c).

5.42   Let $l_1 = l_2 = l$ in Table 5.1; list the eigenfunctions Ω_{mn} corresponding to the eigenvalues $25\pi^2/l^2$ and $100\pi^2/l^2$.

5.43   Find a formal solution to the following mathematical model of heat conduction in an electrically-heated plate:

$$u_t = k\nabla^2 u + q(x, y), \quad 0 < x < 1, \quad 0 < y < 1, \quad 0 < t$$

$u \equiv 0$ on the boundaries of the region $0 < x, y < 1$

$$u(x, y, 0) = U_0(x, y), \quad 0 \le x, y \le 1$$

5.44   Find $u = u(x, y, t)$ in Prob. 5.43 for

(a) $q(x, y) = 100 \sin \pi x \sin 5\pi y$
$U_0(x, y) = 50 \sin 4\pi x \sin \sqrt{5}\pi y$

(b) $q(x, y) = Ae^{kt}$
$U_0(x, y) = 100$

Note: The concepts of a two-dimensional eigenvalue problem are directly extensible to three dimensions. Accordingly, consider a bare, homogeneous, thermal nuclear reactor. When such a reactor is at precisely the critical state, just as many neutrons are produced by fission as are lost by absorption within the reactor and leakage through the boundaries. At the critical state, the thermal neutron flux ϕ is described by

$$\nabla^2 \phi(x, y, z) + B_m^2 \phi(x, y, z) = 0$$

where B_m is the so-called "material buckling" and is dependent only on the material and composition of the reactor medium.

In the theory of reactor design it is shown that for a critical system, the flux ϕ is also given by a solution to

$$\nabla^2 \phi + B_g^2 \phi = 0$$

subject to the condition that the thermal flux ϕ shall go to zero at the effective boundaries of the reactor (see, e.g., Glasstone and Edlund, *Nuclear Reactor Theory*, Van Nostrand, New York, 1952). Here B_g^2 is the "geometric buckling" and is the lowest eigenvalue of the equation and its boundary conditions; B_g depends only on the geometry of the reactor.

5.45 For a reactor built in the shape of a rectangular parallelepiped with sides of lengths a, b, and c, show how B_g is related to the geometry. Determine the functional form of ϕ for this B_g.

5.46 Suppose that $B_m^2 = 37.2 \times 10^{-4}\,\text{cm}^{-2}$ (a uranium-beryllium system). Find the size of a critical cubical reactor made of this material.

5.47 Describe the lines along which the eigenfunctions (5.95) are identically zero. Plot these lines for the eigenfunctions corresponding to $\lambda_{mn}^2 = 2\pi^2$, $5\pi^2$, and $13\pi^2$.

5.48 Find a formal solution to Prob. 5.22(a).

5.49 Find a formal solution and give a physical interpretation of Prob. 5.22(b).

5.50 Establish the necessary conditions to be imposed on $z_0(x, y)$ and $V_0(x, y)$ in (5.91) if the solution to the problem (5.89) to (5.91) [given by (5.97) to (5.99)] is to be twice continuously differentiable in $0 < x, y < 1$.

5.51 The kinetic energy of vibration of a rectangular membrane is

$$\text{KE} = \tfrac{1}{2}\rho \int_0^{l_2} \int_0^{l_1} z_t^2 \, dx \, dy$$

while the potential energy of position is given by

$$\text{PE} = \tfrac{1}{2}T \int_0^{l_2} \int_0^{l_1} (z_x^2 + z_y^2) \, dx \, dy$$

Find the kinetic and potential energies of the vibrations described by (5.97). [*Hint*: Convert the solution to the second form in (5.96), and express your result in terms of

$$\phi_{mn} = A_{mn} \cos (c\lambda_{mn}t + \varepsilon_{mn}).]$$

5.52 Using the results of Prob. 5.51, show that the total energy of the membrane is constant and given by

$$E = \tfrac{1}{8}\rho l_1 l_2 c^2 \sum_{m=1}^{\infty} \sum_{n=1}^{\infty} \lambda_{mn}^2 A_{mn}^2$$

Show then that the total energy is equal simply to the sum of the total energies of each of the individual eigenvibrations. Do not forget that $T/\rho = c^2$.

5.53 A uniform, oscillating pressure with frequency $f = 50$ Hz is applied to the upper surface of the membrane analyzed in Sec. 5.2.2. What is the minimum tension T required to ensure that the fundamental frequency exceeds the forcing frequency? Let $\rho = 0.005$, $l_1 = l_2 = 2$.

5.54 For the membrane of Prob. 5.53, what is the frequency required for another oscillating pressure to excite the second overtone by resonant interaction? Let $T = 50$.

5.55 Sketch the nodal lines of the linear sum of *all* the eigenfunctions Ω_{mn} corresponding to the eigenvalue

(a) $13\pi^2$ (b) $17\pi^2$

in the system (5.95).

5.56   Suppose that the eigenvalue problem for a nonuniform beam is

$$Y'''' - \lambda^4 p(y)Y = 0$$

$$Y(0) = Y''(0) = Y(l) = Y''(l) = 0$$

(a) Prove that all the eigenvalues are positive if $p(y) \geq 0$, but $p(y) \not\equiv 0$.

(b) Prove that eigenfunctions corresponding to distinct eigenvalues are orthogonal if they both exist and $p(y) \not\equiv 0$. (*Hint:* Construct the equivalent of Green's identities.)

5.57   Carry out parts (a) and (b) of Prob. 5.56 for the following eigenvalue problem for a beam with variable density and flexural rigidity:

$$[r(y)Y''(y)]'' + \lambda^2 \rho(y)Y(y) = 0$$

$$Y(0) = Y''(0) = Y(l) = Y''(l) = 0$$

5.58   Obtain a formal solution for the vibrations of the cantilevered beam in Table 5.2. A careful sketch of the plots required to evaluate the eigenvalues will suffice in lieu of explicit values for them. Derive an asymptotic expression for the larger eigenvalues.

5.59   Solve Prob. 5.58 by using a computer to find the eigenvalues and determine the series expansion coefficients for the case when

$$z(y, 0) = \frac{\delta y}{l}$$

$$z_t(y, 0) = 0$$

5.60   Derive an appropriate mathematical model for the beam shown in Fig. 5.60P. Assume that the beam is uniform, that the necessary dimensions are given, and that z_0 and V_0 are given functions of y. Note that $z(l, t) = z_t(l, t) = 0, 0 \leq t$.

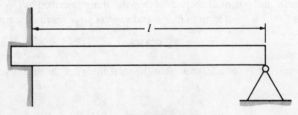

FIGURE 5.60P

5.61   For the model of Prob. 5.60, find an equation for the eigenvalues of the eigenvalue problem derived from the model. Then determine the eigenvalues accurately. What are the frequencies of vibration of the eigenvibrations z_n?

5.62   Consider a doubly cantilevered beam (both ends clamped in place).
(a) Derive an appropriate mathematical model for arbitrary initial conditions.

(b) Find an equation for the eigenvalues of the eigenvalue problem derived from the preceding model.

(c) Find the eigenvalues (within some accuracy tolerance) and eigenfunctions for the above.

(d) Complete a formal solution to the model of part (a).

5.63   If Probs. 5.58 (or 5.59) and 5.62 are worked, compare the distribution of natural frequencies of vibration of the two systems. Did clamping the free end of the cantilevered beam increase the fundamental frequency?

5.64   Suppose that we have a tapered beam such that

$$EI = r(y)$$

$$\rho = p(y)$$

(a) Derive a mathematical model for such a beam when it is simply supported at each end.

(b) Find an eigenvalue problem for this situation; see Prob. 5.57.

5.65   Find a formal solution $z(y, t)$ for the following mathematical model of a simply supported beam under the influence of gravity:

$$z_{tt} + c^2 z_{yyyy} = -g, \qquad 0 < y < 1, \quad 0 < t$$
$$z(0, t) = z(1, t) = 0,$$
$$z_{yy}(0, t) = z_{yy}(1, t) = 0, \qquad 0 < t$$
$$z(y, 0) = 0,$$
$$z_t(y, 0) = \sin \pi x, \qquad 0 \leq y \leq 1$$

5.66   For the model of Prob. 5.65, find the shape of the beam due to the gravity influence only. Could this time-independent solution be used to remove the inhomogeneous term in that model? Solve Prob. 5.65 using this idea as a start.

5.67   Find $z(y, t)$ if

$$z_{tt} + c^2 z_{yyyy} = \sin \pi t \cos \pi y, \qquad 0 < y < 1, \quad 0 < t$$
$$z(0, t) = z(1, t) = 0,$$
$$z_{yy}(0, t) = z_{yy}(1, t) = 0, \qquad 0 < t$$
$$z(y, 0) = 0,$$
$$z_t(y, 0) = 0, \qquad 0 \leq y \leq 1$$

Give a physical interpretation of this model.

5.68   Consider a cantilevered, uniform beam. Derive a mathematical model for such a beam if an oscillating vertical force F_v is applied to the free end, where

$$F_v = F \cos \omega t$$

5.69   Find $z(y, t)$ for the model of Prob. 5.68.

5.70   If ω is given in Prob. 5.68, what minimum value of EI/ρ is required to prevent resonant interaction between the oscillating force F_v and the beam itself?

5.71   Find $z(y, t)$ for the simply supported beam in Table 5.2 if

$$z_t(y, 0) = 0$$

$$z(y, 0) = \sin \left(\frac{\pi y}{l} \right)$$

$$z(0, t) = \sin \omega t$$

while all the other conditions and the governing equation are unchanged.

5.72   The complete eigenfunction-expansion solution to (5.111) through (5.113) is given by (5.124) to (5.126). What necessary conditions must $z_0(y)$ and $V_0(y)$ satisfy if the solution $z(y, t)$ is to be four times continuously differentiable with respect to y and twice continuously differentiable with respect to t? How fast do the coefficients A_{0n} and A_{1n} decay under these circumstances—for example, like $1/n^4$? (*Hint:* Check the discussions of Chap. 3.)

CHAPTER 6

THE QUALITATIVE QUESTIONS

6.1 INTRODUCTION

The logical progression in predicting the behavior of a physical system mathematically begins with a concise description of the system and continues with the construction of a mathematical model. Next, the testing of this mathematical model should follow to ensure that there exists one and only one solution that varies continuously with changes in prescribed auxiliary data or equation coefficients. In the interest of developing our power to solve partial differential equations, we have generally ignored these qualitative questions of existence, uniqueness, and continuity, being satisfied to concentrate on the final quantitative step of solving and interpreting the mathematical models and their solutions. In two particular cases, we answered some of the qualitative questions. Immediately following solution of our first model by separation of variables in Sec. 3.2, it was shown that the solution (3.36) existed as a uniformly convergent infinite series within the problem domain and was continuous with respect to changes in the initial data. Then, in Example 5.1, Sec. 5.1.3, it was formally shown that the series solution satisfied the differential equation.

In Chaps. 3 through 5 methods for obtaining the apparent solutions to linear mathematical models solvable by separation of variables and eigenfunction expansions were demonstrated. Now let us turn back to the qualitative questions and establish the adequacy of our linear models. Although the very general Cauchy problem will be examined because it yields a key result, the main focus in this chapter is divided between (a) demonstration of uniqueness and continuity of solutions in a general manner and without explicit knowledge of the solutions and (b) verification that series solutions are convergent and do indeed satisfy the conditions of the model, thus establishing existence *a posteriori*. Only continuous, bounded solutions and models with at least continuous and bounded data are treated. We restrict ourselves to these rather limited conditions to gain the essence of the methods without the complications arising from discontinuities. The results obtained are particularly important, because they establish rigorously the conditions for well-posed models derived in Chap. 2 for a range of physical systems. When we turn in Chap. 10 to numerical solution of models that are not solvable analytically or that are nonlinear, the ground rules for the simple linear models become an essential, but unfortunately only heuristic, guide to establishing well-posed models.

Establishing the adequacy of mathematical models is one of the most interesting and challenging subjects of applied mathematics. Over the years a number of sophisticated techniques have been derived, particularly to prove the existence in general domains of solutions to general equations. The history of the development of a proper existence proof for the Dirichlet problem for the Laplace equation outlined by Kellogg [1] illustrates the difficulties to be encountered. Green inferred the possibility of solving the Dirichlet problem in 1828, but this was not a proof. Gauss put forth another argument in 1840, but he did not properly restrict the region of the problem. Lord Kelvin in 1847 and Dirichlet in the 1850s advanced techniques based on minimization of an integral (a functional of the variational calculus), but Weierstrauss showed in 1870 that the result was not reliable. Not until 1899 did Hilbert sort out the proper conditions for a reliable result. Indeed, only in 1887 did Poincaré establish by his *méthode de balayage* a broad existence theorem, although Schwarz solved the problem in two dimensions and in 1870 Neumann gave a true existence theorem for convex bounding surfaces by his *method of the arithmetic mean*.

We illustrate here some general methods of demonstrating the uniqueness and continuity of solutions but are satisfied to prove existence *a posteriori* from analysis of specific solutions. Kellogg [1], Petrovsky [2], and Courant and Hilbert [3] provide deeper penetrations into this fascinating subject.

6.2   THE CAUCHY PROBLEM

A *Cauchy Problem* is an initial-value problem for ordinary or partial differential equations or sets of equations. A Cauchy problem can be stated very generally [2; 3, II]; but for an unknown function $z(y, t)$ and a single, second-order partial differential equation, the Cauchy problem is

$$F(y, t, z, z_y, z_t, z_{yt}, z_{yy}, z_{tt}) = 0$$
$$z(y, 0) = z_0(y) \tag{6.1}$$
$$z_t(y, 0) = V_0(y)$$

for $-\infty < y < \infty, 0 \le t$.

A classic result of the existence theory of differential equations is the Cauchy-Kowalewsky theorem that applies to the general Cauchy problem [4] and to (6.1), which is a very restricted, special case. If (6.1) can be brought to the form

$$z_{tt} = \Phi(y, t, p, q, r, s)$$

$$z(y, 0) = z_0(y) \qquad (6.2)$$

$$z_t(y, 0) = V_0(y)$$

and the functions Φ, z_0, and V_0 are analytic* in a neighborhood of a point $(y_0, 0, z_0, p_0, q_0, r_0, s_0)$, the Cauchy–Kowalewsky Theorem states that there exists a unique analytic solution $z(y, t)$ in some neighborhood of $(y_0, 0)$. Here $p = z_y$, $q = z_t$, $r = z_{yy}$, $s = z_{yt}$, $p_0 = z_{0y}$, $q_0 = V_0$, $r_0 = p_{0y}$, and $s_0 = V_{0y}$. Proof of the theorem is straightforward.

First, the presumed analytic solution is obtained as a power series expansion (the Taylor's series) about $(y_0, 0)$. The function value and each derivative of the series are obtained from the initial data, the differential equation, and then successive differentiation of the differential equation. Second, the power series is shown to be convergent and nontrivial in some neighborhood of $(y_0, 0)$. This step is accomplished by *majorizing*† the series—that is, showing that each term of the series is less in absolute value than the corresponding term of an absolutely convergent series. The Cauchy–Kowalewsky theorem can be proved for very general nonlinear systems of N partial differential equations in n independent variables. It is a powerful result but suffers two key weaknesses from our point of view.

First, the power series solution may be valid only in a small neighborhood—that is, locally—whereas we require solutions over complete regions. Second, certain Cauchy problems are not well posed even though the existence and uniqueness of a solution are guaranteed. This point is of great interest.

The simplest Cauchy problem of form (6.2) is the linear problem

$$z_{tt} + \alpha z_{yy} = 0, \qquad -\infty < y < \infty, \quad 0 < t$$

$$z(y, 0) = z_0(y), \qquad \qquad \qquad (6.3)$$

$$z_t(y, 0) = V_0(y), \qquad -\infty < y < \infty$$

where $\alpha = 1$ or -1. For $\alpha = -1$, we recognize (6.3) as the wave equation model of an infinitely long string, and, as such, (6.3) seems a natural model. For $\alpha = 1$, (6.3) becomes a Cauchy problem for Laplace's equation $z_{tt} + z_{yy} = 0$. The existence and uniqueness of a solution are guaranteed for analytic z_0 and V_0!

In 1917 Hadamard [4] first gave the following example. Suppose that we have the almost homogeneous linear problem

$$z_{tt} + z_{yy} = 0$$

$$z(y, 0) = 0 \qquad \qquad (6.4)$$

$$z_t(y, 0) = n^{-\sigma} \sin ny$$

---

* Representable as a power series, convergent in a finite region about a point (see Appendix 2).

† See Sec. 3.2 or 6.4.

with n being a very large positive integer and $\sigma > 0$. The solution of this Cauchy problem is

$$z(y, t) = n^{-\sigma - 1} \sin ny \sinh nt \tag{6.5}$$

Now, $|z_t(y, 0)|$ can be made as small as desired by increasing n so that the initial values differ from zero by an arbitrarily small amount. However, for $t > 0$, (6.5) takes on arbitrarily large values for arbitrarily small t if n is large enough, because $\sinh nt = O(e^{n|t|})$.

For $\alpha = 1$, adding (6.3) to (6.4) gives another linear Cauchy problem with initial conditions differing by an arbitrarily small amount from those of (6.3). By linear superposition, the solution to the new problem differs by an arbitrarily large amount from that of (6.3). Therefore a small change in the data of the Cauchy problem for the Laplace equation induces a large change in the solution; the Cauchy problem for the Laplace equation is not well posed, failing the continuity test!

Our analyses in Chap. 2 showed that in a well-posed model for Laplace's equation, a single boundary condition, specified over a closed region, was appropriate. Kellogg [1], for example, employs integral equation theory to demonstrate the existence of a solution to the well-posed model. We shall prove the uniqueness and continuity of such a solution just below.

6.3   UNIQUENESS AND CONTINUITY OF SOLUTIONS

It is generally possible to suppose that a solution exists for linear models, and then to prove that the solution is unique and varies continuously with respect to the prescribed data. If a convergent Fourier series solution is subsequently found and is shown to satisfy all the conditions of the model, it is clear that a unique, continuous solution exists to the well-posed model.

The objective of this section is to demonstrate, by a series of examples, three basic techniques for proving the uniqueness and the continuity of the solutions to a range of linear mathematical models. The form of proof is invariable. For uniqueness, two nonidentical solutions (e.g., u_1 and u_2), to the model are supposed to exist, to satisfy the same auxiliary conditions, but to differ somewhere within the model domain. Their difference $U = u_2 - u_1$, which satisfies an entirely homogeneous model, is shown to be identically zero—that is, $u_2 \equiv u_1$. From this contradiction, then, two nonidentical solutions cannot exist. For continuity, two solutions u_1 and u_2 to models with slightly different prescribed data are supposed to exist. Their difference $U = u_2 - u_1$ is then shown to be of the same order as the differences between the data; that is, small differences in the data make small changes in the solutions.

The three methods to be considered are an integral method, an energy principle, and maximum-minimum principles. The integral method is based on a general integral relation valid for any sufficiently differentiable function. The energy method uses another integral relation derived from the total energy of the physical system being modeled. Finally, the maximum-minimum principles are derived from consideration of the partial differential equations of particular models.

6.3.1   An Integral Method

In three dimensions, the analysis is based on Gauss' theorem

$$\iint_{\bar{S}} v_n \, dS = \iiint_V \operatorname{div} \boldsymbol{v} \, dV \tag{6.6}$$

and the Green's identity

$$\iint_{\bar{S}} f \frac{\partial g}{\partial n} S = \iiint_V f \, \nabla^2 g \, dV + \iiint_V (\nabla f \cdot \nabla g) \, dV \tag{6.7}$$

derived from (6.6) (see Sec. A.1.4). Here $\boldsymbol{v}$ is at least a continuous vector function of (x, y, z); that is, $\boldsymbol{v} \in C$ in $V + \bar{S}$. The Green's identity (6.7) is valid when f and g are continuous on $V + \bar{S}$ and twice continuously differentiable in V; that is $(f, g) \in C^2$ in V. With regard to $V + \bar{S}$, V is a bounded, simply connected volume, the closed surface $\bar{S}$ forms the complete boundary of V, and $\boldsymbol{n}$ is the outward unit normal vector on $\bar{S}$. It is also necessary that $\bar{S}$ be piecewise smooth;* the normal $\boldsymbol{n}$ then varies continuously over any smooth portion of $\bar{S}$ and is uniquely defined everywhere but on the curves marking the edges of smooth portions.

EXAMPLE 6.1   *The Dirichlet Model for Poisson's Equation.* Let us try to prove that the solution $u \in C^2$ in V and satisfying the Dirichlet model:

$$\nabla^2 u = F \quad \text{in } V \tag{6.8a}$$

$$u = G \quad \text{on } \bar{S} \tag{6.8b}$$

is unique when F and $G \in C$ on $V + \bar{S}$ and $\bar{S}$, respectively. Physically, we can think here of steady-state heat conduction in a solid with the temperature $u = G(x, y, z)$ prescribed on $\bar{S}$ and $F(x, y, z)$ representing heat sources in V of strength $-KF$ per unit volume (see Sec. 2.2.1).

We postulate that two solutions u_1 and u_2 to (6.8) exist, are nonidentical in V, and $\in C^2$ in V. Let $U = u_2 - u_1$. Then U satisfies

$$\nabla^2 U = 0 \quad \text{in } V$$
$$U = 0 \quad \text{on } \bar{S} \tag{6.9}$$

As $U \in C^2$ in V and clearly $\in C$ on $\bar{S}$, we may use the Green's identity (6.7). In (6.7),

$$\nabla f \cdot \nabla g = (f_x \boldsymbol{i} + f_y \boldsymbol{j} + f_z \boldsymbol{k}) \cdot (g_x \boldsymbol{i} + g_y \boldsymbol{j} + g_z \boldsymbol{k}) = f_x g_x + f_y g_x + f_z g_z$$

Let $f = g = U$; from (6.7),

$$\iint_{\bar{S}} U \frac{\partial U}{\partial n} \, dS = \iiint_V U \, \nabla^2 U \, dV + \iiint_V \left[\left(\frac{\partial U}{\partial x}\right)^2 + \left(\frac{\partial U}{\partial y}\right)^2 + \left(\frac{\partial U}{\partial z}\right)^2 \right] dV \tag{6.10}$$

---

* If $\bar{S}$ is defined in space by the continuous implicit relation $\Phi(x, y, z)$, $\bar{S}$ is smooth wherever Φ has continuous derivatives with respect to x, y, and z. The piecewise-smooth surface is a patchwork of a finite number of smooth portions.

But $U \equiv 0$ on $\bar{S}$ while $\nabla^2 U \equiv 0$ in V; thus (6.10) becomes

$$\iiint_V \left[\left(\frac{\partial U}{\partial x} \right)^2 + \left(\frac{\partial U}{\partial y} \right)^2 + \left(\frac{\partial U}{\partial z} \right)^2 \right] dV = 0 \tag{6.11}$$

The term in brackets is always positive unless the first derivatives of U vanish. Unless they vanish everywhere in V, the value of the integral (6.11) will not be zero. Therefore

$$\frac{\partial U}{\partial x} = \frac{\partial U}{\partial y} = \frac{\partial U}{\partial z} = 0$$

and in V, U is a constant that equals zero on $\bar{S}$. Accordingly, $U \equiv 0$ everywhere, meaning that $u_1 \equiv u_2$ in contradiction to the hypothesis that there are two non-identical solutions. The Dirichlet model (6.8) has a unique solution.

EXAMPLE 6.2 *The Neumann Model for Poisson's Equation.* Show that the solution $u \in C^2$ in $V, \in C^1$ on $\bar{S}$, and satisfying the Neumann model

$$\nabla^2 u = F \quad \text{in } V \tag{6.12a}$$

$$\frac{\partial u}{\partial n} = G \quad \text{on } \bar{S} \tag{6.12b}$$

is unique when $(F, G) \in C$ and $\boldsymbol{n}$ is uniquely defined on $\bar{S}$—for example, $\bar{S}$ is smooth.

First, a solution to (6.12) does not exist in general. Why? Because $u \in C^2$ in V, (6.6) must hold for any $\boldsymbol{v} = \nabla u$. As $v_n = \boldsymbol{v} \cdot \boldsymbol{n}$ and div $\nabla u = \nabla^2 u$, (6.6) becomes

$$\iint_{\bar{S}} \frac{\partial u}{\partial n} \, dS = \iiint_V \nabla^2 u \tag{6.13}$$

which is a condition that must be satisfied by a solution to (6.12); (6.13) is called the *Neumann Compatibility Condition.* If

$$\iint_{\bar{S}} G \, dS \neq \iiint_V F \, dV$$

no solution can exist to the Neumann model. If $\nabla^2 u = 0$, for example,

$$\iint_{\bar{S}} \frac{\partial u}{\partial n} \, dS = 0$$

is required.

If (6.12) is a model for steady-state heat conduction in a solid, (6.12b) represents a prescription of the flux $f_n = -K \, \partial u / \partial n$ through each portion of the bounding surface. The total flux through $\bar{S}$ is, for constant K,

$$-K \iint_{\bar{S}} \frac{\partial u}{\partial n} \, dS = -K \iint_{\bar{S}} G \, dS$$

On the other hand, the heat generated in V by the sources of strength $-KF$ is

$$-K \int \int \int_V F \, dV$$

In a steady state, the heat flux through the boundary must just balance the heat generated in the interior; that is,

$$\int \int_{\bar{S}} \frac{\partial u}{\partial n} \, dS = \int \int_{\bar{S}} G \, dS = \int \int \int_V F \, dV = \int \int \int_V \nabla^2 u \, dV$$

But this is precisely the compatibility condition (6.13).

The uniqueness proof for (6.12) is brief. Let $U = u_2 - u_1$, where u_2 and u_1 are the presumed nonidentical solutions to (6.12). Then U satisfies

$$\nabla^2 U = 0 \quad \text{in } V$$

$$\frac{\partial U}{\partial n} = 0 \quad \text{on } \bar{S} \tag{6.14}$$

Note that any constant is a solution to (6.14). Again (6.10) holds for U, and, in view of (6.14), we have

$$\int \int \int_V \left[\left(\frac{\partial U}{\partial x}\right)^2 + \left(\frac{\partial U}{\partial y}\right)^2 + \left(\frac{\partial U}{\partial z}\right)^2 \right] dV = 0$$

[see (6.11)]. Thus U is a constant in V. As a constant is a solution of (6.14), it is possible for $u_2 = u_1 +$ constant. Therefore the *solution to the Neumann model* (6.12) *is unique only up to an additive arbitrary constant.* This is reasonable physically for the heat conduction model, since an arbitrary uniform change in temperature does not alter the temperature gradients or heat fluxes in $V + \bar{S}$.

EXAMPLE 6.3   *The Heat Equation.* Consider heat conduction in a solid V, with bounding surface $\bar{S}$, thermal conductivity K, density ρ, and specific heat c, according to the model

$$u_t = k \nabla^2 u + F \quad \text{in } V, \quad t > 0 \tag{6.15a}$$

$$u = G \quad \text{on } \bar{S}, \quad t \geq 0 \tag{6.15b}$$

$$u = u_0 \quad \text{in } V \text{ at } t = 0 \tag{6.15c}$$

where $F(x, y, z, t)$, $G(x, y, z, t)$, and $u_0(x, y, z) \in C$. Here K, ρ, and c (and $k = K/\rho c$) are taken to be constant and positive.

Assume that a solution u exists for (6.15) and that u is C^2 with respect to (x, y, z) and C^1 with respect to t in V. Let us show that this solution is unique. To begin, let $U = u_2 - u_1$ as before, where u_1 and u_2 are two nonidentical solutions to (6.15). Clearly, U satisfies

$$U_t = k \nabla^2 U \quad \text{in } V, \quad t > 0 \tag{6.16a}$$

$$U = 0 \quad \text{on } \bar{S}, \quad t \geq 0 \tag{6.16b}$$

$$U = 0 \quad \text{in } V \text{ at } t = 0 \tag{6.16c}$$

In order to make use of Green's identity (6.7), we consider the functional (Q is a function of the function U; see Chap. 7)

$$Q(t) = \rho^2 c^2 \int \int \int_V U^2 \, dV \geq 0 \tag{6.17}$$

which is at least C^1 with respect to t and represents the square of the internal energy in the solid V. Differentiating (6.17) with respect to t and using (6.16a) produce

$$\frac{Q'(t)}{\rho^2 c^2} = \int \int \int_V 2UU_t \, dV = 2k \int \int \int_V U \nabla^2 U \, dV$$

According to (6.7) with $f = g = U$ and to (6.16b),

$$\int \int \int_V U \nabla^2 U \, dV = - \int \int \int_V \left[\left(\frac{\partial U}{\partial x} \right)^2 + \left(\frac{\partial U}{\partial y} \right)^2 + \left(\frac{\partial U}{\partial z} \right)^2 \right] dV$$

This gives

$$\frac{Q'(t)}{\rho^2 c^2} = -2k \int \int \int_V \left[\left(\frac{\partial U}{\partial x} \right)^2 + \left(\frac{\partial U}{\partial y} \right)^2 + \left(\frac{\partial U}{\partial z} \right)^2 \right] dV \leq 0 \tag{6.18}$$

for $0 < t$.

Now $Q(0) = 0$ according to (6.17) and (6.16c); hence, according to (6.18), we find

$$Q(t) = \int_0^t Q'(\tau) \, d\tau + Q(0) = \int_0^t Q'(\tau) \, d\tau \leq 0$$

By definition (6.17), $Q(t) \geq 0$. This conflict is resolved only if $Q(t) \equiv 0$. As $U^2 \geq 0$ in (6.17), U must be zero also. Thus $u_2 \equiv u_1$ and the solution u to (6.15) is unique.

Petrovsky [2] and Sagan [5] use a method similar to that in Example 6.3 to demonstrate the uniqueness and continuity of the solution to the mathematical model for the vibrations of a membrane. They reduce and transform the functional

$$I(t) = \int_0^T \int \int_R z_t(z_{tt} - \nabla^2 z) \, dA \, dt$$

where $z_{tt} = \nabla^2 z$ on R, $0 \leq t \leq T$, for R in the (x, y) plane. However, the analysis leads to consideration of the same results obtained by the energy analysis described just below; hence their procedure is not repeated here.

No proofs of continuity have been presented in this section on integral methods. Continuity follows as a trivial extension of the uniqueness proofs based on the maximum-minimum principles proved in Sec. 6.3.3 for Dirichlet models. The extension of the integral methods to continuity is more difficult and is not attempted here (see Petrovsky [2]).

6.3.2   An Energy Method

Energy methods are based on consideration of the behavior of the total energy of a physical system as a function of time. As an example, let us find an expression for the total energy $E(t)$ of a membrane undergoing small transverse vibrations. If the edge of the membrane is fixed or only laterally restrained, the total energy is composed of the sum of the kinetic and potential energies over the membrane region R in the x–y plane.

The kinetic energy of a small element of membrane (see Fig. 2.2 and Prob. 5.51) is

$$\Delta KE = \tfrac{1}{2} \text{mass} \cdot (\text{velocity})^2 = \tfrac{1}{2} \rho \, dA \, (z_t)^2$$

where $dA = dx \, dy$. The total kinetic energy is

$$KE = \frac{1}{2} \iint\limits_{R} \rho (z_t)^2 \, dA \tag{6.19}$$

where $\rho(x, y)$ is the density and $z(x, y, t)$ is the transverse displacement of the membrane.

The potential energy of position of the membrane is equal to the work done in moving the membrane from its zero-displacement state to some other state at time t. The work done on an element $dx \, dy$ of membrane is the tension force T times the change in length of lines in the membrane element parallel to each of the coordinate axes x and y. If the zero-displacement lengths of these lines are the differential lengths dx and dy, their lengths at time t are

$$[(dx)^2 + (dz)^2]^{1/2}_{y = \text{constant}} \quad \text{and} \quad [(dy)^2 + (dz)^2]^{1/2}_{x = \text{constant}}$$

(see Fig. 6.1). To the first order, T is constant (Sec. 2.2.2). Consequently, the work done on an element is

$$\begin{aligned}
dW &= T\{[(dx)^2 + (dz)^2]^{1/2} - dx\} \, dy \\
&\quad + T\{[(dy)^2 + (dz)^2]^{1/2} - dy\} \, dx \\
&= T \, dx \, dy \{[1 + (z_x)^2]^{1/2} - 1\} \\
&\quad + T \, dx \, dy \{[1 + (z_y)^2]^{1/2} - 1\}
\end{aligned} \tag{6.20}$$

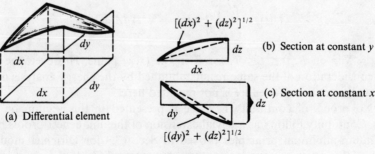

(a) Differential element

(b) Section at constant y

(c) Section at constant x

FIGURE 6.1

But under the small amplitude assumption (Sec. 2.2.2),

$$[1 + (z_x)^2]^{1/2} - 1 = 1 + \tfrac{1}{2}(z_x)^2 + O[(z_x)^3]$$
$$[1 + (z_y)^2]^{1/2} - 1 = 1 + \tfrac{1}{2}(z_y)^2 + O[(z_y)^3]$$

and the derivatives are small compared to unity. Neglecting higher terms and introducing these results in (6.20) yield

$$dW = \{\tfrac{1}{2}T(z_x)^2 + \tfrac{1}{2}T(z_y)^2\}\, dx\, dy$$

Thus

$$PE = \frac{1}{2}\int\int_R T\{(z_x)^2 + (z_y)^2\}\, dA \tag{6.21}$$

and the total energy is, for $T > 0$ and $\rho > 0$,

$$E(t) = KE + PE = \frac{1}{2}\int\int_R [T\{(z_x)^2 + (z_y)^2\} + \rho(z_t)^2]\, dA \geq 0 \tag{6.22}$$

As all the terms in this integral are positive, $E(t) \equiv 0$ means that all the first derivatives of z are zero. Let's use these results in a uniqueness proof.

EXAMPLE 6.4   *The Vibration of a Membrane.* Consider the model of the small transverse vibrations of a membrane

$$z_{tt} = \frac{T}{\rho}\nabla^2 z + F \quad \text{in } R, \quad t > 0 \tag{6.23a}$$

$$z = G \quad \text{on } B, \quad t > 0 \tag{6.23b}$$

$$\begin{aligned} z &= z_0 \\ z_t &= V_0 \end{aligned} \quad \text{at } t = 0 \text{ in } R + B \tag{6.23c}$$

where R is a finite region in (x, y) completely bounded by the piecewise-smooth, closed curve B. We assume that F, G, z_0, and $V_0 \in C$ on $R + B$ or B as appropriate. The solution $z \in C^2$ in R and $\in C$ on B with respect to x and y and $z \in C^1$ in $R + B$ with respect to t.

To prove that z is a unique solution to (6.23), we assume that two nonidentical solutions z_1 and z_2 exist. Their difference $Z = z_2 - z_1$ satisfies

$$Z_{tt} = \frac{T}{\rho}\nabla^2 Z \quad \text{in } R, \quad t > 0$$

$$Z \equiv 0 \quad \text{on } B, \quad t > 0 \tag{6.24}$$

$$\begin{aligned} Z &\equiv 0, \\ Z_t &\equiv 0, \end{aligned} \quad \text{in } R + B, \quad t \overset{\cdot}{=} 0$$

From (6.22), the energy $E(t)$ of the system (6.24) is zero at $t = 0$; that is, $E(0) = 0$. What happens for $t > 0$? First,

$$E'(t) = \int\int_R (T\{Z_x Z_{xt} + Z_y Z_{yt}\} + \rho Z_t Z_{tt})\, dA \tag{6.25}$$

Now, treating the integrals involving T as iterated integrals, we can write

$$\int\int_R Z_x Z_{xt}\, dA = \int_{y_{B1}}^{y_{B2}}\left\{\int_{x_1(y)}^{x_2(y)} Z_x Z_{xt}\, dx\right\} dy$$

and

$$\iint_R Z_y Z_{yt} \, dA = \int_{x_{B1}}^{x_{B2}} \left\{ \int_{y_1(x)}^{y_2(x)} Z_y Z_{yt} \, dy \right\} dx$$

(see Fig. 6.2). Each inner integral can be integrated by parts. For example,

$$\int_{x_1(y)}^{x_2(y)} Z_x Z_{xt} \, dx = [Z_x Z_t]_{x_1(y)}^{x_2(y)} - \int_{x_1(y)}^{x_2(y)} Z_t Z_{xx} \, dx$$

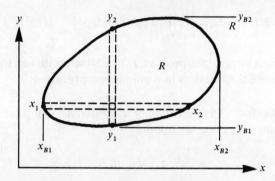

FIGURE 6.2   Membrane region.

As the bracketed term is zero on the boundary (why?),

$$\int_{x_1(y)}^{x_2(y)} Z_x Z_{xt} \, dx = - \int_{x_1(y)}^{x_2(y)} Z_t Z_{xx} \, dx$$

It is easy to show then (see the Problems) that

$$\iint_R T\{Z_x Z_{xt} + Z_y Z_{yt}\} \, dA = - \iint_R T Z_t \, \nabla^2 Z \, dA \tag{6.26}$$

Now (6.25) becomes, on introduction of (6.26),

$$E'(t) = \iint_R \{\rho Z_{tt} - T \nabla^2 Z\} Z_t \, dA \equiv 0$$

because of (6.24). Thus, because $E(0) = 0$,

$$E(t) = \int_0^t E'(\tau) \, d\tau + E(0) \equiv 0 \tag{6.27}$$

But recall from (6.22) that (6.27) implies $Z_x = Z_y = Z_t = 0$ in R. Accordingly, Z must be constant. As $Z = 0$ on B, we have $Z \equiv 0$ in $R + B$ and $z_2 \equiv z_1$. The solution z to (6.23) is therefore unique.

Uniqueness for models with the second and third boundary conditions and proofs of continuity are considered in the Problems.

6.3.3   Maximum and Minimum Principles

For the Laplace equation $\nabla^2 u = 0$ and the heat equation $u_t = k\nabla^2 u$, we shall show that a continuous solution u of these equations in a bounded region R takes both its maximum and minimum values on the boundary B of R or, in the case of the heat equation, initially. These results form the basis for very simple uniqueness and continuity proofs.

We establish two maximum-minimum theorems using a two-dimensional region R in the x–y plane. The same basic technique is used in each proof.

Consider first the Laplace equation $\nabla^2 u = 0$ in R. Bounded continuous solutions u of Laplace's equation are *harmonic functions*. Harmonic functions epitomize the smoothness of the solutions to elliptic equations because harmonic functions are analytic with respect to their independent variables [1, 2].

THEOREM 6.1   *A Maximum-Minimum Principle.* Let the harmonic function $u(x, y)$ be continuous on the closure $\bar{R} = R + B$ of the plane, bounded, closed, and simply connected region R; then $u(x, y)$ can be neither larger than its maximum on the boundary B nor smaller than its minimum on B.

Proof: We construct a proof by contradiction. Define $\phi(x, y) = \frac{1}{4}\varepsilon(x^2 + y^2)$, $\varepsilon \geq 0$. Let the origin of (x, y) lie in R so that $0 \leq \phi(x, y) \leq \frac{1}{4}\varepsilon\rho^2$, where ρ is the diameter of the smallest circle enclosing $\bar{R}$ with center at $(0, 0)$; ρ is less than or equal to the maximum distance across R. Let M be the maximum value and m be the minimum value of the harmonic function $u(x, y)$ on the boundary B.

First, $\nabla^2\phi = \varepsilon \geq 0$. Therefore, for $U^+ = u + \phi$, where $\nabla^2 u = 0$ for the harmonic function $u(x, y)$,

$$\nabla^2 U^+ \geq 0, \qquad U^+ \geq u \quad \text{in } \bar{R} \tag{6.28}$$

while for $U^- = u - \phi$,

$$\nabla^2 U^- \leq 0, \qquad U^- \leq u \quad \text{in } \bar{R} \tag{6.29}$$

because ϕ is nonnegative.

Suppose that U^+ takes its maximum value at some point in R but not on B. At a maximum point, $U_x^+ = U_y^+ = 0$, $U_{xx}^+ \leq 0$, and $U_{yy}^+ \leq 0$. This means that $\nabla^2 U^+ = U_{xx}^+ + U_{yy}^+ \leq 0$ at the point of maximum in contradiction to the first relation of (6.28). Accordingly, U^+ can only take its maximum value on B where

$$U^+ \leq M + \tfrac{1}{4}\varepsilon\rho^2 \tag{6.30}$$

Suppose that U^- takes its minimum value at some point in R but not on B. At a minimum point, $U_x^- = U_y^- = 0$, $U_{xx}^- \geq 0$, and $U_{yy}^- \geq 0$. At the proposed minimum point, then, $\nabla^2 U^- \geq 0$ in contradiction to the first relation of (6.29). Accordingly, U^- can only take its minimum value on B where

$$U^- \geq m - \tfrac{1}{4}\varepsilon\rho^2 \tag{6.31}$$

From the relations in (6.28) and (6.29), $-\varepsilon = \nabla^2 U^- \leq \nabla^2 u \leq \nabla^2 U^+ = \varepsilon$ and $U^- \leq u \leq U^+$; that is,

$$m - \tfrac{1}{4}\varepsilon\rho^2 \leq u \leq M + \tfrac{1}{4}\varepsilon\rho^2$$

Letting $\varepsilon \to 0$ yields $m \le u \le M$ for $\nabla^2 u = 0$. Therefore the harmonic function u can neither be larger than its maximum on B nor smaller than its minimum on B.

$$Q.E.D.$$

A consequence of the preceding theorem is that if a harmonic function u has a maximum at a point in R, then u must be constant in R; that is, u takes its maximum everywhere in $\bar{R}$. This result is called the strong form of the maximum principle by Courant and Hilbert [3, II, pp. 326 ff]. In their proof (actually formulated by E. Hopf), they obtain the interesting result (which we shall not prove):

THEOREM 6.2 *The Positive Normal Derivative.* For the harmonic function $u(x, y)$ of Theorem 6.1, the outward normal derivative $\partial u/\partial n$ at the boundary B of R is strictly positive at the points of B where $u(x, y)$ takes its maximum unless $u(x, y)$ is a constant on $\bar{R}$.

EXAMPLE 6.5 *The Dirichlet Model for Poisson's Equation.* Consider the solution $u(x, y) \in C^2$ in R satisfying the Dirichlet model:

$$\nabla^2 u = F \quad \text{in } R$$
$$u = G \quad \text{on } B \tag{6.32}$$

when $(F, G) \in C$ on $\bar{R} = R + B$ and B, respectively.

Let $U = u_2 - u_1$, where u_2 and u_1 are presumed to be two nonidentical solutions to (6.32). Then U satisfies

$$\nabla^2 U = 0 \quad \text{in } R$$
$$U = 0 \quad \text{on } B$$

and is a harmonic function. The values of U in R must be bounded by the maximum and minimum values of U on B. Therefore $U \equiv 0$ in $\bar{R}$ and the solution to (6.32) is unique!

Now we can also prove that $u(x, y)$ is continuous with respect to small changes in the data function $G(x, y)$—namely, that the change in u (caused by a change in G) is of the same order as the change in G. Let u_1 be the unique solution to the original problem (6.32), and let u_2 be the unique solution to the model

$$\nabla^2 u_2 = F \quad \text{in } R$$
$$u_2 = G + \Delta \quad \text{on } B \tag{6.33}$$

where $\Delta(x, y) \in C$ on B and $|\Delta(x, y)| \le \varepsilon > 0$.

Now $U = u_2 - u_1$ satisfies

$$\nabla^2 U = 0 \quad \text{in } R$$
$$U = \Delta \quad \text{on } B$$

According to Theorem 6.1, U is bounded by the maximum and minimum values of Δ. Thus $|U| \le |\Delta| \le \varepsilon$ or

$$|u_2 - u_1| \le \varepsilon$$

A small change of order ε in the boundary values produces an equally small change in the solution.

Q.E.D.

Theorem 6.2 can be used to show that the Neumann model (see Example 6.2) is unique up to an additive constant (see the Problems).

Now, consider the heat equation model in two dimensions:

$$u_t = k(u_{xx} + u_{yy}) \quad \text{in } R, \quad 0 < t$$
$$u = G \quad \text{on } B, \quad 0 < t \tag{6.34}$$
$$u = u_0 \quad \text{on } \bar{R} = R + B, \quad t = 0$$

Here $k > 0$; $G(x, y, t)$ and $u_0(x, y)$ are of class C on B and in $\bar{R}$, respectively; and R is a bounded, simply connected, and closed region with a complete bounding curve B in the x–y plane.

THEOREM 6.3 *A Maximum-Minimum Principle.* A continuous solution $u(x, y, t)$ of the heat equation in the finite cylinder $[\bar{R}: 0 \leq t \leq T < \infty]$ can neither be larger than its maximum nor smaller than its minimum on the surface $\bar{S}$ composed of the bounding cylinder $[B: 0 \leq t \leq T]$ and the base $[R: t = 0]$. The continuous solution $u(x, y, t)$ takes its maximum and minimum values on the boundaries or initially.

Proof: Essentially we need only repeat the proof of Theorem 6.1. Let ϕ be defined as before. Let M be the maximum value and m the minimum value of $u(x, y, t)$ on $\bar{S}$. Again, $\nabla^2\phi = \varepsilon > 0$, and we let $U^+ = u + \phi$ and $U^- = u - \phi$. This gives $U^+ \leq M + \frac{1}{2}\varepsilon\rho^2$ and $U^- \geq m - \frac{1}{2}\varepsilon\rho^2$ on $\bar{S}$, while $U^- \leq u \leq U^+$ generally.

Suppose that U^+ takes its maximum value at some point (x_0, y_0, t_0) in the finite cylinder $[R: 0 < t \leq T]$ but not on $\bar{S}$. For a maximum U_{tt}^+, U_{xx}^+ and $U_{yy}^+ \leq 0$ and U_x^+ and $U_y^+ = 0$ at (x_0, y_0, t_0), the point of the supposed interior maximum. If $t_0 < T$, $U_t^+ = 0$. If $t_0 = T$, it is possible that $U^+(x_0, y_0, t_0 - \tau) < U^+(x_0, y_0, t_0)$ for small τ so that only $U_t^+ \geq 0$ can be assumed. It follows that, at (x_0, y_0, t_0),

$$U_t^+ - k\nabla^2 U^+ \geq 0 \tag{6.35}$$

Because $u_t - k\nabla^2 u = 0$ and $\nabla^2\phi = \varepsilon > 0$, the definition of $U^+ = u + \phi$ yields

$$U_t^+ - k\nabla^2 U^+ \leq 0$$

which contradicts (6.35). Thus an interior maximum is impossible and

$$U^+ \leq M + \tfrac{1}{4}\varepsilon\rho^2$$

Supposing that U^- takes its minimum inside $\bar{S}$ at (x_1, y_1, t_1) yields the analogous result

$$U^- \geq m - \tfrac{1}{4}\varepsilon\rho^2$$

Accordingly, $m - \tfrac{1}{4}\varepsilon\rho^2 \leq u \leq M + \tfrac{1}{4}\varepsilon\rho^2$ in $\bar{R}$. Letting $\varepsilon \to 0$ gives $m \leq u \leq M$.

Q.E.D.

The uniqueness and continuity of continuous solutions to the general heat equation model

$$u_t = k \nabla^2 u + F \quad \text{in } R, \quad 0 < t$$
$$u = G \quad \text{on } B, \quad 0 < t \tag{6.36}$$
$$u = u_0 \quad \text{on } \bar{R}, \quad t = 0$$

in the finite region R follow from Theorem 6.3, as did the similar results from Theorem 6.1 (see Example 6.5 and the Problems). Theorem 6.3 can also be used to show that the solution to the heat equation on the entire x–y plane is unique if the solution is bounded. Boundedness is a necessary condition for uniqueness. It is well known [6, 7] that

$$u_\infty(x, t) = xt^{-3/2} \exp \left\{ \frac{-x^2}{4kt} \right\}$$

is a solution of the one-dimensional, homogeneous heat model

$$u_t = ku_{xx}, \quad 0 < x, \quad 0 < t$$
$$u(0, t) = 0, \quad 0 < t$$
$$u(x, 0) = 0, \quad 0 < x$$

and that $|u_\infty| \to \infty$ as $t \to 0$ and $x \to 0$ such that $x^2 = c^2 t$. Thus if u is a bounded solution to

$$u_t = ku_{xx} + f(x, t), \quad 0 < x, \quad 0 < t$$
$$u(0, t) = g(t), \quad 0 < t \tag{6.37}$$
$$u(x, 0) = u_0(x), \quad 0 < x$$

then $U = u + cu_\infty$, where c is an arbitrary constant, is another solution to (6.37). The solution to (6.37) is not unique when the solution may be in the class of unbounded functions.

EXAMPLE 6.6 *Uniqueness for the Heat Equation on an Infinite Domain.* Prove that the continuous, bounded solution $u(x, y, t)$ to the model

$$u_t = k \nabla^2 u + F(x, y, t), \quad -\infty < x < \infty, -\infty < y < \infty, 0 < t$$
$$u(x, y, 0) = u_0(x, y), \quad -\infty < x < \infty, -\infty < y < \infty \tag{6.38}$$

is unique when $k > 0$, $F \in C$ in the half-space $0 \leq t$, and $u_0 \in C$ on the x–y plane.

Proof: (This proof is an extension of Tychonov and Samarski's [8] equivalent one-dimensionsal proof.) Let the maximum absolute value of u be the finite constant M so $|u(x, y, t)| \leq M$. Define the continuous function

$$\phi(x, y, t) = \frac{2M}{R^2} (x^2 + y^2 + 4kt)$$

in the cylinder ($r^2 = x^2 + y^2 \leq R^2, 0 \leq t \leq T < \infty$). Then

$$\phi(x, y, t) = 2M + \frac{8kt}{R^2} \quad \text{on } r = R, \quad 0 \leq t \leq T$$

$$\phi(x, y, 0) = \frac{2M(x^2 + y^2)}{R^2} \quad \text{on } 0 \leq r \leq R$$

and ϕ satisfies the heat equation

$$\phi_t = k \nabla^2 \phi$$

in $0 \leq r < R, 0 < t \leq T$.

Suppose that two nonidentical solutions u_1 and u_2 exist to (6.38). Then $U = u_2 - u_1$ satisfies the model

$$
\begin{aligned}
U_t &= k \nabla^2 U, & -\infty < x < \infty, \quad -\infty < y < \infty, \quad 0 < t \\
U(x, y, 0) &= 0, & -\infty < x < \infty, \quad -\infty < y < \infty
\end{aligned}
\tag{6.39}
$$

and

$$|U(x, y, t)| = |u_2 - u_1| \leq |u_2| + |u_1| \leq 2M$$

But now

$$|\phi(x, y, 0)| \geq |U(x, y, 0)| \quad \text{in } 0 \leq r \leq R$$

$$|\phi(x, y, t)| \geq 2M \geq |U(x, y, t)| \quad \text{on } r = R, \quad 0 \leq t \leq T$$

In the finite region $r \leq R$, the maximum-minimum Theorem 6.3 applies, so

$$|U(x, y, t)| \leq |\phi(x, y, t)| \quad \text{in } 0 \leq r \leq R, \quad 0 \leq t \leq T$$

or

$$|U(x, y, t)| \leq \frac{2M}{R^2}(x^2 + y^2 + 4kt) \tag{6.40}$$

For fixed (x, y, t), (6.40) is valid for all finite $R > 0$. Letting $R \to \infty$ produces

$$|U(x, y, t)| \leq 0$$

that is, $u_2 \equiv u_1$. Therefore, in the class of bounded, continuous functions, the solution to (6.38) is unique.   Q.E.D.

6.4   THE WELL-POSED MODEL

According to our terms of reference there exists a unique solution for the well-posed model that varies continuously with the prescribed auxiliary data or equation coefficients. In this chapter it has been established that, if they exist, the solutions to a wide range of the models considered in the previous five chapters are unique and continuous with respect to changes in prescribed data. Where two- or three-dimensional models were used in the proofs, the same results are generally obtained for greater or lesser numbers of dimensions (see the Problems).

To complete the demonstration that the models of the previous five chapters are well posed, it remains only to verify that the formal solutions, obtained as infinite series, exist as uniformly convergent series that satisfy all the conditions of the model. The technique is well known [2, 6, 7, 8, 9]. In order to illustrate it, we establish the existence of the solutions to three models solved as examples in Chap. 3—namely, those given by (3.14), (3.63), and (3.81) for the heat, Laplace, and wave equations, respectively. The exercises contain other examples, models with greater numbers of independent variables, higher-order equations, and so on.

We restrict ourselves to at least continuous and bounded prescribed data. Berg and McGregor [6] provide some theory for piecewise-continuous data. Our proofs rely on the properties of uniformly convergent infinite series; an approach based on Abel's test (also used in [7, 9], for example) is adopted. Statements of the necessary theorems and properties of uniformly convergent infinite series are collected in Appendix 1, Sec. A.1.2, for ready reference. Kaplan [10] and Hyslop [11] provide complete proofs for the series, while derivations of Abel's test are given by Churchill [7], Greenspan [9], and Hyslop [11].

EXAMPLE 6.7 *Existence for the Heat Equation.* The model considered in Sec. 3.2 is

$$u_t = ku_{xx}, \qquad 0 < t, \ \ 0 < x < 1, \ \ 0 < k$$

$$u(0, t) = u(1, t) = 0, \qquad 0 < t \tag{6.41}$$

$$u(x, 0) = u_0(x), \qquad 0 \le x \le 1$$

The formal solution (3.36) is

$$u(x, t) = \sum_{n=1}^{\infty} c_{1n} e^{-n^2\pi^2 kt} \sin n\pi x \tag{6.42}$$

with

$$c_{1n} = 2 \int_0^1 u_0(\xi) \sin n\pi\xi \, d\xi \tag{6.43}$$

Assumptions

The formulation (6.41) contains the inherent assumptions (from our definition of terms and model derivation) that

$$u(x_0, t_0) = \lim_{\substack{x \to x_0 \\ t \to t_0}} u(x, t), \qquad 0 < x_0 < 1, \ \ 0 < t_0$$

$$u(0, t) = \lim_{x \to 0^+} u(x, t), \qquad 0 < t$$

$$u(1, t) = \lim_{x \to 1^-} u(x, t), \qquad 0 < t$$

$$u(x, 0) = \lim_{t \to 0^+} u(x, t), \qquad 0 \le x \le 1$$

These mean that the solution $u(x, t)$ must be continuous on $[0 \le x \le 1, 0 \le t]$. We add the assumptions that $u_0(x)$ is continuous and bounded by a constant $M < \infty$,

$u_0'(x)$ is bounded by $M' < \infty$ and piecewise continuous, $u_0(0) = u_0(1) = 0$, and $|u_0''(x)| < M'' < \infty$ on $0 \le x \le 1$. It follows that the Fourier series representation of the initial condition, namely,

$$u_0(x) = \sum_{n=1}^{\infty} c_{1n} \sin n\pi x \tag{6.44}$$

converges uniformly on $0 \le x \le 1$ (see Sec. 3.3.2, Theorem 3.2, and Prob. 3.23).

Convergence

First, we repeat briefly the result from Sec. 3.2. The coefficients c_{1n} of the convergent Fourier series (6.44) are given by (6.43) and are bounded. As $|\sin n\pi \xi| \le 1$, $|c_{1n}| \le 2M$. Accordingly, (6.42) can be written as

$$\frac{u(x, t)}{2M} = \sum_{n=1}^{\infty} \alpha_n e^{-n^2\pi^2 kt} \sin n\pi x \tag{6.45}$$

where

$$|\alpha_n| \le \frac{|c_{1n}|}{2M} \le 1$$

The series

$$S_c(t) = \sum_{n=1}^{\infty} f_n(t) \qquad f_n(t) = e^{-n^2\pi^2 kt}$$

is absolutely convergent for any fixed $t > 0$ because of the ratio test ([10, 11] or Sec. A.1.2). Clearly, the absolute value of each term in (6.45) is less than or equal to the corresponding $f_n(t)$. Therefore (6.45) and hence (6.42) are uniformly convergent in $0 < t$ according to the Weierstrass M-test ([10, 11] or Sec. A.1.2). The sum $u(x, t)$ of the uniformly convergent series (6.42) of continuous functions is also known to be continuous.

On the other hand, the Fourier series (6.44) is uniformly convergent, while we can write (6.42) as

$$u(x, t) = \sum_{n=1}^{\infty} f_n(t)c_{1n} \sin n\pi x \tag{6.46}$$

where the $f_n(t)$ were defined above. In $0 \le t, 0 \le f_{n+1}(t) \le f_n(t) \le 1$, so $f_n(t)$ is a *positive, monotonic, decreasing function* of n. It follows that, by virtue of Abel's test for series of functions ([7, 9, 11] or Sec. A.1.2), the solution series (6.42) for $u(x, t)$ is uniformly convergent on $0 \le t$. As $\lim_{t \to 0^+} f_n(t) = 1$, the uniformly convergent series (6.42) has as a limit

$$\lim_{t \to 0^+} u(x, t) = u_0(x)$$

that is, the solution (6.42) satisfies the initial condition of the model.

Now (6.42) can be differentiated term by term, and the series of derivatives are equal to the derivatives of $u(x, t)$ if the series of derivatives are uniformly convergent. Consider, from (6.42),

$$u_t = \sum_{n=1}^{\infty} (-n^2\pi^2 k)c_{1n}e^{-n^2\pi^2 kt} \sin n\pi x \tag{6.47}$$

or, from (6.45),

$$\frac{u_t(x, t)}{2M} = \sum_{n=1}^{\infty} (-n^2\pi^2 k)\alpha_n e^{-n^2\pi^2 kt} \sin n\pi x \qquad (6.48)$$

Now $|\alpha_n| \, |\sin n\pi x| \leq 1$ in (6.48), and the resulting majorizing series

$$S_t = \sum_{n=1}^{\infty} (-n^2\pi^2 k)e^{-n^2\pi^2 kt}$$

is absolutely convergent for any fixed $t > 0$ by virtue of the ratio test. Accordingly, (6.48) and hence (6.47) are uniformly convergent in $[0 \leq x \leq 1, 0 < t]$. Similarly,

$$u_{xx} = \sum_{n=1}^{\infty} -n^2\pi^2 c_{1n} e^{-n^2\pi^2 kt} \sin n\pi x$$

is uniformly convergent on $[0 \leq x \leq 1, 0 < t]$. Thus u_t and u_{xx} exist as uniformly convergent series of continuous functions and are therefore continuous on $0 \leq x \leq 1$, $0 < t$.

In summary, we have established that the series solution (6.42) is uniformly convergent to a continuous function in $[0 \leq x \leq 1, 0 \leq t]$ with continuous first derivatives with respect to x and t and a continuous second derivative with respect to x in $[0 \leq x \leq 1, 0 < t]$. The solution (6.42) converges to $u_0(x)$ at $t = 0$. Because term-by-term differentiation is possible and because each term of (6.42) satisfies the differential equation and boundary conditions in (6.41), the solution series satisfies these as well. Thus we have proved that a continuous solution to (6.41) exists as a uniformly convergent infinite series. This solution is known to be unique (see the Problems) and continuous with respect to the data; therefore the model (6.41) for the heat equation is well posed.

EXAMPLE 6.8   *Existence for the Laplace Equation.* The model of Example 3.1 in Sec. 3.4 is

$$\nabla^2 u = u_{xx} + u_{yy} = 0, \qquad 0 < x < l_1, \quad 0 < y < l_2$$

$$u(0, y) = u(l_1, y) = 0, \qquad 0 \leq y \leq l_2$$

$$u(x, 0) = T_1(x),$$
$$\qquad\qquad\qquad\qquad 0 < x < l_1 \qquad (6.49)$$
$$u(x, l_2) = T_2(x),$$

The formal solution (3.70) can be written as

$$u(x, y) = \frac{2}{l_1} \sum_{n=1}^{\infty} \{C_n(y) + D_n(y)\} \sin \frac{n\pi}{l_1} x \qquad (6.50)$$

where

$$C_n(y) = \left(\cosh \frac{n\pi}{l_1} y - \coth \frac{n\pi}{l_1} l_2 \sinh \frac{n\pi}{l_1} y\right) \int_0^{l_1} T_1(\xi) \sin \frac{n\pi}{l_1} \xi \, d\xi$$

$$= \frac{\sinh (n\pi/l_1)(l_2 - y)}{\sinh (n\pi/l_1)l_2} \int_0^{l_1} T_1(\xi) \sin \frac{n\pi}{l_1} \xi \, d\xi, \qquad 0 \leq y \leq l_2 \qquad (6.51)$$

and

$$D_n(y) = \frac{\sinh (n\pi/l_1)y}{\sinh (n\pi/l_1)l_2} \int_0^{l_1} T_2(\xi) \sin \frac{n\pi}{l_1} \xi \, d\xi, \qquad 0 \le y \le l_2 \qquad (6.52)$$

The solution $u(x, y)$ to (6.49) must be continuous on $[0 \le x \le l_1, 0 \le y \le l_2]$. To ensure the uniform convergence of the Fourier series representations

$$T_1(x) = \frac{2}{l_1} \sum_{n=1}^{\infty} \{C_n(0) + D_n(0)\} \sin \frac{n\pi}{l_1} x$$

$$= \frac{2}{l_1} \sum_{n=1}^{\infty} C_n(0) \sin \frac{n\pi}{l_1} x, \qquad 0 \le x \le l_1 \qquad (6.53)$$

and

$$T_2(x) = \frac{2}{l_1} \sum_{n=1}^{\infty} \{C_n(l_2) + D_n(l_2)\} \sin \frac{n\pi}{l_1} x$$

$$= \frac{2}{l_1} \sum_{n=1}^{\infty} D_n(l_2) \sin \frac{n\pi}{l_1} x, \qquad 0 \le x \le l_1 \qquad (6.54)$$

it is sufficient that T_1 and T_2 be piecewise smooth (the function is continuous) with bounded second derivatives in $0 \le x \le l_1$ and take the values $T_1(0) = T_2(0) = T_1(l_1) = T_2(l_1) = 0$.

Now

$$0 < f_n(y) = \frac{\sinh (n\pi/l_1)(l_2 - y)}{\sinh (n\pi/l_1)l_2} < 1, \qquad 0 < y < l_2$$

and

$$0 < g_n(y) = \frac{\sinh (n\pi/l_1)y}{\sinh (n\pi/l_1)l_2} < 1, \qquad 0 < y < l_2$$

As a result of the behavior of the sinh function, we have

$$f_{n+1}(y) \le f_n(y) \le 1,$$
$$g_{n+1}(y) \le g_n(y) \le 1, \qquad 0 < y < l_2$$
$$f_n(l_2) = g_n(0) = 0$$
$$f_n(0) = g_n(l_2) = 1$$

Therefore f_n and g_n are monotomic decreasing functions of n. Consequently, each term in the series

$$\frac{2}{l_1} \sum_{n=1}^{\infty} C_n(y) \sin \frac{n\pi}{l_1} x = \frac{2}{l_1} \sum_{n=1}^{\infty} C_n(0) f_n(y) \sin \frac{n\pi}{l_1} x$$

and

$$\frac{2}{l_1} \sum_{n=1}^{\infty} D_n(y) \sin \frac{n\pi}{l_1} x = \frac{2}{l_1} \sum_{n=1}^{\infty} D_n(0) g_n(y) \sin \frac{n\pi}{l_1} x$$

is of the same sign as and in absolute value less than or equal to its equivalent term in the convergent series (6.53) and (6.54). By virtue of Abel's test, (6.50) is a uniformly convergent series on $[0 \le x \le l_1, 0 \le y \le l_2]$; its sum $u(x, y)$ is continuous there and clearly satisfies the boundary conditions [each term satisfies the homogeneous conditions and (6.50) goes over to the series for T_1 and T_2 in the limit].

Because each term in (6.50) satisfies the Laplace equation, to complete our existence statement we need only establish that the second derivatives of (6.50) are uniformly convergent in $[0 < x < l_1, 0 < y < l_2]$ so that u_{xx} and u_{yy} exist. Consider

$$u_{xx} = -\frac{2}{l_1} \sum_{n=1}^{\infty} \left(\frac{n^2\pi^2}{l_1^2}\right) \{C_n(y) + D_n(y)\} \sin\frac{n\pi}{l_1}x \tag{6.55}$$

and

$$u_{yy} = \frac{2}{l_1} \sum_{n=1}^{\infty} \left(\frac{n^2\pi^2}{l_1^2}\right) \{C_n(y) + D_n(y)\} \sin\frac{n\pi}{l_1}x \tag{6.56}$$

(It is obvious that $u_{xx} + u_{yy} = 0$ whether or not the series converge.)

Now, T_1 and T_2 are bounded, say, $|T_1| \le M_1 < \infty$ and $|T_2| \le M_2 < \infty$. Thus

$$|C_n(y)| \le \frac{M_1 l_1}{\sinh (n\pi/l_1)l_2} \sinh\frac{n\pi}{l_1}(l_2 - y) \tag{6.57}$$

and

$$|D_n(y)| \le \frac{M_2 l_1}{\sinh (n\pi/l_1)l_2} \sinh\frac{n\pi}{l_1}y \tag{6.58}$$

For any fixed y in $0 < y < l_2$ the series of positive constants

$$\sum_{n=1}^{\infty} \left(\frac{n^2\pi^2}{l_1^2}\right)\frac{M_1 l_1 \sinh (n\pi/l_1)(l_2 - y)}{\sinh (n\pi/l_1)l_2} \tag{6.59}$$

and

$$\sum_{n=1}^{\infty} \left(\frac{n^2\pi^2}{l_1^2}\right)\frac{M_2 l_1 \sinh (n\pi/l_1)y}{\sinh (n\pi/l_1)l_2} \tag{6.60}$$

are absolutely convergent according to the ratio test because

$$\frac{\sinh (n\pi/l_1)(l_2 - y)}{\sinh (n\pi/l_1)l_2} = O(e^{-(n\pi/l_1)y}), \qquad 0 < y < l_2$$

and

$$\frac{\sinh (n\pi/l_1)y}{\sinh (n\pi/l_1)l_2} = O(e^{-n\pi/l_1(l_2 - y)}), \qquad 0 < l_2 - y < l_2$$

as $n \to \infty$, and consequently the ratio of consecutive terms ($n + 1$st over nth) approaches zero as $n \to \infty$. It follows from the absolute convergence of (6.59) and (6.60) and the bounds (6.57) and (6.58) that, according to the Weierstrass M-test, the series (6.55) and (6.56) are uniformly convergent on $[0 < x < l_1, 0 < y < l_2]$ and u_{xx} and u_{yy} are continuous there. This completes the demonstration of the existence of a solution $u(x, y) \in C$ for the model (6.49).

EXAMPLE 6.9 *Existence for the Wave Equation.* The model of Example 3.3 in Sec. 3.4 may be generalized to

$$z_{tt} = c^2 z_{yy}, \qquad 0 < y < l, \quad 0 < t$$

$$z_y(0, t) = z_y(l, t) = 0, \qquad 0 < t$$

$$z(y, 0) = z_0(y), \qquad \qquad \qquad (6.61)$$

$$z_t(y, 0) = V_0(y), \qquad 0 \le y \le l$$

In this case, the formal solution is [see (3.94)]

$$z(y, t) = \frac{1}{l} \int_0^l z_0(\xi)\, d\xi + \frac{2}{l} \sum_{n=1}^{\infty} \left\{ A_n \cos\frac{n\pi}{l} ct + B_n \sin\frac{n\pi}{l} ct \right\} \cos\frac{n\pi}{l} y \qquad (6.62)$$

where

$$A_n = \int_0^l z_0(\xi) \cos\frac{n\pi}{l}\xi\, d\xi \qquad (6.63)$$

and

$$B_n = \frac{1}{c(n\pi/l)} \int_0^l V_0(\xi) \cos\frac{n\pi}{l}\xi\, d\xi \qquad (6.64)$$

The arguments for this example are different from those of Example 6.8. To ensure the uniform convergence of the Fourier series representations

$$z_0(y) = \frac{1}{l} \int_0^l z_0(\xi)\, d\xi + \frac{2}{l} \sum_{n=1}^{\infty} A_n \cos\frac{n\pi}{l} y, \qquad 0 \le y \le l \qquad (6.65)$$

and

$$V_0(y) = \frac{2}{l} \sum_{n=1}^{\infty} B_n \cos\frac{n\pi}{l} y, \qquad 0 \le y \le l \qquad (6.66)$$

it is more than sufficient (see the proof of Theorem 3.2) that z_0 and V_0 be piecewise very smooth (the function and its first derivative are continuous, the second derivative is piecewise continuous and bounded) in $0 \le y \le l$, $z_0(0) = z_0(l)$, $V_0(0) = V_0(l)$, and $z_0'(0) = z_0'(l) = V_0'(0) = V_0'(l) = 0$. In (6.62), for every fixed value of $t \ge 0$,

$$\left| \cos\frac{n\pi ct}{l} \right| \le 1 \quad \text{and} \quad \left| \sin\frac{n\pi ct}{l} \right| \le 1$$

so that the two series with A_n and B_n in (6.62) also converge uniformly on $[0 \le y \le l, 0 \le t]$ by virtue of the Weierstrass M-test. This means that $z(y, t)$ is continuous there and satisfies the first initial condition.

In Chap. 9, Sec. 9.3.2, we derive by direct integration the d'Alembert solution

$$z(y, t) = \frac{1}{2}[z_0(y - ct) + z_0(y + ct)] + \frac{1}{2c} \int_{y-ct}^{y+ct} V_0(\tau)\, d\tau$$

to the wave equation for an infinite string. This solution is valid under the conditions of continuity specified for z_0 and V_0. In fact, if the domain of definition of z_0 and V_0 is properly extended beyond $0 \le y \le l$—for example, by *odd* periodic extensions in

$nl \leq y \leq (n + 1)l$—the d'Alembert solution is a solution to (6.61) (see Sec. 9.3.2). We also show that while z and its first derivatives are continuous in $-\infty < y < \infty, 0 \leq t$, its second derivatives may be discontinuous along the *characteristic lines* $y \pm ct$ = constant.

In the present case, the specified conditions on z_0 and V_0 are not sufficient to guarantee convergence of the series for the derivatives of z that must exist to satisfy the second initial condition, the boundary conditions, and the differential equation. From the proof of Theorem 3.2, Sec. 3.3.2, we have that the absolute value of A_n and B_n depends on the smoothness of z_0 and V_0. For $z \in C^2$ in $0 \leq y \leq l, 0 \leq t$, we would have to show that the majorizing series of constants obtained by differentiating (6.62) twice with respect to y or t, namely,

$$\frac{\pi^2}{l^2} \sum_{n=1}^{\infty} n^2 \{|A_n| + |B_n|\} \tag{6.67}$$

converge absolutely because the series for z_t, z_y, z_{tt}, and z_{yy} will then converge uniformly according to the Weierstrass M-test, and $z_t(y, 0)$, $z_y(0, t)$, and $z_y(l, t)$ will satisfy the auxiliary conditions.

The harmonic series (Sec. A.1.2)

$$M \sum \frac{1}{n^{\sigma}}$$

converges for $\sigma > 1$, where M is a finite constant. Therefore in (6.67) we require

$$\frac{\pi^2}{l^2} n^2 \{|A_n| + |B_n|\} \leq M n^{-\sigma}$$

$$|A_n| + |B_n| \leq \frac{M l^2}{\pi^2 n^{3+\varepsilon}}, \qquad \varepsilon > 0$$

For z_0 and $V_0 \in C^4$ or $\in C^3$ with bounded fourth derivatives,

$$|A_n| = O(n^{-4}) \quad \text{and} \quad |B_n| = O(n^{-4})$$

Accordingly, with this method of proof we can show that $z(y, t)$ exists as a twice-continuously differentiable infinite series in $[0 \leq y \leq l, 0 \leq t]$ and that it satisfies the model (6.61) if $z_0(y)$ and $V_0(y) \in C^4$ or $\in C^3$ with $|z_0^{(4)}|$ and $|V_0^{(4)}| < \infty$.

REFERENCES

1. O. D. Kellog, *Foundations of Potential Theory*. New York: Dover, 1953.

2. I. G. Petrovsky, *Lectures on Partial Differential Equations* (trans. from the Russian by A. Shenitzer). New York: Interscience (a division of John Wiley & Sons), 1954.

3. R. Courant and D. Hilbert, *Methods of Mathematical Physics*, Vols. I & II. New York: Interscience (a division of John Wiley & Sons), 1953 & 1962.

4. J. Hadamard, *Lectures on Cauchy's Problem in Linear Partial Differential Equations*. New York: Dover, 1952.

5. H. Sagan, *Boundary and Eigenvalue Problems in Mathematical Physics*. New York: John Wiley & Sons, 1961.

6. P. W. Berg and J. L. McGregor, *Elementary Partial Differential Equations*. San Francisco: Holden-Day, 1966.

7. R. V. Churchill, *Fourier Series and Boundary Value Problems*, 2nd ed. New York: McGraw-Hill, 1963.

8. A. N. Tychonov and A. A. Samarski, *Partial Differential Equations of Mathematical Physics*, Vol. I. San Francisco: Holden-Day, 1964.

9. D. Greenspan, *Introduction to Partial Differential Equations*. New York: McGraw-Hill, 1961.

10. W. Kaplan, *Advanced Calculus*. Reading, Mass.: Addison-Wesley, 1952.

11. J. M. Hyslop, *Infinite Series*, 5th ed. New York: Interscience (a division of John Wiley & Sons), 1954.

PROBLEMS

6.1   Consider the Cauchy problem

$$z_{tt} = c^2 z_{yy}, \qquad -\infty < y < \infty, 0 < t$$

$$z(y, 0) = z_0(y),$$
$$z_t(y, 0) = V_0(y), \qquad -\infty < y < \infty$$

with z_0 and V_0 being analytic functions. Expand the solution as a Taylor series about $(0, 0)$, and show how the terms of the series can be found explicitly in terms of z_0 and V_0.

6.2   Show that the solution of the Cauchy problem for the biharmonic equation

$$\nabla^2(\nabla^2 z) = z_{xxxx} + 2z_{xxyy} + z_{yyyy} = 0, \qquad -\infty < x < \infty, 0 < y$$

$$z(x, 0) = z_0(x),$$
$$z_y(x, 0) = V_0(x),$$
$$z_{yy}(x, 0) = A_0(x), \qquad -\infty < x < \infty$$
$$z_{yyy}(x, 0) = M_0(x),$$

with analytic initial data is not well posed.

6.3   Derive the Green's identity (6.7) from Gauss' theorem (6.6).

6.4   Prove the uniqueness of the solution $u(x, y) \in C^2$ in R of the Dirichlet model

$$\nabla^2 u = F(x, y) \quad \text{in } R$$

$$u = G(x, y) \quad \text{on } B$$

where $\bar{R} = R + B$. What conditions must be imposed on $R, B, F,$ and G?

6.5   Under the usual assumptions, show that the solutions $u(x, y)$ to the following models are unique:

$$\nabla^2 u = F(x, y) \quad \text{in } R$$

with

(a) $u = G(x, y) \quad \text{on } B_1$
     $u_n = g(x, y) \quad \text{on } B_2$

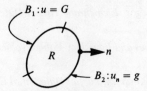

FIGURE 6.5P(a)

(b) $u_n + hu = g(x, y)$ on B of R, $h(x, y) \geq 0$

(c) $u_n + hu = g(x, y)$ on B_1, $h \geq 0$
    $u = G(x, y)$ on B_2

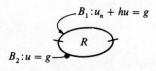

FIGURE 6.5P(c)

(d) $u_n + hu = g(x, y)$ on B_1, $h \geq 0$
    $u_n = G(x, y)$ on B_2

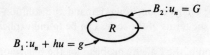

FIGURE 6.5P(d)

6.6 Prove that the solution $u(x, y, z) \in C^2$ in V satisfying

$$\nabla^2 u = F \quad \text{in } V$$

$$\frac{\partial u}{\partial n} + hu = G \quad \text{on } \bar{S}$$

is unique when the function $h \geq 0$.

6.7 Derive uniqueness proofs for the following two-point boundary-value problems by use of the one-dimensional Green's identities (4.13) or (4.14):

(a) $X'' - \lambda^2 X = F(x)$, $0 < x < 1$, $\lambda^2 > 0$
    $X(0) = X_0$
    $X(1) = X_1$

(b) $[e^x X']' - \lambda^2 e^x X = F(x)$, $0 < x < l$, $\lambda^2 > 0$
    $X'(0) = X'_0$
    $X(l) = X_l$

(c) $X'' + x^{-1} X' - \lambda^2 X = F(x)$, $0 < x < 1$, $\lambda^2 > 0$
    $X'(0) = 0$
    $X(1) = X_1$

(d) $X'' = F(x)$, $0 < x < 1$
    $X'(0) = f_0$
    $X'(1) = f_1$

Is some relation between F, f_0, and f_1 required for existence of the solution (that you can obtain by direct integration)? Can you interpret this in terms of steady heat conduction in a rod?

6.8 Prove the uniqueness of solutions to the following models:

(a) $u_t = k \nabla^2 u + F(x, y, z, t)$ in V, $t > 0$
$u_n = G(x, y, z, t)$ on $\bar{S}$, $t \geq 0$
$u = u_0(x, y, z)$ in V, $t = 0$

Are any special conditions on F and G required? Is the solution truly unique?

(b) $u_t = k \nabla^2 u + F(x, y, z, t)$ in V, $t > 0$
$u_n + h(x, y, z)u = G(x, y, z, t)$ on $\bar{S}$, $t \geq 0$, $h \geq 0$
$u = u_0(x, y, z)$ in V, $t = 0$

(c) $u_t = k \nabla^2 u + F(x, y, z, t)$ in V, $t > 0$
$u_n = G(x, y, z, t)$ on $\bar{S}_1$, $t \geq 0$
$u = g(x, y, z, t)$ on $\bar{S}_2$, $t \geq 0$
$u = u_0(x, y, z)$ in V, $t = 0$
where $\bar{S} = \bar{S}_1 + \bar{S}_2$.

(d) Part (c) with $u_n = -hu + G$ on $\bar{S}_1$, $t \geq 0$, $h \geq 0$.

6.9 Derive uniqueness proofs for the heat equation initial-boundary-value problems with all three types of inhomogeneous boundary conditions, alone or mixed, if

$$u_t = ku_{xx} + f(x, t), \qquad 0 < x < l, \quad 0 < t$$

[Hint: Use the internal energy integral

$$Q(t) = \rho^2 c^2 \int_0^l U^2(x, t)\, dx \geq 0$$

and the Green's identity (4.13).]

6.10 Derive uniqueness proofs for the initial-boundary-value problems with all three types of inhomogeneous boundary conditions, alone or mixed, for the wave equation

$$z_{tt} = \frac{T}{\rho} z_{yy} + F(y, t), \qquad 0 < y < l, \quad 0 < t$$

for a string. How is the result altered if the equation is

$$\rho z_{tt} = (T z_y)y + F(y, t), \qquad 0 < y < l, \quad 0 < t$$

when $\rho = \rho(y)$ and $T = T(y)$? [Hint: Use an energy approach; for the boundary conditions of the third kind, you can show $E'(t) \leq 0$. Does this help?]

6.11 Show for Example 6.4 that

$$\iint_R T\{Z_x Z_{xt} + Z_y Z_{yt}\}\, dA = -\iint_R TZ_t \nabla^2 Z\, dA$$

6.12 Repeat Prob. 6.11 under the condition that $Z_n = 0$ on B, $t > 0$.

6.13 Use the result of Prob. 6.12 to prove the uniqueness of the solution to the Neumann model for a vibrating membrane.

6.14 Consider the linear model on $\bar{R} = R + B$:

$$z_{tt} = c^2 \nabla^2 z \quad \text{in } R$$
$$z \equiv 0 \quad \text{on } B$$
$$\begin{aligned} z &= \varepsilon\phi(x, y), \\ z_t &= \varepsilon\psi(x, y), \end{aligned} \quad \text{in } R, \quad t = 0$$

Show that the total energy

$$E(t) = O(\varepsilon^2)$$

if ϕ and $\psi \in C^1$ are bounded by a finite constant M. Next, show that because the first derivatives of z must be $O(\varepsilon)$, z is of order ε for a bounded, finite region R. This proves the continuity with respect to the initial data of the membrane model. Why?

6.15 Repeat Prob. 6.14 for a freely supported membrane—that is, for $z_n = 0$ on B. Is this model well posed or physically reasonable? What happens if $\int_R \psi(x, y)\, dx\, dy \neq 0$?

6.16 Repeat Probs. 6.14 and 6.15 for a vibrating string of finite length l.

6.17 Prove Theorem 6.1 for a function $u(x, y, z)$ harmonic in a volume V with closed boundary $\bar{S}$.

6.18 Prove that Theorem 6.1 is valid for the "harmonic" function $X(x)$ satisfying $X''(x) = 0$ on $0 < x < l$. Is the result intuitively obvious? Why?

6.19 Prove an appropriate uniqueness theorem for the function $u(x, y)$ harmonic in R and satisfying $u_n = g$ on B. What condition must g satisfy? [Hint: Use Theorem 6.2.]

6.20 Prove that the solution to the model

$$\nabla^2 u = F \quad \text{in } R$$
$$u = G \quad \text{on } B_1,$$
$$u_n = g \quad \text{on } B_2, \qquad B = B_1 + B_2$$

is unique. [Hint: Can you use Theorem 6.2?]

6.21 An employee turns in a report to you on a set of *measurements* that he made of temperature in a circular flat plate (governing equation $\nabla^2 u = 0$); the report contains the following graph of isotherms. You tell the employee that he has made a mistake and must rerun the entire experiment. Give a mathematical proof to back your decision.

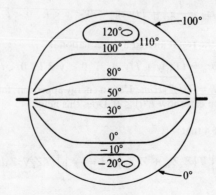

FIGURE 6.21P

6.22 Prove the uniqueness and continuity of continuous solutions to the heat conduction model (6.36).

6.23 Derive maximum-minimum theorems for general heat conduction models governed by

(a) $u_t = ku_{xx} + A(x, t)$, $0 < x < l$, $0 < t$, $0 < k$
(b) $u_t = k\nabla^2 u + A(x, y, t)$ in V, $0 < t$

for the appropriate regions.

6.24 Prove that the bounded continuous solution to the model

$$u_t = ku_{xx} + A(x, t), \qquad -\infty < x < \infty, \quad 0 < t, \quad 0 < k$$

$$u(x, 0) = u_0(x), \qquad -\infty < x < \infty$$

is unique and continuous with respect to the initial data.

6.25 Prove that the problem

$$\nabla^2 \Omega - \Omega = 0 \quad \text{in } R$$

$$\Omega \equiv 0 \quad \text{on } B$$

for $\Omega(x, y)$ has only the trivial solution $\Omega \equiv 0$. [*Hint:* Can you use a Green's identity?]

6.26 Use an integral method to prove the uniqueness of the solution to the Dirichlet model for the Helmholtz equation

$$\nabla^2 u - k^2 u = F(x, y, z) \quad \text{in } V$$

where $u = u(x, y, z)$ and $k^2 > 0$.

6.27 Repeat Prob. 6.26 for a Neumann model.

6.28 Prove that the beam models of Table 5.2 have unique solutions. [*Hint:* Can you derive an energy integral and a useful Green's identity (see Sec. 5.3.2)?]

6.29 Prove that the model given by (5.36) in Example 5.1 is well posed.

6.30 Prove that the following string vibration model is well posed:

$$z_{tt} = \frac{T}{\rho} z_{yy} + F \sin \omega_1 t, \qquad 0 < y < l, \quad 0 < t$$

$$z_y(0, t) = \frac{F}{T} \sin \omega_2 t,$$

$$\hspace{4cm} 0 < t$$

$$z(l, t) = a \sin \omega_3 t,$$

$$z(y, 0) = z_t(y, 0) = 0, \qquad 0 \le y \le l$$

6.31 Prove that the heat conduction model given by (5.60) to (5.62) is well posed. What conditions are needed on $U_0(x, y)$?

6.32 Under what conditions on z_0 and V_0 can you prove that the membrane model given by (5.89) to (5.91) is well posed? Do it.

6.33 Repeat Prob. 6.32 for the beam model given by (5.111) to (5.113).

6.34 Prove that one of the models solved as homework in Chaps. 3 or 5 is well posed. Establish all continuity conditions needed on auxiliary data.

6.35 Show that all derivatives of the solution (6.42) exist as uniformly convergent series of continuous functions on $0 \le x \le 1, 0 < t$.

6.36   Prove that a piecewise-smooth function $T(x)$ satisfying $T(0) = T(l) = 0$ and with $|T''(x)| < \infty$ in $0 \le x \le l$ has a uniformly convergent Fourier series representation

$$\frac{2}{l} \sum_{n=1}^{\infty} \left\{ \int_0^l T(\xi) \sin \frac{n\pi}{l} \xi \, d\xi \right\} \sin \frac{n\pi}{l} x$$

6.37   If $f_n(y) = \sinh ny/\sinh nl$, show that

$$f_{n+1}(y) \le f_n(y), \qquad 0 \le y \le l$$

6.38   Show that for large t,

$$\sinh pt = O(e^{pt})$$

so

$$\frac{\sinh pt}{\sinh p\tau} = O(e^{p(t-\tau)})$$

6.39   Express the solution to (6.61) in terms of the d'Alembert solution by extending z_0 and V_0 to $-\infty < y < \infty$ in a periodic manner.

6.40   Repeat Example 6.9, filling in all missing details of the proof.

6.41   Show that, in general, if $f \in C^m$ on $-l \le x \le l$, the coefficients of its Fourier series

$$\frac{1}{2}c_0 + \sum_{n=1}^{\infty} c_n \cos \frac{n\pi}{l} x + s_n \sin \frac{n\pi}{l} x$$

behave as $|c_n| = O(n^{-m})$ and $|s_n| = O(n^{-m})$.

CHAPTER 7

AN INTRODUCTION TO
GREEN'S FUNCTIONS

For those mathematical models for which we can find a suitable coordinate system such that the partial differential equation will separate and the auxiliary conditions are appropriately applied (see Sec. 3.5), the methods of separation of variables and eigenfunction expansions are useful. However, the solution is obtained as an infinite series that can be slowly convergent and can obscure the essential behavior of the solution at key points—for example, near boundaries or initially.

Our goal in this chapter is to introduce the *Green's function*, typically written as $G(P, Q)$, where P and Q are two points in the space domain of the problem under consideration. The Green's function becomes part of a closed-form solution *for linear models*, employing an integral representation or summation. Perhaps, more significantly, the Green's function permits representation of solutions as the result of *influences* or *disturbances*. The Green's function is the response at P to an influence or disturbance at any point Q. By adding the responses of disturbances in all parts of the domain, we achieve a total solution.

To begin, we take as our point of departure several problems and their solutions from earlier chapters. Then we examine the point source or disturbance function, the *Dirac δ-function*, and gain considerable insight into the behavior of solutions. Third, we develop a number of formal and useful relations for Green's functions. The last section of the chapter is a brief summary.

7.1   A HEURISTIC DEVELOPMENT OF A GREEN'S FUNCTION

Let us begin with Example 5.1, Sec. 5.1.3, the mathematical model of heat conduction in a thin, insulated rod with heat sources present:

$$u_t - ku_{xx} = \frac{A}{\rho c}, \qquad 0 < x < l, \quad 0 < t$$

$$
\begin{aligned}
u(0, t) &= 0, \\
&\qquad\qquad 0 < t \\
u(l, t) &= 0,
\end{aligned}
\tag{7.1}
$$

$$u(x, 0) = u_0(x), \qquad 0 \le x \le l$$

where ρ and c are constants, A is at least a continuous function of x and t, and $u_0(x)$ is continuous with a continuous first derivative. The full solution (5.47) to (7.1) is

$$u(x, t) = \sum_{n=1}^{\infty} \left[\frac{2}{l} \int_0^l u_0(\xi) X_n(\xi)\, d\xi\ e^{-\lambda_n^2 kt} \right.$$

$$\left. + \frac{2}{l} \int_0^t e^{-\lambda_n^2 k(t-\tau)} \int_0^l \frac{A(\xi, \tau)}{\rho c} X_n(\xi)\, d\xi\, d\tau \right] X_n(x) \quad (7.2)$$

in which

$$X_n(x) = \sin \lambda_n x \qquad \lambda_n^2 = \left(\frac{n\pi}{l} \right)^2, \qquad n \ge 1 \tag{7.3}$$

are the eigenfunctions and eigenvalues of the related homogeneous problem [see Eqs. (5.37) to (5.39)].

Now, we need only rearrange (7.2), making the substitution $\tilde{A}(x, t) = A(x, t)/\rho c$ for convenience and recalling that (7.2) is the unique solution to (7.1) according to our work in Chap. 6. Moreover, we proved directly in Sec. 5.1.3 that (7.2) satisfies the conditions of (7.1). An analysis parallel to the one given in Sec. 3.2 will show that the series in (7.2) is uniformly convergent for $t > 0$. Thus it is permissible to exchange the order of integration and summation in (7.2). The result is

$$u(x, t) = \int_0^l \left[\sum_{n=1}^{\infty} \frac{e^{-\lambda_n^2 kt} X_n(x) X_n(\xi)}{l/2} \right] u_0(\xi)\, d\xi$$

$$+ \int_0^t \int_0^l \left[\sum_{n=1}^{\infty} \frac{e^{-\lambda_n^2 k(t-\tau)} X_n(x) X_n(\xi)}{l/2} \right] \tilde{A}(\xi, \tau)\, d\xi\, d\tau$$

As the normalizing constant

$$N_n = \int_0^l X_n^2(\xi)\, d\xi = \frac{l}{2}$$

we can write

$$u(x, t) = \int_0^l G(x, \xi; t) u_0(\xi)\, d\xi + \int_0^t \int_0^l G(x, \xi; t - \tau) \tilde{A}(\xi, \tau)\, d\xi\, d\tau \tag{7.4}$$

where

$$G(x, \xi; t) = \sum_{n=1}^{\infty} \frac{e^{-\lambda_n^2 kt} X_n(x) X_n(\xi)}{N_n} \tag{7.5}$$

is called the *Green's function* (t is treated as a parameter). If we grant that one is able to obtain G by some separate process (and in perhaps some other form), we see immediately that the solution to the inhomogeneous, initial-boundary-value problem (7.1) is given directly by the integral form (7.4). Also, it follows from (7.5) that $G(x, \xi; t) = G(\xi, x; t)$; that is, the Green's function is symmetric. The series (7.5) is *bilinear* in x and ξ and is easily shown to be uniformly convergent for either x or ξ with $t > 0$ and $0 \le x, \xi \le l$ (see Sec. 3.2).

Several useful examples can be extracted from the solution (7.4) and (7.5) after we note carefully that the single Green's function (7.5) is the *kernel* for both parts of the integral-form solution (7.4). Thus the inhomogeneity $\tilde{A}(x, t)$ in the governing equation is accounted for, as well as the initial values $u_0(x)$. Green's functions, in general, are the basis for integral representation of solutions to

1. Inhomogeneous partial differential equations with homogeneous auxiliary conditions in terms of volume or space integrals (here over part of the x–t space).

2. Homogeneous partial differential equations with prescribed boundary or initial conditions in terms of surface or line integrals (here over the line $t = 0$, $0 \le x \le l$).

EXAMPLE 7.1   Set $A(x, t)/\rho c \equiv 0$. Then, from (7.1) and (7.4),

$$u_t = k u_{xx}, \qquad 0 < x < l, \qquad 0 < t$$

$$u(0, t) = u(l, t) = 0, \qquad 0 < t$$

$$u(x, 0) = u_0(x), \qquad 0 \le x \le l$$

and

$$u(x, t) = \int_0^l G(x, \xi; t) u_0(\xi) \, d\xi \tag{7.6}$$

where $G(x, \xi; t)$ is still given by (7.5). The temperature u at a point x and time t is given by the sum (integral) of the responses G to the initial temperature (or influence) u_0 over the whole rod. Again, the solution (7.6) can be written formally and a search undertaken to find the appropriate G if it is unknown.

EXAMPLE 7.2   Set $A(x, t)/\rho c = k P(x)$ and $U(x) = \lim_{t \to \infty} u(x, t)$, assuming that a steady state exists. From (7.1), we obtain the steady-state heat conduction problem

$$U_{xx} = -P(x), \qquad 0 < x < l$$

$$U(0) = 0 \tag{7.7}$$

$$U(l) = 0$$

which is an inhomogeneous, two-point boundary-value problem for an ordinary differential equation. In (7.2), with $A/\rho c = kP$ and $\lambda_n^2 > 0$,

$$\lim_{t \to \infty} \{ e^{-\lambda_n^2 kt} \} = 0$$

$$\lim_{t \to \infty} \left\{ -\frac{2}{l} \int_0^t e^{-\lambda_n^2 k(t-\tau)} \int_0^l kP(\xi)X_n(\xi)\,d\xi\,d\tau \right\} = \frac{2}{\lambda_n^2 l} \int_0^l P(\xi)X_n(\xi)\,d\xi$$

Therefore, as $N_n = l/2$,

$$U(x) = \lim_{t \to \infty} u(x, t) = \int_0^l \left[\sum_{n=1}^{\infty} \frac{X_n(x)X_n(\xi)}{\lambda_n^2 N_n} \right] P(\xi)\,d\xi$$

or

$$U(x) = \int_0^l G(x, \xi)P(\xi)\,d\xi \tag{7.8}$$

where the Green's function (for an ordinary differential equation)

$$G(x, \xi) = \sum_{n=1}^{\infty} \frac{X_n(x)X_n(\xi)}{\lambda_n^2 N_n} \tag{7.9}$$

is a symmetric, bilinear series formed from the characteristic functions and numbers of the eigenvalue problem that yields our λ_n^2, X_n, and N_n; namely,

$$X'' + \lambda^2 X = 0$$

$$X(0) = X(l) = 0$$

The solution (7.8) to (7.7) exposes the Green's function (7.9) as a weighting function that assigns the proper size of influence caused by $P(\xi)$ along the rod to the solution at a particular x-point. The solution at x is then the summation of all the influences from the other points in the rod; hence $G(x, \xi)$ is called the *influence function* also.

Our development led us to an important form of the Green's function; namely, it can often be expressed directly in terms of the eigenvalues and eigenfunctions of a related eigenvalue problem. Now, we need to know more about the Green's function. For example, just what equation does the Green's function satisfy? A great deal can be learned through the use of what is called the Dirac δ-function.

7.2   THE DIRAC δ-FUNCTION

In Chap. 2 we derived Eq. (2.47) for the small transverse vibrations z of a string under the action of an external force $F(z, y, t)$ per unit of mass. If $F = F(y)$ alone and all transient motion is damped, (2.47) becomes

$$z_{yy} = \frac{-\rho F(y)}{T} = -f(y) \tag{7.10}$$

where f is the normalized force per unit length of string, and we suppose (7.10) to be applicable over the total length of the string, be it finite or infinite.

Now we consider $f(y)$ to be applied in a special way—namely, concentrated near $y = 0$—so

$$f(y) = \begin{cases} 0, & |y| > \varepsilon \\ \dfrac{1}{2\varepsilon}\left(1 + \cos\dfrac{\pi}{\varepsilon}y\right), & |y| \le \varepsilon \end{cases}$$

and the total force applied to the string

$$\bar{f} = \int_{-\varepsilon}^{\varepsilon} f(y)\, dy = 1$$

for any small $\varepsilon > 0$. As $\varepsilon \to 0$, $f(0) \to \infty$ while $\bar{f}$ remains unity, and a finite load tends to be applied over a zone of zero size (see Fig. 7.1). Thus we have a point load. It is natural to define a "general point load"

$$\delta(y - \xi) = \lim_{\varepsilon \to 0} \begin{cases} 0, & |y - \xi| > \varepsilon \\ \dfrac{1}{2\varepsilon}\left[1 + \cos\dfrac{\pi}{\varepsilon}(y - \xi)\right], & |y - \xi| \le \varepsilon \end{cases}$$

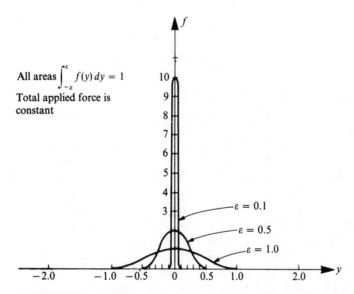

All areas $\displaystyle\int_{-\varepsilon}^{\varepsilon} f(y)\, dy = 1$

Total applied force is constant

$\varepsilon = 0.1$

$\varepsilon = 0.5$

$\varepsilon = 1.0$

FIGURE 7.1   Limiting values of concentrated load function $f(y)$.

A general force is

$$f(y) = \tilde{f}\, \delta(y - \xi)$$

where $\tilde{f}$ is a constant equal to the total force applied and concentrated near $y = \xi$. The point load δ has several significant properties:

$$\delta(y - \xi) = 0, \qquad y \ne \xi \tag{7.11}$$

$$\int_{a}^{b} \delta(y - \xi)\, d\xi = \begin{cases} 0, & a, b < y \quad \text{or} \quad y < a, b \\ 1, & a \le y \le b \end{cases}$$

and

$$\int_{-\infty}^{\infty} \delta(y - \xi) \, d\xi = 1 \tag{7.12}$$

Furthermore, consider the *convolution* * of a continuous function $\phi(x)$ with our point load $\delta(y - \xi)$

$$\phi * \delta = \int_{-\infty}^{\infty} \phi(\xi) \, \delta(y - \xi) \, d\xi$$

Formally, we can exchange the limit and integration processes so

$$\phi * \delta = \lim_{\varepsilon \to 0} \int_{y-\varepsilon}^{y+\varepsilon} \phi(\xi) \frac{1}{2\varepsilon} \left[1 + \cos \frac{\pi}{\varepsilon}(y - \xi) \right] d\xi$$

$$= \lim_{\varepsilon \to 0} \left\{ \frac{\phi(y)}{2\varepsilon} \int_{y-\varepsilon}^{y+\varepsilon} \left[1 + \cos \frac{\pi}{\varepsilon}(y - \xi) \right] d\xi \right\}$$

$$= \lim_{\varepsilon \to 0} \frac{\phi(y)}{2\varepsilon}(2\varepsilon) = \phi(y)$$

Hence

$$\int_{-\infty}^{\infty} \phi(\xi) \, \delta(y - \xi) \, d\xi = \phi(y) \tag{7.13}$$

and $\delta(y - \xi)$ has the *reproducing property*.

The "general point load" δ has numerous physical applications and significances and is called the Dirac δ-function [1]. Laurent Schwartz [2] was apparently the first to outline a theory that justifies the existence and use of the δ-function and all its derivatives. His *Theory of Distributions* is powerful and takes its name from the interpretation of "ideal functions" [3, II], such as Dirac's δ-function and its derivatives, as mass distributions, force distributions, electric charge distributions, and so on. Friedman [4] points out quite clearly that the properties (7.11) and (7.12) are contradictory and mathematical nonsense; namely, if a function is zero everywhere except at one point, its integral is necessarily zero, without regard for the definition of the integral used. However, within the context of the Theory of Distributions, the properties (7.11) and (7.12) and their consequence (7.13) are consistent, legitimate, and eminently useful. Although it is beyond the scope of this book to develop any proofs or explore the Theory of Distributions, it is worthwhile to outline a few key points and to summarize the properties of the δ-function, its derivatives, and its integral.

7.2.1   Differentiation, Integration, and Other Features

The δ-function is not a function according to the usual definition in which a function has a definite value for each point in its domain. The δ-function is something more general, and Dirac [1] suggested that its use be confined to simple expressions where no mathematical inconsistencies arise. Indeed, the underlying concept of Schwartz's Theory of Distributions [2] is to consider only values of the integrals of symbolic or ideal functions (e.g., the δ-function) but never values of the function itself. Accordingly, our brief discussion focuses on the δ-function properties and consequences of integrals involving the function and its derivatives. We follow Friedman's presentation [4]* to some extent here and in Sec. 7.3.

So far we have established the following about the δ-function:

$$\delta(x) = 0, \qquad x \neq 0$$

$$\int_{-\infty}^{\infty} \delta(x)\, dx = 1$$

$$\int_{-\infty}^{\infty} \phi(x)\, \delta(x)\, dx = \phi(0)$$

(7.14)

and

$$\int_{-\infty}^{\infty} \phi(\xi)\, \delta(x - \xi)\, d\xi = \phi(x)$$

for every arbitrary continuous function $\phi(x)$. Detailed proofs of these properties and justification of what follows are found in Refs. 2 and 5.

The δ-function is handled algebraically as if it were an ordinary function. However, Friedman [4] shows that any equation involving the δ-function can be understood in the following sense: if the equation is multiplied by $\phi(x)$ and integrated from $-\infty$ to ∞ and (7.14) is used to evaluate integrals, the result is a correct equation involving ordinary functions. For example, if $\psi(x)$ is some arbitrary continuous function, show that

$$\psi(x)\, \delta(x - \xi) = \psi(\xi)\, \delta(x - \xi)$$

Let $\psi(x)\phi(x) = g(x)$; from (7.14),

$$\int_{-\infty}^{\infty} \psi(x)\phi(x)\, \delta(x - \xi)\, dx = \int_{-\infty}^{\infty} g(x)\, \delta(x - \xi)\, dx = g(\xi) = \psi(\xi)\phi(\xi)$$

while

$$\int_{-\infty}^{\infty} \psi(\xi)\phi(x)\, \delta(x - \xi)\, dx = \psi(\xi) \int_{-\infty}^{\infty} \phi(x)\, \delta(x - \xi)\, dx = \psi(\xi)\phi(\xi)$$

Thus the ordinary function $\phi(\xi)$ replaces the δ-function in the equation and the equality is proved.

The foregoing interpretation of equations leads us naturally to the concept of derivatives of the symbolic δ-function. An integration property of ordinary functions is embodied in integration by parts, where if $f(x)$ and $\phi(x)$ are continuous and have a continuous derivative,

$$\int_{-\infty}^{\infty} f'(x)\phi(x)\, dx = f\phi \Big|_{-\infty}^{\infty} - \int_{-\infty}^{\infty} f(x)\phi'(x)\, dx$$

(7.15)

if the integrals and limits exist. For our purposes, it is sufficient to assume that $\phi(x)$ is a *testing function* that is defined to be continuous, have continuous derivatives of all

* B. Friedman, *Principles and Techniques of Applied Mathematics.* Copyright © 1956 by John Wiley & Sons. Used by permission of John Wiley & Sons, Inc.

orders, and vanish identically outside some finite interval. Then (7.15) becomes

$$I = \int_{-\infty}^{\infty} f'(x)\phi(x)\,dx = -\int_{-\infty}^{\infty} f(x)\phi'(x)\,dx$$

We call I, the left-hand integral, a *functional* because, for given f, $I[\phi(x)]$ depends on the testing function $\phi(x)$ and thus is a function of a function.

Accordingly, the symbolic derivative $s'(x)$ is defined by requiring that the integration by parts relationship

$$\int_{-\infty}^{\infty} s'(x)\phi(x)\,dx = -\int_{-\infty}^{\infty} s(x)\phi'(x)\,dx \qquad (7.16)$$

hold for every testing function $\phi(x)$. The right-hand side of (7.16) always exists, so the left-hand side is used to define the relationship that must hold if $s'(x)$ is to be the derivative of $s(x)$. For the δ-function,

$$I_{\delta'} = \int_{-\infty}^{\infty} \delta'(x)\phi(x)\,dx = -\int_{-\infty}^{\infty} \delta(x)\phi'(x)\,dx = -\phi'(0)$$

that is, the operation $\delta'(x)$ leads to a functional $I_{\delta'}$ that assigns the value $-\phi'(0)$ to the testing function $\phi(x)$. Similarly, the functional I_{δ} assigns the value $\phi(0)$ to the testing function $\phi(x)$ [see Eq. (7.14)].

If we proceed, we have

$$I_{\delta''} = \int_{-\infty}^{\infty} \delta''(x)\phi(x)\,dx = -\int_{-\infty}^{\infty} \delta'(x)\phi'(x)\,dx = \phi''(0)$$

and so forth to describe the derivatives of the δ-function.

Now consider the well-known *Heaviside "unit function"* [3, II] defined in terms of ordinary functions as

$$H(x) = \begin{cases} 0, & x < 0 \\ 1, & x \geq 0 \end{cases} \qquad (7.17)$$

Thus H is well defined except that at $x = 0$, where it has a discontinuity, its derivative is undefined. The functional

$$I_H = \int_{-\infty}^{\infty} H(x)\phi(x)\,dx = \int_{0}^{\infty} \phi(x)\,dx$$

exists. More interestingly,

$$I_{H'} = \int_{-\infty}^{\infty} H'(x)\phi(x)\,dx = -\int_{-\infty}^{\infty} H(x)\phi'(x)\,dx$$

$$= -\int_{0}^{\infty} \phi'(x)\,dx = \phi(0)$$

and

$$I_{\delta} = \int_{-\infty}^{\infty} \delta(x)\phi(x)\,dx = \phi(0)$$

Therefore

$$H'(x) = \delta(x)$$

and the integral of the δ-function is the Heaviside "unit function."

The definitions of the δ-function and its properties are easily extended to greater numbers of dimensions. Indeed, the n-dimensional δ-function is the product of n one-dimensional δ-functions. For example,

$$\iiint_{V_\infty} \phi(Q)\, \delta(P, Q)\, dV_Q = \phi(P) \tag{7.18}$$

where $P = (x, y, z)$ and $Q = (\xi, \eta, \zeta)$ in three dimensions, while

$$\delta(P, Q) = \delta(x - \xi)\, \delta(y - \eta)\, \delta(z - \zeta) \tag{7.19}$$

and the integral on Q over the volume V_∞ extends from $-\infty$ to ∞ in each coordinate direction. Of course, $\phi(Q)$ is presumed to be a three-dimensional testing function (see above). Naturally,

$$\iiint_{V_\infty} \delta(P, Q)\, dV_Q = 1 \tag{7.20}$$

7.2.2   Physical Interpretations and Applications

We are now in a position to establish the physical meaning of the δ-function in our models. Two examples give the basic idea.

First, consider Eq. (2.16) for heat conduction

$$\rho c u_t - [(K u_x)_x + (K u_y)_y + (K u_z)_z] = A \tag{7.21}$$

Suppose that we set $A = \rho c \delta$, where A is the rate of heat generation per unit volume by sources at a point, ρ is the density, and c is the specific heat. Now, if

$$\delta = \delta(P, Q)\, \delta(t - \tau) \tag{7.22}$$

where (Q, τ) is a fixed point in time-space,

$$\int_0^t \iiint_V \rho c\, \delta\, dV_Q\, dt = \rho(P) c(P)$$

when ρ and c are continuous functions of position alone and the volume integral encloses point Q while $0 \leq \tau < t$. But

$$\int_0^t \iiint_V A\, dV_Q\, dt = q$$

where q is the total quantity of heat produced by sources in V during time t. Therefore, as $\delta \equiv 0$,* when $P \neq Q$ and $t \neq \tau$, the δ-function (7.22) is equivalent in (7.21) to a

---

*In view of this property, the usual infinite domain integrals can easily be truncated as done here and below; namely,

$$\int_{-\infty}^{\infty} \delta(x)\, dx = \int_{-\varepsilon}^{\varepsilon} \delta(x)\, dx = 1, \qquad \varepsilon > 0, \text{ etc.}$$

heat source of intensity $A = \rho(Q)c(Q)$ appearing instantaneously at a point in space and time and producing a total quantity of heat $q = \rho(Q)c(Q)$ in an instant.

Second, consider the wave equation (2.34b) for vibrations of a membrane under the action of a force F per unit mass of membrane:

$$z_{tt} - \frac{T}{\rho}\nabla^2 z = F \quad \text{or} \quad \rho z_{tt} - T\nabla^2 z = \rho F \tag{7.23}$$

where T is the tension (force per unit length), ρ is the density (mass unit area), and z is the displacement. The total force f exerted on the membrane is

$$f = \iint_A \rho F \, dA$$

while the impulse (force $\times$ time) given to the membrane in a given time is

$$I = \int_0^t \iint_A \rho F \, dA \, dt$$

If $\rho F = \delta(P, Q; t) = \delta(x - \xi)\,\delta(y - \eta)\,\delta(t - \tau)$, where $P = (x, y)$ and $Q = (\xi, \eta)$, then

$$f = \iint_A \rho F \, dA = \delta(t - \tau), \qquad (P, Q) \in A$$

while

$$I = \int_0^t \iint_A \rho F \, dA \, dt = \int_0^t f = 1$$

provided that P and $Q \in A$ ($\in$ means "belongs to the region or set") and $0 \le \tau < t$. Thus the δ-function $\delta(P, Q; t)$ is equivalent to a point load (see Sec. 7.2 above) that occurs at point Q on the membrane instantaneously at time τ and that imparts a unit *impulse* to the membrane at the point Q in an instant of time.

EXAMPLE 7.3 *The Static Deflection of a String under the Action of a Gravity Force.* From (2.78), the model is, for $l = 1$,

$$z_{yy} = \frac{\rho g}{T} = \text{constant} \tag{7.24}$$

$$z(0) = z(1) = 0 \tag{7.25}$$

From (2.81), the solution is

$$z = \frac{\rho g}{2T} y(y - 1) \tag{7.26}$$

From (7.7) to (7.9), the Green's function solution for $l = 1$ is

$$z(y) = \int_0^1 G(y, \eta)P(\eta) \, d\eta \tag{7.27}$$

where $P(\eta) = -\rho g/T$ and

$$G(y, \eta) = \frac{2}{\pi^2} \sum_{n=1}^{\infty} \frac{\sin n\pi y \sin n\pi\eta}{n^2}$$

(Recall that $N_n = \frac{1}{2}$, $\lambda_n^2 = n^2\pi^2$, and $X_n = \sin n\pi y$ for this case.)

Using Jolley [6], we find that

$$\sum_{n=1}^{\infty} \frac{\sin n\pi y \sin n\pi\eta}{n^2} = \begin{cases} \dfrac{\pi^2}{2}\eta(1 - y), & \eta < y \\ \dfrac{\pi^2}{2}y(1 - \eta), & y < \eta \end{cases}$$

so

$$G(y, \eta) = \begin{cases} (1 - \eta)y, & y < \eta \\ (1 - y)\acute{\eta}, & \eta < y \end{cases} \tag{7.28}$$

It follows that

$$z(y) = \int_0^y (1 - y)\eta P(\eta)\, d\eta + \int_y^1 (1 - \eta)y P(\eta)\, d\eta$$

As $P(\eta) = -\rho g/T$, performance of the indicated integrations yields

$$z(y) = \frac{-\rho g}{T}\left[(1 - y)\frac{\eta^2}{2}\Big|_0^y - y\frac{(1 - \eta)^2}{2}\Big|_y^1\right]$$

$$= \frac{-\rho g}{2T}[y^2(1 - y) + y(1 - y)^2]$$

$$= \frac{-\rho g}{2T}y(1 - y) = \frac{\rho g}{2T}y(y - 1)$$

Therefore the Green's function solution reduces to the original solution (7.26) as expected, but the original solution was obtained by direct integration, not by a series technique!

Now consider the related problem

$$z_{yy} = -\delta(y - \eta), \qquad 0 < y, \eta < 1$$
$$z(0) = z(1) \tag{7.29}$$

in which the point load δ is applied at $y = \eta$ along the string. First, integrate the basic equation across the point load so that

$$\int_{\eta - \varepsilon/2}^{\eta + \varepsilon/2} z_{yy}\, dy = -\int_{\eta - \varepsilon/2}^{\eta + \varepsilon/2} \delta(y - \eta)\, dy = -1, \qquad \varepsilon > 0$$

Then

$$z_y\big|_{\eta + \varepsilon/2} - z_y\big|_{\eta - \varepsilon/2} = -1$$

There is a unit jump in the derivative of z—that is, the slope of the string—across the load point. Otherwise $z_y = K_1, y < \eta$, while $z_y = K_2, y > \eta$. We have then

$$y < \eta: z = K_1 y + K_3$$
$$y > \eta: z = K_2 y + K_4$$
$$y = 0: z = 0$$
$$y = 1: z = 1$$

and

$$K_2 - K_1 = -1 \quad \text{or} \quad K_1 = K_2 + 1$$

It is easy to solve for the K_i; we obtain $K_1 = 1 - \eta, K_2 = -\eta, K_3 = 0$, and $K_4 = \eta$. Thus

$$z(y) = \begin{cases} (1 - \eta)y, & y < \eta \\ (1 - y)\eta, & \eta < y \end{cases} \tag{7.30}$$

and for the point load $\delta(y - \eta)$ at η, the displacement $z(y)$ is equal to the Green's function; that is,

$$z(y) = G(y, \eta)$$

The Green's function must satisfy the equation set

$$G_{yy} = -\delta(y - \eta)$$
$$G(0, \eta) = G(1, \eta) = 0$$

We see the preceding result directly by using (7.27) and the reproducing property of the δ-function; as $P(y) = \delta(y - \eta)$,

$$z(y) = \int_0^1 G(y, \xi)[\delta(\xi - \eta)] \, d\xi = G(y, \eta)$$

The Green's function represents here the shape of the string caused by a unit-point load applied at the point η. As previously inferred, $G(y, \eta)$ is an influence function, and the total of all influences along the string gives the string shape at any point. Also, we again see from (7.28) that $G(y, \eta)$ is symmetric; that is, the displacement at y caused by a point force at η is equal to the displacement at η caused by a point force applied at y!

Of course, we could have solved (7.29) directly. After all,

$$z_y = \int z_{yy} \, dy = -\int \delta(y - \eta) \, dy = -H(y - \eta) + c_1(\eta)$$

because $H'(x) = \delta(x)$; $c_1(\eta)$ is arbitrary. Then

$$\int z_y \, dy = -\int H(y - \eta) \, dy + c_1(\eta)y + c_2(\eta)$$

or

$$z = -(y - \eta)H(y - \eta) + c_1(\eta)y + c_2(\eta)$$

as the reader can easily verify. Now, $0 < \eta < 1$, so at $y = 0$, $H(-\eta) = 0$, and

$$z(0) = 0 = c_2(\eta)$$

and, similarly,

$$z(1) = 0 = -(1 - \eta) + c_1(\eta)$$

The final result is

$$z(y) = -(y - \eta)H(y - \eta) + (1 - \eta)y$$

or

$$z(y) = \begin{cases} (1 - \eta)y, & y < \eta \\ (1 - y)\eta, & \eta < y \end{cases}$$

Thus direct use of the Heaviside "unit function" and our symbolic function relations of the last section yield the same solution as (7.30) obtained by formal, normal mathematics.

EXAMPLE 7.4   *Heat Conduction in a Rod* (from Example 7.1, Sec. 7.1). Let the initial temperature $u_0(x) = \delta(x - \eta)$. We have the amount of heat released at $t = 0$

$$q = \rho c \int_0^l u_0(x)\, dx = \rho c \int_0^l \delta(x - \eta)\, dx = \rho c$$

and from (7.6) the temperature is

$$u(x, t) = G(x, \eta; t)$$

Thus our initial condition is equivalent to instantaneously releasing a quantity of heat ρc at the initial time at a point. Again, $G(x, \eta; t)$ represents the influence throughout the time domain of the point source of heat, and we observe that, in this case, $G(x, \eta; t)$ satisfies

$$G_t - kG_{xx} = 0, \qquad 0 < x < l, \quad 0 < t$$

$$G(0, \eta; t) = G(l, \eta; t) = 0, \qquad 0 < t$$

$$G(x, \eta; 0) = \delta(x - \eta), \qquad 0 < x, \eta < l$$

EXAMPLE 7.5   *Heat Conduction in a Rod* (caused by the presence of a heat source of strength ρc). We set $A/\rho c = \delta(x - \eta; t - \bar{\tau})$ and $u_0(x) = 0$, so (7.1) becomes

$$u_t = ku_{xx} = \delta(x - \eta; t - \bar{\tau}), \qquad 0 < x, \eta < l, \quad 0 < t, \bar{\tau}$$

$$u(0, t) = u(l, t) = 0, \qquad 0 < t \qquad\qquad (7.31)$$

$$u(x, 0) = 0, \qquad 0 \leq x \leq l$$

From (7.4),

$$u(x, t) = \int_0^t \int_0^l G(x, \xi; t - \tau)\, \delta(\xi - \eta; \tau - \bar{\tau})\, d\xi\, d\tau \qquad\qquad (7.32)$$

where G is given by (7.5). For (7.32), the properties of the two-dimensional δ-function yield

$$u(x, t) = \begin{cases} 0, & t < \bar{\tau} \\ G(x, \eta; t - \bar{\tau}), & \bar{\tau} \leq t \end{cases} \tag{7.33}$$

Thus G satisfies the model

$$G_t - kG_{xx} = \delta(x - \eta; t - \bar{\tau}), \qquad 0 < x, \eta < l, \quad 0 < t, \bar{\tau}$$

$$G(0, \xi; t) = G(l, \xi; t) = G(x, \xi; 0) = 0, \qquad 0 < \bar{\tau}$$

(see the Green's function model in the previous example).

Physically, (7.33) shows that in the conduction model the velocity of heat transfer is infinite because, at the instant $t = \bar{\tau}$ when the heat source of strength $q = \rho c$ appears, the temperature in the bar changes to a nonzero value everywhere. Thus this Green's function study reveals a weakness in our mathematical model. In particular, our experimental law of conduction does not exactly account for the molecular motion concept of heat flow in conduction, which predicts a rapid, but finite, heat propagation velocity (see Sec. 2.2.1). The error in the model is, however, negligible for most applications.

7.3   GREEN'S FUNCTIONS

In the previous section we saw that the one-dimensional Green's function $G(x, \xi)$ satisfied the mathematical model with boundary conditions of the first kind:

$$G_{xx} = -\delta(x - \xi), \qquad 0 < x, \xi < l$$

$$G(0, \xi) = G(l, \xi) = 0 \tag{7.34}$$

The solution to this model was obtained in the form of a bilinear series

$$G(x, \xi) = \sum_{n=1}^{\infty} \frac{X_n(x)X_n(\xi)}{\lambda_n^2 N_n} \tag{7.35}$$

where X_n and λ_n^2 were the solutions of the one-dimensional eigenvalue problem

$$X_n'' + \lambda_n^2 X_n = 0, \qquad 0 < x < l$$

$$X_n(0) = X_n(1) = 0 \tag{7.36}$$

and

$$N_n = \int_0^l X_n^2(\xi)\, d\xi \tag{7.37}$$

However, the solution was obtained by direct integration in Example 7.3 of the previous section as

$$G(x, \xi) = \begin{cases} (1 - \xi)x, & x < \xi \\ (1 - x)\xi, & \xi < x \end{cases} \tag{7.38}$$

for $l = 1$, and summation of the series confirmed that (7.35) and (7.38) were identical.

It is left as an exercise to show that the natural generalization to Sturm–Liouville form (see Chap. 4) is valid—namely, that the solution

$$G(x, \xi) = \sum_{n=1}^{\infty} \frac{X_n(x)X_n(\xi)}{\lambda_n^2 N_n}$$

is valid for the model

$$[rG_x]_x + q(x)G = -\delta(x - \xi), \qquad 0 < x, \xi < l$$
$$G(0, \xi) = G(l, \xi) = 0 \tag{7.39}$$

if the X_n and λ_n^2 are solutions of the related Sturm–Liouville eigenvalue problem

$$[rX_n']' + [q(x) + \lambda_n^2 p(x)]X_n = 0, \qquad 0 < x < l$$
$$X_n(0) = X_n(l) = 0$$

The generalization to two dimensions follows the preceding pattern, and the discussion of double Fourier series in Sec. 5.2 gives us the analytical basis for our operations. For example, suppose that we have steady-state heat conduction in a plate of unit dimensions. For the square region $R: 0 < x < 1, 0 < y < 1$ with boundary C, so the *closure* $\bar{R}$ of R is $0 \le x \le 1, 0 \le y \le 1$, the model is

$$\nabla^2 u = -F(x, y) \qquad \text{in } R$$
$$u = 0 \qquad \text{on } C \tag{7.40}$$

In Chap. 5 we showed that the Ω_{mn} satisfying the Helmholtz eigenvalue problem

$$\nabla^2 \Omega + \lambda^2 \Omega = 0 \qquad \text{in } R$$
$$\Omega = 0 \qquad \text{on } C \tag{7.41}$$

were a complete set (see Sec. 5.2) of eigenfunctions with eigenvalues λ_{mn}^2. The Ω_{mn} and λ_{mn}^2 were given explicitly by (5.95). If the functions u and F in (7.40) are continuous with continuous first derivatives, double Fourier series representations of these functions will converge absolutely and uniformly on R.

We let

$$u(x, y) = \sum_n \sum_m A_{mn}\Omega_{mn} \tag{7.42}$$

and

$$F(x, y) = \sum_n \sum_m f_{mn}\Omega_{mn} \tag{7.43}$$

Our solution u satisfies the problem boundary conditions. Introducing (7.42) and (7.43) in (7.40) produces

$$\sum_n \sum_m A_{mn} \nabla^2 \Omega_{mn} = -\sum_n \sum_m f_{nm}\Omega_{mn}$$

As (7.41) holds, we obtain next

$$\sum_n \sum_m (\lambda_{mn}^2 A_{mn} - f_{mn})\Omega_{mn} = 0 \tag{7.44}$$

But Ω_{mn}, λ_{mn}^2, and f_{mn} are known from (7.41) and (7.43), and $F(x, y)$ is given. Then (7.43) yields

$$f_{mn} = \frac{1}{N_{mn}} \iint_R F(\xi, \eta)\Omega_{mn}(\xi, \eta)\, d\xi\, d\eta \tag{7.45}$$

where

$$N_{mn} = \iint_R \Omega_{mn}^2\, d\xi\, d\eta \tag{7.46}$$

Therefore $A_{mn} = f_{mn}/\lambda_{mn}^2$ because all coefficients of the linearly independent Ω_{mn} in (7.44) must be zero.

Our solution is

$$u(x, y) = \sum_n \sum_m \frac{f_{mn}}{\lambda_{mn}^2}\Omega_{mn}(x, y) \tag{7.47}$$

and using (7.45) and (7.46), we obtain

$$u(x, y) = \sum_n \sum_m \frac{\Omega_{mn}(x, y)}{\lambda_{mn}^2 N_{mn}} \iint_R F(\xi, \eta)\Omega_{mn}(\xi, \eta)\, d\xi\, d\eta$$

In a uniformly convergent series, we can exchange summation and integration so

$$u(x, y) = \iint_R \left\{ \sum_n \sum_m \frac{\Omega_{mn}(x, y)\Omega_{mn}(\xi, \eta)}{\lambda_{mn}^2 N_{mn}} \right\} F(\xi, \eta)\, d\xi\, d\eta$$

As before, the Green's function

$$G(x, y, \xi, \eta) = G(P, Q) = \sum_n \sum_m \frac{\Omega_{mn}(x, y)\Omega_{mn}(\xi, \eta)}{\lambda_{mn}^2 N_{mn}} \tag{7.48}$$

arises directly from a formal eigenfunction expansion, and we can write

$$u(x, y) = \iint_R G(x, y, \xi, \eta)F(\xi, \eta)\, d\xi\, d\eta$$

$$= \iint_R G(P, Q)F(Q)\, dA_Q \tag{7.49}$$

Clearly, from (7.48), $G(Q, P) = G(P, Q)$; that is, the Green's function is symmetric. There also is no doubt that the Green's function (7.48) exists as a uniformly convergent series (see the Problems).

If we set $F(x, y) = \delta(P, E) = \delta(x - v)\,\delta(y - \omega)$ in 7.40, where S is a fixed source point, the reproducing property of the δ-function gives

$$u(x, y) = \iint_R G(P, Q)\,\delta(Q, E)\, dA_Q = G(P, E) = G(x, y, v, \omega)$$

Hence (again) the Green's function is the response or influence at P caused by a point source of heat at E. Obviously,

$$\nabla^2 G = -\delta(P,E) \qquad \text{in } R$$
$$G = 0 \qquad P \text{ on } C; \qquad E \text{ not on } C \tag{7.50}$$

With the foregoing background we can turn to more general concepts of the Green's function, its properties and applications. Consider the general two-dimensional problem

$$\nabla^2 u = -F(P) \qquad \text{in } R$$
$$B[u] = q(P) \qquad \text{on } C \tag{7.51}$$

where $B[u]$ represents the application of one of the three types of boundary condition at every point on C (see Fig. 7.2). The appropriate Green's function $G(P, Q)$ must then satisfy

$$\nabla_P^2 G = -\delta(P, Q) \qquad \text{in } R$$
$$B_P[G] = 0, \qquad P \text{ on } C \tag{7.52}$$

that is, $\nabla_P^2 G \equiv 0$ when $P \neq Q$ and $\nabla_P^2 = \partial^2/\partial x^2 + \partial^2/\partial y^2$.

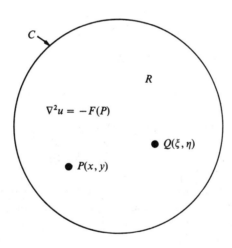

FIGURE 7.2

Let us examine (7.51) and (7.52) in terms of the integral Green's Second Identity given in Appendix 1, Sec. A.1.4. For two functions f and $g \in C^2$,

$$\oint \left(f \frac{\partial g}{\partial n} - g \frac{\partial f}{\partial n} \right) ds = \iint_R (f \nabla^2 g - g \nabla^2 f) \, dx \, dy \tag{7.53}$$

If we recall our discussion of the δ-function and the effect of an integration, we can proceed under the assurance that (7.53) holds for generalized or symbolic functions.

First, is $G(P, Q) = G(Q, P)$ when $G(P, Q) \equiv 0$ for P on C—that is, when G satisfies the Dirichlet boundary condition? Let $f = G(P, Q_1)$ and $g = G(P, Q_2)$ in

(7.53). Then, since $G \equiv 0$ on C, (7.53) becomes, from (7.52),

$$0 = \iint_R [G(P, Q_1) \nabla_P^2 G(P, Q_2) - G(P, Q_2) \nabla_P^2 G(P, Q_1)] \, dx \, dy$$

$$= -\iint_R [G(P, Q_1) \delta(P, Q_2) - G(P, Q_2) \delta(P, Q_1)] \, dx \, dy$$

Hence, from the δ-function reproducing property,

$$G(Q_2, Q_1) - G(Q_1, Q_2) = 0$$

Accordingly, $G(Q_2, Q_1) = G(Q_1, Q_2)$; that is, the Green's function is symmetric.

Second, what is the nature of the Green's function $G(P, Q)$ as $P \to Q$? Suppose that we examine

$$\nabla_P^2 S(P, Q) = -\delta(P, Q) \tag{7.54}$$

near $P = Q$. Because $\delta(P, Q) = \delta(x - \xi)\,\delta(y - \eta)$, the question arises as to whether or not $\delta(P, Q)$ depends on the direction θ in an (r, θ) polar coordinate system centered at Q with

$$r = [(x - \xi)^2 + (y - \eta)^2]^{1/2}$$

$$\theta = \tan^{-1}\left(\frac{y - \eta}{x - \xi}\right)$$

Friedman [4]* suggests that we examine the δ-function definition

$$\iint \phi(P, Q)\,\delta(P, Q)\,dA_P = \phi(Q, Q)$$

where $\phi(P, Q)$ is a test function. In polar coordinates,

$$\int_0^\infty \int_0^{2\pi} \phi(r, \theta)\,\delta(r, \theta) r \, d\theta \, dr = \phi \Big|_{r=0} \tag{7.55}$$

The origin has all values of θ as coordinates, but ϕ is a continuous function and thus is single valued at the origin. The value $\phi|_{r=0}$ must, therefore, be independent of θ. Consequently, because $\delta(r, \theta)$ must have the reproducing property, we replace $\delta(r, \theta)$ by $r^{-1}\,\delta(r)$ temporarily in (7.55) to obtain

$$\int_0^{2\pi} \int_0^\infty \phi(r, \theta)\frac{\delta(r)}{r} r \, dr \, d\theta = \int_0^{2\pi} \phi\Big|_{r=0} d\theta = 2\pi\phi\Big|_{r=0} \tag{7.56}$$

Following Friedman [4],* we deduce from (7.55) and (7.56) that

$$\delta(r, \theta) = \delta(P, Q) = \frac{\delta(r)}{2\pi r}$$

or

$$\delta(P, Q) = \frac{\delta(\mathbf{PQ})}{2\pi \cdot \mathbf{PQ}} \tag{7.57}$$

---

* B. Friedman, *Principles and Techniques of Applied Mathematics.* Copyright © 1956 by John Wiley & Sons. Used by permission of John Wiley & Sons, Inc.

where

$$\mathbf{PQ} = r = [(x - \xi)^2 + (y - \eta)^2]^{1/2}$$

Now return to (7.54) and integrate the equation over a small region R_ε, $\varepsilon > 0$, centered at Q:

$$\iint\limits_{R_\varepsilon} \nabla_P^2 S(P, Q)\, dA_P = -\iint\limits_{R_\varepsilon} \delta(P, Q)\, dA_P \qquad (7.58)$$

Because $\delta(P, Q) \equiv 0$ for $P \neq Q$, the small region R_ε is equivalent to the infinite domain, and

$$\iint\limits_{R_\varepsilon} \delta(P, Q)\, dA_P = 1 \qquad (7.59)$$

by definition. From Gauss' theorem (A.1.5) with $v = \nabla g$,

$$\int_{R_\varepsilon} \nabla_P^2 S(P, Q)\, dA_P = \oint_{C_\varepsilon} \frac{\partial S}{\partial n}(P, Q)\, ds_P \qquad (7.60)$$

where n is the outward normal and s is the arc length on the curve C_ε bounding R_ε. Now, (7.59) and (7.60) reduce (7.58) to

$$\oint_{C_\varepsilon} \frac{\partial S}{\partial n}\, ds_P = -1, \qquad \varepsilon > 0 \qquad (7.61)$$

As $\partial/\partial n = \partial/\partial r$ on the circle C_ε about Q,

$$\oint_{C_\varepsilon} \frac{\partial S}{\partial r}\, ds_P = -1$$

However, $\delta(P, Q)$ is independent of direction and dependent only on r for P near Q according to (7.57). Thus, from (7.54), $\nabla^2 S$ and so $\partial S/\partial n$ are also functions only of r in this case in which no boundary conditions are imposed. If $S = S(r)$ alone, $\partial S/\partial r$ is constant on C_ε so

$$\frac{\partial S}{\partial r} \oint_{C_\varepsilon} ds_P = -1$$

and

$$\frac{\partial S}{\partial r} = \frac{-1}{2\pi r}$$

as

$$\oint_{C_\varepsilon} ds_P = \int_0^{2\pi} r\, d\theta = 2\pi r$$

Thus, finally,

$$S(P, Q) = \frac{-1}{2\pi} \ln r = \frac{-1}{2\pi} \ln \mathbf{PQ} \qquad (7.62)$$

A similar result, namely,

$$S_3(P, Q) = \frac{-1}{4\pi r}$$

can be derived for three dimensions (see the Problems).

The solution (7.62), which has the property (7.61) in the limit—that is,

$$\lim_{\varepsilon \to 0} \oint_{C_\varepsilon} \frac{\partial S}{\partial n} \, ds_P = \lim_{\varepsilon \to 0} \int_0^{2\pi} \left(\frac{-1}{2\pi r}\right) r \, d\theta = -1$$

and has a singularity at one fixed point Q, is called a *fundamental singularity* [7] of the equation considered. In this case,

$$S(P, Q) = \frac{-1}{2\pi} \ln r = \frac{-1}{2\pi} \ln \mathbf{PQ} \tag{7.63}$$

is the fundamental singularity of the two-dimensional Laplace equation

$$\nabla^2 u = u_{xx} + u_{yy} = 0$$

while

$$S(P, Q) = \frac{-1}{4\pi r} = \frac{-1}{4\pi \mathbf{PQ}} \tag{7.64}$$

is the fundamental singularity of the three-dimensional Laplace equation

$$\nabla^2 u = u_{xx} + u_{yy} + u_{zz} = 0$$

Returning to (7.52), we see that our S determined as fundamental singularities satisfy the equation

$$\nabla_P^2 S(P, Q) = -\delta(P, Q) \qquad \text{in } R$$

but not the boundary conditions. Accordingly, the Green's function is easily constructed by the linear superposition of $S(P, Q)$ and a harmonic function $H(P, Q)$ that satisfies

$$\nabla_P^2 H(P, Q) \equiv 0 \qquad \text{in } R$$

$$B_P[H(P, Q) + S(P, Q)] \equiv 0 \qquad \text{on } C \tag{7.65}$$

We find that

$$G(P, Q) = S(P, Q) + H(P, Q) \tag{7.66}$$

satisfies (7.52) and is composed of a clearly identifiable singularity and a regular, well-behaved, harmonic function. We shall construct some specific examples later.

Return to the Green's Second Identity (7.53) and use $f = u(P)$ and $g = G(P, Q)$, where u satisfies (7.51) and G satisfies (7.52). For simplicity, let

$$B_P[\ ] = 0 \text{ be } [\ ] = 0 \qquad \text{on } C$$

That is, $u(P) = q(P)$ and $G(P, Q) = 0$ on C. We have

$$\oint_C \left[u(Q)\frac{\partial G}{\partial n_Q}(P, Q) - G(P, Q)\frac{\partial u(Q)}{\partial n_Q}\right] ds_Q = \iint_R [u(Q)\nabla_Q^2 G - G(P, Q)\nabla_Q^2 u] \, d\xi \, d\eta \tag{7.67}$$

Using the known values in (7.67) yields

$$\oint_C \left[q(Q)\frac{\partial G}{\partial n_Q}(P, Q) \right] ds_Q = \iint_R [-u(Q)\,\delta(P, Q) + G(P, Q)F(Q)]\,d\xi\,d\eta$$

or after using the reproducing property of $\delta(P, Q)$ and some rearrangement,

$$u(P) = \iint_R F(Q)G(P, Q)\,d\xi\,d\eta - \oint_C q(Q)\frac{\partial G}{\partial n_Q}(P, Q)\,ds_Q \tag{7.68}$$

Thus (7.68) gives a closed-form solution in terms of the Green's function $G(P, Q)$ for the general inhomogeneous problem (7.51) with Dirichlet boundary conditions on C. From (7.63), (7.65), and (7.66), we have

$$G(P, Q) = \frac{-1}{2\pi} \ln \mathbf{PQ} + H(P, Q) \tag{7.69}$$

and the problem is reduced to finding $H(P, Q)$. Similar results are obtained for three-dimensional problems in the Problems.

Following Bergman and Schiffer [7], we identify three general Green's functions with the three types of boundary-value problems for Eq. (7.51). The first is the Green's function given above for the Dirichlet problem. The second is the Neumann's function

$$N(P, Q) = S(P, Q) + \bar{n}(P, Q) \tag{7.70}$$

for the Neumann problem (see the compatibility condition discussed in Chap. 6 for this problem)

$$\nabla_P^2 u = -F(P) \quad \text{in } R$$

$$\frac{\partial u}{\partial n_P}(P) = q(P) \quad \text{on } C \tag{7.71}$$

$$\oint_C q\,ds_P = \iint_R F(P)\,dA_P$$

Here $N(P, Q)$ satisfies [7]

$$\nabla_P^2 N = -\delta(P, Q) \quad \text{in } R$$

$$\frac{\partial N}{\partial n_P}(P, Q) = \frac{-1}{L} \quad \text{on } C \tag{7.72}$$

where L is the length of C. It follows that the solution of (7.71) by (7.70) requires that the regular harmonic function $\bar{n}(P, Q)$ satisfying

$$\nabla_P^2 \bar{n}(P, Q) = 0 \quad \text{in } R$$

$$\frac{\partial \bar{n}}{\partial n_P}(P, Q) = -\frac{\partial S}{\partial n_P}(P, Q) - \frac{1}{L} \quad \text{on } C \tag{7.73}$$

must be found.

It is easy to show again by use of (7.53) that $N(P, Q) = N(Q, P)$; that is, the Neumann's function is symmetric. Similarly, (7.53) yields

$$\oint_C \left[u(Q)\frac{\partial N}{\partial n_Q} - N\frac{\partial u(Q)}{\partial n_Q} \right] ds_Q = \iint_R [u(Q) \nabla_Q^2 N - N \nabla_Q^2 u] \, d\xi \, d\eta$$

or from (7.71) to (7.73)

$$-\frac{1}{L}\oint_C u(Q) \, ds_q - \oint_C N(P, Q)q(Q) \, ds_Q = \iint_R [-u(Q) \, \delta(P, Q) + N(P, Q)F(Q)] \, d\xi \, d\eta$$

Thus

$$u(P) = \iint_R F(Q)N(P, Q) \, d\xi \, d\eta + \oint_C q(Q)N(P, Q) \, ds_Q + \frac{1}{L}\oint_C u(Q) \, ds_Q \qquad (7.74)$$

The term

$$\frac{1}{L}\oint_C u(Q) \, dQ = \tilde{C}$$

is a constant and reminds us that the solution to the Neumann problem is not unique but is determined only to within an additive constant. Indeed, (7.72) is only sufficient to define $N(P, Q)$ to within an additive constant also. It is not possible to set $\partial N/\partial n_P = 0$ on C for the same reason that $u(P, Q)$ must satisfy the compatibility condition in (7.71) (see the Problems).

For the string and heat models studied in the previous sections, the Neumann problem also presents certain difficulties. For example, a series solution for the Green's function in the form (7.5) or (7.9) is not possible because now the smallest eigenvalue is zero. For the string, a Neumann support implies free ends and a point force causes the string to depart arbitrarily far from its rest point. For the Neumann string problem, Courant and Hilbert [3, I] prescribe a "Green's function in the generalized sense" $k(x, \xi)$, which we cannot discuss here save to say that $k(x, \xi)$ has the symmetry property and can be constructed in approximately the same manner as a regular Green's function.

The third general function is the Robin's function for boundary conditions of the third kind. Again we have

$$\tilde{R}(P, Q) = S(P, Q) + \bar{r}(P, Q) \qquad (7.75)$$

where, for h being a function of P on C,

$$\nabla_P^2 \tilde{R} = -\delta(P) \qquad \text{in } R$$

$$\frac{\partial \tilde{R}}{\partial n_P}(P) - h\tilde{R}(P) = 0 \qquad \text{on } C \qquad (7.76)$$

$\bar{r}$ is the regular harmonic function satisfying

$$\nabla_P^2 \bar{r} = 0 \qquad \text{in } R$$

$$\frac{\partial \bar{r}}{\partial n_P}(P) - h\bar{r}(P) = -\left[\frac{\partial S}{\partial n_P}(P) - hS(P) \right] \qquad \text{on } C \qquad (7.77)$$

and

$$\nabla_p^2 u = -F(P) \qquad \text{in } R$$

$$\frac{\partial u}{\partial n_P} - hu = q(P) \qquad \text{on } C$$

(7.78)

Bergman and Shiffer [7] call G, N, and $\tilde{R}$ the *fundamental functions* of the equation

$$\nabla_p^2 u = 0 \qquad \text{in } R$$

These functions have a fundamental singularity in the domain R and prescribed behavior on the boundary.

It is well beyond our scope to go further into a general study of Green's functions, but the references provide a fertile ground for advanced readers. To complete this chapter, we consider construction of several Green's functions by the *method of images*, which yields closed-form solutions by deductive reasoning.

EXAMPLE 7.6   *Green's Function for the Half-Plane $y > 0$ (Fig. 7.3).* We require

$$\nabla_P^2 G = -\delta(P, Q) \qquad \text{in } y > 0$$

$$G(P, Q) = 0 \qquad \text{on } y = 0$$

and already know that

$$G(P, Q) = \frac{-1}{2\pi} \ln \mathbf{PQ} + H(P, Q)$$

where H must be harmonic and regular in $y > 0$. Now on $y = 0$,

$$G(P', Q) = \frac{-1}{2\pi} \ln \mathbf{P'Q} + H(P', Q)$$

$$= \frac{-1}{2\pi} \ln \left[(x' - \xi)^2 + \eta^2 \right]^{1/2} + H(x', 0, \xi, \eta)$$

$$= \frac{-1}{2\pi} \ln r' + H = 0$$

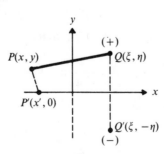

FIGURE 7.3

Therefore

$$H = \frac{1}{2\pi} \ln r' \qquad \text{on } y = 0$$

The *method of images* requires that we define an *image singularity* or point source across the boundary in question from the fundamental singularity. The image singularity must have just the strength, location, and character to successfully oppose the original one at the boundary. In the present case, it is perhaps clear that a singularity located at Q' (Fig. 7.3) and with opposite sign to that at Q is just what is needed. Let us choose

$$H(P, Q) = H(P, Q') = \frac{1}{2\pi} \ln r^*$$

where

$$r^* = [(x - \xi)^2 + (y + \eta)^2]^{1/2}$$

H is harmonic and regular in $y > 0$ because it has no singularity there and $\ln r^*$ is a solution of Laplace's equation. On $y = 0$,

$$H(P', Q) = \frac{1}{2\pi} \ln r'$$

as required. Our result is then

$$G(P, Q) = \frac{-1}{2\pi}(\ln r - \ln r^*)$$

$$= \frac{-1}{2\pi} \ln \frac{r}{r^*}$$

$$= \frac{-1}{2\pi} \ln \left[\frac{(x - \xi)^2 + (y - \eta)^2}{(x - \xi)^2 + (y + \eta)^2}\right]^{1/2}$$

EXAMPLE 7.7   *Green's Function for the Circle.*

$$x^2 + y^2 \leq \rho_0^2 \quad \text{or} \quad \rho_P \leq \rho_0, \qquad 0 < \theta \leq 2\pi \quad \text{(Fig. 7.4)}$$

We require

$$\nabla_P^2 G = -\delta(P, Q) \qquad \text{in } x^2 + y^2 < \rho_0^2$$

$$G(P, Q) = 0 \qquad \text{on } x^2 + y^2 = \rho_0^2$$

and know, in terms of the notation in Fig. 7.4, that

$$G(P, Q) = \frac{-1}{2\pi} \ln r + H \tag{7.79}$$

where H must be harmonic and regular in $x^2 + y^2 < \rho_0^2$, and on $\rho_P^2 = \rho_0^2 = x^2 + y^2$:

$$H = \frac{1}{2\pi} \ln r' \tag{7.80}$$

Because our method of images suggests the need for a singularity across the boundary, we place Q' on the line passing through O and Q and with $\rho^* > \rho_0$. Reflection across the circle requires not a simple linear relationship as for the half-plane, but an inverse relationship, because the interior of the circle corresponds to the entire exterior and $\rho \to 0$ to $\rho^* \to \infty$, while $\rho \to \rho_0$ corresponds to $\rho^* \to \rho_0$. Accordingly,

$$\rho^*\rho = \rho_0^2 \tag{7.81}$$

Now, H must satisfy (7.80) as $P \to P'$ and $\rho_P \to \rho_0$; then we have the geometric relationships described by the inset on Fig. 7.4. The triangles $OP'Q$ and $OP'Q'$ are similar because they share the common included angle at O, and the pairs of sides **OP'** and **OQ** and **OQ'** and **OP'** are proportional as a consequence of (7.81); that is,

$$\frac{\rho_0}{\rho} = \frac{\rho^*}{\rho_0}$$

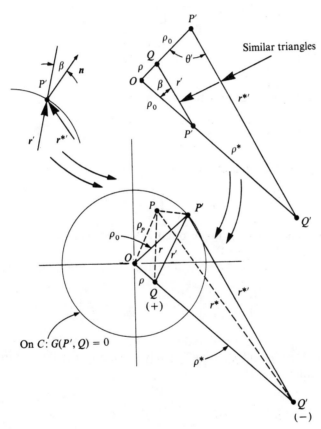

FIGURE 7.4

It follows that

$$\frac{r^{*\prime}}{r'} = \frac{\rho_0}{\rho} = \frac{\rho^*}{\rho_0}$$

whence

$$\frac{\rho r^{*\prime}}{\rho_0} = r' \tag{7.82}$$

Clearly, if we let

$$H(P, Q) = \frac{1}{2\pi} \ln \frac{\rho r^*}{\rho_0} \tag{7.83}$$

we have, by virtue of (7.82),

$$H(P', Q) = \frac{1}{2\pi} \ln \frac{\rho r^{*'}}{\rho_0} = \frac{1}{2\pi} \ln r' \tag{}$$

and (7.80) is satisfied. Our Green's function (7.79) is then

$$G(P, Q) = -\frac{1}{2\pi} \left[\ln r - \ln \frac{\rho r^*}{\rho_0} \right]$$

$$= -\frac{1}{2\pi} \ln \left(\frac{\rho_0 r}{\rho r^*} \right) \tag{7.84}$$

Suppose that we seek now to solve the problem

$$\nabla^2 u = 0 \text{ on } \rho < \rho_0, \qquad 0 < \theta \le 2\pi$$

$$u = q(\theta) \text{ on } \rho = \rho_0 \tag{7.85}$$

where (ρ, θ) are polar coordinates centered at point O (Fig. 7.4). From (7.68), we write

$$u(\rho, \theta) = -\oint_C q \frac{\partial G}{\partial n_P} \, ds_P \tag{7.86}$$

where for convenience we have taken point P to the boundary (but, of course, G is symmetric so no problem arises).

We need to calculate the normal derivative in (7.86); in general,

$$\frac{\partial G}{\partial n} = -\frac{1}{2\pi} \left[\frac{\partial}{\partial n} (\ln r) - \frac{\partial}{\partial n} \left(\ln \frac{\rho r^*}{\rho_0} \right) \right] \tag{7.87}$$

where n is an exterior unit normal and r and r^* are the magnitudes of vectors r and r^* (see Fig. 7.4). Here ρ and ρ_0 are effectively constants, marking source locations. Now let us examine

$$\frac{\partial}{\partial n} (\ln r) = \frac{1}{r} \frac{\partial r}{\partial n} \quad \text{and} \quad \frac{\partial}{\partial n} \left(\ln \frac{\rho r^*}{\rho_0} \right) = \frac{1}{r^*} \frac{\partial r^*}{\partial n} \tag{7.88}$$

A simple limiting geometric argument (see the Problems) shows that (see Fig. 7.4) at P'

$$\left. \frac{\partial r}{\partial n} \right|_{P'} = \cos \beta = \left. \frac{r \cdot n}{r} \right|_{P'} \tag{7.89}$$

Similarly, at P'

$$\left. \frac{\partial r^*}{\partial n} \right|_{P'} = \left. \frac{r^* \cdot n}{r^*} \right|_{P'} = \cos \theta' \tag{7.90}$$

The cosine law for triangles gives us, for $OP'Q'$,

$$\rho^{*2} = r^{*'2} + \rho_0^2 - 2\rho_0 r^{*'} \cos \theta' \tag{7.91}$$

and for OQP'

$$\rho^2 = \rho_0^2 + r'^2 - 2\rho_0 r' \cos \beta \tag{7.92}$$

Therefore at the boundary point P',

$$\left. \frac{\partial r}{\partial n} \right|_{P'} = -\frac{\rho^2 - \rho_0^2 - r'^2}{2\rho_0 r'} = \frac{\rho_0^2 + r'^2 - \rho^2}{2\rho_0 r'}$$

$$\left. \frac{\partial r^*}{\partial n} \right|_{P'} = -\frac{\rho^{*2} - r^{*'2} - \rho_0^2}{2\rho_0 r^{*'}} = \frac{\rho_0^2 + (r'^2 \rho_0^2/\rho^2) - (\rho_0^4/\rho^2)}{2\rho_0^2 r'/\rho} \tag{7.93}$$

by virtue of (7.82).

The Green's function derivative

$$\left. \frac{\partial G}{\partial n} \right|_{P'} = -\frac{1}{2\pi} \left[\frac{1}{r'} \frac{\rho_0^2 + r'^2 - \rho^2}{2\rho_0 r'} - \frac{1}{r^{*'}} \frac{\rho_0^2 + (r'^2 \rho_0^2/\rho^2) - (\rho_0^4/\rho^2)}{2\rho_0 r'/\rho} \right]$$

Since $r^{*'} = r'\rho_0/\rho$, this expression can be greatly simplified to

$$\left. \frac{\partial G}{\partial n} \right|_{P'} = -\frac{1}{2\pi\rho_0} \frac{\rho_0^2 - \rho^2}{r'^2}$$

Thus, from (7.86),

$$u(\rho, \theta) = \frac{1}{2\pi} \oint_C q \frac{\rho_0^2 - \rho^2}{r'^2} \frac{ds_P}{\rho_0}$$

But, on C, $q = q(\theta)$, $ds_P = ds_{P'} = \rho_0 \, d\theta_{P'}$ and from the cosine law,

$$r'^2 = \rho^2 + \rho_0^2 - 2\rho_0\rho \cos(\theta_{P'} - \theta)$$

The final result is

$$u(\rho, \theta) = \frac{1}{2\pi} \int_0^{2\pi} q(\theta_{P'}) \frac{\rho_0^2 - \rho^2}{\rho^2 + \rho_0^2 - 2\rho_0\rho \cos(\theta_{P'} - \theta)} \, d\theta_{P'} \tag{7.94}$$

or

$$u(\rho, \theta) = \frac{\rho_0^2 - \rho^2}{2\pi} \int_0^{2\pi} \frac{q(\theta_{P'}) \, d\theta_{P'}}{\rho^2 + \rho_0^2 - 2\rho_0\rho \cos(\theta_{P'} - \theta)}, \qquad \rho < \rho_0 \tag{7.95}$$

This is the *Poisson Integral Formula* for the interior of the circle $\rho < \rho_0, 0 < \theta \le 2\pi$. For a continuous function $q(\theta)$ that is periodic and has a square-integrable first derivative, the integral (7.95) yields a continuous function.

An interesting result called the *Mean-Value Theorem* arises for $\rho = 0$; then, from (7.95),

$$u(0, \theta) = \frac{1}{2\pi} \int_0^{2\pi} q(\theta_{P'}) \, d\theta_{P'}$$

That is, if u is harmonic in any circle, the value of u at the center is the average of the boundary values of u.

7.4 SUMMARY

In this chapter we explored a new way of expressing solutions to ordinary and partial differential equations in terms of an integral and a fundamental function, in lieu of series or eigenfunction expansions. The fundamental function, usually called the Green's function, represented the influence or response of a system to a unit point load or source. The total response was the *linear superposition* through integration of the responses throughout the system; thus the method is restricted to linear models.

The symbolic function or distribution, the Dirac δ-function, provided a key to the understanding of the behavior of the fundamental functions. Indeed, for a class of equations—namely, $\nabla^2 u = -F$ in a region R—we found that the fundamental singularity S for all cases was

$$S(P, Q) = -\frac{1}{2\pi} \ln \mathbf{PQ}$$

for two dimensions; and if certain boundary conditions were prescribed on the boundary C of R, it was only necessary to add a function, harmonic in R and just canceling the appropriate boundary values of S on C, to S to generate the fundamental solutions. They, of course, are used to solve very general problems in u.

Series expansions, in eigenvalues and eigenfunctions of a related eigenvalue problem, and the method of images were used to generate fundamental solutions for partial differential equations, whereas in the case of some boundary-value problems for ordinary differential equations, we were able to find the fundamental solutions by direct integration.

We have only touched briefly on an important aspect of mathematics in this chapter, neglecting, for example, a great deal of the potential theory of harmonic functions. The Green's function or fundamental solution approach has great power and many applications in pure and applied mathematics; Refs. 3, 4, 7, and 8 provide a penetrating coverage of deeper insights, further topics, and results.

REFERENCES

1. P. A. M. Dirac, *The Principles of Quantum Mechanics*, 3rd ed. Oxford: Clarendon Press, 1949.

2. L. Schwartz, *Théorie des Distributions*, Vols. 1 & 2. Paris: Hermann & Cie, 1950–1951.

3. R. Courant and D. Hilbert, *Methods of Mathematical Physics*, Vols. I & II. New York: Interscience (a division of John Wiley & Sons), 1953 & 1962.

4. B. Friedman, *Principles and Techniques of Applied Mathematics*. New York: John Wiley & Sons, 1956.

5. I. M. Gel'fand and G. E. Shilov, *Generalized Functions*, Vol. 1, *Properties and Operations* (trans. by E. Saletan). New York: Academic Press, 1964.

6. L. B. W. Jolley, *Summation of Series*, 2nd revised ed. New York: Dover, 1961.

7. S. Bergman and M. Schiffer, *Kernel Functions and Elliptic Partial Differential Equations in Mathematical Physics*. New York: Academic Press, 1953.

8. O. D. Kellogg, *Foundations of Potential Theory*. New York: Dover, 1953.

PROBLEMS

7.1 Prove that the bilinear series (7.5) is uniformly convergent in x or ξ for X_n and λ_n^2 given by (7.3) and $t > 0$. Show then that $G(x, \xi; t)$ is a continuous and differentiable function of (x, ξ, t) for $t > 0$ (see Appendix 1).

7.2 Find the bilinear series for G for the model (5.17) to (5.19), and express the solution to the model in integral form employing G.

7.3 Find the bilinear series for G for the model in Example 3.1, and express the solution in integral form.

7.4 Repeat Prob. 7.3 for Example 3.2 (provided that $\lambda_n^2 \neq 0$).

7.5 Find the bilinear series for G in each case:

(a) Prob. 3.6   (b) Prob. 3.7

(c) Prob. 3.35   (d) Prob. 3.37

7.6 Find the bilinear series for G in each case and express the solution of the model in terms of G:

(a) Prob. 5.1(b)   (b) Prob. 5.2(a)

(c) Prob. 5.4(a)   (d) Prob. 5.6(a)

(e) Prob. 5.6(b)   (f) Prob. 5.16

(g) Prob. 5.21

7.7 Find a bilinear series for a Green's function, and sum the series to obtain explicit expressions for G for ordinary differential equations by using the characteristic values and functions from the following (be sure to specify the general ordinary differential equation of the Green's function):

(a) $X'' + \lambda^2 X = 0, \qquad X'(0) = X(1) = 0$

(b) $X'' + \lambda^2 X = 0, \qquad X(0) = X'(1) = 0$

(c) $X'' + \lambda^2 X = 0, \quad X(0) = -X(1), \quad X'(0) = -X'(1)$

[*Hint:* See Jolley [6] for summations of series.]

7.8 Using the Green's functions obtained in Prob. 7.7, solve the following models of steady-state heat conduction, sketch a typical Green's function, give a physical interpretation of the Green's function and the model, and sketch the solution $u(x)$:

(a) $u_{xx} = -\cos\dfrac{\pi x}{2}, \qquad 0 < x < 1, \quad u_x(0) = u(1) = 0$

(b) $u_{xx} = -1, \qquad 0 < x < 1, \quad u(0) = u_x(1) = 0$

7.9 Repeat Prob. 7.8 for the cases below of the deflection of a string under a distributed load:

(a) $z_{yy} = -\sin \pi y, \qquad 0 < y < 1, \quad z_y(0) = z(1) = 0$

(b) $z_{yy} = -(1 - y^2), \qquad 0 < y < 1, \quad z(0) = z_y(1) = 0$

7.10 Find δ''' and δ^{iv}.

7.11 Find H'', where H is the Heaviside unit function.

7.12 Calculate $\int H(y - \eta)\, dy$.

7.13   Find the Green's function representing the solution of the following model of an impulsively struck string:

$$z_{tt} - C^2 z_{yy} = \delta(y - \eta), \qquad 0 < y, \eta < 1, \quad 0 < t$$
$$z(0, t) = z(1, t) = 0, \qquad 0 < t$$
$$z(y, 0) = z_t(y, 0) = 0, \qquad 0 < y < 1$$

7.14   Repeat Prob. 7.13 with a drag or resistance term proportional to z_t added to the left side of the differential equation—that is, with $z_{tt} + Dz_t - C^2 z_{yy} = \delta(y - \eta)$.

7.15   Find the Green's function representing the solution of the following model, and give a physical interpretation of the model:

$$z_{tt} + Dz_t - C^2 z_{yy} = 0, \qquad 0 < y < 1, \quad 0 < t$$
$$z_y(0, t) = z(1, t) = 0, \qquad 0 < t$$
$$z(y, 0) = 0,$$
$$z_t(y, 0) = \delta(y - \eta), \qquad 0 \le y \le 1, \quad 0 < \eta < 1$$

7.16   Obtain Green's functions for the following conditions by direct integration:

(a) $G_{yy} = -\delta(y - \eta), \qquad G(0, \eta) = G_y(1, \eta) = 0, \qquad 0 < y, \eta < 1$

(b) $G_{xx} = -\delta(x - \xi), \qquad G(-1, \xi) = G(1, \xi) = 0, \qquad -1 < x, \xi < 1$

(c) $G_{xx} + \dfrac{1}{x} G_x = -\delta(x - \xi), \qquad G_x(0, \xi) = G(1, \xi) = 0, \qquad 0 < x, \xi < 1$

(d) $G_{yyyy} = -\delta(y - \eta), \qquad G(0, \eta) = G_{yy}(0, \eta) = G(1, \eta) = G_{yy}(1, \eta) = 0, \qquad 0 < y, \eta < 1$

(e) $G_{xx} = \delta(x - \xi), \quad G_x(0, \xi) = -\frac{1}{2}, \quad G_x(1, \xi) = \frac{1}{2}, \qquad 0 < x, \ \xi < 1$

Why are these conditions appropriate?

7.17   Find the steady-state deflection of a beam of uniform cross section under the constant load $q = EI/\rho$ and with simply supported ends at $y = 0$ and $y = 1$. [*Hint:* Check Chap. 5 and Prob. 7.16(d).]

7.18   Repeat Prob. 7.17 with $q = (EI/\rho)(\frac{1}{2} - y)$ and with cantilevered ends at $y = 0$ and $y = 1$.

7.19   Show that the Green's function satisfying

$$G_t - kG_{xx} = -\delta(x - \eta; t - \bar{\tau}), \qquad 0 < x, \ \eta < l, \ 0 < t, \ \bar{\tau}$$

$$G(0, \eta; t) = G(l, \eta; t) = G(x, \eta; 0) = 0$$

when $\bar{\tau} > 0$, satisfies

$$G_t - kG_{xx} = 0, \qquad 0 < x, \ \eta < l, \ 0 < t$$
$$G(0, \eta; t) = G(l, \eta; t) = 0, \qquad 0 < t, \ 0 < \eta < l$$
$$G(x, \eta; 0) = \delta(x - \eta), \qquad 0 < x, \ \eta < l$$

when $\bar{\tau} = 0$.

7.20   Assume that the eigenvalues λ_n^2 and eigenfunctions X_n satisfying

$$[r(x)X'(x)]' + [q(x) + \lambda^2 p(x)]X(x) = 0, \qquad 0 < x < l$$

$$X(0) = X(l) = 0$$

are known. Deduce the bilinear series for a Green's function by solving

$$[ru_x]_x + qu = -P(x), \qquad 0 < x < l$$

$$u(0) = u(l) = 0$$

Give a physical interpretation.

7.21 Calculate the jump in G_x across the point load in the case of the equation

$$[r(x)G_x(x, \xi)]_x + q(x)G(x, \xi) = -\delta(x - \xi)$$

7.22 Calculate the static deflection of a unit radius, circular membrane with fixed edge under a unit load at the center. Sketch the result.

7.23 Calculate the static deflection of a unit radius, circular membrane with fixed edge under the action of gravity alone.

7.24 Using the δ-function's properties, prove that (7.35) is a solution to (7.34) under conditions (7.36) and (7.37). [*Hint:* Proceed formally, using orthogonality to get relations involving ordinary functions.]

7.25 A unit load is applied at ξ on a string and induces a displacement $z(x, \xi)$ at x. What displacement at ξ is caused by a three-unit load at x?

7.26 If a heat source of strength Q at $x = 0.75$ makes the temperature in a rod equal $T°$F at $x = 0.25$, what strength source at $x = 0.25$ is required to make the temperature $T^2°$F at $x = 0.75$?

7.27 Prove that the bilinear series for the Green's function (7.48) is uniformly convergent and that G is continuous. [*Hint:* As $|\Omega_{mn}| \le 1$, prove that the majorizing series of constants $1/\lambda_{mn}^2 N_{mn}$ converges.]

7.28 Find a bilinear series representation for the Green's function for the model in Prob. 5.12.

7.29 Find a bilinear series representation for the Green's function for the static displacement by an arbitrary (steady) load of a membrane with the boundary condition prescribed in Prob. 5.22(a).

7.30 Find the solution—that is, the response or Green's function—for the following models of a unit square membrane acted on by a damping force proportional to the velocity of points on the membrane (air or water surrounding the membrane can induce such a resistance force):

(a) $z_{tt} + Dz_t - C^2 \nabla^2 z = \delta(x - \xi; y - \eta; t - \tau), \qquad 0 < x, y < 1, \quad 0 < t$
$z \equiv 0$ on the boundary;
at rest at $t = 0$

(b) $z_{tt} + Dz_t - C^2 \nabla^2 z = 0, \qquad 0 < x, y < 1, \quad 0 < t$
$z \equiv 0$ on the boundary
$z(x, y, 0) = 0,$
$z_t(x, y, 0) = \delta(x - \xi, y - \eta), \qquad 0 < x, y < 1$

Give physical interpretations in each case.

7.31 Prove that (7.64) is the proper fundamental singularity for $\nabla^2 u = 0, u = u(x, y, z)$.

7.32 Derive Green's Second Identity for functions f and $g \in C^2$ and satisfying the Helmholtz equation

$$\nabla^2 u + g(P)u = 0 \qquad \text{on } R$$

7.33 Define the equation to be satisfied by the Green's function for the equation in Prob. 7.32.

7.34   For the model

$$\nabla^2 u + g(P)u = f(P) \qquad \text{in } R$$

$$u \equiv 0, \qquad P \text{ on } C$$

express u in terms of the Green's function defined in Prob. 7.33 and satisfying appropriate boundary conditions. [*Hint:* See Prob. 7.32.]

7.35   If

$$S(P, Q) = -\frac{1}{2\pi} \ln \mathbf{PQ} + s(P, Q)$$

what equation must $s(P, Q)$ satisfy if S is to be the fundamental singularity of the Helmholtz equation in Prob. 7.32? [*Hint:* Check Prob. 7.33.]

7.36   Carry out the analyses leading to the equivalent of (7.65) through (7.69) for the three-dimensional problem in R with $u = q$ on C, assuming (7.64) is established.

7.37   Prove that the Neumann function is symmetric; that is, $N(P, Q) = N(Q, P)$.

7.38   Use the properties of the δ-function to show that (7.72) satisfies the compatibility condition of (7.71) for Neumann problems on any region $\bar{R} = R + C$.

7.39   Given $\tilde{R}$ for $\bar{R} = R + C$, find u if

$$\nabla_P^2 u = -F(p) \qquad \text{in } R$$

$$\frac{\partial u}{\partial n_p} - h(P)u = q(P) \qquad \text{on } C$$

7.40   Prove that $\tilde{R}$ is symmetric.

7.41   Find the Neumann function $N(P, Q)$ for the half-plane $y > 0$ by the method of images. [*Hint:* What is $1/L$?]

7.42   Find the Green's function $G(P, Q)$ for the quadrant $x > 0, y > 0$. [*Hint:* Put in enough images!]

7.43   Find the Green's function $G(P, Q)$ for the sector $\rho > 0, 0 < \theta < \pi/4$ of the plane.

7.44   Find the mixed Neumann–Green's function $M(P, Q)$ satisfying

$$\nabla_P^2 M(P, Q) = -\delta(P, Q), \qquad 0 < x, \quad 0 < y$$
$$M(P, Q) = 0, \qquad P = (0, y), \quad y > 0$$

$$\frac{\partial M}{\partial n_P}(P, Q) = 0, \qquad P = (x, 0), \quad x > 0$$

[*Hint:* Try images.]

7.45   Find $u(x, y)$ if

(a) $\nabla^2 u = F(x, y)$ in $y > 0$, $u = 0$ on $y = 0$.

(b) $\nabla^2 u = 0$ in $y > 0$, $u = u_0(x)$ on $y = 0$.

7.46   Find $u(x, y)$ by use of Green's functions when $\nabla^2 u = 0$ in $x > 0, y > 0$, and

(a) $u_x(0, y) = -1$ on $y > 0$
     $u(x, 0) = 1$ on $x \geq 0$

(b) $u_x(0, y) = -1$ on $y > 0$
     $u_y(x, 0) = 1$ on $x \geq 0$

7.47   Determine the Green's function for the unit sphere.

7.48   Using vector algebra, prove (7.89) and (7.90).

7.49   Heat conduction in a plate is modeled by

$$\nabla^2 u = 0, \qquad 0 \le \rho < 1, \quad 0 \le \theta < 2\pi$$

$$u(1, \theta) = \sin \theta \,°F, \qquad 0 \le \theta < 2\pi$$

Find the temperature $u(\rho, \theta)$ and, in particular, $u(0, \theta)$.

7.50   If, in Prob. 7.49,

(a) $u(1, \theta) = \cos^2 \theta \,°F$, $0 \le \theta < 2\pi$, find $u(0, \theta)$.

(b) $u(1, \theta) = \begin{cases} 1\,°F, & 0 \le \theta < \pi, \\ 0, & \pi \le \theta < 2\pi, \end{cases}$ find $u(0, \theta)$.

7.51   Determine the Poisson integral formula for the exterior of the circle ($\rho > 1$) with data prescribed on the circle $\rho = 1$.

7.52   Determine the Poisson integral formula for the sphere when the region R is

(a) $\rho > 1$ (the exterior of the sphere).

(b) $\rho < 1$ (the interior of the sphere).

7.53   Find the temperature in the center of a conducting sphere if the upper half is at $100\,°F$ while the lower half is at $50\,°F$.

7.54   Find u in $\bar{R} : \rho \le 1$ if

$$\nabla^2 u = F(\rho, \theta) \qquad \text{in } R$$

$$u = 0 \qquad \text{on } C$$

7.55   Determine the Neumann function for the circle $\rho < \rho_0$, and obtain the equivalent integral representation (see the Poisson integral formula)

$$u(\rho, \theta) = \frac{\rho_0}{2\pi} \int_0^{2\pi} q(\theta_{P'}) \ln \left[\frac{\rho_0^2 + \rho^2 - \rho_0 \rho \cos(\theta_{P'} - \theta)}{\rho_0^2} \right] d\theta_{P'}$$

7.56   Repeat Prob. 7.55 for the region $\rho > \rho_0$, the external problem.

7.57   Find the Neumann function for the sphere for [8]

(a) the region $\bar{R} : \rho \le 1$.
(b) the region $\bar{R} : \rho \ge 1$.

CHAPTER 8

INTEGRAL TRANSFORMS
AND INFINITE DOMAINS

8.1   INTRODUCTION

In Chap. 7, Green's functions were employed in presenting problem solutions in an integral form—for example,

$$U(x) = \int_0^l G(x, \xi)u(\xi) \, d\xi$$

This integral can be viewed as a function of the "parameter" x and the function $U(x)$ as the *transformation* of the class of functions $u(\xi)$ from their ξ-domain to the x-domain. The Green's function $G(x, \xi)$ is then called the *kernel* of the *integral transform* $U(x)$. In this chapter we examine several *linear* mathematical models with semi-infinite or finite space domains and discover the utility and applicability of integral transforms of the general type

$$T\{\phi(\eta)\} = \Phi(\xi) = \int_a^b K(\xi, \eta)\phi(\eta) \, d\eta \qquad (8.1)$$

with kernel $K(\xi, \eta)$.

One important property of $\Phi(\xi)$ is easily deduced. Suppose that

$$\phi(\eta) = c_1\phi_1(\eta) + c_2\phi_2(\eta)$$

where c_1 and c_2 are constants. Then, provided that ϕ_1 and ϕ_2 have transforms according to (8.1)—that is, provided the necessary integrals exist,

$$\Phi(\xi) = T\{c_1\phi_1(\eta) + c_2\phi_2(\eta)\} = \int_a^b K(\xi, \eta)[c_1\phi_1(\eta) + c_2\phi_2(\eta)]\, d\eta$$

$$= c_1 \int_a^b K(\xi, \eta)\phi_1(\eta)\, d\eta + c_2 \int_a^b K(\xi, \eta)\phi_2(\eta)\, d\eta$$

or

$$T\{c_1\phi_1 + c_2\phi_2\} = c_1 T\{\phi_1\} + c_2 T\{\phi_2\}$$

Thus the integral transforms are *linear operators* (see Sec. 2.4).

An important question is whether or not there is an *inverse operator* T^{-1} such that

$$\phi(\eta) = T^{-1}\{\Phi\} \tag{8.2}$$

The existence of a *transform pair*—namely, the transform and its inverse—is the key to our applications. The pattern is to transform a *given model* from an η-space to a ξ-space where, presumably, obtaining the solution is easier. Then, using the inverse operator, we transform the *solution* back to the η-space.

Among the many possible kernels K and limits (a, b) for transform (8.1), three sets that have direct application to partial differential equations are treated here. All three feature infinite space domains for both variable η and parameter ξ because solutions of models with such domains are of practical interest and the Fourier series, applicable for finite domains and periodic functions, is no longer appropriate.

If $a = -\infty$, $b = \infty$, and $K(\xi, \eta) = e^{i\xi\eta}/2\pi$, where $i = e^{i\pi/2} = \sqrt{-1}$ (recall that $e^{i\xi\eta} = \cos\xi\eta + i\sin\xi\eta$), then (8.1) is the *Fourier Transform*

$$F(\xi) = \frac{1}{2\pi} \int_{-\infty}^{\infty} e^{i\xi\eta} f(\eta)\, d\eta \tag{8.3}$$

with the inverse transform being

$$f(\eta) = \int_{-\infty}^{\infty} F(\xi)\, e^{-i\xi\eta}\, d\xi \tag{8.4}$$

This transform pair and its companion Fourier sine and cosine transforms are used in the direct solution of heat and diffusion models and of vibration models for strings and beams.

Another Fourier-type transform pair is the *Hankel Transform* of order n:

$$H_n(\xi) = \int_0^{\infty} \eta J_n(\xi\eta) h(\eta)\, d\eta \tag{8.5}$$

with its inverse

$$h(\eta) = \int_0^{\infty} \xi H_n(\xi) J_n(\xi\eta)\, d\xi \tag{8.6}$$

where J_n is the nth-order Bessel function (see A.2.38). This pair is applicable to problems of heat flow in domains where polar coordinates are relevant for physical reasons.

The third transform pair is the *Laplace Transform*

$$L(\xi) = \mathscr{L}\{l(\eta)\} = \int_0^\infty e^{-\xi\eta} l(\eta)\, d\eta \tag{8.7}$$

and its inverse defined by

$$l(\eta) = \mathscr{L}^{-1}\{L(\xi)\} \tag{8.8}$$

Applications for the Laplace transform are widely spread in the fields of ordinary and partial differential equations. Rainville [1] in a monograph on the Laplace transform treats the solution of both ordinary and partial differential equations involved in vibration, electric circuit, wave, heat, and diffusion models.

8.2   FOURIER INTEGRAL TRANSFORMS

The development of an integral representation for infinite intervals is accomplished by an example based on material in Chaps. 3 and 4. A limit process is used. First, a problem in a finite domain is solved. Second, the domain is extended to infinity. Finally, the Fourier transform pair is deduced from the extended solution.

8.2.1   A Limit Process

The classic Fourier heat ring model described in Sec. 4.4 is an excellent base for our analysis because a clear physical meaning can be attributed to the limit process. Physically, the ring-shaped conductor is laterally insulated so that heat conduction occurs in one dimension along the circumference of the ring (Fig. 8.1).

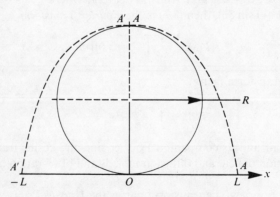

FIGURE 8.1   Fourier heat ring.

The mathematical model for the temperature u in the ring is

$$u_t = ku_{xx}, \qquad -L < x < L, \quad 0 < t \tag{8.9a}$$

$$\begin{aligned} u(L, t) &= u(-L, t), \\ u_x(L, t) &= u_x(-L, t), \end{aligned} \qquad 0 < t \tag{8.9b}$$

$$u(x, 0) = u_0(x), \qquad -L \leq x \leq L \tag{8.9c}$$

$$|u(x, t)| < \infty, \qquad -L \leq x \leq L, \quad 0 \leq t \tag{8.9d}$$

The last condition is precisely that required (see Chap. 6) to guarantee that a unique solution exists.

We can arbitrarily assign the origin O to the heat ring AOA' so that A goes to L, A' to $-L$, and the compatibility boundary conditions on temperature and heat flux hold across $A'A$. From a geometric point of view, $L = \pi R$; thus through R we make both the ring and the model domain change size. In particular, as the ring gets very large with $R \to \infty$, $L \to \infty$ simultaneously.

According to Example 4.6, Sec. 4.4, separation of variables in (8.9), with $u(x, t) = X(x)T(t)$, produces the eigenvalue problem (note that L replaces unity used in Sec. 4.4)

$$X'' + \lambda^2 X = 0, \qquad -L < x < L$$
$$X(-L) = X(L)$$
$$X'(-L) = X'(L) \tag{8.10}$$

with the linearly independent eigenfunctions

$$X_{n1}(x) = \cos \lambda_n x$$
$$X_{n2}(x) = \sin \lambda_n x \tag{8.11}$$

corresponding to each eigenvalue $\lambda_n^2 = (n\pi/L)^2$, $n \geq 0$. Separation of variables also gives

$$T' + \lambda^2 k T = 0$$

so the particular solutions

$$u_n(x, t) = e^{-\lambda_n^2 k t}(A_n X_{n1} + B_n X_{n2})$$

satisfy (8.9a) and (8.9b).

The complete, and clearly bounded, solution is

$$u(x, t) = \sum_{n=0}^{\infty} e^{-\lambda_n^2 k t}(A_n X_{n1} + B_n X_{n2}) \tag{8.12}$$

At $t = 0$, we require

$$u(x, 0) = u_0(x) = \sum_{n=0}^{\infty} (A_n X_{n1} + B_n X_{n2}) \tag{8.13}$$

The X_{n1} and X_{n2} are orthogonal on $-L \leq x \leq L$ with respect to the weight function $p = 1$ (see Theorem 4.2', Sec. 4.4, and the Problems). The normalizing constants

$$N_{ni} = L, \qquad n > 0, \quad i = 1, 2$$
$$N_{01} = 2L$$

($X_{02} \equiv 0$, so no eigenfunction exists for this subscript value). Application of the orthogonality relations

$$\int_{-L}^{L} X_{n1} X_{m1}\, dx = 0 \quad \text{and} \quad \int_{-L}^{L} X_{n2} X_{m2}\, dx = 0, \qquad m \neq n$$

and

$$\int_{-L}^{L} X_{n1} X_{m2} \, dx = 0$$

to (8.13) gives

$$\int_{-L}^{L} X_{m1} u_0(x) \, dx = N_{m1} A_m \quad \text{and} \quad \int_{-L}^{L} X_{m2} u_0(x) \, dx = N_{m2} B_m$$

In sum, (8.13) can now be written as

$$u(x, 0) = u_0(x) = \frac{1}{2L} \int_{-L}^{L} u_0(\xi) \, d\xi + \sum_{n=1}^{\infty} \frac{1}{L} \int_{-L}^{L} u_0(\xi) \cos \frac{n\pi}{L} \xi \, d\xi \cos \frac{n\pi}{L} x$$

$$+ \sum_{n=1}^{\infty} \frac{1}{L} \int_{-L}^{L} u_0(\xi) \sin \frac{n\pi}{L} \xi \, d\xi \sin \frac{n\pi}{L} x \qquad (8.14)$$

Next, we examine what occurs as the radius R of the ring becomes very large and the points A and A' recede infinitely far from our view. The set $\{\lambda_n^2\}$, which is the spectrum of the eigenvalue problem, is discrete for finite L. For example,

$$|\lambda_{n+1}^2 - \lambda_n^2| = \frac{\pi^2}{L^2} \neq 0$$

for $L < \infty$. As $L \to \infty$, the spectrum becomes continuous and the eigenvalues λ_n^2 are distributed everywhere on the real positive axis from zero to infinity; clearly,

$$\lim_{L \to \infty} \{\lambda_{n+1}^2 - \lambda_n^2\} = \lim_{L \to \infty} \frac{\pi^2}{L^2} = 0$$

As $\lambda_n^2 = n^2 \pi^2 / L^2$, let $\Delta \lambda = \pi/L$. Then $\lambda_{n+1} - \lambda_n = \Delta \lambda$ and $\lim_{L \to \infty} \Delta \lambda = 0$. From (8.14), it is appropriate that n and L approach infinity such that $n/L \to \infty$ as $n \to \infty$ and $L \to \infty$. This ensures that the eigenvalues λ_n^2 are distributed over the positive real axis because, for $n < \infty$,

$$\lambda_n^2 = \frac{\pi^2 n^2}{L^2} \to 0 \quad \text{as } L \to \infty$$

while

$$\lambda_n^2 = \frac{\pi^2 n^2}{L^2} \to \infty \quad \text{as } n \to \infty \text{ and } L \to \infty$$

Accordingly, (8.14) is

$$u(x, 0) = u_0(x) = \frac{1}{2L} \int_{-L}^{L} u_0(\xi) \, d\xi + \frac{1}{\pi} \sum_{n=1}^{\infty} \int_{-L}^{L} u_0(\xi) \cos \lambda_n \xi \, d\xi \cos \lambda_n x \, \Delta \lambda$$

$$+ \frac{1}{\pi} \sum_{n=1}^{\infty} \int_{-L}^{L} u_0(\xi) \sin \lambda_n \xi \, d\xi \sin \lambda_n x \, \Delta \lambda \qquad (8.15)$$

As $L \to \infty$,

$$\lim_{\substack{\Delta \lambda \to \infty \\ L \to \infty}} \sum_{n=1}^{\infty} f(x, \xi, \lambda_n) \, \Delta \lambda = \int_0^{\infty} f(x, \xi, \lambda) \, d\lambda = I$$

which is similar to the formal limiting process for the definition of the improper integral I. If

$$\lim_{L \to \infty} \int_{-L}^{L} u_0(\xi)\, d\xi < \infty \tag{8.16}$$

then as $L \to \infty$, (8.15) becomes

$$u(x, 0) = u_0(x) = \frac{1}{\pi} \int_0^\infty d\lambda \left\{ \int_{-\infty}^\infty u_0(\xi)[\cos \lambda\xi \cos \lambda x + \sin \lambda\xi \sin \lambda x]\, d\xi \right\} \tag{8.17}$$

because the first term on the right-hand side of (8.15) disappears under condition (8.16).

As a result of the trigonometric identity,

$$\cos \lambda\xi \cos \lambda x + \sin \lambda\xi \sin \lambda x = \cos \lambda(\xi - x)$$

and with $u_0(x) = f(x)$, (8.17) can be written in the form of the *Fourier Integral Formula*

$$f(x) = \frac{1}{\pi} \int_0^\infty d\lambda \left[\int_{-\infty}^\infty f(\xi) \cos \lambda(\xi - x)\, d\xi \right] \tag{8.18}$$

that forms the cornerstone of our analysis.

Before dwelling on (8.18), its validity, and applications, let us return to the solution (8.12) of (8.9) and develop some valuable results in an example.

EXAMPLE 8.1   *Heat Conduction in the Fourier Heat Ring* (Fig. 8.1). Let

$$u_0(x) = \begin{cases} U_0, & |x| < x_0 < \infty \\ 0, & |x| \ge x_0 \end{cases} \tag{8.19}$$

where U_0 and x_0 are finite constants. To generate this condition, one could make a large ring in two halves, keep one in a deep freezer and one in boiling water, then join them to start the experiment at $t = 0$.

From (8.14), the solution (8.12) is, for L finite,

$$u(x, t) = \frac{1}{2L} \int_{-L}^{L} u_0(\xi)\, d\xi + \sum_{n=1}^\infty \frac{e^{-\lambda_n^2 kt}}{L} \int_{-L}^{L} u_0(\xi)(\cos \lambda_n\xi \cos \lambda_n x + \sin \lambda_n\xi \sin \lambda_n x)\, d\xi \tag{8.20}$$

and as $L \to \infty$

$$u(x, t) = \frac{1}{\pi} \int_0^\infty e^{-\lambda^2 kt}\, d\lambda \left(\int_{-\infty}^\infty u_0(\xi) \cos \lambda(\xi - x)\, d\xi \right) \tag{8.21}$$

because (8.19) satisfies (8.16); that is,

$$\lim_{L \to \infty} \int_{-L}^{L} u_0(\xi)\, d\xi = \lim_{L \to \infty} \left(\int_{-L}^{-x_0} 0\, dx + \int_{-x_0}^{x_0} U_0\, dx + \int_{x_0}^{L} 0\, dx \right) = 2U_0 x_0 < \infty$$

Thus (8.21) is the Fourier integral solution of the model

$$u_t = k u_{xx}, \qquad -\infty < x < \infty, \quad 0 < t$$

$$u(x, 0) = u_0(x), \qquad -\infty < x < \infty \tag{8.22}$$

$$|u(x, t)| < \infty$$

The boundary conditions are now insignificant because they are applied at infinity and do not have an effect in the finite region about the origin—that is, in $|x| < \infty$. [It is easy (see the Problems) to verify this point by performing a derivation with either Dirichlet or Neumann boundary conditions at A and A' and achieving the same result (8.21).]

Exchanging the order of integration in (8.21) gives

$$u(x, t) = \frac{1}{\pi} \int_{-\infty}^{\infty} u_0(\xi) \, d\xi \int_0^{\infty} e^{-\lambda^2 kt} \cos \lambda(\xi - x) \, d\lambda$$

[The exchange is justified provided only that $\int_{-\infty}^{\infty} |u_0(\xi)| \, d\xi$ exists.] But (see the Problems)

$$\int_0^{\infty} e^{-\lambda^2 kt} \cos \lambda(\xi - x) \, d\lambda = \left(\frac{\pi}{4kt}\right)^{1/2} \exp\left\{-\left[\frac{(\xi - x)^2}{4kt}\right]\right\}$$

so then

$$u(x, t) = \left(\frac{1}{4\pi kt}\right)^{1/2} \int_{-\infty}^{\infty} u_0(\xi) \exp\left\{-\left[\frac{(\xi - x)^2}{4kt}\right]\right\} d\xi \tag{8.23}$$

We see that

$$G(x, \xi; t) = \left(\frac{1}{4\pi kt}\right)^{1/2} \exp\left\{-\left[\frac{(\xi - x)^2}{4kt}\right]\right\} \tag{8.24}$$

is the Green's function for the model.

For the initial condition (8.19), (8.23) can be brought to a particularly simple result. Introducing (8.19) in (8.23) yields

$$u(x, t) = U_0\left(\frac{1}{4\pi kt}\right)^{1/2} \int_{-x_0}^{x_0} \exp\left\{-\left[\frac{(\xi - x)^2}{4kt}\right]\right\} d\xi \tag{8.25}$$

It is easy to verify that (8.25) is a bounded solution to the prescribed model.

Now, the *error function* erf x [3, Chap. 7] is a tabulated function given by the integral

$$\text{erf } x = \frac{2}{\pi^{1/2}} \int_0^x e^{-\eta^2} \, d\eta \tag{8.26}$$

and the *complementary error function* is

$$\text{erfc } x = 1 - \text{erf } x = \frac{2}{\pi^{1/2}} \int_x^{\infty} e^{-\eta^2} \, d\eta \tag{8.27}$$

Although erf x cannot be evaluated in terms of elementary functions (a power series expansion is possible),

$$\text{erf } \infty = \frac{2}{\pi^{1/2}} \int_0^{\infty} e^{-\eta^2} \, d\eta = 1 \tag{8.28}$$

so

$$\text{erfc } \infty = 0 \qquad \text{erfc } 0 = 1 \tag{8.29}$$

The form of (8.26) suggests the change of variable $\eta = (\xi - x)/(4kt)^{1/2}$ in (8.25).

The upper and lower limits in the integral in (8.25) are, in terms of η,

$$\eta_{\text{upper}} = \frac{x_0 - x}{(4kt)^{1/2}}$$

$$\eta_{\text{lower}} = \frac{-x_0 - x}{(4kt)^{1/2}}$$

while

$$d\eta = \frac{d\xi}{(4kt)^{1/2}}$$

Accordingly, (8.25) becomes

$$u(x, t) = \frac{U_0}{\pi^{1/2}} \int_{-(x_0+x)/(4kt)^{1/2}}^{(x_0-x)/(4kt)^{1/2}} e^{-\eta^2} \, d\eta$$

or

$$u(x, t) = \frac{U_0}{2} \left[\frac{2}{\pi^{1/2}} \int_0^{(x_0-x)/(4kt)^{1/2}} e^{-\eta^2} \, d\eta + \frac{2}{\pi^{1/2}} \int_{-(x_0+x)/(4kt)^{1/2}}^0 e^{-\eta^2} \, d\eta \right]$$

Replacing η by $-\rho$ in the second integral gives the penultimate form

$$u(x, t) = \frac{U_0}{2} \left[\frac{2}{\pi^{1/2}} \int_0^{(x_0-x)/(4kt)^{1/2}} e^{-\eta^2} \, d\eta + \frac{2}{\pi^{1/2}} \int_0^{(x_0+x)/(4kt)^{1/2}} e^{-\rho^2} \, d\rho \right]$$

Comparison of this result with (8.26) indicates that

$$u(x, t) = \frac{U_0}{2} \left\{ \text{erf} \left[\frac{x_0 - x}{(4kt)^{1/2}} \right] + \text{erf} \left[\frac{x_0 + x}{(4kt)^{1/2}} \right] \right\} \tag{8.30}$$

for $-\infty < x < \infty, 0 < t$.

Thus we have an explicit solution for the heat conduction in an infinitely long rod in terms not of integrals or series, but of a tabulated function (very much like sine or cosine, really!). The spread of heat in the rod with time is easily visualized by plotting the solution (8.30) (see the Problems).

The validity of the Fourier integral formula (8.18) can be verified by extension of the principles used to verify the convergence of the Fourier series (see Sec. 3.3.1). Consider the following theorem:

THEOREM 8.1   Suppose that a function f is piecewise smooth* on every finite interval and absolutely integrable on $(-\infty, \infty)$; that is, $f(x) \in L^1(-\infty, \infty)$ or

$$\int_{-\infty}^{\infty} |f(\xi)| \, d\xi$$

---

* A function $f(x)$ is *piecewise smooth* on any finite interval if the interval can be subdivided into a finite number of subintervals such that $f(x)$ is continuous on each closed subinterval [i.e., has finite limits $f(x_i^+)$ and $f(x_i^-)$ at the left and right ends of each subinterval] and has continuous first derivatives in the closed subinterval (see Prob. 3.20 and Ref. [2]). Thus $f(x) \in C^1$ on each closed subinterval.

exists. The Fourier integral formula (8.18) represents $f(x)$ in the form

$$\frac{1}{2}\{f(x^+) + f(x^-)\} = \frac{1}{\pi}\int_0^\infty d\lambda \int_{-\infty}^\infty f(\xi)\cos\lambda(\xi - x)\,d\xi \tag{8.31}$$

Proof: Consider the integral

$$I_N = \int_0^N d\lambda \int_{-\infty}^\infty f(\xi)\cos\lambda(\xi - x)\,d\xi \tag{8.32}$$

where N is an arbitrary large number. Because of the assumed properties of f and because

$$|f(\xi)\cos\lambda(\xi - x)| \le |f(\xi)|$$

the integral I_N exists and an exchange of the order of integration in (8.32) is permissible. As a result, we have

$$I_N = \int_{-\infty}^\infty f(\xi)\,d\xi \int_0^N \cos\lambda(\xi - x)\,d\lambda \tag{8.33}$$

Now

$$\int_0^N \cos\lambda(\xi - x)\,d\lambda = \frac{\sin\lambda(\xi - x)}{\xi - x}\bigg|_0^N = \frac{\sin N(\xi - x)}{\xi - x}$$

for all N and $\xi - x$ as

$$\lim_{\xi \to x}\frac{\sin\lambda(\xi - x)}{\xi - x} = \lambda$$

Therefore (8.33) becomes

$$I_N = \int_{-\infty}^\infty f(\xi)\frac{\sin N(\xi - x)}{\xi - x}\,d\xi$$

while setting $\eta = \xi - x$ yields

$$I_N = \int_{-\infty}^\infty f(x + \eta)\frac{\sin N\eta}{\eta}\,d\eta \tag{8.34}$$

In Sec. 3.3.1 and Prob. 3.21 it was shown that, for any finite interval $a < \eta < b$ and with f as defined above,

$$\lim_{\beta \to \infty}\int_a^b f(\eta)\sin\beta\eta\,d\eta = 0 \tag{8.35}$$

The extended Riemann–Lebesgue lemma for an infinite domain is

$$\lim_{\beta \to \infty}\int_{-\infty}^\infty f(\eta)\sin\beta\eta\,d\eta = 0 \tag{8.36}$$

Proof of (8.36) (see also the Problems): Kaplan [2] points out the close relation between improper integrals and infinite series. Indeed, because

$$\int_{-\infty}^\infty |f(\eta)|\,d\eta$$

exists (i.e., is convergent), the infinite series

$$\sum_{n=-\infty}^{\infty} \int_{x_n}^{x_{n+1}} |f(\eta)| \, d\eta = \sum_{n=-\infty}^{\infty} M_n < \infty$$

converges absolutely to a finite sum and each of the positive constants M_n is bounded. The x_i are the endpoints of finite intervals, chosen here for convenience to coincide with subintervals over which $f(x) \in C^1$. Because for the continuous functions

$$a_n = \int_{x_n}^{x_{n+1}} f(\eta) \sin \beta n \, d\eta$$

we have

$$|a_n| = \left| \int_{x_n}^{x_{n+1}} f(\eta) \sin \beta \eta \, d\eta \right| \leq M_n$$

the series $\sum_{n=-\infty}^{\infty} a_n$ is uniformly convergent according to the Weierstrass M-test ([2] or Appendix A.1.2).

Thus

$$\lim_{\beta \to \infty} \int_{-\infty}^{\infty} f(\eta) \sin \beta \eta \, d\eta = \lim_{\beta \to \infty} \left[\sum_{n=-\infty}^{\infty} \int_{x_n}^{x_{n+1}} f(\eta) \sin \beta \eta \, d\eta \right]$$

$$= \lim_{\beta \to \infty} \left(\sum_{n=-\infty}^{\infty} a_n \right) = \sum_{n=-\infty}^{\infty} \left(\lim_{\beta \to \infty} a_n \right)$$

where the exchange of limit processes (the limit and the infinite summation) is permitted because of the uniform convergence ([2] or Appendix A.1.2). It follows from (8.35) that

$$\lim_{\beta \to \infty} a_n \equiv 0$$

Hence

$$\lim_{\beta \to \infty} \int_{-\infty}^{\infty} f(\eta) \sin \beta \eta \, d\eta = 0 \qquad \text{Q.E.D.}$$

Returning now to the proof of Theorem 8.1, we write symbolically

$$I_N = \left[\int_{-\infty}^{-\varepsilon} + \int_{-\varepsilon}^{\varepsilon} + \int_{\varepsilon}^{\infty} \right] f(x + \eta) \frac{\sin N\eta}{\eta} \, d\eta$$

for a small $\varepsilon > 0$. Clearly, $f(x + \eta)/\eta$ is piecewise smooth in $|\eta| > \varepsilon$, so the first and third integrals vanish as $N \to \infty$. Thus, from (8.32) and the preceding discussions,

$$I_\infty = \int_0^\infty d\lambda \int_{-\infty}^\infty f(\xi) \cos \lambda(\xi - x) \, d\xi = \lim_{N \to \infty} \int_{-\varepsilon}^\varepsilon f(x + \eta) \frac{\sin N\eta}{\eta} \, d\eta \qquad (8.37)$$

In the region $|\eta| \leq \varepsilon$ near $\eta = 0$,

$$f(x + \eta) = f(x^+) + f'(\overline{x^+})\eta, \qquad \eta > 0$$

and

$$f(x + \eta) = f(x^-) + f'(\overline{x^-})\eta, \qquad \eta < 0$$

where $0 \leq \overline{x^+} \leq \varepsilon$ and $-\varepsilon \leq \overline{x^-} \leq 0$, but $\overline{x^+}$ and $\overline{x^-}$ depend on η according to the mean-value theorem of calculus [2]. The right-hand integral in (8.37) becomes

$$\int_{-\varepsilon}^{\varepsilon} f(x + \eta) \frac{\sin N\eta}{\eta} d\eta = f(x^+) \int_0^{\varepsilon} \frac{\sin N\eta}{\eta} d\eta + f(x^-) \int_{-\varepsilon}^0 \frac{\sin N\eta}{\eta} d\eta$$

$$+ \int_0^{\varepsilon} f'(\overline{x^+}) \sin N\eta \, d\eta + \int_{-\varepsilon}^0 f'(\overline{x^-}) \sin N\eta \, d\eta$$

In the limit as $N \to \infty$, we let $t = N\eta$ in the preceding equations with the result that*

$$\lim_{N \to \infty} \int_0^{\varepsilon} \frac{\sin N\eta}{\eta} d\eta = \lim_{N \to \infty} \int_0^{N_\varepsilon} \frac{\sin t}{t} dt = \int_0^{\infty} \frac{\sin t}{t} dt = \frac{\pi}{2}$$

$$\lim_{N \to \infty} \int_{-\varepsilon}^0 \frac{\sin N\eta}{\eta} d\eta = \frac{\pi}{2}$$

$$\lim_{N \to \infty} \int_{-\varepsilon}^0 f'(\overline{x^-}) \sin N\eta \, d\eta = \lim_{N \to \infty} \int_0^{\varepsilon} f'(\overline{x^+}) \sin N\eta \, d\eta = 0$$

Thus (8.37) becomes

$$I_\infty = \int_0^{\infty} d\lambda \int_{-\infty}^{\infty} f(\xi) \cos \lambda(\xi - x) \, d\xi = \frac{\pi}{2} \left\{ f(x^+) + f(x^-) \right\}$$

to confirm the validity of the Fourier integral formula (8.31).   Q.E.D.

The preceding theorem establishes (8.18) as well as (8.31) if we understand that $f(x) = \frac{1}{2}\{f(x^+) + f(x^-)\}$ when appropriate for piecewise-smooth functions. Using the trigonometric identity employed to arrive at (8.18) to put the Fourier integral formula back in the form (8.17) gives

$$f(x) = \frac{1}{\pi} \int_0^{\infty} d\lambda \left[\int_{-\infty}^{\infty} f(\xi) \cos \lambda\xi \cos \lambda x \, d\xi + \int_{-\infty}^{\infty} f(\xi) \sin \lambda\xi \sin \lambda x \, d\xi \right] \quad (8.38)$$

or by analogy with the Fourier series (3.45)

$$f(x) = \int_0^{\infty} [c(\lambda) \cos \lambda x + s(\lambda) \sin \lambda x] \, d\lambda \quad (8.39a)$$

where

$$c(\lambda) = \frac{1}{\pi} \int_{-\infty}^{\infty} f(\xi) \cos \lambda\xi \, d\xi \quad (8.39b)$$

$$s(\lambda) = \frac{1}{\pi} \int_{-\infty}^{\infty} f(\xi) \sin \lambda\xi \, d\xi \quad (8.39c)$$

---

* In Sec. 3.3.1 we proved

$$f(x) = \lim_{k \to \infty} PS_k = \lim_{k \to \infty} \frac{1}{\pi} \int_{-\pi}^{\pi} f(x + \eta) \frac{\sin [k + \frac{1}{2}]\eta}{2 \sin \eta/2} d\eta$$

For $k + \frac{1}{2} = N$ and $t = (k + \frac{1}{2})\eta = N\eta$, a suitable choice for $f(x)$ yields the desired results.

These results exactly parallel the full-range Fourier series expansion; we should expect similar analogous results for the half-range cosine and sine series expansions.

Consider that $f(x) = f(-x)$ so that $f(x)$ is an *even* function of x. From (8.39c) and (8.39b),

$$s(\lambda) = \frac{1}{\pi}\left\{\left[\int_{-\infty}^{0} + \int_{0}^{\infty}\right]f(\xi)\sin\lambda\xi\,d\xi\right\}$$

$$= \frac{1}{\pi}\left\{-\int_{0}^{\infty} f(-\rho)\sin\lambda\rho\,d\rho + \int_{0}^{\infty} f(\xi)\sin\lambda\xi\,d\xi\right\} = 0$$

$$c(\lambda) = \frac{1}{\pi}\left\{\left[\int_{-\infty}^{0} + \int_{0}^{\infty}\right]f(\xi)\cos\lambda\xi\,d\xi\right\} = \frac{2}{\pi}\int_{0}^{\infty} f(\xi)\cos\lambda\xi\,d\xi$$

and for $f(x)$ on $0 < x < \infty$,

$$f(x) = \int_{0}^{\infty} c(\lambda)\cos\lambda x\,d\lambda \tag{8.40a}$$

with*

$$c(\lambda) = \frac{2}{\pi}\int_{0}^{\infty} f(\xi)\cos\lambda\xi\,d\xi \tag{8.40b}$$

Equations (8.40) are a *Fourier Cosine Transform* pair; $c(\lambda)$ is the cosine transform of $f(x)$. The condition on f from Theorem 8.1 for the existence of the transforms is now

$$\int_{0}^{\infty} |f(x)|\,dx < \infty$$

Similarly, if $f(x) = -f(-x)$ so that $f(x)$ is an *odd* function of x, $c(\lambda) = 0$, while

$$f(x) = \int_{0}^{\infty} s(\lambda)\sin\lambda x\,d\lambda \tag{8.41a}$$

and

$$s(\lambda) = \frac{2}{\pi}\int_{0}^{\infty} f(\xi)\sin\lambda\xi\,d\xi \tag{8.41b}$$

Thus Eqs. (8.41) provide a representation for $f(x)$ on $0 < x < \infty$ and are the *Fourier Sine Transform* pair. The sine transform of $f(x)$ is $s(\lambda)$; again we require

$$\int_{0}^{\infty} |f(x)|\,dx < \infty$$

In the Fourier integral formula (8.18),

$$\int_{0}^{\infty} \cos\lambda(\xi - x)\,d\lambda = \frac{1}{2}\int_{-\infty}^{\infty} \cos\lambda(\xi - x)\,d\lambda$$

---

* The factor $2/\pi$ can be placed where desired and symmetrical form results if $(2/\pi)^{1/2}$ is used on both equations.

because the cosine is an even function of λ. Thus (8.18) can be written

$$f(x) = \frac{1}{2\pi} \int_{-\infty}^{\infty} d\lambda \int_{-\infty}^{\infty} f(\xi) \cos \lambda(\xi - x) \, d\xi \tag{8.42}$$

Introducing

$$\cos \lambda(\xi - x) = \tfrac{1}{2}[e^{i\lambda(\xi-x)} + e^{-i\lambda(\xi-x)}]$$

in (8.42) gives

$$f(x) = \frac{1}{4\pi}\left[\int_{-\infty}^{\infty} e^{-i\lambda x} \, d\lambda \int_{-\infty}^{\infty} f(\xi)e^{i\lambda\xi} \, d\xi + \int_{-\infty}^{\infty} e^{i\lambda x} \, d\lambda \int_{-\infty}^{\infty} f(\xi)e^{-i\lambda\xi} \, d\xi \right]$$

A change of variables that changes the sign of both dummy variables in either pair of these integrals shows that the pairs are identical. Thus

$$f(x) = \frac{1}{2\pi} \int_{-\infty}^{\infty} e^{-i\lambda x} \, d\lambda \int_{-\infty}^{\infty} f(\xi)e^{i\lambda\xi} \, d\xi = \frac{1}{2\pi} \int_{-\infty}^{\infty} e^{i\lambda x} \, d\lambda \int_{-\infty}^{\infty} f(\xi)e^{-i\lambda\xi} \, d\xi$$

The *Fourier Transform* pair is

$$F(\lambda) = \frac{1}{2\pi} \int_{-\infty}^{\infty} f(\xi)e^{i\lambda\xi} \, d\xi \tag{8.43a}$$

and

$$f(x) = \int_{-\infty}^{\infty} F(\lambda)e^{-i\lambda x} \, d\lambda \tag{8.43b}$$

8.2.2   Applications of the Limit Process

EXAMPLE 8.2   *Fluid Flow of a High-Speed Jet from a Nozzle.* The flow of a plane stream of ideal fluid (see Sec. 2.2.3) from a nozzle (Fig. 8.2) leads to an interesting Dirichlet model in a finite region with a solution involving infinite integrals.

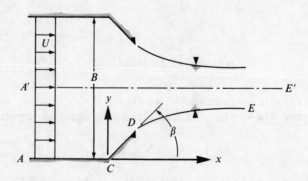

FIGURE 8.2   Jet from a nozzle.

The complete problem of determining the form of the jet and the fluid velocities was formulated and solved by the author [4]. However, we are concerned here only with solving the intermediate problem for the stream function $\psi(q, \chi)$, whose spatial derivatives give the fluid velocity components. The polar coordinates (q, χ) in this case represent the magnitude q of the velocity and its direction χ with respect to the centerline of the flow. The mathematical model for ψ (see Fig. 8.3) is

$$\nabla^2\psi = \psi_{qq} + \frac{1}{q}\psi_q + \frac{1}{q^2}\psi_{\chi\chi} = 0, \qquad 0 < q < 1, \quad 0 < \chi < \beta \qquad (8.44a)$$

$$\psi(q, 0) = f(q), \qquad 0 < q < 1 \qquad (8.44b)$$

$$\psi(1, \chi) = 0, \qquad 0 < \chi \leq \beta \qquad (8.44c)$$

$$\psi(q, \beta) = 0, \qquad 0 \leq q \leq 1 \qquad (8.44d)$$

on the sector of the unit circle $0 \leq \chi \leq \beta$. The constants U, B, β are given and ψ is discontinuous on $\chi = 0$ because $f(q) = 0$ on $q < U$ and $f(q) = -UB/2$ on $q \geq U$.

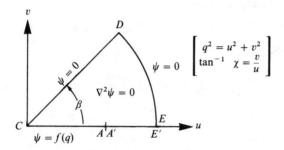

FIGURE 8.3 Stream function on sector of circle.

The infinite integrals in the solution arise because $q \to 0$ and because of the apparent singularity of the Laplace equation (8.44a) in the polar coordinates (q, χ). Indeed, the model (8.44) appears to be missing the implied condition

$$\psi(0, \chi) = 0, \qquad 0 < \chi < \beta$$

To begin, we solve the related but conventional problem for $u(r, \theta)$:

$$\nabla^2 u = u_{rr} + \frac{1}{r}u_r + \frac{1}{r^2}u_{\theta\theta} = 0, \qquad a < r < 1, \quad 0 < \theta < \gamma$$

$$
\begin{aligned}
u(a, \theta) &= 0, & 0 < \theta < \gamma & \quad \text{(\textit{Note:} equivalent to implied} \\
u(1, \theta) &= 0, & 0 < \theta \leq \gamma & \quad \text{condition above)} \\
u(r, 0) &= 0, & a \leq r \leq 1 & \\
u(r, \gamma) &= f(r), & a < r < 1 &
\end{aligned}
\qquad (8.45)
$$

where $f(r)$ is prescribed, γ is a constant, and $0 < a \ll 1$. Using $u(r, \theta) = \phi(r)T(\theta)$ and the method of separation of variables produces the eigenvalue problem

$$r^2\phi'' + r\phi' + \lambda^2\phi = 0, \qquad a < r < 1$$
$$\phi(1) = \phi(a) = 0 \qquad (8.46)$$

and

$$T'' - \lambda^2 T = 0, \qquad 0 < \theta < \gamma$$
$$T(0) = 0 \qquad (8.47)$$

The solution to (8.47) is (see Sec. 3.4, Example 3.1)

$$T(\theta) = \frac{c_1}{\lambda} \sinh \lambda\theta$$

Now, the ordinary differential equation in (8.46) has the Sturm–Liouville form

$$[r\phi']' + \frac{\lambda^2}{r}\phi = 0 \tag{8.48}$$

so that the eigenfunctions are orthogonal with respect to $p = r^{-1}$ and a formal attack with a power series solution or $\phi = r^{\pm i\lambda}$ would indeed yield the desired results. However, it is convenient to reduce new problems to old problems that we have already solved. This is such a case, for if $\rho = \ln r$, then $a \leq r \leq 1$ implies $\ln a \leq \rho \leq 0$ and $d\rho/dr = 1/r$; (8.48) becomes

$$\phi'' + \lambda^2\phi = 0$$

where $\phi = \phi(\rho)$ because

$$\phi_r = \frac{1}{r}\phi_\rho \quad \text{or} \quad r\phi_r = \phi_\rho$$

Whence

$$(r\phi_r)_r = \phi_{\rho\rho}\frac{d\rho}{dr} = \frac{1}{r}\phi_{\rho\rho}$$

so

$$r(r\phi_r)_r = \phi_{\rho\rho}$$

In terms of ρ,

$$\phi'' + \lambda^2\phi = 0, \qquad \ln a < \rho < 0$$
$$\phi(\ln a) = \phi(0) = 0 \tag{8.49}$$

We know that the eigenvalues and eigenfunctions for (8.49) are

$$\lambda_n^2 = \left(\frac{n\pi}{\ln a}\right)^2 \qquad \phi_n(\rho) = \sin \lambda_n\rho, \qquad n > 0$$

where, for convenience, $\lambda_n = -n\pi/\ln a$ because $\ln a < 0$ for $0 < a < 1$. Thus

$$\lambda_n^2 = \left(\frac{n\pi}{\ln a}\right)^2 \qquad \phi_n(r) = \sin(\lambda_n \ln r), \qquad n > 0 \tag{8.50}$$

are the eigenvalues and eigenfunctions for (8.46). Also,

$$\int_{\ln a}^0 \phi_n(\rho)\phi_m(\rho)\,d\rho = 0 \qquad \text{for } m \neq n$$

and

$$\int_{\ln a}^0 \phi_n^2(\rho)\,d\rho = \frac{-\ln a}{2}$$

(see Sec. 3.2 and Example 3.1, Sec. 3.4) because of the orthogonality of the $\phi_n(\rho)$ of (8.49). Therefore, for $\phi_n(r)$,

$$\int_a^1 \frac{1}{r} \phi_n(r)\phi_m(r)\, dr = 0, \qquad m \neq n \tag{8.51}$$

and

$$\int_a^1 \frac{1}{r} \phi_n^2(r)\, dr = -\frac{\ln a}{2} = N_n \tag{8.52}$$

because $\rho = \ln r$ and $d\rho = r^{-1}\, dr$. Note that (8.51) confirms that the eigenfunctions $\phi_n(r)$ of (8.46) and (8.48) are orthogonal with respect to the weight function $p = r^{-1}$.

Now, using our results, (8.51) and (8.52) in the usual way produce (see the Problems)

$$u(r, \theta) = \frac{2}{\pi} \sum_{n=1}^{\infty} \left(\frac{-\pi}{\ln a}\right) \frac{\sinh \lambda_n \theta}{\sinh \lambda_n \gamma} \int_a^1 \frac{f(\eta)}{\eta} \sin (\lambda_n \ln \eta)\, d\eta \sin (\lambda_n \ln r) \tag{8.53}$$

If $\Delta\lambda = \lambda_{n+1} - \lambda_n = -\pi/\ln a$ [from (8.50)], (8.53) can be written

$$u(r, \theta) = \frac{2}{\pi} \sum_{n=1}^{\infty} \frac{\sinh \lambda_n \theta}{\sinh \lambda_n \gamma} \sin (\lambda_n \ln r) \int_a^1 \frac{f(\eta)}{\eta} \sin (\lambda_n \ln \eta)\, d\eta\, \Delta\lambda$$

As $a \to 0$, $\Delta\lambda \to 0^+$ because $\ln a \to -\infty$, while $\lim_{a\to 0}\{\lim_{n\to\infty} \lambda_n\} = \infty$ as before in our limit process. Then, for $a = 0$,

$$u(r, \theta) = \frac{2}{\pi} \int_0^{\infty} \frac{\sinh \lambda\theta}{\sinh \lambda\gamma} \sin (\lambda \ln r) \int_0^1 \frac{f(\eta)}{\eta} \sin (\lambda \ln \eta)\, d\eta\, d\lambda$$

For $a = 0$, if we compare (8.44) and (8.45), we see that letting $\gamma = \beta$, $r = q$, and $\theta = \beta - \chi$ suggests $u(r, \theta) = \psi(q, \chi)$. Immediately,

$$u(r, \gamma) = \psi(q, 0) = f(q)$$

and

$$\psi(q, \chi) = \frac{2}{\pi} \int_0^{\infty} \frac{\sinh \lambda(\beta - \chi)}{\sinh \lambda\beta} \sin (\lambda \ln q) \int_0^1 \frac{f(\eta)}{\eta} \sin (\lambda \ln \eta)\, d\eta\, d\lambda \tag{8.54}$$

is the solution to (8.44).

It is easy to show (see the Problems) that the improper integral in (8.54) converges provided that

$$\left| \int_0^1 \frac{f(\eta)}{\eta} \sin (\lambda \ln \eta)\, d\eta \right| < \infty$$

Thus the solution exists. In order to establish the validity of the representation (8.54) at $\chi = 0$, set $\rho = -\ln q$ and $\xi = -\ln \eta$; then (8.54) becomes, at $\chi = 0$,

$$\psi(e^{-\rho}, 0) = f(e^{-\rho}) = \frac{2}{\pi} \int_0^{\infty} \sin (-\lambda\rho)\, d\lambda \int_{\infty}^0 f(e^{-\xi}) \sin (-\lambda\xi)(-d\xi) \tag{8.55}$$

as $d\xi = -d\eta/\eta$. If $F(\rho) = f(e^{-\rho})$, (8.55) becomes

$$F(\rho) = \frac{2}{\pi} \int_0^{\infty} \sin \lambda\rho\, d\lambda \int_0^{\infty} F(\xi) \sin \lambda\xi\, d\xi$$

because the sine function is odd. But this is exactly the Fourier sine transform (8.41), valid when $F(\rho) \in L^1(0, \infty)$—that is, when

$$\int_0^\infty |F(\xi)| \, d\xi$$

exists. Thus (8.54) is a valid representation at $\chi = 0$ when the improper integral

$$\int_0^1 |f(\eta)| \frac{d\eta}{\eta} \tag{8.56}$$

exists.

EXAMPLE 8.3   *Vibration of a Large Circular Membrane.* We derived in Sec. 2.2.2 a mathematical model for the small transverse vibrations of a circular membrane with fixed circumference and finite radius R. In Sec. 4.4 we solved the eigenvalue problem for this model. It is natural to return to these results and obtain the solution for a very large membrane by letting $R \to \infty$.

From (2.63), the model for the small, free transverse vibrations, symmetric about the origin, of a circular membrane with fixed circumference is, where $z(r, t)$ is the displacement,

$$z_{tt} = c^2 \left(z_{rr} + \frac{1}{r} z_r \right), \qquad 0 < r < R, \quad 0 < t \tag{8.57a}$$

$$z(R, t) = 0, \qquad 0 < t \tag{8.57b}$$

$$z_r(0, t) = 0, \qquad 0 < t \tag{8.57c}$$

$$z(r, 0) = z_0(r), \qquad 0 \le r \le R \tag{8.57d}$$

$$z_t(r, 0) = V_0(r), \qquad 0 \le r \le R \tag{8.57e}$$

Separation of variables in (8.57a to c) through the use of the product form

$$z(r, t) = \phi(r)T(t)$$

yields an eigenvalue problem for $\phi(r)$

$$\phi'' + \frac{1}{r}\phi' + \lambda^2 \phi = 0, \qquad 0 < r < R$$

$$\phi'(0) = \phi(R) = 0 \tag{8.58}$$

and, for $T(t)$, the equation

$$T'' + c^2 \lambda^2 T = 0 \tag{8.59}$$

The solution to (8.59) is [see (3.84)]

$$T(t) = A_0 \cos c\lambda t + \frac{A_1}{c\lambda} \sin c\lambda t$$

while in Example 4.7, Sec. 4.4, we found the eigenfunctions and eigenvalues of (8.58) to be

$$\phi_n(r) = J_0(\lambda_n r) \qquad \lambda_n^2 = \left(\frac{\alpha_n}{R} \right)^2, \qquad n > 0$$

where the α_n are the roots of the Bessel's function of zero order J_0—that is,

$$J_0(\alpha_n) = 0$$

Therefore the proposed series solution to (8.57) is

$$z(r, t) = \sum_{n=1}^{\infty} \left(A_{0n} \cos c\lambda_n t + \frac{A_{1n}}{c\lambda_n} \sin c\lambda_n t \right) J_0(\lambda_n r) \tag{8.60}$$

At $t = 0$, we require, according to (8.57d and e),

$$z(r, 0) = z_0(r) = \sum_{n=1}^{\infty} A_{0n} J_0(\lambda_n r) \tag{8.61a}$$

and

$$z_t(r, 0) = V_0(r) = \sum_{n=1}^{\infty} A_{1n} J_0(\lambda_n r) \tag{8.61b}$$

The ordinary differential equation in (8.58) has the Sturm–Liouville form (Chap. 4)

$$[r\phi']' + \lambda^2 r\phi = 0$$

so the eigenfunctions $\phi_n(r) = J_0(\lambda_n r)$ are orthogonal with respect to $p = r$; that is,

$$\int_0^R r\phi_n(r)\phi_m(r)\, dr = \int_0^R rJ_0\left(\frac{\alpha_n}{R}r\right)J_0\left(\frac{\alpha_m}{R}r\right)dr = 0, \qquad m \neq n$$

Then, from Appendix 3, Eq. (A.3.27), we have

$$N_n = \int_0^R r\phi_n^2\, dr = \int_0^R rJ_0^2\left(\frac{\alpha_n}{R}r\right)dr = \frac{R^2}{2}[J_0^2(\alpha_n) + J_1^2(\alpha_n)]$$

As $J_0(\alpha_n) = 0$, $N_n = \frac{1}{2}R^2 J_1^2(\alpha_n) \neq 0$ because J_0 and J_1 have no common roots. Application of these orthogonality relations to (8.61) leads in the usual way to

$$A_{0m} = \frac{2}{R^2 J_1^2(\alpha_m)} \int_0^R rJ_0(\lambda_m r)z_0(r)\, dr$$

and

$$A_{1m} = \frac{2c\lambda_m}{R^2 J_1^2(\alpha_m)} \int_0^R rJ_0(\lambda_m r)V_0(r)\, dr$$

The complete solution to the finite model (8.57) is, from (8.60) and the above,

$$z(r, t) = \sum_{n=1}^{\infty} \frac{2J_0(\lambda_n r)}{R^2 J_1^2(\alpha_n)} \left[\cos c\lambda_n t \int_0^R \rho J_0(\lambda_n \rho)z_0(\rho)\, d\rho \right.$$

$$\left. + \sin c\lambda_n t \int_0^R \rho J_0(\lambda_n \rho)V_0(\rho)\, d\rho \right] \tag{8.62a}$$

while Eqs. (8.61) become

$$z_0(r) = \sum_{n=1}^{\infty} \frac{2J_0(\lambda_n r)}{R^2 J_1^2(\alpha_n)} \int_0^R \rho J_0(\lambda_n \rho)z_0(\rho)\, d\rho \tag{8.62b}$$

and

$$V_0(r) = \sum_{n=1}^{\infty} \frac{2J_0(\lambda_n r)}{R^2 J_1^2(\alpha_n)} \int_0^R \rho J_0(\lambda_n \rho) V_0(\rho) \, d\rho \qquad (8.62c)$$

Both (8.62b) and (8.62c) have the form

$$f(r) = \sum_{n=1}^{\infty} f_{bn} J_0(\lambda_n r), \qquad f_{bn} = \frac{1}{N_n} \int_0^R \rho J_0(\lambda_n \rho) f(\rho) \, d\rho$$

of a *Fourier–Bessel* series. It is our goal to see if, as $R \to \infty$, these series become Fourier–Bessel integrals or Hankel transforms. It is convenient to deal only with (8.62b); (8.62a) and (8.62c) have the same form and the results for (8.62b) apply equally to all (8.62).

For our usual procedure in the limit process and from examination of the Hankel transforms (8.5) and (8.6), we expect to be able to replace $2/R^2 J_1^2(\alpha_n)$ by $\lambda_n \Delta\lambda$ so that, as $R \to \infty$, $\Delta\lambda \to 0$ and the series becomes an integral. The key here is the not-obvious behavior of $J_1^2(\alpha_n)$. However, from (A.3.18) in Appendix 3, we find that asymptotically for large argument x,

$$-J_0'(x) = J_1(x) = \left(\frac{2}{\pi x}\right)^{1/2} \left[\cos\left(x - \frac{3\pi}{4}\right) + O(|x|^{-1})\right]$$

$$J_0(x) = \left(\frac{2}{\pi x}\right)^{1/2} \left[\cos\left(x - \frac{\pi}{4}\right) + O(|x|^{-1})\right]$$

The roots of $J_0(\alpha_n) = 0$ are approximately $\alpha_n \approx (n - \frac{1}{4})\pi$ as α_n becomes large. By choosing a value N large enough, we can make

$$|\alpha_n - (n - \tfrac{1}{4})\pi| < \varepsilon, \qquad n > N$$

for some arbitrarily small ε and

$$\left| J_1^2(\alpha_n) - \frac{2}{\pi \alpha_n} \right| < \delta, \qquad n > N$$

for arbitrarily small δ. [$J_1^2(\alpha_n) \neq 0$ because J_0 and J_1 have no common roots.]
For $n > N$,

$$\lambda_n = \frac{\alpha_n}{R} \approx \frac{n\pi}{R} - \frac{\pi}{4R}$$

so

$$\Delta\lambda = \lambda_{n+1} - \lambda_n = \frac{\pi}{R}$$

and

$$\frac{2}{R^2 J_1^2(\alpha_n)} \approx \frac{\pi \alpha_n}{R^2} = \lambda_n \Delta\lambda, \qquad n > N$$

as we hoped. Accordingly, following the suggestion of Weber [5, p. 199] (see also Bowman [6]), we write (8.62b) as

$$z_0(r) = \sum_{n=1}^{N} \frac{2J_0(\lambda_n r)}{R^2 J_1^2(\alpha_n)} \int_0^R \rho J_0(\lambda_n \rho) z_0(\rho) \, d\rho + \sum_{n=N}^{\infty} \lambda_n \Delta\lambda J_0(\lambda_n r) \int_0^R \rho J_0(\lambda_n \rho) z_0(\rho) \, d\rho$$

Again $\lim_{R \to \infty} \{\lim_{n \to \infty} \lambda_n\} \to \infty$. As we let $R \to \infty$, every term in the first series vanishes, whereas, for $n = M$,

$$\lim_{R \to \infty} \{\lambda_N\} = \lim_{R \to \infty} \left\{ \frac{\alpha_N}{R} \right\} = 0$$

Thus the second series becomes formally an integral with lower limit zero and upper limit infinity; that is,

$$z(r) = \int_0^\infty \lambda J_0(\lambda r)\, d\lambda \int_0^\infty \rho J_0(\lambda \rho) z_0(\rho)\, d\rho \qquad (8.63)$$

which is precisely a Hankel transform of order zero [see (8.5) and (8.6)]. For (8.63) to be valid [7, 8] it is sufficient that z_0 be piecewise smooth on every finite interval and

$$\int_0^\infty \rho^{1/2} |z_0(\rho)|\, d\rho < \infty \qquad (8.64)$$

Then (8.63) is correct if we interpret

$$z_0(r) = \tfrac{1}{2}\{z_0(r^+) + z_0(r^-)\}$$

at any points of discontinuity. Indeed, although we do not study Hankel transforms further here, a general representation of $z_0(r)$ under the foregoing conditions

$$\tfrac{1}{2}\{z_0(r^+) + z_0(r^-)\} = \int_0^\infty \lambda J_n(\lambda r)\, d\lambda \int_0^\infty \rho J_n(\lambda \rho) z_0(\rho)\, d\rho$$

is valid [7, 8].

Finally, as $R \to \infty$, (8.62a) becomes

$$z(r, t) = \int_0^\infty \lambda J_0(\lambda r)\, d\lambda \int_0^\infty \rho J_0(\lambda \rho)\{\cos c\lambda t\, z_0(\rho) + \sin c\lambda t\, V_0(\rho)\}\, d\rho \qquad (8.65)$$

In each case above, the eigenfunctions corresponding to the eigenvalues of the discrete spectrum of the finite problem become solutions of an infinite eigenvalue problem that has no boundary conditions. The spectrum of the infinite problem is the continuum of positive real numbers. The summation of the series in the finite problem becomes an integral summation over the continuous spectrum in the infinite problem. The limit process provides a plausible basis, in general, for generating continuous spectra and eigenfunction representations through integrals ([9], pp. 339-343, for instance).

8.2.3   Direct Use of Transform Pairs

Now let us proceed to use transforms directly. To do so, we need to know the specific properties of transforms; in particular, since we are going to employ them to transform differential equations, the transforms of derivatives must be known.

The Fourier transforms (8.40), (8.41), and (8.43) are valid under the general requirement that $f(x) \in L^1(a, \infty)$—that is, the integral

$$\int_{-a}^\infty |f(x)|\, dx \qquad (8.66)$$

exists—where for the cases considered here a is either 0 or ∞. It is easy to show (see the Problems) that a *necessary* condition for the existence of (8.66) is

$$\lim_{|x| \to \infty} f(x) = 0$$

for piecewise-smooth functions. The derivatives of the transform are obtained by integration by parts. From (8.1), with $d\phi/d\eta$ replacing ϕ and under the assumption that K and ϕ and their derivatives are bounded and continuous,

$$\int_a^b K(\xi, \eta)\frac{d\phi}{d\eta}\, d\eta = K(\xi, \eta)\phi(\eta)\Big|_a^b - \int_a^b \frac{\partial K}{\partial \eta}\phi(\eta)\, d\eta \tag{8.67}$$

and, similarly,

$$\int_a^b K(\xi, \eta)\frac{d^2\phi}{d\eta^2}\, d\eta = K(\xi, \eta)\frac{d\phi}{d\eta}(\eta)\Big|_a^b - \int_a^b \frac{\partial K}{\partial \eta}\frac{d\phi}{d\eta}\, d\eta$$

$$= \left[K(\xi, \eta)\frac{d\phi}{d\eta}(\eta) - \frac{\partial K}{\partial \eta}(\xi, \eta)\phi(\eta) \right]\Big|_a^b + \int_a^b \frac{\partial^2 K}{\partial \eta^2}\phi(\eta)\, d\eta \tag{8.68}$$

The Fourier transform is, from (8.43a),

$$F(\lambda) = \frac{1}{2\pi}\int_{-\infty}^{\infty} f(\xi)e^{i\lambda\xi}\, d\xi \tag{8.69}$$

the kernel is $K = (1/2\pi)e^{i\lambda\xi}$ so, with the variables being (λ, ξ) now,

$$\frac{\partial K}{\partial \xi} = i\lambda K, \qquad \frac{\partial^2 K}{\partial \xi^2} = (i\lambda)^2 K = -\lambda^2 K$$

From (8.67) and (8.68) for f and f' continuous and f'' piecewise smooth,

$$\frac{1}{2\pi}\int_{-\infty}^{\infty}\frac{df}{d\xi}e^{i\lambda\xi}\, d\xi = \frac{1}{2\pi}e^{i\lambda\xi}f(\xi)\Big|_{-\infty}^{\infty} - \frac{i\lambda}{2\pi}\int_{-\infty}^{\infty} f(\xi)e^{i\lambda\xi}\, d\xi \tag{8.70}$$

and

$$\frac{1}{2\pi}\int_{-\infty}^{\infty}\frac{d^2f}{d\xi^2}e^{i\lambda\xi}\, d\xi = \frac{1}{2\pi}\left[e^{i\lambda\xi}\frac{df}{d\xi}(\xi) - i\lambda e^{i\lambda\xi}f(\xi) \right]\Big|_{-\infty}^{\infty} + \frac{(i\lambda)^2}{2\pi}\int_{-\infty}^{\infty} f(\xi)e^{i\lambda\xi}\, d\xi \tag{8.71}$$

But $\lim_{|x| \to \infty} f(x) = 0$ is required for (8.69) and its inverse to exist, while $\lim_{|x| \to \infty} f'(x) = 0$ is required for (8.70) and its inverse to exist. Therefore the evaluated terms in (8.70) and (8.71) vanish and

$$\frac{1}{2\pi}\int_{-\infty}^{\infty}\frac{df}{d\xi}e^{i\lambda\xi}\, d\xi = \frac{-i\lambda}{2\pi}\int_{-\infty}^{\infty} f(\xi)e^{i\lambda\xi}\, d\xi = -i\lambda F(\lambda)$$

$$\frac{1}{2\pi}\int_{-\infty}^{\infty}\frac{d^2f}{d\xi^2}e^{i\lambda\xi}\, d\xi = (i\lambda)^2 F(\lambda) = -\lambda^2 F(\lambda)$$

Following the same procedure for the sine and cosine transforms (left to the Problems), we have in sum:

THEOREM 8.2   Suppose that a continuous function $f(x)$ has a continuous first derivative and a piecewise-smooth second derivative on the appropriate interval

($|x| < \infty$ or $0 < x < \infty$). If the function and its derivatives are absolutely integrable— that is, $\in L^1$ on the appropriate interval—and both $f(x) \to 0$ and $f'(x) \to 0*$ as $|x| \to \infty$, the Fourier transforms are as shown in the table.

Function	Fourier Transform	Sine Transform	Cosine Transform
$f(x)$	$F(\lambda) = \dfrac{1}{2\pi} \displaystyle\int_{-\infty}^{\infty} f(\xi) e^{i\lambda\xi}\, d\xi$	$s(\lambda) = \dfrac{2}{\pi} \displaystyle\int_{0}^{\infty} f(\xi) \sin \lambda\xi\, d\xi$	$c(\lambda) = \dfrac{2}{\pi} \displaystyle\int_{0}^{\infty} f(\xi) \cos \lambda\xi\, d\xi$
$f'(x)$	$-i\lambda F(\lambda)$	$-\lambda c(\lambda)$	$-\dfrac{2}{\pi} f(0) + \lambda s(\lambda)$
$f''(x)$	$-\lambda^2 F(\lambda)$	$\dfrac{2}{\pi} f(0) - \lambda^2 s(\lambda)$	$-\dfrac{2}{\pi} f'(0) - \lambda^2 c(\lambda)$

For many mathematical models of physical systems, it is reasonable to expect continuous solutions with continuous derivatives. Similarly, the limit in Theorem 8.2 on f (and hence f') at infinity is reasonable for many physical problems when we consider infinite intervals. The interest in such cases is usually some finite interval far from certain boundary conditions that might otherwise affect the solution. Accordingly, behavior at infinity is not of primary concern, and, for bounded solutions, the mathematically imposed limitation on f is acceptable.

In the application of Theorem 8.2 to partial differential equations, $f(x)$ is replaced by $u(x, t)$. The second variable is treated as a parameter; that is, the transform is valid for every particular fixed value of t. Also, for models with second-order derivatives in the differential equation and a semi-infinite domain, the appropriate form of the transform is fixed by the function or derivative value prescribed in the boundary condition at the origin (see the sine and cosine transforms in Theorem 8.2).

The best way to gain an understanding of the transform method is to work several examples. A natural first example is the model solved in Sec. 8.2.1—that is, the infinitely large Fourier heat ring.

EXAMPLE 8.4   From (8.22), a model for $u(x, t)$ is

$$u_t = k u_{xx}, \qquad -\infty < x < \infty, \quad 0 < t \tag{8.72a}$$

$$u(x, 0) = u_0(x), \qquad -\infty < x < \infty \tag{8.72b}$$

$$|u(x, t)| < \infty \tag{8.72c}$$

$$\lim_{|x| \to \infty} u(x, t) = 0, \qquad 0 \le t$$

$$\lim_{|x| \to \infty} u_x(x, t) = 0, \qquad 0 \le t \tag{8.72d}$$

$$\int_{-\infty}^{\infty} |u_0(x)|\, dx < \infty$$

with $u_0(x)$ piecewise smooth and where (8.72d) are conditions imposed to ensure the validity of the transforms used. The requirement $u(x, t) \in L^1(-\infty, \infty)$, $0 \le t$, is equivalent to (8.72d).

---

* The result $f'(x) \to 0$ follows from the Law of Mean [2] for the function $f(x)$, as defined, if $f(x) \to 0$. Thus $f(x) \to 0$ or $f'(x) \to 0$ are not separate requirements but are consequences.

We transform (8.72a and b) with respect to x by the transform [see (8.43a)]

$$U(\lambda, t) = \frac{1}{2\pi} \int_{-\infty}^{\infty} u(x, t)e^{i\lambda x} \, dx \tag{8.73a}$$

According to (8.43b),

$$u(x, t) = \int_{-\infty}^{\infty} U(\lambda, t)e^{-i\lambda x} \, d\lambda \tag{8.73b}$$

From (8.73a) and Theorem 8.2,

$$\frac{1}{2\pi} \int_{-\infty}^{\infty} u_t(x, t)e^{i\lambda x} \, dx = \frac{\partial U}{\partial t}(\lambda, t)$$

because differentiation under the integral is permissible for absolutely convergent integrals—that is, for $u(x, t) \in L^1(-\infty, \infty)$—and

$$\frac{1}{2\pi} \int_{-\infty}^{\infty} u_{xx}(x, t)e^{i\lambda x} \, dx = -\lambda^2 U(\lambda, t)$$

The transforms of (8.72a and b) are then

$$\frac{\partial U}{\partial t} = -\lambda^2 kU, \qquad U(\lambda, 0) = \frac{1}{2\pi} \int_{-\infty}^{\infty} u_0(x)e^{i\lambda x} \, dx \tag{8.74}$$

This is an initial-value problem for an ordinary differential equation with λ as a parameter. Therefore the transform reduces the initial-value problem for a partial differential equation to an initial-value problem for an ordinary differential equation. From (A.2.1) and (A.2.3) in Appendix 2 or from Chap. 3, the solution to (8.74) is

$$U(\lambda, t) = U(\lambda, 0)e^{-\lambda^2 kt} \tag{8.75}$$

Having now solved the model in the transform λ-space, we transform the solution back to x-space using (8.73b); thus

$$u(x, t) = \int_{-\infty}^{\infty} U(\lambda, 0)e^{-\lambda^2 kt}e^{-i\lambda x} \, d\lambda$$

$$= \frac{1}{2\pi} \int_{-\infty}^{\infty} \int_{-\infty}^{\infty} u_0(\xi)e^{i\lambda \xi} \, d\xi \, e^{-\lambda^2 kt - i\lambda x} \, d\lambda$$

or

$$u(x, t) = \frac{1}{2\pi} \int_{-\infty}^{\infty} e^{-\lambda^2 kt} \, d\lambda \int_{-\infty}^{\infty} u_0(\xi)e^{i\lambda(\xi - x)} \, d\xi \tag{8.76}$$

which is the solution to (8.72).

To regain the solution form (8.21) obtained previously, we write (8.76) as

$$u(x, t) = \frac{1}{2\pi} \left[\int_{-\infty}^{0} e^{-\lambda^2 kt} \, d\lambda \int_{-\infty}^{\infty} u_0(\xi)e^{i\lambda(\xi - x)} \, d\xi + \int_{0}^{\infty} e^{-\lambda^2 kt} \, d\lambda \int_{-\infty}^{\infty} u_0(\xi)e^{i\lambda(\xi - x)} \, d\xi \right]$$

Putting $\rho = -\lambda$ so $d\rho = -d\lambda$ in the first pair of integrals produces

$$u(x, t) = \frac{1}{2\pi} \left\{ \int_0^\infty e^{-\rho^2 kt} \, d\rho \int_{-\infty}^\infty u_0(\xi) e^{-i\rho(\xi - x)} \, d\xi \right.$$

$$\left. + \int_0^\infty e^{-\lambda^2 kt} \, d\lambda \int_{-\infty}^\infty u_0(\xi) e^{i\lambda(\xi - x)} \, d\xi \right\}$$

$$= \frac{1}{2\pi} \left\{ \int_0^\infty e^{-\lambda^2 kt} \, d\lambda \int_{-\infty}^\infty u_0(\xi) [e^{-i\lambda(\xi - x)} + e^{i\lambda(\xi - x)}] \, d\xi \right\}$$

As $e^{-i\lambda(\xi - x)} + e^{i\lambda(\xi - x)} = 2 \cos \lambda(\xi - x)$,

$$u(x, t) = \frac{1}{\pi} \int_0^\infty e^{-\lambda^2 kt} \, d\lambda \int_{-\infty}^\infty u_0(\xi) \cos \lambda (\xi - x) \, d\xi$$

which is precisely equivalent to (8.21). The operations leading to (8.23) then follow naturally.

On the other hand, (8.23) can be achieved directly from (8.76). Write (8.76) as

$$u(x, t) = \frac{1}{2\pi} \int_{-\infty}^\infty d\lambda \int_{-\infty}^\infty u_0(\xi) e^{i\lambda(\xi - x) - \lambda^2 kt} \, d\xi \tag{8.77}$$

Exchanging the order of integration [see the comments preceding (8.23)] leads to the inner integral

$$I_i = \int_{-\infty}^\infty e^{i\lambda(\xi - x) - \lambda^2 kt} \, d\lambda = \int_{-\infty}^\infty e^{i\lambda\rho} e^{-\lambda^2 kt} \, d\lambda, \qquad \rho = \xi - x$$

But $e^{i\lambda\rho} e^{-\lambda^2 kt} = e^{-\lambda^2 kt} (\cos \lambda\rho + i \sin \lambda\rho)$, and because the sine is an odd function,

$$\int_{-\infty}^\infty e^{-\lambda^2 kt} \sin \lambda\rho \, d\lambda = 0$$

Therefore, since the cosine is an even function,

$$I_i = \int_{-\infty}^\infty e^{-\lambda^2 kt} \cos \lambda\rho \, d\lambda = 2 \int_0^\infty e^{-\lambda^2 kt} \cos \lambda\rho \, d\lambda$$

The integral on the far right has the well-known value [see the equation prior to (8.23) and the Problems] $\pi^{1/2}(4kt)^{-1/2} \exp[-\rho^2/4kt]$. Accordingly,

$$I_i = \int_{-\infty}^\infty e^{-\lambda^2 kt} e^{i\lambda\rho} \, d\lambda = \left(\frac{\pi}{4kt} \right)^{1/2} \exp\left(-\frac{\rho^2}{4kt} \right). \tag{8.78}$$

and (8.77) becomes with $\rho = \xi - x$ again

$$u(x, t) = \frac{1}{(4\pi kt)^{1/2}} \int_{-\infty}^\infty u_0(\xi) \exp\left\{ -\left[\frac{(\xi - x)^2}{4kt} \right] \right\} \, d\xi$$

which equals (8.23) as expected.

If $f(x) = e^{-x^2kt}$, (8.78) shows us that the Fourier transform is

$$F(\lambda) = \frac{1}{2\pi} \int_{-\infty}^{\infty} e^{-x^2kt} e^{i\lambda x} dx = (4\pi kt)^{-1/2} \exp\left(-\frac{\lambda^2}{4kt}\right)$$

But then

$$f(x) = e^{-x^2kt} = \int_{-\infty}^{\infty} F(\lambda)e^{-i\lambda x} d\lambda = \frac{1}{2\pi} \int_{-\infty}^{\infty} \left(\frac{\pi}{kt}\right)^{1/2} e^{-\lambda^2/4kt} e^{-i\lambda x} d\lambda$$

and $\exp(-\lambda^2 kt)$ is seen to be the Fourier transform of $(\pi/kt)^{1/2} \exp(-x^2/4kt)$. Fourier transform pairs can often be determined by evaluation of such specific integrals. Several useful results are tabulated in Appendix 4. The list is not extensive; excellent comprehensive tables [10] edited by Erdélyi are readily available, so it is unnecessary to include large tables of transforms in textbooks.

EXAMPLE 8.5   *Steady Heat Conduction in the Corner of a Large Insulated Plate.* Suppose that the model for the temperature $u(x, y)$ is

$$\nabla^2 u = u_{xx} + u_{yy} = 0, \qquad 0 < x, \quad 0 < y \tag{8.79a}$$

$$u(0, y) = f(y), \qquad 0 \le y \tag{8.79b}$$

$$u_y(x, 0) = 0, \qquad 0 < x \tag{8.79c}$$

$$|u(x, y)| < \infty$$

$$u(x, y) \in L^1(0, \infty) \qquad \text{for } x \text{ and } y \tag{8.79d}$$

The solution to (8.79) by transforms can be carried out by transforming with respect to either variable. From Theorem 8.2, a sine transform

$$U(\lambda, y) = \frac{2}{\pi} \int_0^{\infty} u(x, y) \sin \lambda x \, dx \tag{8.80}$$

is required for the x direction because $u(0, y)$ is prescribed; however, for the y direction, the cosine transform

$$U(x, \lambda) = \frac{2}{\pi} \int_0^{\infty} u(x, y) \cos \lambda y \, dy \tag{8.81}$$

is appropriate because $u_y(x, 0)$ is given.

Proceeding with (8.80) leads to the transforms of (8.79a and c):

$$\frac{2}{\pi} \lambda u(0, y) - \lambda^2 U(\lambda, y) + \frac{\partial^2 U}{\partial y^2}(\lambda, y) = 0 \tag{8.82}$$

$$\frac{\partial U}{\partial \lambda}(\lambda, 0) = 0 \tag{8.83}$$

Also, $u(x, y) \to 0$ as $y \to \infty$, so (8.80) gives

$$\lim_{y \to \infty} U(\lambda, y) = 0 \tag{8.84}$$

Equations (8.82) to (8.84) constitute a well-posed, ordinary-differential-equation, boundary-value problem for $U(\lambda, y)$ (with λ again treated as a parameter). The standard form for (8.82) is [after introduction of (8.79b)]

$$\frac{\partial^2 U}{\partial y^2} - \lambda^2 U = -\frac{2}{\pi} \lambda f$$

and comparison of this with Example A.4, Appendix 2, shows us that the general solution is*

$$U(\lambda, y) = A(\lambda) \cosh \lambda y + \frac{B(\lambda)}{\lambda} \sinh \lambda y$$

$$+ \frac{1}{\lambda} \sinh \lambda y \int_0^y \left(-\frac{2\lambda f(\tau)}{\pi} \right) \cosh \lambda \tau \, d\tau$$

$$- \frac{1}{\lambda} \cosh \lambda y \int_0^y \left(-\frac{2\lambda f(\tau)}{\pi} \right) \sinh \lambda \tau \, d\tau \qquad (8.85)$$

Now (8.83) gives

$$\frac{\partial U}{\partial y}(\lambda, 0) = 0 = B(\lambda)$$

and then (8.84) leads to

$$\lim_{y \to \infty} \left\{ \cosh \lambda y \left[A - \frac{2}{\pi} \left(\int_0^y f(\tau) \left\{ \frac{\sinh \lambda y}{\cosh \lambda y} \cosh \lambda \tau - \frac{\cosh \lambda y}{\cosh \lambda y} \sinh \lambda \tau \right\} d\tau \right) \right] \right\} = 0$$

It follows that, as $\lim_{y \to \infty} \tanh \lambda y = 1$,

$$A = \frac{2}{\pi} \int_0^\infty f(\tau) \{ \cosh \lambda \tau - \sinh \lambda \tau \} \, d\tau$$

But

$$\cosh \lambda \tau - \sinh \lambda \tau = \tfrac{1}{2}(e^{\lambda \tau} + e^{-\lambda \tau} - e^{\lambda \tau} + e^{-\lambda \tau}) = e^{-\lambda \tau}$$

whence

$$A = \frac{2}{\pi} \int_0^\infty f(\tau) e^{-\lambda \tau} \, d\tau \qquad (8.86)$$

Using the identity

$$\sinh \lambda y \cosh \lambda \tau - \cosh \lambda y \sinh \lambda \tau = \sinh \lambda(y - \tau)$$

and (8.86) in (8.85) with $B(\lambda) = 0$ from above yields

$$U(\lambda, y) = \frac{2}{\pi} \left[\cosh \lambda y \int_0^\infty f(\tau) e^{-\lambda \tau} \, d\tau - \int_0^y f(\tau) \sinh \lambda(y - \tau) \, d\tau \right]$$

The solution is given by inverting or transforming $U(\lambda, y)$ with the inverse transform

$$u(x, y) = \int_0^\infty U(\lambda, y) \sin \lambda x \, d\lambda$$

* Recall that $\sin i\lambda y = i \sinh \lambda y$ and $\cosh i\lambda y = \cos \lambda y$.

This inversion appears tedious, but it is possible; a simpler result is obtained by writing the general solution (8.85) in exponential form (see the Problems). The cosine transform gives the simplest approach because the related boundary condition is homogeneous.

Using (8.81) on (8.79a and b) yields (check Theorem 8.2)

$$\frac{\partial^2 U}{\partial x^2}(x, \lambda) - \frac{2}{\pi}u_y(x, 0) - \lambda^2 U(x, \lambda) = 0$$

and

$$U(0, \lambda) = \frac{2}{\pi}\int_0^\infty u(0, y) \cos \lambda y \, dy = \frac{2}{\pi}\int_0^\infty f(y) \cos \lambda y \, dy = F(\lambda) = \text{known} \quad (8.87)$$

From the limiting condition on u as $x \to \infty$, $\lim_{x \to \infty} U(x, \lambda) = 0$. The complete boundary-value problem is

$$\frac{\partial^2 U}{\partial x^2} - \lambda^2 U = 0$$

$$U(0, \lambda) = F(\lambda)$$

$$\lim_{x \to \infty} U(x, \lambda) = 0$$

A general solution for the equation is

$$U(x, \lambda) = A(\lambda) \cosh \lambda x + \frac{B(\lambda)}{\lambda} \sinh \lambda x$$

From the limiting condition as $x \to \infty$, we must have $B(\lambda) = -\lambda A(\lambda)$; using the exponential forms of the hyperbolic functions produces

$$U(x, \lambda) = A(\lambda)e^{-\lambda x}$$

It follows that $A(\lambda) = F(\lambda)$, so

$$U(x, \lambda) = F(\lambda)e^{-\lambda x}$$

Thus

$$u(x, y) = \int_0^\infty U(x, \lambda) \cos \lambda y \, d\lambda = \int_0^\infty F(\lambda)e^{-\lambda x} \cos \lambda y \, d\lambda$$

From (8.87),

$$u(x, y) = \frac{2}{\pi}\int_0^\infty e^{-\lambda x} d\lambda \int_0^\infty f(\tau) \cos \lambda \tau \cos \lambda y \, d\tau$$

Now

$$\cos \lambda \tau \cos \lambda y = \tfrac{1}{2}[\cos \lambda(y + \tau) + \cos \lambda(y - \tau)]$$

so after an exchange in the order of integration, the inner integral is

$$I_i = \frac{1}{2}\int_0^\infty e^{-\lambda x} \cos \lambda(y + \tau) \, d\lambda + \frac{1}{2}\int_0^\infty e^{-\lambda x} \cos \lambda(y - \tau) \, d\lambda$$

These integrals are well known (see the Problems) and

$$I_i = \frac{1}{2}\left[\frac{x}{x^2 + (y + \tau)^2} + \frac{x}{x^2 + (y - \tau)^2}\right]$$

Therefore

$$u(x, y) = \frac{x}{\pi}\int_0^\infty f(\tau)\left[\frac{1}{x^2 + (y + \tau)^2} + \frac{1}{x^2 + (y - \tau)^2}\right] d\tau$$

In view of the uniqueness (see Chap. 6) of the solution, this result is identical to that obtained with the sine transform (see Prob. 8.35).

Interestingly, if we proceed formally for the case $f(y) \equiv 1$, in spite of the fact that such a function violates the limiting conditions, we find (see the Problems) that

$$u(x, y) = 1$$

which is physically reasonable. For

$$f(y) = \begin{cases} 1, & y \le y_0 \\ 0, & y > y_0 \end{cases}$$

$$u(x, y) = \frac{1}{\pi}\left[\tan^{-1}\left(\frac{y_0 + y}{x}\right) + \tan^{-1}\left(\frac{y_0 - y}{x}\right)\right]$$

Here

$$\lim_{x \to \infty} u(x, y) = 0$$

clearly; as $y \to \infty$, $y_0 + y \to y$ and $y_0 - y \to -y$, so

$$\lim_{y \to \infty} u(x, y) = 0$$

also. Similar results exist for the derivatives so the solution is properly behaved.

EXAMPLE 8.6   *The Forced Vibrations of a Very Long String.* As an approximation, consider the small transverse vibrations of an infinitely long string. From (2.47) and (2.50) to (2.51), the model for the displacement $z(y, t)$ is

$$z_{tt} = c^2 z_{yy} + f(y, t), \qquad -\infty < y < \infty, \quad 0 < t \tag{8.88a}$$

$$\begin{aligned} z(y, 0) &= z_0(y), \\ z_t(y, 0) &= V_0(y), \end{aligned} \qquad -\infty < y < \infty \tag{8.88b}$$

$$\begin{aligned} |z(y, t)| &< \infty, \\ z(y, t) &\in L^1(-\infty, \infty), \qquad 0 \le t \end{aligned} \tag{8.88c}$$

where $f(y, t)$ is a force per unit mass acting in the z direction on the string.

Application of the Fourier transform

$$Z(\lambda, t) = \frac{1}{2\pi}\int_{-\infty}^\infty z(y, t)e^{i\lambda y}\, dy \tag{8.89}$$

in (8.88a and b) yields

$$\frac{\partial^2 Z}{\partial t^2}(\lambda, t) = -\lambda^2 c^2 Z(\lambda, t) + F(\lambda, t) \tag{8.90}$$

$$Z(\lambda, 0) = \frac{1}{2\pi} \int_{-\infty}^{\infty} z_0(y) e^{i\lambda y} \, dy = Z_0(\lambda) \tag{8.91}$$

$$\frac{\partial Z}{\partial t}(\lambda, 0) = \frac{1}{2\pi} \int_{-\infty}^{\infty} V_0(y) e^{i\lambda y} \, dy = \tilde{V}_0(\lambda) \tag{8.92}$$

where

$$F(\lambda, t) = \frac{1}{2\pi} \int_{-\infty}^{\infty} f(y, t) e^{i\lambda y} \, dy \tag{8.93}$$

Equations (8.90) to (8.92) comprise an initial-value problem for an ordinary differential equation with λ as a parameter. Using our experience from the previous example [recall (A.2.55), Appendix 2], we find quickly that

$$Z(\lambda, t) = Z_0(\lambda) \cos c\lambda t + \frac{\tilde{V}_0(\lambda)}{c\lambda} \sin c\lambda t + \frac{1}{c\lambda} \int_0^t F(\lambda, \tau) \sin c\lambda(t - \tau) \, d\tau \tag{8.94}$$

Inserting (8.94) in the inverse of (8.89) yields the formal solution

$$z(y, t) = \int_{-\infty}^{\infty} Z(\lambda, t) e^{-i\lambda y} \, d\lambda = \int_{-\infty}^{\infty} Z_0(\lambda) \cos c\lambda t \, e^{-i\lambda y} \, d\lambda$$

$$+ \int_{-\infty}^{\infty} \frac{\tilde{V}_0(\lambda)}{c\lambda} \sin c\lambda t \, e^{-i\lambda y} \, d\lambda + \int_{-\infty}^{\infty} \frac{e^{-i\lambda y}}{c\lambda} \int_0^t F(\lambda, \tau) \sin c\lambda(t - \tau) \, d\tau \, d\lambda \tag{8.95}$$

Because (8.95) is a simple linear sum of the effects of initial displacement, initial velocity, and forcing function, it is convenient to treat each effect separately.

First, let $f(y, t) = 0$ and $V_0(y) = 0$; (8.95) becomes with the insertion of (8.91)

$$z(y, t) = \frac{1}{2\pi} \int_{-\infty}^{\infty} \int_{-\infty}^{\infty} z_0(\xi) e^{i\lambda\xi} \, d\xi \cos c\lambda t \, e^{-i\lambda y} \, d\lambda$$

$$= \frac{1}{2\pi} \int_{-\infty}^{\infty} \cos c\lambda t \, e^{-i\lambda y} \, d\lambda \int_{-\infty}^{\infty} z_0(\xi) e^{i\lambda\xi} \, d\xi \tag{8.96}$$

To evaluate (8.96), we replace $\cos c\lambda t$ by $\frac{1}{2}(\exp\{ic\lambda t\} + \exp\{-ic\lambda t\})$, and integrals of the form

$$I_\pm = \frac{1}{2\pi} \int_{-\infty}^{\infty} z_0(\xi) e^{i\lambda(\xi \pm ct)} \, d\xi = e^{\pm ict\lambda} Z_0(\lambda)$$

emerge. With $\xi \pm ct = \rho, d\rho = d\xi$,

$$I_\pm = \frac{1}{2\pi} \int_{-\infty}^{\infty} z_0(\rho \pm ct) e^{i\lambda\rho} \, d\rho = e^{\pm ic\lambda t} Z_0(\lambda)$$

Thus the Fourier transform of $f(x - p)$ is $e^{ip\lambda}F(\lambda)$. Similarly,

$$\frac{1}{2\pi}\int_{-\infty}^{\infty} e^{ip\xi}f(\xi)e^{i\lambda\xi}\,d\xi = \frac{1}{2\pi}\int_{-\infty}^{\infty} f(\xi)e^{i\xi(\lambda-p)}\,d\xi = F(\lambda - p)$$

so the Fourier transform of $e^{ipx}f(x)$ is $F(\lambda - p)$. These results are stated as

THEOREM 8.3   *The Translation Theorem.* Under the conditions of Theorem 8.2, the following relationships hold:

Function	Fourier Transform
$f(x - p)$	$e^{i\lambda p}F(\lambda)$
$e^{ipx}f(x)$	$F(\lambda - p)$

Now (8.96) becomes

$$z(y, t) = \frac{1}{2}\int_{-\infty}^{\infty} e^{-i\lambda y}\,d\lambda\left[\frac{1}{2\pi}\int_{-\infty}^{\infty} z_0(\xi)e^{ic\lambda t}e^{i\lambda\xi}\,d\xi + \frac{1}{2\pi}\int_{-\infty}^{\infty} z_0(\xi)e^{-ic\lambda t}e^{i\lambda\xi}\,d\xi\right]$$

$$= \frac{1}{2}\int_{-\infty}^{\infty} e^{-i\lambda y}[Z_0(\lambda)e^{ic\lambda t} + Z_0(\lambda)e^{-ic\lambda t}]\,d\lambda$$

According to Theorem 8.3, this equation is equivalent to

$$z(y, t) = \tfrac{1}{2}[z_0(y - ct) + z_0(y + ct)] \tag{8.97}$$

when $f(y, t) \equiv V_0(y) \equiv 0$. Now, let $z_0(y) \equiv f(y, t) \equiv 0$; (8.95) becomes

$$z(y, t) = \int_{-\infty}^{\infty} e^{-i\lambda y}\sin c\lambda t\,\frac{\tilde{V}_0(\lambda)}{c\lambda}\,d\lambda$$

Using

$$\sin c\lambda t = \frac{1}{2i}\{\exp(ic\lambda t) - \exp(-ic\lambda t)\}$$

gives a term of the form

$$\frac{1}{2ic\lambda}[e^{ic\lambda t} - e^{-ic\lambda t}] = \frac{1}{2}\int_{-t}^{t} e^{ic\lambda\tau}\,d\tau$$

Thus

$$z(y, t) = \frac{1}{2}\int_{-\infty}^{\infty} e^{-i\lambda y}\tilde{V}_0(\lambda)\int_{-t}^{t} e^{ic\lambda\tau}\,d\tau\,d\lambda = \frac{1}{2}\int_{-t}^{t}\,d\tau\int_{-\infty}^{\infty}\tilde{V}_0(\lambda)e^{ic\lambda\tau}e^{-i\lambda y}\,d\lambda$$

From Theorem 8.3 and with $\rho = y - c\tau$, we find

$$z(y, t) = \frac{1}{2}\int_{-t}^{t} V_0(y - c\tau)\,d\tau = \frac{1}{2c}\int_{y-ct}^{y+ct} V_0(\rho)\,d\rho \tag{8.98}$$

In case only $f(y, t) \equiv 0$ in the original problem (8.88), the *d'Alembert* solution

$$z(y, t) = \frac{1}{2}[z_0(y - ct) + z_0(y + ct)] + \frac{1}{2c}\int_{y-ct}^{y+ct} V_0(\rho)\,d\rho$$

is obtained. In Chap. 9, Sec. 9.3.2, this solution is obtained by use of characteristics and is discussed in detail.

Finally, we let $z_0(y) \equiv V_0(y) \equiv 0$; (8.95) becomes

$$z(y, t) = \int_{-\infty}^{\infty} \int_0^t F(\lambda, \tau) e^{-i\lambda y} \frac{\sin c\lambda(t - \tau)}{c\lambda} \, d\tau \, d\lambda \qquad (8.99)$$

Following precisely the procedure leading to (8.98), we let $\rho = t - \tau$ and

$$\frac{\sin c\lambda(t - \tau)}{c\lambda} = \frac{1}{2ic\lambda}(e^{ic\lambda\rho} - e^{-ic\lambda\rho}) = \frac{1}{2} \int_{-\rho}^{\rho} e^{ic\lambda\eta} \, d\eta$$

$$= \frac{1}{2} \int_{-(t-\tau)}^{t-\tau} e^{ic\lambda\eta} \, d\eta$$

Then (8.99) can be written (after the permissible changes in the order of integration)

$$z(y, t) = \frac{1}{2} \int_0^t d\tau \int_{-(t-\tau)}^{t-\tau} d\eta \int_{-\infty}^{\infty} F(\lambda, \tau) e^{ic\eta} e^{-i\lambda y} \, d\lambda$$

The last integral equals $f(y - c\eta, \tau)$ according to Theorem 8.3. With $p = y - c\eta$ so $dp = -c \, d\eta$, we have then

$$z(y, t) = \frac{1}{2c} \int_0^t \int_{y-c(t-\tau)}^{y+c(t-\tau)} f(p, \tau) \, dp \, d\tau \qquad (8.100)$$

as the displacement by a force $f(y, t)$ of a very long string, initially at rest and with zero displacement.

8.2.4   Applications with the Dirac δ-function; Convolutions

In Chap. 7 introduction of the δ-function representation of impulsive disturbances or initial conditions led to the establishment of the Green's functions and fundamental singularities or source terms for various equations. On infinite domains, the δ-function and Fourier transforms can be used to obtain explicit formulas for the Green's functions.

Consider, first, the one-dimensional heat conduction model. Suppose that, for $u(x, t)$, a model is

$$u_t - ku_{xx} = \delta(x - x_0, t - t_0), \qquad -\infty < x < \infty, \quad 0 < t$$

$$u(x, 0) = 0, \qquad -\infty < x < \infty$$

with other appropriate limiting conditions [see (8.72)]. Using the Fourier transforms. (8.73) gives, for $U(\lambda, t)$,

$$U_t + \lambda^2 kU = \frac{e^{i\lambda x_0}}{2\pi} \delta(t - t_0) \qquad U(\lambda, 0) = 0 \qquad (8.101)$$

because

$$F(\lambda, t) = \frac{1}{2\pi} \int_{-\infty}^{\infty} \delta(x - x_0, t - t_0) e^{i\lambda x} \, dx$$

$$= \frac{1}{2\pi} \delta(t - t_0) \int_{-\infty}^{\infty} \delta(x - x_0) e^{i\lambda x} \, dx = \frac{e^{i\lambda x_0}}{2\pi} \delta(t - t_0)$$

according to the reproducing property of the δ-function. From Sec. A.2.1, Appendix 2, the solution to (8.101) is

$$U(\lambda, t) = U(\lambda, 0)e^{-\lambda^2 kt} + \frac{e^{i\lambda x_0}}{2\pi} \int_0^t \delta(\tau - t_0)e^{\lambda^2 k(\tau - t)}\, d\tau$$

$$= 0 + \begin{cases} 0, & t < t_0 \\ e^{i\lambda x_0}e^{\lambda^2 k(t_0 - t)}, & t_0 < t \end{cases}$$

(8.102)

We write the last result in the form [see (7.17)]

$$U(\lambda, t) = H(t - t_0)\exp\left[-\lambda^2 k(t - t_0) + i\lambda x_0\right]$$

From (8.73b),

$$u(x, t) = \int_{-\infty}^{\infty} U(\lambda, t)e^{i\lambda x}\, d\lambda$$

$$= \frac{H(t - t_0)}{2\pi} \int_{-\infty}^{\infty} \exp\left[-\lambda^2 k(t - t_0)\right] \exp\left[-i\lambda(x - x_0)\right]\, d\lambda$$

$$= \frac{H(\eta)}{2\pi} 2 \int_0^{\infty} e^{-\lambda^2 k\eta} \cos \lambda\rho\, d\lambda$$

$$= \frac{H(\eta)}{2\pi} \frac{\pi^{1/2}}{(k\eta)^{1/2}} \exp\left(-\frac{\rho^2}{4k\eta}\right)$$

(8.103)

if $\rho = x - x_0$ while $\eta = t - t_0$ [check the same manipulations in the previous section leading to (8.78)].

Accordingly, the Green's function (i.e., the solution to the δ-function model) is

$$G(x, x_0; t - t_0) = G(x - x_0; t - t_0) = \frac{H(t - t_0)}{[4\pi k(t - t_0)]^{1/2}} \exp\left[\frac{-(x - x_0)^2}{4k(t - t_0)}\right]$$

(8.104)

and we conclude that [the formal derivation is a repeat of the preceding derivation with $f(x, t)$ replacing δ]

$$u(x, t) = \int_0^t \int_{-\infty}^{\infty} G(x - \xi; t - \tau)f(\xi, \tau)\, d\xi\, d\tau$$

(8.105)

We see that $G = 0$ when $\tau > t$, so t may be replaced by ∞ in the upper limit of (8.105), and adding $H(t_0)$ to (8.104) makes $G = 0$ when $t_0 < 0$, so the lower limit in (8.105) can be placed at $-\infty$. In sum, we have, for

$$u_t - ku_{xx} = f(x, t), \qquad -\infty < x < \infty, \quad 0 < t$$

$$u(x, 0) = u_0(x), \qquad -\infty < x < \infty$$

(8.106)

the solution [compare to (7.4) for the finite model (7.1) and to (8.23) and (8.24)]

$$u(x, t) = \int_{-\infty}^{\infty} G(x - \xi; t)u_0(\xi)\, d\xi + \int_{-\infty}^{\infty} \int_{-\infty}^{\infty} G(x - \xi; t - \tau)f(\xi, \tau)\, d\xi\, d\tau$$

(8.107)

where if $x - \xi = \rho$ and $t - \tau = \eta$,

$$G(\rho\,;\eta) = \frac{H(\eta)H(\tau)}{(4\pi k\eta)^{1/2}} \exp\left(-\frac{\rho^2}{4k\eta}\right) \tag{8.108}$$

Here $G(x - x_0, t - t_0)$ is the fundamental singularity or Green's function for the heat equation—that is, the response to an instantaneous heat source at $x = x_0$ and $t = t_0$.

The preceding derivations depended on the reproducing property of the δ-function and the Fourier transform of δ. Let us examine these in more detail. In Sec. 7.2 we defined the *convolution*

$$\phi * \delta = \int_{-\infty}^{\infty} \phi(\xi)\,\delta(y - \xi)\,d\xi$$

of the δ-function and a test function. This gave

$$\phi(\xi) = \int_{-\infty}^{\infty} \phi(x)\,\delta(\xi - x)\,dx = \int_{-\infty}^{\infty} \phi(\xi - x)\,\delta(x)\,dx$$

As $\delta(x) = \delta(-x)$, for $\xi = 0$ and $\phi = e^{i\lambda x}/2\pi$,

$$\frac{1}{2\pi}\int_{-\infty}^{\infty} e^{i\lambda x}\,\delta(x)\,dx = \frac{e^{i\lambda\cdot 0}}{2\pi} = \frac{1}{2\pi} = F_\delta$$

Thus the Fourier transform F_δ of $\delta(x)$ is $(2\pi)^{-1}$. The formal completion of the transform by using the inverse relation (8.43b) gives a definition of the δ-function:

$$\delta(x) = \frac{1}{2\pi}\int_{-\infty}^{\infty} e^{-i\lambda x}\,d\lambda$$

Similarly, for $f(x - p) = \delta(x - p)$,

$$\frac{1}{2\pi}\int_{-\infty}^{\infty} \delta(x - p)e^{i\lambda x}\,dx = \frac{1}{2\pi}e^{i\lambda p} = e^{i\lambda p}F_\delta$$

which agrees with the translation theorem (Theorem 8.3).

The general convolution of two ordinary functions is

$$a * b = \int_{-\infty}^{\infty} a(\xi)b(x - \xi)\,d\xi = \int_{-\infty}^{\infty} a(x - \xi)b(\xi)\,d\xi$$

where the second integral follows from the first when $\eta = x - \xi$ is used in the first. The Fourier transform of $a * b$ is

$$F(a * b) = \frac{1}{2\pi}\int_{-\infty}^{\infty} a * b\, e^{i\lambda x}\,dx = \frac{1}{2\pi}\int_{-\infty}^{\infty}\int_{-\infty}^{\infty} a(\xi)b(x - \xi)\,d\xi\, e^{i\lambda x}\,dx$$

$$= \frac{1}{2\pi}\int_{-\infty}^{\infty} a(\xi)\,d\xi \int_{-\infty}^{\infty} b(x - \xi)e^{i\lambda x}\,dx$$

if suitable limits are placed on a and b to justify the change of the order of integration—for example, a and b are piecewise smooth and $\in L^1(-\infty, \infty)$. From Theorem 8.3,

$$\frac{1}{2\pi}\int_{-\infty}^{\infty} b(x - \xi)e^{i\lambda x}\,dx = e^{i\lambda\xi}B(\lambda)$$

Therefore

$$F(a * b) = \int_{-\infty}^{\infty} a(\xi)e^{i\lambda\xi} \, d\xi \, B(\lambda) = 2\pi A(\lambda)B(\lambda)$$

According to the Fourier inversion formula (8.43b),

$$a * b = \int_{-\infty}^{\infty} F(a * b)e^{-i\lambda x} \, d\lambda = 2\pi \int_{-\infty}^{\infty} A(\lambda)B(\lambda)e^{-i\lambda x} \, d\lambda$$

Thus

$$\int_{-\infty}^{\infty} a(\xi)b(x - \xi) \, d\xi = 2\pi \int_{-\infty}^{\infty} A(\lambda)B(\lambda)e^{-i\lambda x} \, d\lambda$$

Finally, let the convolution of the transforms be

$$A * B = \int_{-\infty}^{\infty} A(\mu)B(\lambda - \mu) \, d\mu = \int_{-\infty}^{\infty} A(\lambda - \mu)B(\mu) \, d\mu$$

As $B(\lambda - \mu)$ is the transform of $e^{-i\mu x}b(x)$,

$$A * B = \frac{1}{2\pi} \int_{-\infty}^{\infty} A(\mu)e^{-i\mu x} \int_{-\infty}^{\infty} b(x)e^{i\lambda x} \, dx \, d\mu$$

But

$$A(\mu) = \frac{1}{2\pi} \int_{-\infty}^{\infty} a(x)e^{i\mu x} \, dx$$

so

$$a(x) = \int_{-\infty}^{\infty} A(\mu)e^{-i\mu x} \, d\mu$$

Therefore, after changing the order of integration,

$$A * B = \frac{1}{2\pi} \int_{-\infty}^{\infty} a(x)b(x)e^{i\lambda x} \, dx$$

or

$$A * B = F(ab)$$

The convolution results can be codified in a theorem.

THEOREM 8.4   *Convolution Theorem.* Under the conditions on two functions $a(x)$ and $b(x)$ of Theorem 8.2, the convolution

$$a * b = \int_{-\infty}^{\infty} a(\xi)b(x - \xi) \, d\xi = \int_{-\infty}^{\infty} a(x - \xi)b(\xi) \, d\xi$$

exists and

(a) the Fourier transform of the convolution equals 2π times the product of the transforms $A(\lambda)$ and $B(\lambda)$ of a and b.

(b) the convolution

$$A * B = \int_{-\infty}^{\infty} A(\mu)B(\lambda - \mu)\, d\mu = \int_{-\infty}^{\infty} A(\lambda - \mu)B(\mu)\, d\mu$$

of the transforms A and B is equal to the transform of the product $a \cdot b$.
(c) the convolution $a * b$ is equal to 2π times the inverse transform of the product $A \cdot B$.

Now from the solution (8.107), we observe, according to Theorem 8.4, that a convolution theorem can be given for the general heat model (8.106):

THEOREM 8.5   *Solution of the Heat Problem by Convolution.* Given $G(\rho; \eta)$, according to (8.108) and with appropriate limits on $f(x, t)$ and $u_0(x)$,
(a) the solution to the initial-value problem of the heat conduction model (8.106) in the absence of sources is the *single convolution*

$$u(x, t) = \int_{-\infty}^{\infty} G(x - \xi; t)u_0(\xi)\, d\xi = \int_{-\infty}^{\infty} G(\xi; t)u_0(x - \xi)\, d\xi$$

(b) the solution to the inhomogeneous one-dimensional heat conduction model (8.106) with zero initial values and sources present is the *double convolution*

$$u(x, t) = \int_{-\infty}^{\infty} \int_{-\infty}^{\infty} G(x - \xi; t - \tau)f(\xi, \tau)\, d\xi\, d\tau$$

$$= \int_{-\infty}^{\infty} \int_{-\infty}^{\infty} G(\xi; \tau)f(x - \xi, t - \tau)\, d\xi\, d\tau$$

EXAMPLE 8.7   *An Impulse Acting on a Very Long String.* In the model of Example 8.6, we let $z_0(y) \equiv V_0(y) \equiv 0$. The force per unit mass is $f(y, t)$; ρf is the force per unit length of string. Thus the impulse

$$I = \int_{-\infty}^{\infty} \int_{-\infty}^{\infty} \rho f\, dy\, dt$$

is imparted to the string from $-\infty < y < \infty$ and over all time $-\infty < t < \infty$. To obtain a unit impulse at $t = t_0, y = y_0$, we set $f = \delta(y - y_0, t - t_0)/\rho$. Provided that $t_0 \geq 0$ and $|y_0| < \infty$,

$$I = \int_{0}^{\infty} \int_{-\infty}^{\infty} \delta(y - y_0, t - t_0)\, dy\, dt = 1$$

and the displacement z is given by (8.100) as

$$z(y, t) = \frac{1}{2c\rho} \int_{0}^{t} \int_{y - c(t - \tau)}^{y + c(t - \tau)} \delta(p - y_0, \tau - t_0)\, dp\, d\tau \qquad (8.109)$$

We must examine the integral

$$I_\delta = \int_{y - c(t - \tau)}^{y + c(t - \tau)} \delta(p - y_0, \tau - t_0)\, dp = \delta(\tau - t_0) \int_{y - c(t - \tau)}^{y + c(t - \tau)} \delta(p - y_0)\, dp$$

In Sec. 7.2.1 we found $H'(x) = \delta(x)$, so

$$I_\delta = \delta(\tau - t_0) \int_{y-c(t-\tau)}^{y+c(t-\tau)} H'(p - y_0)\, dp = \delta(\tau - t_0) \int_{y-y_0-c(t-\tau)}^{y-y_0+c(t-\tau)} H'(\rho)\, d\rho$$

$$= \delta(\tau - t_0)[H(y - y_0 + c(t - \tau)) - H(y - y_0 - c(t - \tau))]$$

Thus (8.109) is

$$z(y, t) = \frac{1}{2c\rho} \int_0^t [H\{y - y_0 + c(t - \tau)\} - H\{y - y_0 - c(t - \tau)\}]\, \delta(\tau - t_0)\, d\tau$$

or

$$z(y, t) = \frac{1}{2c\rho} \begin{cases} 0, & t_0 > t \geq 0 \\ H\{y - y_0 + c(t - t_0)\} - H\{y - y_0 - c(t - t_0)\}, & 0 \leq t_0 \leq t \end{cases}$$

A particularly simple result is obtained for an initial impulse at $y_0 = 0$—that is, with $t_0 = 0$ also—

$$z(y, t) = \frac{1}{2c\rho}\{H(y + ct) - H(y - ct)\}$$

Thus an initial impulse at the origin creates a zone of displacement $z = (2c\rho)^{-1}$ whose edges propagate along the so-called *characteristic lines* $y \pm ct = 0$. These lines are discussed in detail in Chap. 9. For now, a plot of the solution $z(y, t)$ in a y-t plane (Fig. 8.4) shows that the point impulse produces a discontinuous solution and that the points of discontinuity propagate along the characteristics. The discontinuities do *not* spread in this solution of the wave equation, whereas they do for the heat equation as the result of the *diffusion* of the heat in the rod, for example.

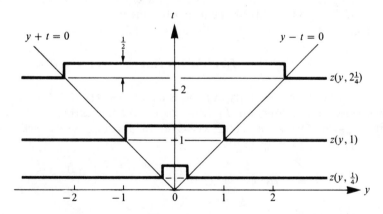

FIGURE 8.4 Impulsive solution of the wave equation ($c = \rho = 1$).

8.3 THE LAPLACE TRANSFORM

The Fourier transforms of the previous section have limitations; two are most obvious. First, if the form of the equation to be transformed changes, the form of the transform changes; for instance, Example 8.3 led to a Hankel transform pair with respect to the space variable r. Second, the functions transformed must approach zero as the independent variable transformed approaches infinity. This condition excludes transformation of some models involving, for example, periodic boundary conditions or forcing functions that do not vanish at infinity.

We perceive a need, then, particularly with relation to the semi-infinite region, say, $t \geq 0$, for an integral transform of a function $\phi(t)$, where $\phi(t)$ is not necessarily zero as $t \to \infty$. The Laplace transform (8.7) satisfies this need as the transform integral

$$\mathscr{L}\{\phi(t)\} = \Phi(p) = \int_0^\infty \phi(t)e^{-pt}\,dt \tag{8.110}$$

exists for real p and t (and is indeed absolutely convergent) provided only that on $0 \leq t$

$$|\phi(t)| = O(e^{\gamma t}) \text{ as } t \to \infty \tag{8.111}$$

for $p > \gamma \geq 0$. Then ϕ is said to be of *exponential order* as $t \to \infty$ (Sec. A.1.1). A major impetus to the development of the Laplace transform methodology was its use as a replacement for the symbolic and somewhat obscure Heaviside's operational calculus [11, 12]; the transform has become the mainstay of the modern operational calculus. General conditions for the validity of the Laplace transform (8.110) and its inverse can be established by an analysis based on complex function theory [12]. Churchill [12] shows that if $\phi(t)$ is a real-valued function, sectionally continuous on each finite interval and of exponential order according to (8.111) on $0 \leq t$, then $\Phi(p)$ is an analytic function (see Sec. 2.6 or Sec. A.2.2) of p, where $p = \gamma' + i\beta$ is a complex variable, $\gamma' > \gamma$, and $\gamma \geq 0$ remains real.

There is also a close relationship between the Fourier and Laplace transforms. This relationship is used here to establish suitable conditions for the validity of the Laplace transform and to establish the form of its inverse.

From (8.43) and Theorem 8.1, the integral relation

$$\frac{1}{2\pi}\int_{-\infty}^\infty e^{-i\lambda x}\,d\lambda \int_{-\infty}^\infty f(\xi)e^{i\lambda\xi}\,d\xi = f(x), \qquad -\infty < x < \infty \tag{8.112}$$

is valid at every point of continuity of f and is equal to $\frac{1}{2}\{f(x^+) + f(x^-)\}$ otherwise for all piecewise-smooth functions $f \in L^1(-\infty, \infty)$. We saw earlier that this implied $f(x) \to 0$ as $|x| \to \infty$. Define a new piecewise-smooth function $\phi(x)$ of *exponential order* $\gamma \geq 0$ such that, for $\gamma' > \gamma$,

$$f(x) = H(x)e^{-\gamma'x}\phi(x) = \begin{cases} e^{-\gamma'x}\phi(x), & x \geq 0 \\ 0, & x < 0 \end{cases} \tag{8.113}$$

Equation (8.112) becomes

$$e^{-\gamma'x}\phi(x) = \frac{1}{2\pi}\int_{-\infty}^\infty e^{-i\lambda x}\,d\lambda \int_0^\infty e^{-\gamma'\xi}\phi(\xi)e^{i\lambda\xi}\,d\xi, \qquad 0 \leq x < \infty \tag{8.114}$$

and as $f \in L^1(-\infty, \infty)$,

$$\int_0^\infty e^{-\gamma'x}|\phi(x)|\,dx < \infty \tag{8.115}$$

The transform (8.114) can be written

$$\phi(x) = \frac{1}{2\pi} \int_{-\infty}^{\infty} e^{(\gamma' - i\lambda)x} \, d\lambda \int_{0}^{\infty} \phi(\xi) e^{-(\gamma' - i\lambda)\xi} \, d\xi, \qquad 0 \le x < \infty$$

Let $p = \gamma' - i\lambda$ so $dp = -i \, d\lambda$. Then

$$\phi(x) = \frac{1}{2\pi i} \int_{\gamma' - i\infty}^{\gamma' + i\infty} e^{px} \, dp \int_{0}^{\infty} \phi(\xi) e^{-p\xi} \, d\xi \tag{8.116}$$

According to (8.110), the Laplace transform of $\phi(x)$ is

$$\mathscr{L}\{\phi(x)\} = \Phi(p) = \int_{0}^{\infty} \phi(x) e^{-px} \, dx \tag{8.117}$$

Introduction of (8.117) into (8.116) provides the explicit inverse transform

$$\phi(x) = \frac{1}{2\pi i} \int_{\gamma' - i\infty}^{\gamma' + i\infty} \Phi(p) e^{px} \, dp \tag{8.118}$$

By combining these results—that is, (8.115), (8.117), and (8.118), and the above-mentioned proof by Churchill—we obtain

THEOREM 8.6   Let $\phi(x)$ be piecewise smooth and of the order $O(e^{\gamma x})$ when $0 \le x$. Then the Laplace transform of $\phi(x)$

$$\mathscr{L}\{\phi(x)\} = \Phi(p) = \int_{0}^{\infty} \phi(x) e^{-px} \, dx$$

is an analytic function of the complex variable $p = \gamma' + i\beta$ in the half-plane $\gamma' > \gamma$. Furthermore, the integral

$$\mathscr{L}^{-1}\{\Phi(p)\} = \frac{1}{2\pi i} \int_{\gamma' - i\infty}^{\gamma' + i\infty} \Phi(p) e^{px} \, dp$$

evaluated along any line Re $(p) = \gamma' > \gamma$ converges to $\phi(x)$ at every point of continuity of ϕ and to $\frac{1}{2}\{\phi(x^+) + \phi(x^-)\}$ otherwise, independently of the value of γ'. Thus $\mathscr{L}^{-1}\{\mathscr{L}\{\phi(x)\}\} = \phi(x)$.

The Laplace transform and the inverse transform can be evaluated by direct integration, by application of complex contour integration and residue theory in the case of the inversion integral, or by reference to a set of standard tables [3, 10]. The contour and residue method [11, 12] is important for advanced applications; however, for our introductory discussion, direct integration of a few simple cases, use of the linearity of the transform and inverse, and reference to our brief table of transforms in Appendix 4 and to the comprehensive tables in Refs. [3] and [10] are sufficient.

Direct integration with the use of integration by parts and standard integral tables [13] establishes transforms of a few simple functions (see Appendix 4).

EXAMPLE 8.8   *Laplace Transforms.*

1. $\phi(x) = 1$ (of exponential order $\gamma = 0$)

$$\Phi(p) = \int_0^\infty e^{-px}\,dx = \frac{1}{p}[e^{-px}]\Big|_0^\infty = \frac{1}{p}, \qquad p > 0$$

2. $\phi(x) = x^n$ (of exponential order $\gamma = 0$)

$$\Phi(p) = \int_0^\infty x^n e^{-px}\,dx = \frac{\Gamma(1+n)}{p^{n+1}}, \qquad n > -1, \quad p > 0$$

where the *Gamma function*

$$\Gamma(x) = \int_0^\infty e^{-\beta}\beta^{x-1}\,d\beta$$

For positive integers n, $\Gamma(n) = (n-1)!$ or direct integration by parts yields

$$\Phi(p) = \int_0^\infty x^n e^{-px}\,dx = \frac{n!}{p^{n+1}}, \qquad p > 0$$

3. $\phi(x) = e^{\alpha x}$ (of exponential order $\gamma = \alpha$)

$$\Phi(p) = \int_0^\infty e^{\alpha x} e^{-px}\,dx = \int_0^\infty e^{-(p-\alpha)x}\,dx = \frac{1}{p-\alpha}, \qquad p > \alpha$$

4. $\phi(x) = \cos \alpha x$ (of exponential order $\gamma = 0$)

$$\Phi(p) = \int_0^\infty \cos \alpha x\, e^{-px}\,dx = \frac{p}{p^2 + \alpha^2}, \qquad p > 0$$

5. $\phi(x) = \sin \alpha x$ (of exponential order $\gamma = 0$)

$$\Phi(p) = \int_0^\infty \sin \alpha x\, e^{-px}\,dx = \frac{\alpha}{p^2 + \alpha^2}, \qquad p > 0$$

6. $\phi(x) = \cosh \alpha x$ (of exponential order $\gamma = \alpha$)

$$\Phi(p) = \int_0^\infty \cosh \alpha x\, e^{-px}\,dx = \frac{p}{p^2 - \alpha^2}, \qquad p > |\alpha|$$

7. $\phi(x) = \sinh \alpha x$ (of exponential order $\gamma = \alpha$)

$$\Phi(p) = \int_0^\infty \sinh \alpha x\, e^{-px}\,dx = \frac{\alpha}{p^2 - \alpha^2}, \qquad p > |\alpha|$$

8. $\phi(x) = \delta(x - \alpha)$ and $\phi(x) = H(x - \alpha)$ (of exponential order $\gamma = 0$)

$$\mathscr{L}\{\delta(x - \alpha)\} = \int_0^\infty \delta(x - \alpha)\, e^{-px}\,dx = e^{-p\alpha}, \qquad p > 0$$

$$\mathscr{L}\{H(x - \alpha)\} = \int_0^\infty H(x - \alpha)e^{-px}\,dx = \int_\alpha^\infty e^{-px}\,dx = \frac{e^{-p\alpha}}{p}, \qquad p > 0$$

EXAMPLE 8.9   *Inverse Laplace Transforms.* From Example 8.8 we have immediately

1. $\mathscr{L}^{-1}\left\{\dfrac{1}{p}\right\} = 1$

2. $\mathscr{L}^{-1}\left\{\dfrac{\Gamma(1+n)}{p^{n+1}}\right\} = x^n$ or $\mathscr{L}^{-1}\left\{\dfrac{1}{p^{n+1}}\right\} = \dfrac{x^n}{\Gamma(1+n)}$

3. $\mathscr{L}^{-1}\left\{\dfrac{1}{p-\alpha}\right\} = e^{\alpha x}$

4. $\mathscr{L}^{-1}\left\{\dfrac{\alpha}{p^2+\alpha^2}\right\} = \cos \alpha x$ $\mathscr{L}^{-1}\left\{\dfrac{\alpha}{p^2+\alpha^2}\right\} = \sin \alpha x$

5. $\mathscr{L}^{-1}\left\{\dfrac{p}{p^2-\alpha^2}\right\} = \cosh \alpha x$ $\mathscr{L}^{-1}\left\{\dfrac{\alpha}{p^2-\alpha^2}\right\} = \sinh \alpha x$

We show below that the transform solutions $\Phi(p)$ to differential equations can often be decomposed by the method of partial fractions. Then, because of the linearity of the transform, a number of simple fractions whose inverses are known can be summed to represent the more complicated original form whose inverse is the sum of the fraction inverses.

Using as a guide the relations developed and used for Fourier transforms, we now proceed to establish the properties of the Laplace transform needed for the solution of ordinary and partial differential equations. From (8.117),

$$\mathscr{L}\{c_1\phi_1(x) + c_2\phi_2(x)\}$$

is

$$\Phi(p) = \int_0^\infty [c_1\phi_1(x) + c_2\phi_2(x)]e^{-px}\,dx$$

where c_1 and c_2 are arbitrary constants while ϕ_1 and ϕ_2 satisfy (8.115) for, say, $\gamma_1 \geq \gamma_2$, respectively. Then, for $p > \gamma_1 \geq \gamma_2$,

$$\Phi(p) = c_1 \int_0^\infty \phi_1(x)e^{-px}\,dx + c_2 \int_0^\infty \phi_2(x)e^{-px}\,dx$$

exists; thus the Laplace transform is linear (see Sec. 8.1)—that is,

$$\mathscr{L}\{c_1\phi_1(x) + c_2\phi_2(x)\} = c_1\mathscr{L}\{\phi_1(x)\} + c_2\mathscr{L}\{\phi_2(x)\} = c_1\Phi_1(p) + c_2\Phi_2(p)$$

Examination of (8.118) reveals that the inverse transform is also linear; for example,

$$\mathscr{L}^{-1}\left\{\sum_{n=1}^{N} c_i\Phi_i(p)\right\} = \sum_{n=1}^{N} c_i\phi_i(x) \tag{8.119}$$

The transform of $\phi'(x)$ is

$$\mathscr{L}\{\phi'(x)\} = \int_0^\infty \phi'(x)e^{-px}\,dx, \quad 0 \leq x \tag{8.120}$$

We assume that ϕ' is piecewise smooth and of exponential order $\gamma_1 > 0$. It follows that the integral (8.120) is absolutely and uniformly convergent for $p > \gamma_1$; furthermore, $\phi(x)$ is of exponential order γ_1. Provided that ϕ is also continuous on $0 \leq x$, integration by parts in (8.120) (see Sec. 8.2.3) produces

$$\mathcal{L}\{\phi'(x)\} = \phi(x)e^{-px}\big|_0^\infty + p\int_0^\infty \phi(x)e^{-px}\,dx = -\phi(0) + p\mathcal{L}\{\phi(x)\} \qquad (8.121)$$

because $\lim_{x \to \infty} \phi(x)e^{-px} = 0$ for $p > \gamma_1$. Similarly, if $\phi''(x)$ is piecewise smooth and of exponential order $\gamma_2 > 0$, then ϕ' and ϕ are of exponential order γ_2. Provided that both ϕ' and ϕ are continuous on $0 \leq x$,

$$
\begin{aligned}
\mathcal{L}\{\phi''(x)\} &= \int_0^\infty \phi''(x)e^{-px}\,dx = \phi'(x)e^{-px}\big|_0^\infty + p\int_0^\infty \phi'(x)e^{-px}\,dx \\
&= -\phi'(0) + p\mathcal{L}\{\phi'(x)\} \qquad\qquad (8.122) \\
&= -\phi'(0) - p\phi(0) + p^2\mathcal{L}\{\phi(x)\}
\end{aligned}
$$

because $\lim_{x \to \infty} \phi'(x)e^{-px} = 0$ for $p > \gamma_2$. By induction, we obtain the general result

$$\mathcal{L}\{\phi^{(n)}(x)\} = -\sum_{i=2}^n p^{n-i}\phi^{(i-1)}(0) - p^{n-1}\phi(0) + p^n\mathcal{L}\{\phi(x)\}, \qquad 0 \leq x, \quad p > \gamma_n \;(8.123)$$

where $\phi^{(n)}$ is of exponential order $\gamma_n > 0$ and ϕ and its first $n-1$ derivatives are continuous. As with the Fourier transform, the Laplace transform of an ordinary derivative is an algebraic expression; accordingly, we expect the Laplace transform of a partial differential equation to be an ordinary differential equation dependent on a parameter and the transform of an ordinary differential equation to be an algebraic equation.

The Laplace transform possesses the translation property equivalent to Theorem 8.3. Thus, for $\mu \geq 0$,

$$\mathcal{L}\{\phi(x - \mu)\} = \int_0^\infty \phi(x - \mu)e^{-px}\,dx = \int_{-\mu}^\infty \phi(\rho)e^{-p(\rho+\mu)}\,d\rho$$

However, $\phi \equiv 0$ for $x < 0$; therefore

$$\mathcal{L}\{\phi(x - \mu)\} = e^{-p\mu}\int_0^\infty \phi(\rho)e^{-p\rho}\,d\rho = e^{-p\mu}\mathcal{L}\{\phi(x)\} = e^{-p\mu}\Phi(p) \qquad (8.124)$$

Similarly,

$$\mathcal{L}\{e^{\mu x}\phi(x)\} = \int_0^\infty \phi(x)e^{-(p-\mu)x}\,dx = \Phi(p - \mu) \qquad (8.125)$$

Finally, a convolution result can be derived for the Laplace transform through direct use of the inversion integral (8.118) and the idea from Theorem 8.4(c). We write

$$A(p) = \int_0^\infty a(x)e^{-px}\,dx \qquad (8.126)$$

$$B(p) = \int_0^\infty b(\xi)e^{-p\xi}\,d\xi \qquad (8.127)$$

and

$$\frac{1}{2\pi i}\int_{\gamma'-i\infty}^{\gamma'+i\infty} A(p)B(p)e^{px}\,dp \tag{8.128}$$

where a and b satisfy the usual conditions. Introducing (8.127) into (8.128) and performing the permissible change of the order of integration give

$$\frac{1}{2\pi i}\int_{\gamma'-i\infty}^{\gamma'+i\infty} A(p)B(p)e^{px}\,dx = \int_0^\infty b(\xi)e^{-p\xi}\,d\xi \frac{1}{2\pi i}\int_{\gamma'-i\infty}^{\gamma'+i\infty} A(p)e^{px}\,dp$$

$$= \int_0^\infty b(\xi)\,d\xi \frac{1}{2\pi i}\int_{\gamma'-i\infty}^{\gamma'+i\infty} e^{-p\xi}A(p)e^{px}\,dp$$

$$= \int_0^\infty b(\xi)a(x-\xi)\,d\xi$$

according to (8.124). As $a(x-\xi) \equiv 0$ for $\xi > x$—that is, for negative arguments—

$$\frac{1}{2\pi i}\int_{\gamma'-i\infty}^{\gamma'+i\infty} A(p)B(p)e^{px}\,dx = \int_0^x b(\xi)a(x-\xi)\,d\xi$$

or

$$\mathcal{L}^{-1}\{A(p)B(p)\} = \int_0^x b(\xi)a(x-\xi)\,d\xi = \int_0^x a(\xi)b(x-\xi)\,d\xi = a*b \tag{8.129}$$

Thus the convolution $a*b$ of $a(x)$ and $b(x)$, in the sense of the Laplace transform, is equal to the inverse transform of the product of the separate transforms of a and b. Also,

$$\mathcal{L}\{a*b\} = A(p)B(p) \tag{8.130}$$

8.3.1   Application to Ordinary Differential Equations

Because ordinary differential equations with constant coefficients often have solutions in exponential form, the Laplace transform is ideally suited to their solution, whereas the Fourier transforms are not appropriate. Because the Laplace transform of derivatives includes one auxiliary (initial) condition for each order of derivatives, the transform is also seen to be ideally suited to incorporate the differential equation and auxiliary initial conditions conveniently in a single algebraic form. The concepts and applications of the Laplace transform are examined in depth in Refs. [1], [11], and [12]; we examine here only the basic technique in three examples closely related to our previous attempts to solve mathematical models.

The well-known method of partial fractions [1, 12, 13] is a key to the exploitation of the linearity of the Laplace transform and its inverse, as well as to the use of simple or tabulated inverses. Frequently transformation and solution of a problem lead to the requirement for finding inverse transforms of quotients of polynomials in p. Thus

$$\Phi(p) = \frac{N(p)}{D(p)} \tag{8.131}$$

where the numerator N and the denominator D are polynomials of the form

$$N(p) = n_0 + n_1 p + n_2 p^2 + n_3 p^3 + \cdots + n_m p^m$$

$$D(p) = d_0 + d_1 p + d_2 p^2 + d_3 p^3 + \cdots + d_q p^q$$

with $m < q$ and D and N having no roots in common being assumed. The cases $m \geq q$ and common roots can be reduced by formal long division of the polynomials and by factoring and cancellation of common factors, respectively.

Case 1. $D(p)$ has a set of n distinct (nonrepeated) roots p_i or, equivalently, factors $(p - p_i)$. According to the method of partial fractions, we expand the fraction in terms of the factors. This step may be done generally or, as here, sequentially. We write

$$\Phi(p) = \frac{N(p)}{D(p)} = \frac{N(p)}{(p - p_i)Q(p)} = \frac{A_i}{p - p_i} + \frac{F(p)}{Q(p)} \qquad (8.132)$$

where $D(p) = (p - p_i)Q(p)$ and A_i and $F(p)$ are to be determined. Clearing fractions gives

$$N(p) = A_i Q(p) + F(p)(p - p_i)$$

For $p = p_i$,

$$A_i = \frac{N(p_i)}{Q(p_i)}$$

and then

$$F(p) = \frac{N(p)}{p - p_i} - \frac{N(p_i)}{Q(p_i)} Q(p)$$

Having determined A_i, one can repeat the foregoing process on the quotient $F(p)/Q(p)$ by factoring $(p - p_j)$, $i \neq j$, from $Q(p)$, and so on, or, forsaking determination of $F(p)$ until all the A_i are known, simply repeat the original process with another value of A_i.

The general form when written directly is

$$\Phi(p) = \frac{N(p)}{D(p)} = \sum_{i=1}^{n} \frac{A_i}{p - p_i} + \frac{F(p)}{Q(p)}$$

where

$$D(p) = (p - p_1)(p - p_2) \cdots (p - p_n) Q(p) = \prod_{i=1}^{n} (p - p_i)Q(p)$$

Indeed, as $N(p_i) \neq 0$ and $Q(p_i) \neq 0$, by induction from above,

$$A_i = \frac{N(p_i)P_i(p_i)}{Q(p_i)}$$

where

$$P_i(p) = \frac{(p - p_i)}{\displaystyle\prod_{j=1}^{n} (p - p_j)}$$

Case 2. $D(p)$ has a repeated root of order r at $p = a$. The expansion for the repeated root is built from a sequence of factors; that is, we write

$$\Phi(p) = \frac{N(p)}{(p-a)^r Q(p)} = \frac{R_1}{p-a} + \frac{R_2}{(p-a)^2} + \cdots + \frac{R_r}{(p-a)^r} + \frac{F(p)}{Q(p)} \qquad (8.133)$$

where $F(a) \neq 0$ and $Q(a) \neq 0$; $Q(p)$ contains all other distinct root factors of $D(p)$ and must be processed as in Case 1. Clearing fractions gives

$$N(p) = \sum_{i=1}^{r} R_i Q(p)(p-a)^{r-i} + F(p)(p-a)^r$$

Thus

$$N(a) = R_r Q(a) \quad \text{or} \quad R_r = \frac{N(a)}{Q(a)}$$

Letting $G(p) = N(p)/Q(p)$, we observe that

$$G'(p) = \sum_{i=1}^{r-1} R_i(r-i)(p-a)^{r-i-1} + O[(p-a)^{r-1}]$$

and $G'(a) = R_{r-1}$. By induction,

$$G^{(n)}(a) = n! R_{r-n}$$

Once the R_i are known, $F(p)$ can be found and $F(p)$ and $Q(p)$ used to find the expansion of the distinct roots as in Case 1.

Although these cases provide a general, formal means of proceeding, the expansion by partial fractions is most often completed by inspection. The key step in any case is the determination of the factors. The following three examples illustrate the Laplace transform and partial fraction methods.

EXAMPLE 8.10   *An Initial-Value Problem.* In Example 8.6 on the forced vibrations of a very long string, we required the solution to a problem of the form

$$\phi''(t) + c^2 \lambda^2 \phi(t) = F(t)$$

$$\phi(0) = Z_0 \qquad (8.134)$$

$$\phi'(0) = V_0$$

The Laplace transform of $\phi(t)$ is

$$\Phi(p) = \int_0^\infty \phi(t) e^{-pt} \, dt$$

From (8.122) or (8.123), the transform of (8.134) is

$$-\phi'(0) - p\phi(0) + p^2 \Phi(p) + c^2 \lambda^2 \Phi(p) = f(p) \qquad (8.135)$$

where

$$f(p) = \mathscr{L}\{F(t)\} = \int_0^\infty F(t) e^{-pt} \, dt$$

Solving the algebraic problem (8.135) gives

$$\Phi(p) = \frac{f(p)}{p^2 + \lambda^2 c^2} + \frac{\phi'(0) + p\phi(0)}{p^2 + \lambda^2 c^2} = \Phi_1(p) + \Phi_2(p)$$

We seek

$$\phi(t) = \mathscr{L}^{-1}\{\Phi(p)\} = \mathscr{L}^{-1}\{\Phi_1\} + \mathscr{L}^{-1}\{\Phi_2\}$$

From Example 8.9 (4 and 5),

$$\mathscr{L}^{-1}\{\Phi_2\} = \frac{\phi'(0)}{\lambda c} \mathscr{L}^{-1}\left\{\frac{\lambda c}{p^2 + \lambda^2 c^2}\right\} + \phi(0)\mathscr{L}^{-1}\left\{\frac{p}{p^2 + \lambda^2 c^2}\right\}$$

$$= \frac{\phi'(0)}{\lambda c} \sin \lambda ct + \phi(0) \cos \lambda ct$$

Now

$$\mathscr{L}^{-1}\left\{\frac{1}{p^2 + c^2\lambda^2}\right\} = \frac{1}{\lambda c} \sin c\lambda t$$

while

$$\mathscr{L}^{-1}\{f(p)\} = F(t)$$

The convolution (8.129) then gives

$$\mathscr{L}^{-1}\left\{f(p)\frac{1}{p^2 + c^2\lambda^2}\right\} = F * \left(\frac{\sin c\lambda t}{\lambda c}\right) = \frac{1}{c\lambda}\int_0^t F(\tau) \sin c\lambda(t - \tau)\, d\tau$$

Therefore

$$\phi(t) = Z_0 \cos c\lambda t + \frac{V_0}{c\lambda} \sin c\lambda t + \frac{1}{c\lambda}\int_0^t F(\tau) \sin c\lambda(t - \tau)\, d\tau$$

which we see is entirely equivalent to (8.94), for example. If $f(t)$ is of exponential order, then $\phi(t)$ is of exponential order and the use of the transform is valid. Notice that this result permits solutions that grow without bound as $t \to \infty$ as a consequence of the forcing function $F(t)$.

EXAMPLE 8.11   *The General Solution.* In Chap. 9 solution of the model for the flow of current i or voltage v in a telegraph cable leads to the need for the general solution to the ordinary differential equation (Chap. 9, Probs. 9.16 to 9.21)

$$\alpha T'' + \beta T' + \gamma T = 0 \tag{8.136}$$

for $T(t)$ with α, β, and γ being constants. The Laplace transform of $T(t)$ is

$$\Phi(p) = \int_0^\infty T(t)e^{-pt}\, dt$$

and the transform of the equation is

$$\alpha[-T'(0) - pT(0) + p^2\Phi(p)] + \beta[-T(0) + p\Phi(p)] + \gamma\Phi(p) = 0$$

or

$$\Phi(p)(\alpha p^2 + \beta p + \gamma) = \alpha T'(0) + (\alpha p + \beta)T(0)$$

The solution of the algebraic equation is

$$\Phi(p) = \frac{\alpha T'(0) + (\alpha p + \beta)T(0)}{\alpha p^2 + \beta p + \gamma}$$

Now, the denominator $D(p) = \alpha p^2 + \beta p + \gamma$ has the factors

$$\left(p + \frac{\beta}{2\alpha} - \theta^{1/2}\right) \quad \text{and} \quad \left(p + \frac{\beta}{2\alpha} + \theta^{1/2}\right)$$

where $\theta = \beta^2/4\alpha^2 - \gamma/\alpha$, obtained from the roots of the quadratic equation

$$\alpha p^2 + \beta p + \gamma = 0$$

For $\theta \neq 0$, D has a pair of distinct roots; for $\theta = 0$, D has the repeated root $p = -\beta/2\alpha$. Consider $\theta = 0$. We write

$$\Phi(p) = \frac{\alpha T'(0) + \beta T(0) + \alpha p T(0)}{(p + \beta/2\alpha)^2} = \frac{R_1}{(p + \beta/2\alpha)} + \frac{R_2}{(p + \beta/2\alpha)^2}$$

[Here $Q(p)$ is zero because $D(p)$ factors exactly.] Then clearing fractions gives

$$\alpha T'(0) + \beta T(0) + \alpha p T(0) = R_1\left(p + \frac{\beta}{2\alpha}\right) + R_2 \qquad (8.137)$$

For $p = -\beta/2\alpha$,

$$R_2 = \alpha T'(0) + \beta T(0) - \frac{\beta}{2}T(0) = \alpha T'(0) + \frac{\beta}{2}T(0)$$

Differentiating (8.137) with respect to p yields

$$\alpha T(0) = R_1$$

and

$$\Phi(p) = \frac{\alpha T(0)}{p + \beta/2\alpha} + \frac{\alpha T'(0) + (\beta/2)T(0)}{(p + \beta/2\alpha)^2}$$

From Example 8.9(3),

$$\mathscr{L}^{-1}\left\{\frac{1}{p + \beta/2\alpha}\right\} = e^{-(\beta/2\alpha)t}$$

From the translation result (8.125) and Example 8.9(2),

$$\mathscr{L}^{-1}\left\{\frac{1}{p^2}\right\} = \frac{t}{\Gamma(2)} = \frac{t}{1!} = t$$

but

$$\mathscr{L}^{-1}\left\{\frac{1}{(p - \mu)^2}\right\} = te^{\mu t}$$

For $\mu = -\beta/2\alpha$, we obtain the final result

$$\mathscr{L}^{-1}\{\Phi(p)\} = T(t) = \alpha T(0)e^{-(\beta/2\alpha)t} + \left[\alpha T'(0) + \frac{\beta}{2}T(0)\right]te^{-(\beta/2\alpha)t}$$

As no initial conditions are prescribed, $T(0)$ and $T'(0)$ are arbitrary; thus the general solution for (8.136) with $\theta = 0$—that is, $\beta^2 = 4\alpha\gamma$—is

$$T(t) = (A + Bt)e^{-(\beta/2\alpha)t}$$

The solutions for $\theta \neq 0$ involve only exponentials and distin⌐⌐ roots and are left to the Problems.

EXAMPLE 8.12   *A Boundary-V*   ⌐onsider

$$X'' + \lambda^2 X = 0, \qquad \cdot \leq l$$

$$X(0) = X(l) = 0 \tag{8.138}$$

We presume that $X(x)$ exists in the entire region $0 \leq x < \infty$. The Laplace transform of (8.138) is

$$-X'(0) - pX(0) + p^2\Phi(p) + \lambda^2\Phi(p) = 0$$

or

$$\Phi(p) = \frac{X'(0)}{p^2 + \lambda^2}$$

The second boundary condition $X(l) = 0$ is not picked up by the transform while $X'(0)$ is unspecified. From Example 8.9(4),

$$\mathscr{L}^{-1}\{\Phi(p)\} = \frac{X'(0)}{\lambda} \sin \lambda x$$

At $x = l$, we must have

$$\frac{X'(0)}{\lambda} \sin \lambda l = 0 \tag{8.139}$$

which gives a relation between $X'(0)$ and λ for given l. Of course, we recognize (8.138) as an eigenvalue problem, and (8.139) illustrates this point very clearly. Either $X'(0) = 0$ and there is no solution to the two-point boundary-value problem (8.138)—that is, $X \equiv 0$ (Theorem A.2, Appendix 2)—or $\lambda' \sin \lambda l = 0$.

In particular, only for the discrete values

$$\lambda_n^2 = \left(\frac{n\pi}{l}\right)^2, \qquad n = 1, 2, 3, \ldots$$

is $X'(0)$ arbitrary and does a solution exist. The eigenfunctions

$$X_n(x) = \frac{X'(0)}{\lambda_n} \sin \lambda_n x, \qquad 0 \leq x \leq l$$

are solutions to (8.138) and are periodic with period $2\pi/\lambda_n$. Therefore $X_n(x)$ and its periodic extension exist in $0 \leq x < \infty$ and are continuous and of exponential order $\gamma = 0$; hence our use of the transform was legitimate.

8.3.2   Applications to Partial Differential Equations

The technique for applying the Laplace transform to partial differential equations precisely parallels that for the Fourier transforms and employs the basic results and relations derived in the earlier parts of this section. It would be ideal to return now to the Fourier heat ring model on the infinite domain to demonstrate the equivalences of the transforms and the particular merits of each. However, as long as the initial conditions of any model are nonzero, the Laplace transform in time is not the best method if the Fourier or Hankel transforms in the space variables are usable. It is possible to use the Laplace transform, but the transformed equations are inhomogeneous and the inverse transforms are usually difficult to find. For example, the initial-value model for heat conduction in the infinite domain in Example 8.4 can be solved by the Laplace transform only through use of the inversion formula (8.118) and contour integration [14]. (For inhomogeneous linear models, it is often wise to find solutions to individual models, each incorporating only a single inhomogeneous equation or auxiliary condition, and then to add the individual solutions together to achieve the desired total result.)

Our examples for partial differential equations are based on the processes of mass transfer in fluids. Many of our day-to-day experiences involve the process of mass transfer by convection and diffusion. As smoke pours from a tall chimney, the moving air currents *convect* or transport the smoke away at the speed of the wind, while at the same time the smoke mixes with or *diffuses* through the air, carrying it until the smoke concentration is so low that we believe the smoke is no longer there, since we cannot see it. Pollution discharged to streams and rivers is also transported and mixed in much the same way.

In the simplest, one-dimensional motion (x direction only), the fluxes f_C due to convection and f_D due to diffusion of a quantity being transported across a given section x at time t are

$$f_C = UQ \qquad f_D = -DQ_x$$

where U is the speed of the main fluid (centimeters per second); Q is the concentration of the transported quantity, say smoke or dye or bacteria, per unit volume (grams per cubic centimeter); and D is the diffusion coefficient (centimeters squared per second). Here f_D is given by the *Fick's rate equation* that relates the diffusive flux to the negative gradient of concentration (see Fourier's heat law, Sec. 2.2.1). When the diffusion results from the random vibration of molecules in a gas or liquid, Fick's law is valid and D is often essentially a constant that can be determined experimentally. In the wind above the chimney, the diffusion is likely to result from the motion of the turbulent eddies in the wind; Fick's law and constant D are then simplifying assumptions used to gain simple, but approximate, results.

An analysis of a slice Δx thick through a one-dimensional stream leads to a conservation equation for the transported mass (see the Problems and compare to the derivation of the heat equation, Sec. 2.2.1). The resulting partial differential equation is

$$Q_t + UQ_x = DQ_{xx}$$

The following applications explore models of prospective convection-diffusion processes when either one or the other is dominant.

EXAMPLE 8.13   *Pure Convection.* Suppose that the transported quantity is a red dye of strength Q that diffuses slowly in water so that the dye cloud has a motion governed essentially by convection when U is fairly large. A source of dye of concentration Q_0 is available at a point in a one-dimensional stream of constant speed U. Putting the coordinate origin at the source and turning the source on to full strength at time zero lead to a model for $Q(x, t)$:

$$Q_t + U'Q_x = 0, \qquad 0 < x, \quad 0 < t$$

$$Q(0, t) = Q_0, \qquad 0 < t \tag{8.140}$$

$$Q(x, 0) = 0, \qquad 0 \le x$$

We assume that Q and Q_x approach zero as $x \to \infty$ for all t. Note that we have a model with a first-order partial differential equation (see Sec. 9.2).

The Laplace transform of $Q(x, t)$ with respect to t is

$$q(x, p) = \int_0^\infty Q(x, t)e^{-pt}\, dt$$

The transform of (8.140) is

$$-Q(x, 0) + pq(x, p) + Uq_x(x, p) = 0$$

$$q(0, p) = \frac{Q_0}{p}$$

As $Q(x, 0) = 0$,

$$q_x + \frac{p}{U}q = 0 \qquad q(0, p) = \frac{Q_0}{p} \tag{8.141}$$

The solution to (8.141) is well known to us:

$$q(x, p) = \frac{Q_0}{p}e^{-px/U}$$

Now, from Example 8.8(8),

$$\mathscr{L}^{-1}\left\{\frac{1}{p}e^{-pz}\right\} = H(t - \alpha)$$

Accordingly,

$$\mathscr{L}^{-1}\{q(x, p)\} = Q_0\mathscr{L}^{-1}\left\{\frac{1}{p}e^{-p(x/U)}\right\} = Q_0H\left(t - \frac{x}{U}\right)$$

or

$$Q(x, t) = Q_0H\left(t - \frac{x}{U}\right) \tag{8.142}$$

Thus, for $t < x/U$, the dye concentration is zero; while for $t \ge x/U$, the concentration is the full source value Q_0. This first-order *convection equation* provides the simplest of wave-propagation phenomena—in this case, a forward moving wave front (provided that $U > 0$) located at $x = Ut$ and with speed $dx/dt = U$. In addition, the discontinuity between the boundary and initial condition is preserved in the solution and the front does not disperse as time passes, remaining distinct and discontinuous. The wave edge propagates along the *characteristic* line $x - Ut = 0$ (see Sec. 9.2). Thus the Laplace transform method can yield well-behaved and valid discontinuous solutions caused by discontinuities in the auxiliary conditions; this remarkable power is not shared by the Fourier series methods.

If $Q_0 = Q_0(t)$ in lieu of being a constant, we have, in lieu of (8.141),

$$q_x + \frac{p}{U}q = 0 \qquad q(0, p) = \mathscr{L}\{Q_0(t)\} = q_0(p)$$

and need

$$\mathscr{L}^{-1}\{q_0(p)\, e^{-px/U}\}$$

But

$$\mathscr{L}\{Q_0(t - a)H(t - a)\} = \int_0^\infty Q_0(t - a)H(t - a)e^{-pt}\, dt = \int_0^\infty Q_0(t - a)e^{-pt}\, dt$$

$$= e^{-pa}\int_0^\infty Q_0(\tau)e^{-pt}\, d\tau = e^{-pa}q_0(p)$$

Thus

$$\mathscr{L}^{-1}\{q_0(p)e^{-px/U}\} = Q_0\left(t - \frac{x}{U}\right)H\left(t - \frac{x}{U}\right)$$

and

$$Q(x, t) = Q_0\left(t - \frac{x}{U}\right)H\left(t' - \frac{x}{U}\right) \tag{8.143}$$

A change in Q_0 at $x = 0$, $t = t_0$ is felt downstream at any point x only after time $t = t_0 + x/U$.

EXAMPLE 8.14   *Pure Diffusion.* Suppose, in Example 8.13, that the velocity of the fluid U is very slow so that diffusion dominates the convection. The model (8.140) would be then modified to be, for $D > 0$,

$$Q_t = DQ_{xx}, \qquad 0 < x, \quad 0 < t$$

$$Q(0, t) = Q_0, \qquad 0 < t$$

$$Q(x, 0) = 0, \qquad 0 \le x \tag{8.144}$$

$$|Q(x, t)| < \infty$$

with Q and $Q_x \to 0$ as $x \to \infty$ for all t.

The transform of (8.144) is

$$-Q(x, 0) + pq(x, p) = Dq_{xx}(x, p)$$

$$q(0, p) = \frac{Q_0}{p} \tag{8.145}$$

As $Q(x, 0) = 0$, the solution to (8.145) is

$$q(x, p) = Q_0 \frac{1}{p} \exp\left[-\left(\frac{p}{D}\right)^{1/2} x\right] \tag{8.146}$$

because the general solution to the homogeneous equation (for $p > 0$) is

$$q(x, p) = A(p) \exp\left[-\left(\frac{p}{D}\right)^{1/2} x\right] + B(p) \exp\left[\left(\frac{p}{D}\right)^{1/2} x\right]$$

and $q(x, p) \to 0$ as $x \to \infty$ because $Q(x, t) \to 0$. Referring to the Table of Transforms, Appendix 4, we find

$$\mathscr{L}^{-1}\left\{\frac{1}{p} e^{-\alpha p^{1/2}}\right\} = \operatorname{erfc} \frac{\alpha}{2t^{1/2}}$$

and the inverse of (8.146) yields

$$Q(x, t) = Q_0 \operatorname{erfc} \frac{x}{2(Dt)^{1/2}} \tag{8.147}$$

Now it is possible to detect the difference in the solution of the convection and diffusion equations. Here $\operatorname{erfc}(0) = 1$ and $\operatorname{erfc}(\tau) < 1$ for $\tau > 0$. Accordingly, $Q < Q_0$ for all $x > 0$ and $t < \infty$. Indeed, $\operatorname{erfc}(0.5) = 0.52$ [3]; hence $Q \approx 0.5Q_0$ for $x = (Dt)^{1/2}$. If we consider that $Q \approx 0.5Q_0$ represents the location of the advancing "diffusion front," the speed of the front is

$$\frac{dx}{dt} = \frac{1}{2}\left(\frac{D}{t}\right)^{1/2}$$

Thus, whereas the distinct convection front moves with constant speed, the "diffusion front" moves with decreasing speed and is not distinct because $1 > Q/Q_0 > 0$ for all finite x and t.

If $Q_0 = Q_0 f(t)$, (8.146) becomes

$$q(x, p) = q_0(p) \exp\left[-\left(\frac{p}{D}\right)^{1/2} x\right] = Q_0 F(p) \exp\left[-\left(\frac{p}{D}\right)^{1/2} x\right]$$

According to the convolution result (8.129),

$$Q(x, t) = \mathscr{L}^{-1}\left\{q_0(p) \exp\left[-\left(\frac{p}{D}\right)^{1/2} x\right]\right\} = \int_0^t Q_0 f(t - \tau) \frac{x/D^{1/2}}{2(\pi\tau^3)^{1/2}} \exp\left(\frac{x^2/D}{4\tau}\right) d\tau \tag{8.148}$$

because from Appendix 4

$$\mathscr{L}^{-1}\left\{\exp\left[-\left(\frac{p}{D}\right)^{1/2} x\right]\right\} = \frac{x/D^{1/2}}{2(\pi t^3)^{1/2}} \exp\left(\frac{x^2/D}{4t}\right)$$

But replacing t by τ in (8.147) and writing out $\operatorname{erfc}[x/2(D\tau)^{1/2}]$ give

$$Q(x, \tau) = Q_0\left[1 - \frac{2}{\pi^{1/2}} \int_0^{x/2(D\tau)^{1/2}} e^{-\eta^2} d\eta\right]$$

whence, according to Leibnitz's rule [2],

$$\frac{\partial Q(x, \tau)}{\partial \tau} = Q_0 \left[-\frac{2}{\pi^{1/2}} \exp\left(-\frac{x^2/D}{4\tau} \right)\left(-\frac{1}{2} \frac{x/D^{1/2}}{2\tau^{3/2}} \right) \right]$$

$$= Q_0 \left\{ \frac{x/D^{1/2}}{2(\pi\tau^3)^{1/2}} \exp\left(\frac{x^2/D}{4\tau} \right) \right\}$$

Thus, denoting by $\tilde{Q}(x, t)$ the solution to (8.144), we have that

$$Q(x, t) = \int_0^t f(t - \tau)\frac{\partial \tilde{Q}}{\partial \tau}(x, \tau)\, d\tau \tag{8.149}$$

is the solution to the model (8.144) with the constant boundary condition replaced by an equivalent time-varying condition, $Q_0 f(t)$. Equation (8.149) is one simple form of the general *Duhamel's formula* or *theorem* (more general forms are given in [12, 14]).

EXAMPLE 8.15 *Diffusion in a Finite Region.* Suppose now that we install a collector at $x = l$ that removes all the dye in our diffusion-dominated physical system and makes $Q(l, t) = 0$. (Why is this not appropriate for the convection equation?) Then (8.144) becomes

$$Q_t = DQ_{xx}, \qquad 0 < x < l, \quad 0 < t$$

$$Q(0, t) = Q_0 \qquad Q(l, t) = 0, \qquad 0 < t \tag{8.150}$$

$$Q(x, 0) = 0$$

Of course, we can solve (8.150) by the series methods of Chap. 5, but let us try by the Laplace transform technique.

Assuming that Q is of exponential order as $t \to \infty$ means that

$$q(x, p) = \int_0^\infty Q(x, t)e^{-pt}\, dt$$

exists. The transforms of (8.150) are

$$-Q(x, 0) + pq(x, p) = Dq_{xx}(x, p) \tag{8.151}$$

$$q(0, p) = \frac{Q_0}{p} \qquad q(l, p) = 0$$

As $Q(x, 0) = 0$, the general solution to the differential equation can be written [see (8.85)] for convenience in terms of $(l - x)$ in lieu of x (for this eliminates one term in our subsequent expressions):

$$q(x, p) = c_1(p)\cosh\left(\frac{p}{D}\right)^{1/2}(l - x) + \frac{c_2(p)}{(p/D)^{1/2}}\sinh\left(\frac{p}{D}\right)^{1/2}(l - x)$$

Introducing this equation into the conditions in (8.151) gives, because $c_1(p) = 0$,

$$q(x, p) = \frac{Q_0}{p}\frac{\sinh(p/D)^{1/2}(l - x)}{\sinh(p/D)^{1/2}l}$$

We seek

$$Q(x, t) = \mathscr{L}^{-1} \left\{ \frac{Q_0}{p} \frac{\sinh (p/D)^{1/2}(l - x)}{\sinh (p/D)^{1/2}} \right\} \tag{8.152}$$

If $Q_0 = Q_0(t)$, then $q(0, p) = q_0(p)$ and (8.152) must be inverted by the convolution result (8.129) (see the Problems). However, for Q_0 constant, the inversion (8.152) involves only establishing the inverse of the hyperbolic quotient. The usual procedure (see, e.g., [1, 12]) is to expand the quotient in an infinite series of negative exponential powers by the binomial expansion [13]

$$\frac{1}{1 \pm x} = \sum_{n=0}^{\infty} (\mp 1)^n x^n, \qquad |x| < 1 \tag{8.153}$$

Now, with $\lambda = (p/D)^{1/2}$,

$$\frac{\sinh \lambda(l - x)}{\sinh \lambda l} = \frac{e^{\lambda(l-x)} - e^{-\lambda(l-x)}}{e^{\lambda l} - e^{-\lambda l}} = \frac{e^{-\lambda x} - e^{-\lambda(2l-x)}}{1 - e^{-2\lambda l}}$$

$$= [e^{-\lambda x} - e^{-\lambda(2l-x)}] \sum_{n=0}^{\infty} e^{-2\lambda n l}$$

$$= \sum_{n=0}^{\infty} \left\{ e^{-\lambda(2nl + x)} - e^{-\lambda[(2n+2)l - x]} \right\}$$

$$= \sum_{m=0}^{\infty} \left\{ e^{-\lambda(ml + x)} - e^{-\lambda[(m+2)l - x]} \right\}$$

From (8.152) and the above,

$$Q(x, t) = Q_0 \sum_{m=0}^{\infty} \left(\mathscr{L}^{-1} \left\{ \frac{1}{p} \exp \left[-\left(\frac{p}{D} \right)^{1/2} (ml + x) \right] \right\} \right.$$

$$\left. - \mathscr{L}^{-1} \left\{ \frac{1}{p} \exp \left[-\left(\frac{p}{D} \right)^{1/2} ((m + 2)l - x) \right] \right\} \right) \tag{8.154}$$

The transform leading to (8.147) gave (or alternately from Appendix 4)

$$\mathscr{L}^{-1} \left\{ \frac{1}{p} e^{-\alpha p^{1/2}} \right\} = \text{erfc} \frac{\alpha}{2t^{1/2}}$$

Consequently, the final solution to (8.150) is, from (8.154),

$$Q(x, t) = Q_0 \sum_{m=0}^{\infty} \left\{ \text{erfc} \left[\frac{ml + x}{2(Dt)^{1/2}} \right] - \text{erfc} \left[\frac{(m + 2)l - x}{2(Dt)^{1/2}} \right] \right\}$$

Thus the Laplace transform yields a series solution for the finite inhomogeneous problem; however, the *form*, not the answer, is much different from that found by the methods of Chap. 5.

8.4   DISCUSSION

The limit process and integral transforms described in this chapter provide methods for the solution of mathematical models with partial differential equations and infinite or semi-infinite domains, as well as the solution (by Laplace transform) of certain partial differential equation models with finite domains and of initial-value and boundary-value problems for ordinary differential equations. The effect of the transform was to reduce by one the number of independent variables in a given equation; hence, in the cases studied, partial differential equations were reduced to ordinary differential equations dependent on a parameter, while the latter equations could be reduced to algebraic equations. Both the limit process and the transform method are based, as are most of the methods studied by us, on linear superposition. These methods are, therefore, *restricted to linear problems*. However, the solution of inhomogeneous models is handled routinely.

The very simplicity of use and the power of the transforms tend to mask another significant limitation, aside from the requirement of linearity. The transforms described here—namely, the Fourier, Laplace, and Hankel transforms—can only be applied to certain equation forms. For other equation forms, other transforms would have to be developed, and none enjoys the broad usage or has the backup in theory and tabulated results of the three that we have examined.

An integral transform, when applied to a partial differential equation, effectively separates the variables. For example, compare the effect of the Fourier transform (8.73a) on the equation $u_t = ku_{xx}$ in Example 8.4, and the separation of variables in Sec. 3.2 for the same equation. The resulting equation for the time-dependent portion of the product-form solution is the same; in general, however, the separation constant is replaced by the transform parameter raised to a power equal to the order of the transformed derivatives. This situation reveals two things. First, the transform method replaces the summation of product-form solutions by series by a summation of product-form solutions by integral; we saw this happen in the limit process. Second, in Chap. 3 each of the product-form parts had to satisfy a separate ordinary differential equation determined by separation of variables. Now, it follows that, to be effective, the kernel of a transform must be a solution to the ordinary differential equation (for the transformed variable) obtained by separation of variables (see Sec. 5.1, to see that inhomogeneous terms can be neglected). This requirement determines the acceptable form of transform for any model.

EXAMPLE 8.16   *Determination of Acceptable Transforms.*

1. $u_t = ku_{xx}$. By separation of variables, the ordinary differential equations are, say for $u(x, t) = X(x)T(t)$,

$$X'' + \lambda^2 X = 0 \quad \text{and} \quad T' + k\lambda^2 T = 0$$

The kernels of the Fourier transforms are $e^{i\lambda x}, \cos \lambda x, \sin \lambda x$; all satisfy the X equation. The kernel e^{-px} of the Laplace transform satisfies the T equation for $k\lambda^2 = p$. Thus all these transforms are, at first test, appropriate, and examination of the auxiliary conditions and the domain of the model would indicate which transform is to be used.

2. $u_t = u_{rr} + (1/r)u_r$. By separation of variables, with $u(r, t) = R(r)T(t)$,

$$R'' + \frac{1}{r}R' + \lambda^2 R = 0 \quad \text{and} \quad T' + \lambda^2 T = 0$$

Certainly none of the Fourier transform kernels satisfies the R-equation, but the Laplace kernel satisfies the T-equation with $\lambda^2 = p$. However, the kernel $J_0(\lambda r)$ of the Hankel transform of order zero [(8.5) or (8.63)] does satisfy the R-equation; in this case, a Hankel transform is appropriate for the transformation with respect to the space variable.

Thus the kernel of the transform that will succeed is determined largely by the form of the equation to be transformed. A choice is often available between a space- and a time-variable transform—for example, between the sine and cosine Fourier and Laplace transforms in the case of transient heat conduction in a semi-infinite rod. When a choice is available, the guiding rule is convenience. A transform has an advantage only if the transformed equation is easier to solve than the original. For example, the choice between a Fourier and a Laplace transform can depend on which auxiliary conditions are homogeneous (see our examples in Secs. 8.3.2 and 8.2.3). Generally the transform should be chosen so that the resulting ordinary differential or algebraic equations are homogeneous or otherwise as simple as possible to facilitate finding the inverse transform.

The Laplace transform was introduced to deal with equations having solutions potentially of exponential order at infinity rather than the zero required of Fourier transforms. The Laplace transform is also very useful for ordinary differential equations. This transform is most suited to initial-value problems because the unknown values in the transformed equation are the prescribed initial conditions for the original equation. With the Laplace transform and boundary-value problems, the number of conditions at the initial-value end will be less than needed and one is required to carry an unknown condition as part of the problem (see Example 8.12). Hence the Laplace transform is not useful for the Laplace equation on a semi-infinite domain even though its kernel satisfies one of the separated equations, because the conditions on the solution at infinity (conditions are required over every part of the *closed* boundary for an elliptic equation) cannot be incorporated. Of course, the Fourier transforms work well for the Laplace equation because they require the solution to approach zero at infinity.

The Fourier transforms are clearly not suited for use in equations containing variable coefficients depending on the transformed variable, for the kernel will not be a solution of the separated equation [see Example 8.16(2)]. For the Laplace transform, the situation is somewhat different. For partial differential equations with variable coefficients, including the transformed variable in polynomial form (usually time), the transformed equation is a partial differential equation of the same or higher order than the original and with derivatives with respect to the transforming parameter p. Usually little is to be gained by use of the transform in such cases. Ordinary differential equations with polynomial coefficients can be treated in the usual way by Laplace transforms. However, difficulties may arise (a) when the equations have singular solutions at finite points that the bounded transform cannot represent [e.g., Bessel's equation has a singular point at $r = 0$ and a singular solution Y_0 (Appendix 2)] and (b) when an inverse is sought. In such cases, power series solutions (Appendix 2) may be more useful and attainable, although considerable power and scope can be gained for many cases of ordinary and partial differential equations through the use of the Laplace inversion formula (8.118) and contour integration [12, 14].

Higher-order linear equations can be treated also; examples for a vibrating beam with a fourth-order equation are given in the Problems. The kernel is determined by the equation form as outlined above. Similarly, greater numbers of independent variables can be handled—for example, leading for three variables (x, y, t) in heat conduction to double Fourier transforms (see Sec. 5.2). The analogy between single and double series and single and double transforms is complete.

REFERENCES

1. E. D. Rainville, *The Laplace Transform: An Introduction*. New York: Macmillan, 1963.

2. W. Kaplan, *Advanced Calculus*. Reading, Mass.: Addison-Wesley, 1952.

3. M. Abramowitz and I. A. Stegun (Eds.), *Handbook of Mathematical Functions*. New York: Dover, 1965.

4. R. L. Street, "Two-Dimensional Jet and Cavity Flows," *Journal of the Hydraulics Division*, ASCE, Vol. 90, No. HY2, Proc. Paper 3831, March 1964, pp. 141–161.

5. H. Weber, *Die Partiellen Differential-Gleichungen der Mathematischen Physik*, Vol. I. Braunschweig, Germany: Friedr. Vieweg & Sohn, 1910.

6. F. Bowman, *Introduction to Bessel Functions*. New York: Dover, 1958.

7. G. N. Watson, *A Treatise on the Theory of Bessel Functions*, 2nd ed. London: Cambridge University Press, 1944.

8. E. C. Titchmarsh, *Introduction to the Theory of Fourier Integrals*. London: Oxford University Press, 1937.

9. R. Courant and D. Hilbert, *Methods of Mathematical Physics*, Vol. I. New York: Interscience (a division of John Wiley & Sons), 1953.

10. A. Erdélyi (Ed.), *Tables of Integral Transforms; Vol. 1, Fourier, Laplace, and Mellin Transforms; Vol. 2, Bessel and Miscellaneous Transforms*. New York: McGraw-Hill, 1954.

11. H. S. Carslaw and J. C. Jaeger, *Operational Methods in Applied Mathematics*, 2nd ed. London: Oxford University Press, 1953.

12. R. V. Churchill, *Operational Mathematics*, 2nd ed. New York: McGraw-Hill, 1958.

13. C. R. C. *Standard Mathematical Tables*, 20th ed. Cleveland: Chemical Rubber Publishing Co., 1972.

14. H. F. Weinberger, *Partial Differential Equations*. New York: Blaisdell, 1965.

PROBLEMS

8.1 Show that the inverse transform T^{-1} is linear if $T\{\phi\}$ is given by (8.1) and T^{-1} by (8.2).

8.2 Show that T^{-1} and T are commutative—that is, that $T\{T^{-1}\{\ \}\} = T^{-1}\{T\{\ \}\}$.

8.3 Prove that the eigenfunctions X_{n1} and X_{n2} of (8.11) are orthogonal on $-L \leq x \leq L$.

8.4 By solving the following models with a limit process, obtain (8.21) and verify that boundary conditions do not affect the result:

$$u_t = ku_{xx}, \qquad -L < x < L, \qquad 0 < t$$
$$u(x, 0) = U_0(x), \qquad -L \le x \le L$$
$$|u(x, t)| < \infty, \qquad 0 \le t, \quad -L \le x \le L$$

(a) with $u(L, t) = u(-L, t) = 0, \qquad 0 \le t$

(b) with $u_x(L, t) = u_x(-L, t) = 0, \qquad 0 \le t$

8.5   Give a physical interpretation of and apply the limit process of Sec. 8.2.1 to solve each of the following mathematical models:

(a) $u_t = ku_{xx}, \qquad 0 < x, \quad 0 < t$
   $u(0, t) = 0, \qquad 0 < t$
   $u(x, 0) = u_0(x), \qquad 0 \le x$
   $|u(x, t)| < \infty, \qquad 0 \le x, \quad 0 \le t$
   $u(x, t) \in L^1(0, \infty), \qquad 0 \le t$

(b) $u_t = ku_{xx}, \qquad 0 < x, \quad 0 < t$
   $u_x(0, t) = 0, \qquad 0 < t$
   $u(x, 0) = u_0(x), \qquad 0 \le x$
   $|u(x, t)| < \infty, \qquad 0 \le x, \quad 0 \le t$
   $u(x, t) \in L^1(0, \infty), \qquad 0 \le t$

(c) $u_t = ku_{xx} + \alpha u, \qquad -\infty < x < \infty, \quad 0 < t, \quad 0 < \alpha$
   $u(x, 0) = u_0(x), \qquad -\infty < x < \infty$
   $|u(x, t)| < \infty, \qquad -\infty < x < \infty, \quad 0 \le t$
   $u(x, t) \in L^1(-\infty, \infty), \qquad 0 \le t$

(d) $u_{xx} + u_{yy} = 0, \qquad 0 < x, \quad 0 < y$
   $u(x, 0) = 0, \qquad 0 \le x$
   $u_x(0, y) = f(y), \qquad 0 \le y$
   $|u(x, y)| < \infty, \qquad 0 \le x, \quad 0 \le y$
   $u(x, y) \in L^1(0, \infty), \qquad 0 \le x \quad \text{or} \quad 0 \le y$

(e) $z_{tt} = c^2 z_{yy}, \qquad 0 < y, \quad 0 < t$
   $z(0, t) = 0, \qquad 0 \le t$
   $z(y, 0) = 0, \qquad 0 \le y$
   $z_t(y, 0) = V_0(y), \qquad 0 \le y$
   $|z(y, t)| < \infty, \qquad 0 \le y, \qquad 0 \le t$
   $z(y, t) \in L^1(0, \infty), \qquad 0 \le t$

(f) $z_{tt} = c^2 z_{yy} - \alpha z, \qquad 0 < y, \quad 0 < t$
   $z_y(0, t) = 0, \qquad 0 \le t$
   $z(y, 0) = z_0(y), \qquad 0 \le y$
   $z_t(y, 0) = 0, \qquad 0 \le y$
   $|z(y, t)| < \infty$
   $z(y, t) \in L^1(0, \infty), \qquad 0 \le t$

8.6   Use a limit process to find $z(0, t)$ if

$$z_{tt} = z_{yy}, \qquad 0 < y, \quad 0 < t$$
$$z_y(0, t) = 0, \qquad 0 \le t$$
$$z(y, 0) = e^{-y}, \qquad 0 \le y$$
$$z_t(y, 0) = 0, \qquad 0 \le y$$
$$|z(y, t)| < \infty$$
$$z(y, t) \in L^1(0, \infty), \qquad 0 \le t$$

8.7   Carry out the necessary limiting process to obtain the mathematical model and formal solution for the transverse vibrations of an elastic beam of very great length (see Sec. 5.3).

8.8   Use the exponential form of the cosine to evaluate

(a) $\displaystyle\int_0^\infty e^{-\lambda x} \cos \lambda\tau \, d\lambda$

(b) $\displaystyle\int_0^\infty e^{-\lambda^2 kt} \cos \lambda(\xi - x) \, d\lambda$

   [*Hint:* Try completing the square in the integrands.]

8.9   Using (8.24),

(a) find $\lim_{t\to\infty} G(x, \xi; t)$.

(b) plot $G(x, 0; t)$ for a representative set of times $t > 0$.

(c) describe $G(x, 0; 0)$ and give a physical interpretation of $G(x, 0; t)$ for $t \geq 0$.

8.10   Prove that (8.25) is bounded for $t \geq 0$.

8.11   Plot erf x, erfc x, and erf $x^{-1/2}$ on the same graph.

8.12   Using (8.30) with $x_0 = 1$, plot $u(x, t)/U_0$ versus x for $kt = 0, 0.0625, 0.25, 1, 25, \infty$.

8.13   Express the solutions to the following problems in terms of erf and/or erfc:

(a) Prob. 8.5(a) with $u_0(x) = 1$

(b) Prob. 8.5(a) with $u_0(x) = \begin{cases} U_0, & 0 \leq x \leq x_0 \\ 0, & x_0 < x \end{cases}$

(c) Prob. 8.5(c) with $u_0(x) = 1$

8.14   Find $u(x, t)$ if

$$u_t = ku_{xx}, \qquad 0 < x, \quad 0 < t$$
$$u_x(0, t) = 0, \qquad 0 \leq t$$
$$u(x, 0) = \begin{cases} U_0, & 0 < x \leq x_0 \\ 0, & x_0 < x \end{cases}$$
$$|u(x, t)| < \infty, \qquad 0 \leq x, \quad 0 \leq t$$
$$u(x, t) \in L^1(0, \infty), \qquad 0 \leq t$$

8.15   Use a limit process to find $u(x, t)$ for

$$u_t = ku_{xx} + Q(x, t), \qquad 0 < x, \quad 0 < t$$
$$u(0, t) = 0, \qquad 0 \leq t$$
$$u(x, 0) = u_0(x), \qquad 0 \leq x$$
$$|u(x, t)| < \infty, \qquad 0 \leq x, \quad 0 \leq t$$
$$u(x, t) \in L^1(0, \infty), \qquad 0 \leq t$$

8.16   Use a limit process to find $z(y, t)$ for

$$z_{tt} = c^2 z_{yy} + F(y, t), \qquad 0 < y, \quad 0 < t$$
$$z_y(0, t) = 0, \qquad 0 \leq t$$
$$z(y, 0) = 0, \qquad 0 \leq y$$
$$z_t(y, 0) = 0, \qquad 0 \leq y$$
$$|z(y, t)| < \infty, \qquad 0 \leq y, \quad 0 \leq t$$
$$z(y, t) \in L^1(0, \infty), \qquad 0 \leq t$$

8.17   Prove that if $f(x)$ and $f'(x) \in L^1(-\infty, \infty)$, $f(x)$ is continuous in the mean—that is,

$$\lim_{h \to 0} \int_{-\infty}^{\infty} |f(x + h) - f(x)| \, dx = 0$$

[*Hint:* Use the mean-value theorem of calculus.]
Note: A more subtle proof can be used to show that $f(x)$ is continuous in the mean if only $f(x) \in L^1(-\infty, \infty)$.

8.18   Prove the complex Riemann-Lebesgue theorem: if $f(x) \in L^1(-\infty, \infty)$, its Fourier transform vanishes as $|\lambda| \to \infty$. Thus

$$\lim_{|\lambda| \to \infty} \frac{1}{2\pi} \int_{-\infty}^{\infty} f(x) e^{i\lambda x} \, dx = 0$$

[*Hint:* Define the transform $-F(\lambda) = e^{i\pi} F(\lambda)$, let $\xi = x + \pi/\lambda$, and use the general result noted in Prob. 8.17.]

8.19   Use the result of Prob. 8.18 to prove

$$\lim_{\beta \to \infty} \int_{-\infty}^{\infty} f(\eta) \sin \beta\eta \, d\eta = 0$$

and

$$\lim_{\beta \to \infty} \int_{-\infty}^{\infty} f(\eta) \cos \beta\eta \, d\eta = 0$$

for the real function $f(x) \in L^1(-\infty, \infty)$.

8.20   Verify by direct integration that

$$\int_a^1 r^{-1} \phi_n(r) \phi_m(r) \, dr = \begin{cases} 0, & m \neq n \\ -\tfrac{1}{2} \ln a, & m = n \end{cases}$$

for the ϕ_n of (8.50).

8.21   Use the result of Prob. 8.20 to derive (8.53) from (8.50) and

$$u(r, \theta) = \sum_{n=1}^{\infty} c_{1n} \lambda_n^{-1} \sinh \lambda_n \theta \sin (\lambda_n \ln r) \qquad \text{if } u(r, \gamma) = f(r)$$

8.22   Prove that the improper integral in (8.54) converges if

$$\int_0^1 |f(\eta)| \eta^{-1} \, d\eta$$

exists and that this is sufficient to show

$$\left| \int_0^1 f(\eta) \sin (\lambda \ln \eta) \eta^{-1} \, d\eta \right| < \infty$$

8.23   Use a limit process to obtain the mathematical model and the temperature $u(r, t)$ for radial heat conduction in a long, uniformly heated circular cylinder of very great radius if the initial temperature is $u_0(r)$. [*Hint:* Use cylindrical coordinates (r, θ, z), and assume that there are no temperature variations with respect to θ and z.]

8.24   Use a limit process to obtain the mathematical model and the displacement $z(r, t)$ for the transverse vibrations of a very large, circular membrane if $z(r, 0) = 0$, $z_t(r, 0) = (r^2 + 1)^{-3/2}$, and $c^2 = 1$. Evaluate and plot $z(r, t)$ for several values of t. [*Hint:* Evaluate the inner integral by using the Hankel transform results in Appendix 4.]

8.25   Find $z(0, t)$ for Prob. 8.24. [*Hint:* Integrate by parts until original integral is regained; gather terms and evaluate.]

8.26   By a limit process, find $z(r, t)$ if

$$z_{tt} = c^2(z_{rr} + r^{-1}z_r) + e^{-\alpha t}, \qquad 0 < r, \ \ 0 < t, \ \ 0 < \alpha$$
$$z_r(0, t) = 0, \qquad 0 \le t$$
$$z(r, 0) = z_t(r, 0) = 0, \qquad 0 \le r$$
$$|z(r, t)| < \infty$$
$$z(r, t) \text{ satisfies (8.64)}, \qquad 0 \le t$$

8.27   Find $z(0, t)$ for Prob. 8.26.

8.28   The following model describes steady-state dispersion (mixing) of some quantity in a moving, uniform stream of fluid with speed v in the y direction:

$$vC_y = DC_{xx}, \qquad -\infty < x < \infty, \ \ 0 < y$$
$$C(x, 0) = \begin{cases} C_0, & x < 0 \\ 0, & 0 \le x \end{cases}$$
$$|C(x, y)| < \infty, \qquad -\infty < x < \infty, \ \ 0 < y$$

where C is the concentration of the quantity and D is the dispersion coefficient. Heat, dye, bacteria, or water pollutants are dispersible quantities.

(a) Show by application of a passage-to-limit process that

$$C(x, y) = \frac{1}{2}C_0 \operatorname{erfc}\left\{\frac{1}{2}x\left(\frac{Dy}{v}\right)^{-1/2}\right\}$$

(b) Plot $C(x, y)/C_0$ versus x for $y = 0, 20, 80, 320$ cm if $v = 0.007$ cm/sec, $D = 0.00028$ cm^2/ sec. (Put all curves on a single plot of C/C_0 vs. x with $|x| < 10$ and y as a parameter.)

8.29   Use the limit process to solve the following models for the harmonic function $u(x, y)$:

(a) $\nabla^2 u = 0, \qquad 0 < x, \ \ 0 < y < 1$
$u(0, y) = 0, \qquad 0 \le y < 1$
$u(x, 0) = 0, \qquad 0 \le x$
$u(x, 1) = e^{-x}, \qquad 0 < x$
$|u(x, y)| < \infty, \qquad 0 \le x, \ 0 \le y \le 1$
$u(x, y) \in L^1(0, \infty), \qquad 0 \le y \le 1$

(b) $\nabla^2 u = 0, \qquad 0 < x < 1, \ \ 0 < y$
$u_x(0, y) = 0, \qquad 0 \le y$
$u(x, 0) = 1, \qquad 0 \le x \le 1$
$u(1, y) = 0, \qquad 0 < y$
$|u(x, y)| < \infty, \qquad 0 \le x \le 1, \ \ 0 \le y$
$u(x, y) \in L^1(0, \infty), \qquad 0 \le x \le 1$

(c) $\nabla^2 u = 0, \qquad 0 < x, \ \ 0 < y < 1$
$u_x(0, y) = -1, \qquad 0 \le y \le 1$
$u(x, 0) = \operatorname{sech} \pi x, \qquad 0 \le x$
$u_x(x, 1) = 0, \qquad 0 < x$
$|u(x, y)| < \infty, \qquad 0 \le x, \ 0 \le y \le 1$
$u(x, y) \in L^1(0, \infty), \qquad 0 \le y \le 1$

(d) $\nabla^2 u = 0, \qquad -\infty < x < \infty, \ \ 0 < y < 1$
$u(x, 0) = \begin{cases} 1, & -x_0 \le x \le 0 \\ 0, & 0 < x \ \text{ or } \ x < x_0 \end{cases}$

$$u_y(x, 0) = 0, \qquad -\infty < x < \infty$$
$$|u(x, y)| < \infty, \qquad -\infty < x < \infty, \quad 0 \le y \le 1$$
$$u(x, y) \in L^1(-\infty, \infty), \qquad 0 \le y \le 1$$

8.30   Show that if the piecewise-smooth function $f(x) \in L^1(-a, \infty)$, $a = 0$ or ∞, it is necessary that $f(x) \to 0$ as $|x| \to \infty$. [*Hint:* The absolute integral of $f(x)$ converges if and only if the series

$$\sum_{n=1}^{\infty} a_n, \qquad a_n = \int_{a+n-1}^{a+n} |f(x)| \, dx,$$

converges. For convergent series, $\lim_{n \to \infty} a_n = 0$; if the integral of a nonnegative function is zero, the function is identically zero.]

8.31   Use the law of the mean of calculus to show that if the conditions of Prob. 8.30 hold, $\lim_{|x| \to \infty} f'(x) = 0$ also.

8.32   For K and then ϕ discontinuous at $\eta = D$ in (a, b), derive the derivative forms (8.67) and (8.68).

8.33   Derive the derivative forms in Theorem 8.2 for the sine and cosine transforms.

8.34   By induction, derive the Fourier transform of $d^{(n)} f / dx^{(n)}$.

8.35   Complete the solution to Example 8.5 using the sine transform and (8.85)—that is, perform the necessary integrations. Show that it is equivalent to use

$$U(\lambda, y) = A(\lambda) e^{-\lambda y} + B(\lambda) e^{\lambda y} + \frac{1}{2\lambda} e^{\lambda y} \int_0^y \left(\frac{2\lambda f(\tau)}{\pi} \right) e^{-\lambda \tau} \, d\tau - \frac{1}{2\lambda} e^{-\lambda y} \int_0^y \left(\frac{2\lambda f(\tau)}{\pi} \right) e^{\lambda \tau} \, d\tau$$

Be sure that your results agree with those found by use of the cosine transform.

8.36   Verify the solution to Example 8.5 for $f(y) = 1$ by evaluating

$$\int_0^{\infty} f(\xi) [x^2 + (y \pm \xi)^2]^{-1} \, d\xi \qquad \text{for } f(y) = \begin{cases} 1, & y < y_0 \\ 0, & y_0 < y \end{cases}$$

and then letting $y_0 \to \infty$.

8.37   Show that $f(\alpha x)$, $\alpha > 0$, has

(a) the Fourier transform $\alpha^{-1} F(\lambda/\alpha)$.

(b) the cosine transform $\alpha^{-1} c(\lambda/\alpha)$.

8.38   Show that $dF/d\lambda$ is the transform of $ixf(x)$, and find the Fourier transforms of $f(\alpha x) e^{i\beta x}$ and $f(\alpha x) \cos \beta x$ in terms of F.

8.39   Use the cosine transform to obtain the integral representation

$$\text{sech } \pi x = \left(\frac{2}{\pi} \right)^{1/2} \int_0^{\infty} \frac{\cos \lambda x}{1 + \lambda^4} \, d\lambda$$

Evaluate the integral numerically with a computer, and compare with tabulated values of sech πx. Show, also, that

$$\int_0^{\infty} \frac{d\lambda}{1 + \lambda^4} = \left(\frac{\pi}{2} \right)^{1/2}$$

8.40   Use the cosine transform to obtain the integral representation

$$J_0(\alpha x) = \frac{2}{\pi} \int_0^{\alpha} \frac{\cos \lambda x}{(\alpha^2 - \lambda^2)^{1/2}} \, d\lambda, \qquad \alpha > 0$$

and to show that

$$\int_0^\alpha \frac{d\lambda}{(\alpha^2 - \lambda^2)^{1/2}} = \frac{\pi}{2}$$

8.41   Derive the necessary transforms of derivatives for the Hankel transform of order zero to show that

$$\int_0^\infty r\left(f_{rr} + \frac{1}{r}f_r\right) J_0(\lambda r)\, dr = H_0\left(f_{rr} + \frac{1}{r}f_r\right) = -\lambda^2 H_0(\lambda)$$

8.42   Use the sine transform to solve Prob. 8.5(a).

8.43   Use the cosine transform to solve Prob. 8.5(b).

8.44   Use the Fourier transform to solve Prob. 8.5(c).

8.45   Use Fourier transforms to solve

(a) Prob. 8.5(d).   (b) Prob. 8.5(e).

(c) Prob. 8.5(f).   (d) Prob. 8.6.

8.46   Solve Prob. 8.14 by use of transforms.

8.47   Solve Prob. 8.15 by use of the sine transform.

8.48   Solve Prob. 8.16 by use of the cosine transform.

8.49   Solve Prob. 8.23 by direct use of the Hankel transform with $u_0(r) = (r^2 + r_0^2)^{-1/2}$ for known r_0. What is the effect of the size of r_0?

8.50   Use transforms to solve Prob. 8.24.

8.51   Use transforms to solve Prob. 8.26.

8.52   Solve Prob. 8.28 by use of transforms.

8.53   Use transforms to solve Prob. 8.29.

8.54   Find $u(x, y)$ for $\nabla^2 u = 0$ on $y > 0$ with $u(x, 0) = e^{-(x-x_0)^2}$.

8.55   Find $u(x, y)$ for $\nabla^2 u = 0$ on $y > 0$ with $u_y(x, 0) = f(x)$, $|u(x, y)| < \infty$, and $u(x, y) \in L^1(-\infty, \infty), 0 \le y$.

8.56   Find $u(x, t)$ if

$$u_t = ku_{xx}, \qquad x < 0, \quad 0 < t$$

$$u(x, 0) = 0, \qquad x \le 0$$

$$|u(x, t)| < \infty, \qquad x \le 0, \quad 0 \le t$$

$$u(x, t) \in L^1(-\infty, 0), \qquad 0 \le t$$

and

(a) $u(0, t) = f(t), \qquad 0 \le t$

or

(b) $u_x(0, t) = e^{-t}, \qquad 0 \le t$

8.57   Find the evolving water wave pattern on a body of water of infinite extent and uniform depth d if the initial, circularly symmetric surface pattern is

(a) $\eta(r, 0) = a(r^2 + 1)^{-1/2}, \qquad 0 \le r$.

(b) $\eta(r, 0) = \delta(r)$, $0 \le r$.

Plot some typical results for various times with $d = \infty$. [*Hint:* See Probs. 2.23 and 3.54; assume that the surface pressure p and the initial surface velocity η_t are zero.]

8.58   Given

$$u_t = k u_{xx}, \qquad 0 < x, \quad 0 < t$$

$$u(x, 0) = \begin{cases} u_0, & x_0 \le x \le x_1 \\ 0, & x_1 < x \quad \text{or} \quad x < x_0 \end{cases}$$

$$|u(x, t)| < \infty, \qquad 0 \le x, \quad 0 \le t$$

$$u(x, t) \in L^1(0, \infty), \qquad 0 < t$$

find $u(x, t)$ if

(a) $u_x(0, t) = 0$, $0 \le x$.

(b) $u(0, t) = 0$, $0 \le x$.

8.59   Find the displacement $z(y, t)$ of a semi-infinite string with $c^2 = T/\rho$ under the following conditions:

(a) $z(0, t) = \sin \omega t$ with the string at rest initially.

(b) $z_y(0, t) = \cos \omega t$ with the string at rest initially. Give a physical interpretation.

(c) $z_y(0, t) = 0$, $z(y, 0) = \operatorname{sech} y$, $z_t(y, 0) = 0$

(d) $z(0, t) = 1$, $z(y, 0) = e^{-y}$, $z_t(y, 0) = 0$

(e) $z_{tt} = c^2 z_{yy} - kz$, $z_y(0, t) = 0$, $z(y, 0) = \operatorname{sech} y$, $z_t(y, 0) = 0$. Give a physical interpretation.

(f) $z_{tt} = c^2 z_{yy} - ke^{-y} \sin \omega t$, $z(0, t) = 0$, with the string initially at rest. Give a physical interpretation.

8.60   Find the one-dimensional temperature variations $u(x, t)$ in a semi-infinite slab of material with conductivity k under the following conditions:

(a) $u(0, t) = \sin \omega t$, $u(x, 0) = 0$. This model leads to temperature waves;* calculate their amplitude decay and their speed of propagation; for example, follow a point at which temperature is locally a maximum.

(b) $u_x(0, t) = \cos \omega t$, $u(x, 0) = 0$.

(c) $u_t = k u_{xx} + e^{-t}$, $u(0, t) = 0$, $u(x, 0) = 0$.

(d) $u_t = k u_{xx} + e^{-x} \sin \omega t$, $u(0, t) = 0$, $u(x, 0) = 0$.

8.61   Using the results of Prob. 8.60, find

(a) $-K u_x(0, t)$, the flux into the earth, in part (a).

(b) $u(0, t)$ in part (b).

(c) $-K u_x(0, t)$ in parts (c) and (d).

---

*This model represents, approximately, the temperature variations in the surface layers of the earth induced by daily or seasonal air temperature changes.

8.62 Find $u(x, y)$ for $\nabla^2 u = e^{-(x^2 + y^2)}$ on $y > 0$, if

(a) $u(x, 0) = 0$, $-\infty < x < \infty$. Calculate the flux at $y = 0$.

(b) $u_y(x, 0) = 0$, $-\infty < x < \infty$. Calculate the temperature at $y = 0$.

(c) $u_x(0, y) = 0$, $\qquad u(x, 0) = 0$, $\quad 0 < x$.

(d) $u_x(0, y) = 0$, $\qquad u_y(x, 0) = 0$, $\quad 0 < x$.

8.63 Formulate an appropriate model and solve it by using transforms for the transverse vibrations of a beam under the following conditions:

(a) infinite beam with $z(y, 0) = e^{-y^2}$ and $z_t(y, 0) = 0$.

(b) semi-infinite beam at rest initially with a mechanical displacement $z(0, t) = A \sin \omega t$ of the pinned end so $z_{yy}(0, y) = 0$ also.

(c) semi-infinite beam at rest initially with $z_y(0, t) = z_{yyy}(0, t) = 0$ and a distributed load $q/\rho = e^{-y}$ added for $t > 0$.

(d) semi-infinite beam at rest initially with a shear force $Q(0, t) = \sin \omega t$ at the free end.

8.64 Find $F(\lambda)$ for

(a) $f(x) = e^{i\lambda_0 x}$.   (b) $f(x) = \cos \lambda_0 x$.   (c) $f(x) = \sin \lambda_0 x$.

(*Hint:* Consider F_δ.)

8.65 Given the model

$$u_t = k u_{xx} + \delta(x - x_0, t - t_0), \qquad 0 < x, \quad 0 < t$$

$$u(x, 0) = 0, \qquad 0 \le x$$

$$u(x, t) \in L^1(0, \infty), \qquad 0 \le t$$

obtain the Green's functions for

(a) $u(0, t) = 0$.   (b) $u_x(0, t) = 0$.

In each case, also deduce the Green's function by images and previous results for the infinite domain and compare to your present result. Express the solution for arbitrary source and initial conditions in terms of the Green's functions.

8.66 Given a semi-infinite string with the impulsive force $\delta(y - y_0, t - t_0)$ applied, find $z(y, t)$ if the string is initially at rest and

(a) $z(0, t) = 0$.   (b) $z_y(0, t) = 0$.

Deduce the Green's function and solve the equivalent problem with arbitrary forces and initial displacements in each case. [*Hint:* Express initial displacement as odd-even extension to $y < 0$ of prescribed $z_0(y)$, $y > 0$, to facilitate expression of the answer.]

8.67 Find $z(y, t)$ for $t_0 = 0$ and $y_0 = 0$ in Prob. 8.66.

8.68 Given $\nabla^2 u = \delta(x - x_0, y - y_0)$, find $u(x, y)$ if

(a) $0 < y$, $\quad 0 < x$, $\quad u(x, 0) = 0$, $\quad u(0, y) = 0$.

(b) $0 < y$, $\quad 0 < x$, $\quad u_x(0, y) = 0$, $\quad u(x, 0) = 0$.

(c) $0 < y$, $\quad -\infty < x < \infty$, $\quad u_y(x, 0) = 0$.

Discuss the form of the resulting Green's functions, and give a physical interpretation of each case.

8.69 Find the displacement $z(y, t)$ of a semi-infinite beam with a free end if the beam is acted on by the impulsive force $\delta(y - y_0, t - t_0)$ and is initially at rest. Find $z(0, t)$ for $y_0 = t_0 = 0$.

8.70 Use the change of variable $\rho = -\ln q$ and the appropriate transforms to solve (8.44) for $\beta = \pi/2$.

8.71 If $u(x, t)$ is a solution to $u_t = ku_{xx}$ on $0 < x, 0 < t$, show that $\partial^{(n)}u/\partial x^{(n)}$ is also a solution to the same equation for $n \geq 1$; that is, derivatives of solutions to the heat equation are also solutions to the heat equation.

8.72 Using the result of Prob. 8.71, prove that if

$$u_t = ku_{xx}, \qquad 0 < x, \quad 0 < t$$

$$Ku_x(0, t) - Hu(0, t) = 0, \qquad 0 \leq t$$

$$u(x, 0) = u_0(x), \qquad 0 \leq x$$

then $\phi(x, t) = u_x(x, t) - (H/K)u(x, t)$ satisfies

$$\phi_t = k\phi_{xx}, \qquad 0 < x, \quad 0 < t$$

$$\phi(0, t) = 0, \qquad 0 \leq t$$

$$\phi(x, 0) = f(x)$$

where $f(x) = u_0'(x) - (H/K)u_0(x)$. Use this result and a Fourier transform to find $u(x, t)$. [Hint: Once ϕ is known, integrate $\phi = u_x - ku$ with respect to x (t is a parameter) and use original problem for u to evaluate arbitrary functions of t in the integral.]

8.73 Find $u(x, t)$ if

$$u_t = ku_{xx}, \qquad 0 < x, \quad 0 < t$$
$$Ku_x(0, t) - Hu(0, t) = -HF, \qquad 0 \leq t$$
$$u(x, 0) = 0, \quad 0 \leq x$$

and give a physical interpretation.

8.74 Solve Prob. 8.72 with

$$u_0(x) = \begin{cases} U_0, & x \leq x_0 \\ 0, & x_0 < x \end{cases}$$

8.75 Find $z(y, t)$ if

$$z_{tt} = c^2 z_{yy}, \qquad 0 < y, \quad 0 < t$$

$$z_y(0, t) = -\frac{hz(0, t)}{T}, \qquad 0 \leq t$$

$$z(y, 0) = e^{-y}, \qquad 0 \leq y$$
$$z_t(y, 0) = 0, \qquad 0 \leq y$$

and give a physical interpretation. (Hint: See Prob. 8.72.)

8.76 Repeat Prob. 8.75 with $z(y, 0) = z_0 = $ constant, $0 \leq y$.

8.77 Find $\mathscr{L}\{x^n\}$ for positive integers n by integration by parts.

8.78 Verify by direct integration:

(a) $\mathscr{L}\{\cosh \alpha x\} = \dfrac{p}{p^2 - \alpha^2}, \qquad p > |\alpha|$

(b) $\mathcal{L}\{\cos \alpha x\} = \dfrac{p}{p^2 + \alpha^2}$, $p > 0$

(c) $\mathcal{L}\{J_0(\alpha x)\} = \dfrac{1}{(p^2 + \alpha^2)^{1/2}}$, $p > 0$

[*Hint*: Integrate series for J_0 term by term and sum result by using the binomial expansion.]

8.79   If $\phi'(x) = O(e^{\gamma x})$ as $x \to \infty$, show that $\phi(x) = O(e^{\gamma x})$ as $x \to \infty$, provided that ϕ' is piecewise smooth.

8.80   By successive integration by parts, show that

$$\mathcal{L}\{\phi^{(n)}(x)\} = p^n \mathcal{L}\{\phi(x)\} - p^{n-1}\phi(0) - \sum_{i=2}^{n} p^{n-i}\phi^{(i-1)}(0)$$

if only $\phi^{(n)} = O(e^{\gamma_n x})$ as $x \to \infty$ and $p > \gamma_n$.

8.81   Find the following inverse transforms by using partial fractions and/or convolutions:

(a) $\mathcal{L}^{-1}\left\{\dfrac{1}{(p + \alpha)^2 (p - \beta)}\right\}$

(b) $\mathcal{L}^{-1}\left\{\dfrac{\mu p + \nu}{(p + \alpha)(p + \beta)}\right\}$

(c) $\mathcal{L}^{-1}\left\{\dfrac{\mu p^2 + \nu p + \sigma}{(p + \alpha)^3}\right\}$

(d) $\mathcal{L}^{-1}\left\{\dfrac{1}{p^{1/2}(p^{1/2} + \alpha)^2}\right\}$

(e) $\mathcal{L}^{-1}\left\{\dfrac{p^3 - 27}{p^4 + 14p^3 + 68p^2 + 130p + 75}\right\}$

8.82   Find $\phi(t)$ by Laplace transform if $\phi'' + \lambda^2\phi = t$, $\phi(0) = 1$, $\phi'(0) = 0$.

8.83   Find $\phi(t)$ by Laplace transform if $\phi' + \lambda^2\phi = \cos wt$, $\phi(0) = 0$.

8.84   Use Laplace transforms to find $\phi(t)$ in the following cases:

(a) $\alpha\phi'' + \beta\phi' + \gamma\phi = 0$, $\phi(0) = 1$, $\phi'(0) = 0$, $\dfrac{\beta^2}{\gamma} > 4\alpha$

(b) $\alpha\phi'' + \beta\phi' + \gamma\phi = 0$, $\phi(0) = 0$, $\phi'(0) = 1$, $\dfrac{\beta^2}{\gamma} > 4\alpha$

(c) $\phi'' + \phi' + \phi = \cos wt$, $\phi(0) = \phi'(0) = 0$

(d) $\phi'' + \phi' + \phi = \cos \sqrt{\frac{3}{4}}t$, $\phi(0) = \phi'(0) = 0$

(e) $\phi'' + \phi' - \phi = 0$, $\phi(0) = \phi'(0) = 1$

8.85   If ϕ_1 satisfies a second-order, linear ordinary differential equation with $\phi(0) = 1$, $\phi'(0) = 0$, while ϕ_2 satisfies the same equation with $\phi(0) = 0$, $\phi'(0) = 1$, find the ϕ satisfying the same equation with $\phi(0) = A$, $\phi'(0) = B$.

8.86   Find $\phi(t)$ if $\phi'' - \lambda^2\phi = \delta(t - t_0)$, $\phi(0) = \phi'(0) = 0$.

8.87   Find $\phi(t)$ if $\phi'' + \lambda^2\phi = H(t - t_0)$, $\phi(0) = \phi'(0) = 0$.

8.88   Find $\phi(t)$ if $\phi'''' - \lambda^4\phi = F(t)$, $\phi(0) = \phi'(0) = \phi''(0) = \phi'''(0) = 0$.

8.89 Find $R(r)$ if $|R(r)| < \infty$, $R'' + \dfrac{1}{r}R + \lambda^2 R = 0$, $R'(0) = 0$, $0 \le r$.

8.90 Find $\phi(r)$ and λ^2 if $r^2\phi'' + r\phi' + \lambda^2\phi = 0$, $\phi(1) = \phi(a) = 0$, $a \le r \le 1$.

8.91 Find $R(r)$ and λ^2 if $R'(0) = R(1) = 0$, $R'' + \dfrac{1}{r}R + \lambda^2 R = 0$, $0 < r < 1$.

8.92 Find $X(x)$ and λ^2 if $X'(0) = X'(l) = 0$ and $X'' + \lambda^2 X = 0$, $0 < x < l$.

8.93 Derive an equation for the conservation of a dispersing (diffusing) and convecting quantity in a fluid stream. Let Q be the mass of the quantity present per unit volume of fluid with speed U and D be the constant (Fickian) diffusion coefficient. [*Hint:* Follow the derivation in Sec. 2.2.1.]

8.94 Given

$$Q_t + UQ_x = 0, \qquad 0 < x, \quad 0 < t$$

$$Q(0, t) = 0, \qquad 0 \le t$$

$$Q(x, 0) = \begin{cases} 0, & 2\pi < x \\ 1 - \cos x, & 0 < x < 2\pi \end{cases}$$

find $Q(x, t)$ and the flux UQ_x at $x = 0$.

8.95 Given

$$Q_t + UQ_x = 0, \qquad -\infty < x < \infty, \quad 0 < t$$

$$Q(x, 0) = \delta(x), \qquad -\infty < x < \infty$$

find $Q(x, t)$.

8.96 Given

$$Q_t = DQ_{xx}, \qquad 0 < x, \quad 0 < t$$

$$Q_x(0, t) = \frac{F(t)}{D}, \qquad 0 < t$$

$$Q(x, 0) = 0, \qquad 0 \le x$$

find $Q(x, t)$ and give a physical interpretation (is the sign of F important?).

8.97 Given

$$Q_t = DQ_{xx}, \qquad 0 < x, \quad 0 < t$$

$$Q_x(0, t) = 0, \qquad 0 < t$$

$$Q(x, 0) = \delta(x - x_0), \qquad 0 \le x$$

find $Q(x, t)$ and time t_p when $Q = 0.52$ at some x_p in terms of x_0, x_p, and D.

8.98 Given

$$Q_t + UQ_x = DQ_{xx}, \qquad 0 < x, \quad 0 < t$$

$$Q(0, t) = Q_0, \qquad 0 < t$$

$$Q(x, 0) = 0, \qquad 0 \le x$$

find $Q(x, t)$ and plot it for several values of t. Deduce the "speed" of the concentration front. Calculate the ratio of the diffusive and convective fluxes at $x = 0$.

8.99   Plot the solution (8.147) for several t, and verify that $Q \approx 0.52$ at $x = (Dt)^{1/2}$.

8.100   Solve for $u(x, t)$ in Prob. 8.72 by direct application of the Laplace transform to the model for u.

8.101   Solve Prob. 8.73 by direct application of the Laplace transform.

8.102   Find $z(y, t)$ by use of the Laplace transform if the string is always initially at rest:

(a) $z_{tt} = c^2 z_{yy}$, $0 < y,$ $0 < t$
$z(0, t) = a(t)$, $0 < t$
Derive a Duhamel theorem relation for this case.

(b) $z_{tt} = c^2 z_{yy}$, $0 < y,$ $0 < t$

$\vdots$ $z_y(0, t) = \dfrac{F(t)}{T}$, $0 \le t$

(c) $z_{tt} = c^2 z_{yy} - z$, $0 < y,$ $0 < t$
$z(y, 0) = a(t)$, $0 \le t$
Find explicit results for $a(t) = t$.

(d) $z_{tt} = c^2 z_{yy} + \delta(y - y_0, t - t_0)$, $0 < y,$ $0 < t$
$z_y(0, t) = 0$, $0 \le t$

(e) $z_{tt} = z_{yy}$, $0 < y,$ $0 < t$

$z_y(0, t) = \dfrac{\delta(t - t_0)}{T}$, $0 \le t$

Plot $z(y, t)$ versus y for $t = t_0, t_0 + 1, t_0 + 2$.

(f) $z_{tt} = z_{yy}$, $0 < y,$ $0 < t$
$z(0, t) = H(t - t_0)$, $0 \le t$
Plot $z(y, t)$ versus y for $t = t_0, t_0 + 1, t_0 + 2$.

8.103   Derive a Duhamel theorem relation for the model

$Q_t = DQ_{xx}$, $0 < x,$ $0 < t$
$Q_x(0, t) = Q_0(t)$, $0 \le t$
$Q(x, 0) = 0$, $0 \le x$

and then solve the problem for $Q_0(t) = e^{-t}$.

8.104   Find $Q(x, t)$ for Prob. 8.98 if $Q_0 = \sin \omega t$.

8.105   Find $Q(x, t)$ if

$Q_t = DQ_{xx}$, $0 < x,$ $0 < t$
$DQ_x(0, t) = -Q(0, t)$, $0 < t$
$Q(x, 0) = H(x - x_0)$, $0 \le x, x_0$

8.106   Find $Q(x, t)$ if

$Q_t + UQ_x = DQ_{xx}$, $0 < x,$ $0 < t$
$DQ_x(0, t) + Q(0, t) = 0$, $0 < t$
$Q(x, 0) = H(x - x_0)$, $0 \le x, x_0$

8.107   Find $Q(x, t)$ if $_*$

$Q_t + UQ_x = DQ_{xx}$, $0 < x,$ $0 < t$
$DQ_x(0, t) = -1$, $0 < t$
$Q(x, 0) = 0$, $0 \le x$

Calculate $Q(0, t)$ and total material flow through $x = 0$ as a function of time.

8.108   Find $Q(x, t)$ for

$$Q_t + UQ_x = DQ_{xx}, \qquad -\infty < x < \infty, \quad 0 < t$$
$$Q(x, 0) = \delta(x), \qquad -\infty < x < \infty$$

Then deduce the solution for $Q(x, 0) = Q_0(x)$.

8.109   Find the solution $z(r, t)$ to the model

$$z_{tt} = z_{rr} + \frac{1}{r}z_r, \qquad 0 < r, \quad 0 < t$$

$$z_r(0, t) = H(t), \qquad 0 < t$$
$$z(r, 0) = 0, \qquad 0 \le r$$
$$z_t(r, 0) = 0, \qquad 0 \le r$$

8.110   A semi-infinite elastic beam of uniform rectangular cross section is pin-supported at $y = 0$ and is initially at rest. At some time t_0, the support slips so that the end is displaced downward by an amount Δ. Formulate an appropriate model, and find the induced vibrations by use of Laplace transform.

8.111   Find the longitudinal displacements caused by striking the end of an elastic bar (see Prob. 2.4), initially at rest. Let the impulsive force be $-\delta(t - t_0)$ so $z_x(0, t) = -\delta(t - t_0)/AE$. Plot the elastic wave propagation versus x for various times.

8.112   Find $Q(x, t)$ if

$$Q_t = kQ_{xx}, \qquad 0 < x < l, \quad 0 < t$$
$$Q(0, t) = Q_0(t), \qquad 0 < t$$
$$Q(l, t) = 0, \qquad 0 < t$$
$$Q(x, 0) = 0, \qquad 0 \le x \le l$$

[*Hint:* Use the Laplace transform convolution.]

8.113   Use the methods of Sec. 5.1 to solve (8.150). Compare with the Laplace transform solution (Example 8.15) by reduction to the same form or plotting.

8.114   Find $u(x, t)$ if $u_t = ku_{xx}, 0 < x < 1, 0 < t$, and

(a) $u(0, t) = u(1, t) = 0, \qquad 0 < t$
   $u(x, 0) = u_0, \qquad 0 \le x \le 1$

(b) $u_x(0, t) = u(1, t) = 0, \qquad 0 < t$
   $u(x, 0) = u_0(x), \qquad 0 \le x \le 1$

(c) $u_x(0, t) = 0, \qquad 0 < t$
   $u(1, t) = T, \qquad 0 < t$
   $u(x, 0) = 0, \qquad 0 \le x \le 1$

(d) Part (c) with $T = T(t)$.

8.115   Find $z(y, t)$ if $z_{tt} = c^2 z_{yy}, 0 < y < l, 0 < t$, the string is initially at rest, and

(a) $z(0, t) = 0, \qquad 0 < t$
   $z(l, t) = a(t), \qquad 0 < t$

(b) $z_y(0, t) = 0, \qquad 0 < t$
   $z(l, t) = a(t), \qquad 0 < t$

(c) $z(0, t) = 0$, $0 < t$

$$z_y(l, t) = \frac{F(t)}{T}, \quad 0 < t$$

Find $z(l, t)$.

8.116 Formulate a mathematical model for conduction and find the temperature $u(r, t)$ in a sphere of radius R and of material with thermal diffusivity k if initially the temperature is a constant T and the surface temperature is held at zero.

8.117 Use separation of variables to determine the acceptable transforms in the following cases:

(a) $u_t = u_{xx} + ku$ for $u(x, t)$, $0 < x$, $0 < t$

(b) $z_{tt} = c^2 z_{yy} + \alpha z_t + \beta z$ for $z(y, t)$, $0 < y$, $0 < t$

(c) $Q_t + UQ_x = S(x, t)$ for $Q(x, t)$, $0 < x$, $0 < t$

(d) $Q_t + UQ_x = DQ_{xx}$ for $Q(x, t)$, $-\infty < x < \infty$, $0 < t$

(e) $z_{tt} + c^2 z_{yyyy} = 0$ for $z(y, t)$, $0 < y$, $0 < t$

(f) $u_t = k\left(u_{rr} + \frac{2}{r}u_r\right)$ for $u(r, t)$, $0 < r$, $0 < t$

8.118 Find the Laplace transformed equation in each case:

(a) $u_t = ku_{xx} + tu$, $0 < x$, $0 < t$

(b) $z_{yy} = c^2 z_{yy} + t^2 z_t$, $-\infty < y < \infty$, $0 < t$

(c) $Q_t + e^{-t}Q_x = DQ_{xx}$, $-\infty < x < \infty$, $0 < t$

What would you do in this case with the transformed equation? [*Hint:* First show, for example,

$$\frac{\partial}{\partial p}\left[\int_0^\infty u(x, t)\, e^{-pt}\, dt\right] = -\int_0^\infty u(x, t)te^{-pt}\, dt, \text{ etc.}]$$

8.119 Use a limit process on the solution to (5.60) to (5.62) to obtain formally a double Fourier transform relation; that is, let l_1 and $l_2 \to \infty$.

8.120 Find $u(x, y, t)$ for

$$\nabla^2 u = 0, \quad -\infty < x < \infty, \quad -\infty < y < \infty, \quad 0 < t$$
$$u(x, y, 0) = u_0(x, y), \quad -\infty < x < \infty, \quad -\infty < y < \infty$$

8.121 Find $u(x, y, t)$ for Prob. 8.120 if

$$u(x, y, 0) = \begin{cases} u_0, & |x| \le x_0, \ |y| \le y_0 \\ 0, & |x| > x_0, \ |y| > y_0 \end{cases}$$

by direct application of the double transform

$$F(\lambda, \mu) = \frac{1}{4\pi^2}\int_{-\infty}^\infty \int_{-\infty}^\infty f(x, y)\, e^{i(\lambda x + \lambda y)}\, dx\, dy$$

Note that the integral

$$\int_{-\infty}^\infty \int_{-\infty}^\infty |f(x, y)|\, dx\, dy$$

must exist. Why? Can you find the inversion formula directly, albeit formally?

CHAPTER 9

CHARACTERISTICS

9.1 INTRODUCTION

The solution of a first-order or second-order partial differential equation with a single dependent variable and two independent variables can be visualized as a surface in (x, y, z) space. Thus we can use analytic geometry [1] to enhance our understanding of such a problem. This is particularly true for initial-value problems in which we expect the solution to propagate from the region on which the initial data are given.

In the case of first-order and hyperbolic-type second-order equations, information from the initial data propagates over well-defined paths in the surface representing the solution. These propagation paths are called *characteristics*. They were introduced indirectly in Sec. 2.6, where the classification and reduction to canonical form of second-order equations were discussed.

The purpose of this chapter is to explore the physical and mathematical significance of characteristics. Knowledge of their existence gives considerable insight into the expected behavior of a problem's solution, even before the solution is known.

In the following material, attention is restricted to problems with one un-known or dependent variable and two independent variables and to a brief introduction to the subject. Greater depth and breadth can be obtained from Refs. [2, 3, 4, 5]. We begin with consideration of first-order equations because they have a clear geometric interpretation, are relatively simple to handle, and illustrate all the key properties found in second-order equations. Second-order hyperbolic equations, together with the rudiments of numerical calculations with characteristics, then comprise the remainder of the chapter.

9.2   FIRST-ORDER EQUATIONS

The general first-order partial differential equation in two independent variables (x, y) is

$$F(x, y, z, p, q) = 0 \tag{9.1}$$

where, according to the notation introduced in Chap. 1,

$$p = z_x \quad \text{and} \quad q = z_y \tag{9.2}$$

If (9.1) is a quasi-linear equation, it can be written

$$Pp + Qq = R \tag{9.3}$$

where P, Q, and R are functions of x, y, and z but not of p or q. If R is linear in z, and if P and Q are functions of x and y alone, then (9.3) is linear. The major development of this section deals with the quasi-linear equation (9.3), and it is assumed that P, Q, and R, together with their first derivatives, are continuous in the region of the problem under consideration. Also, P and Q are assumed not to vanish simultaneously—that is, $P^2 + Q^2 \neq 0$—in the problem region.

First-order equations arise from a number of physical systems. In geometrical optics, the propagation of light is described in terms of the geometry of light wave fronts and rays that are perpendicular. If the surfaces z = constant represent wave fronts for the propagation of plane waves, the differential equation for z, in the notation of this chapter, is

$$p^2 + q^2 = 1$$

a nonlinear first-order equation [4]. It can be shown that the characteristics of the solution represent light rays in this case.

Another important problem is that of river pollution, and a key quantity to indicate the degree of pollution is the dissolved oxygen content of the river water. If $U(x, t)$ is the velocity of the river water and $S(x, t, O)$ is a source distribution of dissolved oxygen with concentration $O(x, t)$, the equation describing the convection of the oxygen through the fluid [6] is

$$UO_x + O_t = S$$

This so-called Convection Equation is identical to the quasi-linear equation (9.3).

Finally, the propagation of a gravity-driven water wave in shallow water can be described in terms of a first-order equation derived from the conservation of linear momentum in the fluid motion under the wave. This derivation yields the equation

$$(1 + \tfrac{3}{2}z)z_x + z_t = 0$$

when the deviation z of the water wave surface from the still-water level and the derivatives z_x and z_t are small [7]. Again, this equation has the form of (9.3).

As mentioned in Sec. 9.1, the solution $z(x, y)$ to the quasi-linear equation (9.3), for example, can be represented as a surface in (x, y, z) space (Fig. 9.1). This surface is called an *integral surface* because it represents the solution or "integral" of the partial differential equation. The integral surface for (9.3) is represented by the formal identity

$$I(x, y, z) = z(x, y) - z = 0 \qquad (9.4)$$

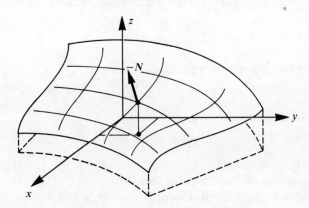

FIGURE 9.1   An integral surface representing a solution of (9.3).

From analytic geometry [1] we know that taking differentials in (9.4) yields the equation of the tangent to the integral surface at any point; hence

$$\frac{\partial I}{\partial x}\, dx + \frac{\partial I}{\partial y}\, dy + \frac{\partial I}{\partial z}\, dz = 0$$

or

$$z_x\, dx + z_y\, dy - 1\, dz = 0$$

The last relation is the total differential

$$dz = p\, dx + q\, dy \qquad (9.5)$$

which is an equation of the tangent plane at any point. Accordingly, the vector $N = p\boldsymbol{i} + q\boldsymbol{j} - 1\boldsymbol{k}$—that is, the vector $(p, q, -1)$—is *normal* to the integral surface (Fig. 9.1) at any point.

The scalar product of N and the vector (P, Q, R) is zero because

$$(P, Q, R) \cdot (p, q, -1) = (P\boldsymbol{i} + Q\boldsymbol{j} + R\boldsymbol{k}) \cdot (p\boldsymbol{i} + q\boldsymbol{j} - 1\boldsymbol{k})$$

$$= Pp + Qq - R = 0$$

from (9.3). Thus (P, Q, R) is perpendicular to N, their scalar product being zero.

Consequently, (P, Q, R) is tangent to the integral solution surface at every point and lies in the plane of the tangent equation (9.5). This means that the first-order equation (9.3) can be viewed as a geometric requirement that any integral or solution surface $z(x, y)$ through the point (x, y, z) must be tangent to the vector (P, Q, R). In fact, by beginning at some point on the integral surface and moving in the direction of the *known* tangent vector (P, Q, R), we move along a line lying entirely in the surface $I(x, y, z) = 0$. This line is called a *characteristic*, and by finding sets of *characteristics* we can define the integral surfaces representing solutions of the first-order partial differential equation (9.3).

Suppose that the *position vector r* of a point on a characteristic curve is

$$r = xi + yj + zk$$

This vector can be expressed parametrically in terms of distance s along a particular curve; then

$$r(s) = x(s)i + y(s)j + z(s)k$$

and the tangent vector to the curve at a particular point is

$$\frac{dr}{ds} = \frac{dx}{ds}i + \frac{dy}{ds}j + \frac{dz}{ds}k$$

The vector $(dx/ds, dy/ds, dz/ds)$ is tangent to the characteristic curve and the solution or integral surface, but (P, Q, R) is also tangent, as shown above. Therefore the components of the two vectors are proportional:

$$\frac{dx/ds}{P} = \frac{dy/ds}{Q} = \frac{dz/ds}{R}$$

or

$$\frac{dx}{P} = \frac{dy}{Q} = \frac{dz}{R} \tag{9.6}$$

The system (9.6) must be satisfied by any characteristic curve in the solution surface. Equivalent systems are

$$\frac{dy}{dx} = \frac{Q}{P}, \qquad \frac{dz}{dx} = \frac{R}{P}$$

or

$$\frac{dx}{dy} = \frac{P}{Q}, \qquad \frac{dz}{dy} = \frac{R}{Q}$$

Actually, (9.6) is only a pair of independent, first-order, ordinary differential equations. The dependent third equation can be obtained from the independent pair. From ordinary differential equation theory [see the references in Appendix 2], we know that the solutions of the pair of equations can be written as two independent functions, $G(x, y, z) = C_1$ and $g(x, y, z) = C_2$, each containing an arbitrary or free parameter C_i. These solutions constitute a two-parameter family of space curves that generate integral surfaces satisfying the first-order partial differential equation (9.3). The space curves are the intersections of the surfaces generated by G and g and specified by values of the parameters C_1 and C_2.

Suppose that we require all characteristics in the integral surface to pass through a given single curve that is not a characteristic—for example, one characteristic passing through each point on the curve. Then a relation between C_1 and C_2 must be found such that the intersections of the surfaces generated by G and g all pass through the given curve. The result is a specific relationship between C_1 and C_2—for example, $C_1 = C_1(C_2)$—so that C_2 remains arbitrary. Thus a single-parameter family of characteristics is sufficient to determine an integral surface. Such a surface is shown schematically in Fig. 9.2. The one-parameter surface is to be contrasted with the two-parameter surfaces generated by G and g in that the latter consists of characteristics that pass uniquely through every point in the (x, y, z) space where P, Q, and R are defined.

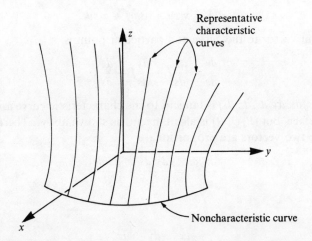

FIGURE 9.2   Integral surface generated by one-parameter family of characteristics.

A problem like the preceding one, in which we ask that the solution or integral surface of (9.3) pass through a prescribed curve, is called a *Cauchy Problem* (or an *Initial-Value Problem* when z is prescribed for $t = 0$). Although Garabedian [3] shows the conditions for the existence and uniqueness of the solution of the general Cauchy problem in a small neighborhood of the prescribed curve, we turn here to specific examples in order to gain insight into the behavior of solutions.

EXAMPLE 9.1   Consider the following convection-type equation for $z(x, t)$ obtained by setting $P = Q = R = 1$ in (9.3) and replacing y by t:

$$z_x + z_t = 1 \tag{9.7}$$

From (9.6), the characteristic equations are

$$\frac{dx}{1} = \frac{dt}{1} = \frac{dz}{1}$$

The equations of the characteristics are

$$\frac{dx}{dt} = 1 \quad \text{and} \quad \frac{dz}{dt} = 1$$

in differential form and

$$x - t = C_1 \quad \text{and} \quad z - t = C_2 \tag{9.8}$$

in integrated form. The constants C_1 and C_2 are arbitrary, so that (9.8) is a two-parameter family. The first of (9.8) gives the projections of the characteristics on the plane of the independent variables, and the lines $x - t = $ constant are often called the *base characteristics* or just *characteristics*. Along each base characteristic, $z - t = $ constant; hence, in general, $C_2 = C_2(C_1)$. That is,

$$z - t = h(x - t) \tag{9.9}$$

where h is an arbitrary function of one variable. Equation (9.9) is the general solution of (9.7).

Prescription of Initial Conditions

1. In a typical Cauchy or initial-value problem, the specification of z on the noncharacteristic line $t = 0$ is expected; that is,

$$z(x, 0) = z_0(x) \tag{9.10}$$

Then, from (9.8), $x = C_1$ and $z = C_2$ on $t = 0$. It follows that the relation between C_1 and C_2 must be: for the choice of C_1 values covering the axis (for each value we generate a characteristic), $C_2 = z_0(C_1)$. More directly, from the general solution (9.9),

$$z - t = z_0(x - t)$$

satisfies (9.10).

2. Suppose that z is prescribed on the characteristic $x - t = K$ such that

$$z(x, t) = z_0(x, t) \qquad \text{on } x - t = K$$

Then, from the general solution (9.9), we have the requirement

$$z_0(x, t) - t = h(K)$$

which is impossible because $z_0(x, t)$ is arbitrarily prescribed while $h(K)$ is constant. Even if we make $z_0(x, t) = t + K_0$ so that the solution can meet the data, it is clear that any $h(x - t)$ that has $h(K) = K_0$ is a solution; that is, an infinite number of solutions is possible [such as $h(x - t) = A(x - t)^n + K_0$ for $K = 0$, any A and $n > 0$]. Accordingly, the Cauchy problem with data prescribed on a characteristic is *improperly posed* because the solution is not unique (see Sec. 6.4).

EXAMPLE 9.2   Consider the convection equation

$$z_x + z_t = 0 \tag{9.11}$$

for $z(x, t)$ with some special initial data. The characteristics equations are [see (9.3) and (9.6)]

$$\frac{dx}{1} = \frac{dt}{1} \quad \text{and} \quad dz = 0$$

leading to

$$x - t = C_1$$

$$z = C_2$$

It follows that if z is prescribed as a function $z_0(x)$ for $t = 0$, then $C_2 = z_0(C_1)$ as C_1 covers the values of the x axis and, in general,

$$z = h(x - t)$$

so

$$z = z_0(x - t) \tag{9.12}$$

Prescription of Initial Conditions

1. Let the initial data be a pulse disturbance represented by

$$z_0(x) = \delta(x)$$

(δ is the Dirac δ-function used in Chap. 7). Then from (9.12),

$$z(x, t) = \delta(x - t)$$

which is plotted schematically in Fig. 9.3. Recall that $\delta(x) = 0$ for $x \neq 0$, so $\delta(x - t) = 0$ for $x \neq t, t > 0$. Thus the solution z is identically zero except along the characteristic through the disturbance location in the initial data. Clearly, *disturbances propagate along the base characteristics.*

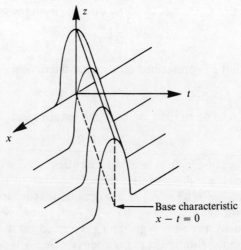

FIGURE 9.3   Schematic of propagation of δ-function initial data.

2. Let the initial data be discontinuous—for example,

$$z_0(x) = H(x - 1) - H(x + 1)$$

where $H(x)$ is the Heaviside unit function (Chap. 7)

$$H(x) = 1, \qquad x > 0$$

$$H(x) = 0, \qquad x \leq 0$$

Then, from (9.12),

$$z(x, t) = H(x - t - 1) - H(x - t + 1)$$

which is sketched in Fig. 9.4. Indeed, now we see that not only do *disturbances propagate along the base characteristics*, but *discontinuities do as well*.

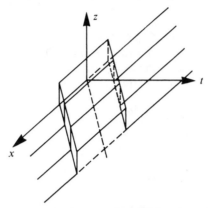

FIGURE 9.4   Schematic of propagation of *H*-function pair initial data.

3. Let the initial data be

$$z_0(x) = R(x)$$

where

$$R(x) = \begin{cases} 0, & |x| > 1 \\ 1 - |x|, & |x| \le 1 \end{cases}$$

From (9.12),

$$z(x, t) = R(x - t)$$

which is sketched in Fig. 9.5. Clearly, jumps in the derivatives of the solution may occur along characteristics and *jumps in the derivatives of the initial data propagate along the base characteristics*.

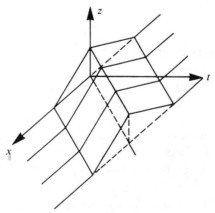

FIGURE 9.5

The propagation of discontinuities and disturbances along the base characteristics also illustrates how they divide the x–t plane. A given section of the initial curve has a well-defined *domain of influence* because that section of data can affect the solution only at those points that lie on the base characteristics through the data. Working backward from a specific section of the solution leads us to define, on the initial data curve, the *domain of dependence* of that section of the solution.

EXAMPLE 9.3   The propagation of a gravity water wave on shallow water provides a good example of a more sophisticated problem, in which the base characteristics are dependent on the solution.* If the water surface elevation z (above the undisturbed level) and its derivatives remain small, the governing equation is

$$(1 + \tfrac{3}{2}z)z_x + z_t = 0, \qquad -\infty < x < \infty, \quad t > 0 \tag{9.13}$$

An appropriate initial condition is

$$z(x, 0) = \begin{cases} \varepsilon(1 + \cos x), & -\pi \le x \le \pi, \ \ 0 < \varepsilon \ll 1 \\ 0, & |x| > \pi \end{cases} \tag{9.14}$$

The equations of the characteristics are [see (9.3) and (9.6)]

$$\frac{dx}{1 + \tfrac{3}{2}z} = \frac{dt}{1} \quad \text{and} \quad dz = 0$$

Therefore, on a characteristic,

$$\frac{dx}{dt} = 1 + \frac{3}{2}z \quad \text{and} \quad z = \text{constant} \tag{9.15}$$

Because z is constant on a characteristic, dx/dt is constant there, too. Thus the characteristics are straight lines, but they are no longer parallel.

From (9.15),

$$x - (1 + \tfrac{3}{2}z)t = C_1$$
$$z = C_2 \tag{9.16}$$

on a characteristic; hence

$$z = h(x - \{1 + \tfrac{3}{2}z\}t)$$

in general. From the initial condition (9.14), it follows that

$$z(x, t) = \begin{cases} \varepsilon[1 + \cos(x - \{1 + \tfrac{3}{2}z\}t)], & |x - \{1 + \tfrac{3}{2}z\}t| \le \pi \\ 0, & |x - \{1 + \tfrac{3}{2}z\}t| > \pi \end{cases} \tag{9.17}$$

so $C_2 = \varepsilon(1 + \cos C_1)$ on $|x - \{1 + \tfrac{3}{2}z\}t| = |C_1| \le \pi$, for example. Figure 9.6a is a plot of the base characteristics (9.16); the values of the constants $(C_1, C_2) = (-3\pi/2, 0)$, $(-\pi, 0), (-\pi/2, \varepsilon), \dots$ are given to identify the particular characteristics shown.

*Adapted with permission from "Mathematical Methods Notes," D. H. Peregrine, University of Bristol, Bristol, England, Spring 1968 (unpublished).

Figure 9.6b shows the propagation profiles and illustrates the nonlinear phenomenon of the steepening of the wave front.

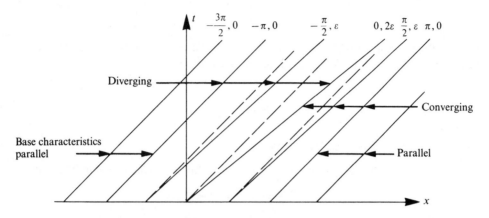

FIGURE 9.6a   Characteristic plane (with values of $(C_1, C_2) = (-3\pi/2, 0), \ldots$ shown on related characteristics).

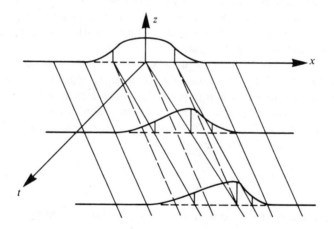

FIGURE 9.6b   Propagation profiles (axes reversed for pictorial clarity).

The solution to (9.13) becomes invalid when the wave front becomes too steep because z_x grows large. Indeed,

$$z_x = -\varepsilon \sin (x - \{1 + \tfrac{3}{2}z\}t)(1 - \tfrac{3}{2}z_x t)$$

or

$$z_x = \frac{-\varepsilon \sin \eta}{1 - \tfrac{3}{2}t\varepsilon \sin \eta}$$

where $\eta = x - \{1 + \tfrac{3}{2}z\}t$. Clearly, $z_x = \infty$, where

$$1 - \tfrac{3}{2}t\varepsilon \sin \eta = 0$$

As η is constant along any characteristic, this condition occurs first on the line where $\eta = \pi/2$, so $\sin \eta = 1$. Therefore $z_x \to \infty$ and the solution becomes invalid as

$$t \to \frac{2}{3\varepsilon}$$

Only in the limit of vanishingly small waves ($\varepsilon \to 0$) does the solution remain valid for large time. The case for $\varepsilon < 0$ is explored in the Problems.

9.3 SECOND-ORDER HYPERBOLIC EQUATIONS

9.3.1 Preliminary Analysis

Consider the general, second-order, quasi-linear partial differential equation

$$ar + 2bs + ct = F(x, y, z, p, q) \tag{9.18}$$

for $z(x, y)$, where

$$r = z_{xx}, \quad s = z_{xy}, \quad t = z_{yy}, \quad p = z_x, \quad q = z_y$$

and a, b, and c are functions of x, y, z, p, and q but not of r, s, or t. Making use of the experience of the previous section, we move immediately to determine if a Cauchy or initial-value problem is appropriate and if characteristics exist for second-order equations in the same sense as for first.

Let I be a curve in the x–y plane with parametric representation $x(l)$ and $y(l)$ in terms of arc length l. It is reasonable, particularly in analogy with initial-value problems for ordinary differential equations, that more data must be given for second-order than for first-order problems. Indeed, we now prescribe the values of both z and z_n along the initial curve I, or, what is equivalent, the values of z, p, and q under the so-called *strip condition* [4] [see (9.5)]

$$\frac{dz}{dl} = p\frac{dx}{dl} + q\frac{dy}{dl} \tag{9.19}$$

which ensures the proper relationship between z, p, and q. Because

$$\frac{\partial z}{\partial n} = p\frac{\partial x}{\partial n} + q\frac{\partial y}{\partial n} \tag{9.20}$$

prescription of dz/dl (i.e., z) and $\partial z/\partial n$ along I is just sufficient to permit calculation of p and q from (9.19) and (9.20).

From the discussion of Sec. 9.2, it is clear that if the solution $z(x, y)$ to (9.18) is considered as an integral surface, the prescribed values $x(l)$, $y(l)$, $z(l)$, $p(l)$, and $q(l)$ represent a curve on the integral surface *and* the normal $N = p\mathbf{i} + q\mathbf{j} - 1\mathbf{k}$ to the surface along the curve. Schiffer [8] points out that by representing a space curve and the normal vector at points on the curve, these five functions of l actually determine an infinitesimal surface element that is shifted along I to describe an infinitesimal strip in the integral surface. He then poses our primary question: for a given strip (x, y, z, p, q), does a unique solution $z(x, y)$ to (9.18) always exist whose integral surface in (x, y, z) space contains the strip?

The question is easily resolved. If the derivatives r, s, and t are to exist, they, together with z, p, and q, must satisfy the differential equation (9.18), the strip condition (9.19), and the conditions obtained from the total derivatives of p and q along I—namely,

$$\frac{dp}{dl} = \frac{\partial p}{\partial x}\frac{dx}{dl} + \frac{\partial p}{\partial y}\frac{dy}{dl} = r\frac{dx}{dl} + s\frac{dy}{dl}$$

$$\frac{dq}{dl} = \frac{\partial q}{\partial x}\frac{dx}{dl} + \frac{\partial q}{\partial y}\frac{dy}{dl} = s\frac{dx}{dl} + t\frac{dy}{dl} \tag{9.21}$$

But (9.21) and (9.18) constitute a set of three simultaneous equations for the three unknowns r, s, and t in terms of known functions and derivatives.

From (9.21) and (9.18),

$$\frac{dx}{dl}r + \frac{dy}{dl}s = \frac{dp}{dl}$$

$$\frac{dx}{dl}s + \frac{dy}{dl}t = \frac{dq}{dl} \tag{9.22}$$

$$ar + 2bs + ct = F$$

The solution to (9.22) is written conveniently in determinant form, according to Cramer's rule [9], as

$$\frac{.r}{D_1} = \frac{s}{D_2} = \frac{t}{D_3} = \frac{1}{D_4} \tag{9.23}$$

where

$$D_1 = \begin{vmatrix} \dfrac{dp}{dl} & \dfrac{dy}{dl} & 0 \\[2mm] \dfrac{dq}{dl} & \dfrac{dx}{dl} & \dfrac{dy}{dl} \\[2mm] F & 2b & c \end{vmatrix} \qquad D_2 = \begin{vmatrix} \dfrac{dx}{dl} & \dfrac{dp}{dl} & 0 \\[2mm] 0 & \dfrac{dq}{dl} & \dfrac{dy}{dl} \\[2mm] a & F & c \end{vmatrix}$$

$$D_3 = \begin{vmatrix} \dfrac{dx}{dl} & \dfrac{dy}{dl} & \dfrac{dp}{dl} \\[2mm] 0 & \dfrac{dx}{dl} & \dfrac{dq}{dl} \\[2mm] a & 2b & F \end{vmatrix} \qquad D_4 = \begin{vmatrix} \dfrac{dx}{dl} & \dfrac{dy}{dl} & 0 \\[2mm] 0 & \dfrac{dx}{dl} & \dfrac{dy}{dl} \\[2mm] a & 2b & c \end{vmatrix}$$

When $D_4 \neq 0$ on the initial curve I, (9.23) gives finite and unique solution values r, s, and t to the system (9.22). Thus the function z and its first two derivatives with respect to x and y are known on I. All higher-order derivatives of z can be obtained by continued differentiation of the differential equation and repetition of the foregoing approach, provided only that $x(l)$ and $y(l)$ are sufficiently differentiable. Consequently, the solution can, at least in the small, be extended uniquely from I to points off I by a Taylor expansion (Appendix 1). More important, as Schiffer [8] notes, two solutions to (9.18) that coincide on I and have the same first derivatives there (i.e., coincide on a prescribed strip) must coincide in all their derivatives. For a solution to be discontinuous across I, it must be discontinuous in its first derivatives at least. Thus the prescription of a strip (x, y, z, p, q) determines a unique solution to (9.18) when $D_4 \neq 0$ on the strip; the Cauchy or initial-value problem appears to be well posed under these conditions. In fact, however, this problem is not continuous with respect to Cauchy data unless Eq. (9.18) is hyperbolic (Chap. 6).

Suppose that I is a curve on which $D_4 \equiv 0$. Then the system (9.22) has no finite solutions unless the compatibility conditions $D_i \equiv 0, i = 1, 2, 3$, are satisfied [9]. Using the property that adding a multiple of any row (or column) of a determinant to a different, parallel row (or column) does not change the determinant value, we find that if any two $D_i = 0$, the remaining $D_i = 0$. The requirement $D_4 = 0$ yields the equation

$$a\left(\frac{dy}{dl}\right)^2 - 2b\left(\frac{dy}{dl}\right)\left(\frac{dx}{dl}\right) + c\left(\frac{dx}{dl}\right)^2 = 0 \tag{9.24}$$

while the condition $D_2 = 0$ (D_2 is convenient because it contains two zeros) ensures $D_1 = D_3 = 0$ and produces

$$a\frac{dp}{dl}\frac{dy}{dl} + c\frac{dq}{dl}\frac{dx}{dl} - F\frac{dx}{dl}\frac{dy}{dl} = 0 \tag{9.25}$$

Under conditions (9.24) and (9.25), the system (9.22) has an infinite number of finite solutions. Thus, along the curve I when $D_4 \equiv 0$, the Cauchy problem in which a strip is given—that is, $x(l)$, $y(l)$, $z(l)$, $p(l)$, and $q(l)$—does not possess a unique solution and therefore is ill-posed. Indeed, the problem possesses many solutions, any two of which may coincide only in the solution z and its first derivatives p and q on the strip.

As a result, so-called *weak discontinuities* [8] (in second and higher derivatives) in the solution z to (9.18) can occur across a curve I on which (9.24)—that is, $D_4 = 0$—is satisfied. Such curves are called *base characteristics* or, for our purposes, simply *characteristics*.

Equation (9.24) contains only total derivatives and can be written

$$a\left(\frac{dy}{dx}\right)^2 - 2b\left(\frac{dy}{dx}\right) + c = 0 \tag{9.26}$$

This equation defines two families of characteristic curves in the (x, y) plane and factors to

$$\left(a\frac{dy}{dx} - b - \{b^2 - ac\}^{1/2}\right)\left(a\frac{dy}{dx} - b + \{b^2 - ac\}^{1/2}\right) = 0 \tag{9.27}$$

which gives the slopes of the two families

$$\frac{dy}{dx} = \frac{b + \{b^2 - ac\}^{1/2}}{a} \quad \text{and} \quad \frac{dy}{dx} = \frac{b - \{b^2 - ac\}^{1/2}}{a} \tag{9.28}$$

Equations (9.28) are precisely the same as (2.106), which gave the transformation of differential equations to canonical form. In general, two characteristic directions exist at each point in the (x, y) plane. The nature of the characteristics is governed by the discriminant (see Sec. 2.6) $b^2 - ac$.

When $b^2 - ac > 0$, the roots in (9.28) are real, Eq. (9.18) is called *hyperbolic*, and there are two *real* characteristic slopes at each point (x, y). The characteristics are, therefore, curves in the real domain of the problem, and weak discontinuities may occur in the solution of hyperbolic equations.

When $b^2 - ac = 0$, Eqs. (9.28) collapse to a single result. Thus there is a single characteristic direction at each point (x, y). Equation (9.18) is called *parabolic* under this condition. In the case of an initial-value problem for the simple heat equation

$$u_{xx} - u_t = 0$$

the family of characteristics lies on the initial data line $t = 0$ (they never cross it and move into the x–t plane) and the characteristics are of no significant value in understanding the behavior of the solution, except that it is clear that no weak discontinuities may exist in the solution because there are no characteristics in (x, t) for $t > 0$.

When $b^2 - ac < 0$, the roots in (9.28) are imaginary and the characteristic slopes are complex. Accordingly, for this case in which (9.18) is called *elliptic*, there are no real characteristics and hence *no* weak discontinuities occur in the solution to elliptic problems in the real plane. In fact, it can be shown that the solutions to well-posed elliptic and parabolic problems are analytic, in spite of discontinuous boundary or initial conditions [4].

Whereas the characteristics for first-order equations were of general interest, the characteristics for second-order equations are of interest only for hyperbolic equations ($b^2 - ac > 0$). For hyperbolic equations, there are two, real characteristic directions given by (9.28) at each point (x, y), and for a solution z to the Cauchy problem to exist along one of these directions, condition (9.25) must be satisfied (even when the solution is constructed from a noncharacteristic strip). In the case of first-order equations, we obtained an equation for the base characteristic through any point, plus an equation for the total derivative of the unknown z to be satisfied along the base characteristic. Now we obtain equations for a pair of characteristics through any point, plus an equation relating the total derivatives of the first derivatives p and q of z along each characteristic. Later we shall see that this information, together with the identity relation

$$dz = p\, dx + q\, dy$$

is just sufficient to allow the step-by-step propagation of the solution to the Cauchy problem for (9.18) along the characteristic curves from a noncharacteristic initial curve I. Furthermore, it follows that because weak discontinuities can exist across characteristics only, discontinuities in second derivatives of z are propagated in the two characteristic directions in the (x, y) plane. Courant and Hilbert [4] show that the characteristics remain carriers of discontinuities in the case of generalized or weak solutions (including distributions) resulting from data with discontinuous first derivatives; however, in the strict sense, the meaning of the governing equation (9.18) excludes discontinuities in the first derivatives p and q.

We next turn to an analysis of the simple wave equation to gain further insight into hyperbolic problems.

9.3.2   The Wave Equation

The mathematical model for the transverse vibrations of a very long, flexible string is (Sec. 2.2.2)

$$z_{tt} - C^2 z_{yy} = 0, \qquad -\infty < y < \infty, \quad 0 < t \tag{9.29a}$$

$$z(y, 0) = Z_0(y), \qquad -\infty < y < \infty \tag{9.29b}$$

$$z_t(y, 0) = V_0(y), \qquad -\infty < y < \infty \tag{9.29c}$$

in which (9.29a) is the wave equation. There are no boundary conditions here because the string is taken to be effectively infinitely long. Thus none of the effects (disturbances) moving on the string at finite speed can either reach infinity or come from infinity in a finite time, and we see below that disturbances do travel at a finite speed.

From Sec. 2.6 we know that a transformation, via the change of variables

$$\xi = y - Ct$$

$$\eta = y + Ct$$

reduces (9.29a) to

$$z_{\xi\eta} = 0 \tag{9.30}$$

Also, comparing (9.29a) with (9.18) shows that $a = 1$, $b = 0$, $c = -C^2$, and $F \equiv 0$ (let $x = t$), so $b^2 - ac = C^2 > 0$; and, from (9.28), the slopes of the real characteristics are

$$\frac{dy}{dt} = \pm C$$

Accordingly, the characteristics are the lines $y \pm Ct = $ constant; that is, $\xi = $ constant and $\eta = $ constant are the two families of characteristics. We call ξ and η characteristic variables or coordinates. Furthermore, the initial curve I (i.e., $t = 0$) is a non-characteristic curve and z, $p = z_t$, and $q = z_y$ are prescribed there, so the initial-value or Cauchy problem (9.29) is well posed.

Returning to (9.30), we see that it can be integrated directly in this simple case. First,

$$z_\xi = A(\xi)$$

where A is an arbitrary function of ξ because only $A_\eta = 0$ is required. Then

$$z = \int^\xi A(\tau)\, d\tau + B(\eta)$$

where B is an arbitrary function of η. Now $\int^\xi A(\tau)\, d\tau$ is also an arbitrary function, so let us set

$$h(\xi) = \int^\xi A(\tau)\, d\tau$$

$$l(\eta) = B(\eta)$$

where both h and l are arbitrary functions of their respective variables.

It follows that

$$z(\xi, \eta) = h(\xi) + l(\eta)$$

is the general solution of (9.30), and provided that we understand that $\xi = y - Ct$ and $\eta = y + Ct$,

$$z(y, t) = z(\xi, \eta) = h(\xi) + l(\eta) \tag{9.31}$$

is the *general solution* to (9.29a).

In order for a solution to (9.29a) to exist along the characteristics ξ and η, the solution must satisfy the compatibility condition (9.25). For the present case, (9.25) reduces to

$$\frac{dp}{dq} = C^2 \frac{dt}{dy} \tag{9.32}$$

because only total derivatives are involved. On ξ-characteristics, $y - Ct = $ constant, so $dt/dy = 1/C$ and (9.32) gives

$$\frac{dp}{dq} = C$$

or

$$p - Cq = \text{constant where } \xi = \text{constant} \tag{9.33}$$

On η-characteristics, $y + Ct = $ constant, so $dt/dy = -1/C$ and (9.32) gives

$$\frac{dp}{dq} = -C$$

or

$$p + Cq = \text{constant where } \eta = \text{constant} \tag{9.34}$$

Now $p = z_t$, while $q = z_y$ here, so applying the chain rule of partial differentiation— for example,

$$z_t = \frac{dh}{d\xi} \frac{\partial \xi}{\partial t} + \frac{dl}{d\eta} \frac{\partial \eta}{\partial t}$$

in (9.31), we have

$$p = -Ch' + Cl' \qquad q = h' + l'$$

and

$$p + Cq = 2Cl'(\eta) \qquad p - Cq = 2Ch'(\xi)$$

Thus (9.31) satisfies (9.33) and (9.34).

It remains to use (9.31) in the initial conditions (9.29b) and (9.29c) in order to establish h and l so that we have a solution to the model. Introducing (9.31) into (9.29b) produces

$$h(y) + l(y) = Z_0(y) \tag{9.35}$$

while putting (9.31) into (9.29c) yields

$$- Ch'(y) + Cl'(y) = V_0(y) \tag{9.36}$$

because $\xi = \eta = y$ for $t = 0$. We can integrate (9.36) directly to remove the derivatives; hence, using a definite integral, we obtain

$$- Ch(y) + Cl(y) = \int_0^y V_0(\tau)\, d\tau + K \tag{9.37}$$

If we multiply (9.35) by C, we obtain

$$Ch(y) + Cl(y) = CZ_0(y) \tag{9.38}$$

First adding (9.37) to (9.38) and then subtracting (9.37) from (9.38) lead to

$$2Cl(y) = CZ_0(y) + \int_0^y V_0(\tau)\, d\tau + K \tag{9.39}$$

and

$$2Ch(y) = CZ_0(y) - \int_0^y V_0(\tau)\, d\tau - K \tag{9.40}$$

Therefore h and l are now known functions, being uniquely determined (except for the integration constant K) by the initial conditions.

We revert to the *proper variables* for each function in (9.31); that is, from (9.40),

$$h(\xi) = \frac{1}{2}Z_0(\xi) - \frac{1}{2C}\int_0^\xi V_0(\tau)\, d\tau - \frac{K}{2C} \tag{9.41a}$$

and from (9.39)

$$l(\eta) = \frac{1}{2}Z_0(\eta) + \frac{1}{2C}\int_0^\eta V_0(\tau)\, d\tau + \frac{K}{2C} \tag{9.41b}$$

Putting (9.41) back into (9.31) gives the model solution

$$z(\dot{y}, t) = \frac{1}{2}Z_0(\xi) + \frac{1}{2}Z_0(\eta) + \frac{1}{2C}\left[\int_0^\eta V_0(\tau)\, d\tau - \int_0^\xi V_0(\tau)\, d\tau\right]$$

or after inversion of the last integral and reversion to the original variables,

$$z(y, t) = \frac{1}{2}[Z_0(y - Ct) + Z_0(y + Ct)] + \frac{1}{2C}\int_{y-Ct}^{y+Ct} V_0(\tau)\, d\tau \tag{9.42}$$

This solution for the model (9.29) can be used to gain further insight into the character of hyperbolic equations, of which (9.29a) is a most simple example.

Recall that Z_0 and V_0 are prescribed at $t = 0$ as functions of y. Thus for any value of $y - Ct$ or $y + Ct$, we look along the line $t = 0$ in the (y, t) plane until we find the equivalent value of y in order to evaluate Z_0 and V_0. For example, suppose that we seek $z(y_0, t_0)$, where y_0 and t_0 represent a specific point in the (y, t) plane. Equation (9.42) then becomes

$$z(y_0, t_0) = \frac{1}{2}[Z_0(y_0 - Ct_0) + Z_0(y_0 + Ct_0)] + \frac{1}{2C} \int_{y_0 - Ct_0}^{y_0 + Ct_0} V_0(\tau) \, d\tau$$

The value of $z(y_0, t_0)$ is determined completely by the value of Z_0 along the line $t = 0$ where $y = y_0 - Ct_0 = \xi_0$ and $y = y_0 + Ct_0 = \eta_0$ and by the integral of the values of V_0 between $y_0 - Ct_0 = \xi_0 \leq y \leq \eta_0 = y + Ct_0$ on $t = 0$. Therefore the solution at a point in the (y, t) plane depends only on a well-defined *portion* of the initial data—namely, that portion marked out by the two characteristics ξ_0 and η_0 through the point (y_0, t_0) (see Fig. 9.7). The values outside of the interval $\xi_0 \leq y \leq \eta_0$ do not affect the solution at (y_0, t_0). Accordingly, this interval cut from the y axis by the characteristics is called the *domain of dependence* for (y_0, t_0). If the characteristic lines are constructed through any point (y, t), it is clear that they cut the line $t = 0$ and neatly block out the domain of dependence in every case (see Fig. 9.7).

A few trial sketches show that the initial data on $y \leq \xi_0$ can influence only points lying to the *left* of the characteristic $\xi_0 = y - Ct = $ constant. Similarly, the initial data on $y \geq \xi_0$ can influence only points lying to the right of the characteristic $\eta_2 = y + Ct = \xi_0 = $ constant. Therefore point A on $t = 0$ at $y = \xi_0$ can only influence (y, t) points lying in the wedge area between ξ_0 and η_2. This area is the *domain of influence* (Fig. 9.7) of point A. Such a domain of influence can be constructed for any point on the initial line $t = 0$. If the point is located at a point of discontinuity in Z_0 or V_0, this discontinuity can propagate along the characteristics from the point but can never cross the characteristics and leave the domain of influence.

Another important feature of the solution (9.42) becomes apparent if we set $V_0(y) \equiv 0$ so that (9.42) reduces to

$$z(y, t) = \tfrac{1}{2}Z_0(y - Ct) + \tfrac{1}{2}Z_0(y + Ct) = \tfrac{1}{2}Z_0(\xi) + \tfrac{1}{2}Z_0(\eta) \tag{9.43}$$

Along a characteristic ξ_0, the solution part $Z_0(y - Ct) = Z_0(\xi_0)$ remains constant. Along a characteristic η_0, the solution part $Z_0(y + Ct) = Z_0(\eta_0)$ remains constant. Therefore, if a pair of characteristics issues from each point on the initial line $t = 0$, we can visualize the initial wave form (remember that there is no initial velocity) splitting into two equal parts and these two parts propagating out along their respective characteristics. One part is a forward traveling wave and moves *without change of form* along the ξ characteristics at a finite speed $dy/dt = C$ that is determined by the ratio of string tension to density (see Sec. 2.2.2); the other part is a rearward traveling wave that moves *without change of form* along the η characteristics at a speed $dy/dt = -C$. The total solution at any time is simply the *sum* of the two wave parts.

Figures 9.8a and 9.8b were prepared to illustrate the motion of waves on a string. The results were drawn by a computer plotter using output from a simple program employing (9.43) with $C^2 = 1$ and the initial conditions (Figure 9.8a)

$$Z_0(y) = \text{sech}^2 (y - 4) + \text{sech}^2 (y + 4), \qquad -\infty < y < \infty \tag{9.44a}$$

and (Figure 9.8b)

$$Z_0(y) = \text{sech}^2 (y - 4) - \text{sech}^2 (y + 4), \qquad -\infty < y < \infty \tag{9.44b}$$

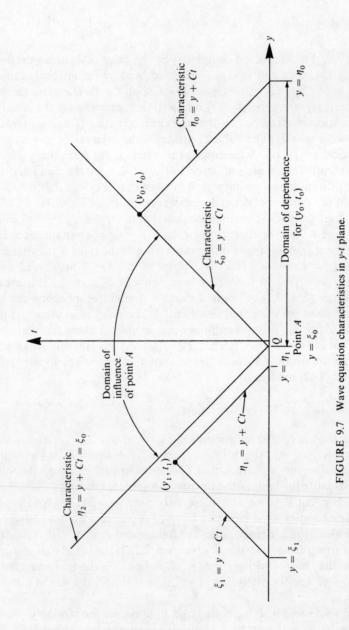

FIGURE 9.7 Wave equation characteristics in y-t plane.

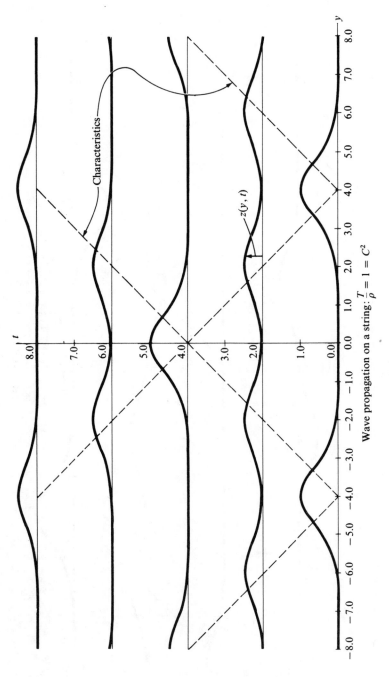

Wave propagation on a string: $\frac{T}{\rho} = 1 = C^2$

FIGURE 9.8a

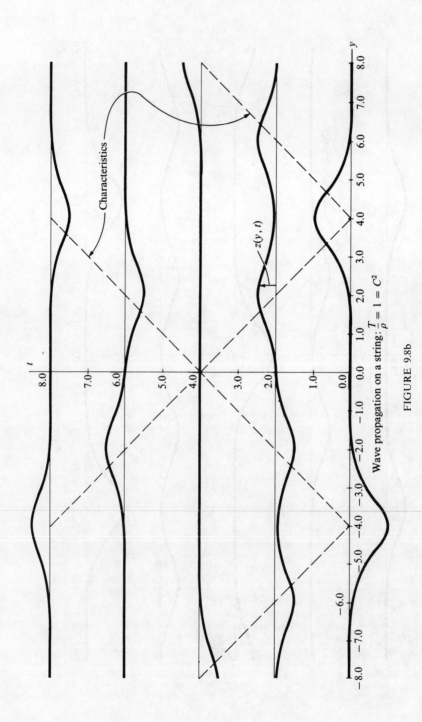

Wave propagation on a string: $\dfrac{T}{\rho} = 1 = C^2$

FIGURE 9.8b

The wave crests in the string are initially located at $y = \pm 4$; characteristics are shown from these points so that the motion can be traced. The appropriate values of the solution function are superimposed on lines $t = 0, 2, 4, 6$, and 8. Can you see how the characteristics play their role? Could you construct a solution from the initial data and characteristics alone (without formally employing the solution equation)?

In Fig. 9.8a and Eq. (9.44a) it is clear that $z(y, t) = z(-y, t)$ and $Z_0(y) = Z_0(-y)$; that is, the solution is even in y. But then $z_y(y, t) = -z_y(-y, t)$, and it follows that as $y \to 0$, we must have

$$z_y(0, t) = 0$$

Thus Fig. 9.8a gives a solution to another problem, the semi-infinite string problem

$$z_{tt} - z_{yy} = 0, \qquad 0 < y < \infty, \quad 0 < t$$

$$z_y(0, t) = 0, \qquad 0 < t$$

$$z(y, 0) = \operatorname{sech}^2(y - 4) + \operatorname{sech}^2(y + 4), \qquad 0 < y < \infty$$

$$z_t(y, 0) = 0, \qquad 0 < y < \infty$$

This result illustrates the *method of images* in which, in this case, the solution to a problem on a semi-infinite interval is obtained by extending the problem across the boundary in such a way that the initial-value problem on the infinite domain satisfies the boundary condition at $y = 0$ for all time. Here an *even* extension or *image* [Eq. (9.44)] leads to a solution satisfying the homogeneous derivative boundary condition.

Figure 9.8b gives a solution to the problem of a semi-infinite string that is fixed with $z(0, t) = 0$ at the end. Clearly, here an *odd image* is required so that $z(y, t) = -z(y, t)$ and $z(0, t) = 0$ is the result.

Consider a general problem

$$z_{tt} - C^2 z_{yy} = 0, \qquad 0 < y < \infty, \quad 0 < t$$

$$z(0, t) = 0, \qquad 0 < t$$

$$z(y, 0) = Z_0(y), \qquad 0 < y < \infty \qquad (9.45)$$

$$z_t(y, 0) = V_0(y), \qquad 0 < y < \infty$$

We seek to generate the appropriate *odd image* so that the solution (9.42) for the infinite string can be used. We need to define Z_0 and V_0 for $y < 0$ so $z(0, t) \equiv 0$. From (9.42),

$$z(0, t) = 0 = \frac{1}{2}[Z_0(-Ct) + Z_0(Ct)] + \frac{1}{2C}\int_{-Ct}^{Ct} V_0(\tau)\, d\tau$$

Treating Z_0 and V_0 independently, we set the term in brackets to zero

$$Z_0(-Ct) + Z_0(Ct) = 0 \qquad (9.46)$$

and the integral to zero

$$\int_{-Ct}^{Ct} V_0(\tau)\, d\tau = 0 \qquad (9.47)$$

Clearly, if $Z_0(-y) = -Z_0(y)$, (9.46) is satisfied; therefore an *odd image* in Z_0 is required. Similarly, if we rewrite (9.47) as

$$\int_{-Ct}^{0} V_0(\tau)\,d\tau + \int_{0}^{Ct} V_0(\tau)\,d\tau = -\int_{Ct}^{0} V_0(-\rho)\,d\rho + \int_{0}^{Ct} V_0(\tau)\,d\tau$$

$$= \int_{0}^{Ct} V_0(-\rho)\,d\rho + \int_{0}^{Ct} V_0(\tau)\,d\tau$$

$$= \int_{0}^{Ct} [V_0(-\beta) + V_0(\beta)]\,d\beta = 0$$

where ρ, τ, and β are dummy variables, we see that $V_0(-y) = -V_0(y)$ is required; that is, an *odd image* is also appropriate for $V_0(y)$.

In closing this section we establish that disturbances and discontinuities really do propagate along characteristics. Let us use the Dirac δ-function $\delta(y)$ and choose $C^2 = 1$,

$$Z_0(y) = \delta\left(y - \frac{1}{2}\right) + \sum_{n=1}^{\infty} (-1)^n \left[\delta\left(y - \frac{1}{2} - n\right) + \delta\left(y - \frac{1}{2} + n\right)\right],$$

$$V_0(y) = 0, \qquad\qquad -\infty < y < \infty$$

for the original string problem (9.29), whose solution now is (9.43) or under these conditions

$$z(y, t) = \frac{1}{2}\left[\delta\left(y - t - \frac{1}{2}\right) + \delta\left(y + t - \frac{1}{2}\right)\right] + \frac{1}{2}\sum_{n=1}^{\infty} (-1)^n \left[\delta\left(y - t - \frac{1}{2} - n\right)\right.$$

$$\left. + \delta\left(y - t - \frac{1}{2} + n\right)\right] + \frac{1}{2}\sum_{n=1}^{\infty} (-1)^n \left[\delta\left(y + t - \frac{1}{2} - n\right)\right.$$

$$\left. + \delta\left(y + t - \frac{1}{2} + n\right)\right]$$

Although this solution is difficult to interpret in written form, a graphical representation with z superimposed on the (y, t) plane is quite revealing. Consider Fig. 9.9, where δ is represented by the small pulses. A short segment of the y axis is shown, as well as the characteristics from each pulse. Note that the disturbances propagate along the characteristics and, particularly, how the disturbances interact. After careful study you should see that in addition to representing a portion of the solution to our original problem, Fig. 9.9 shows, in the segment $0 \le y \le 1$, the evolution of the solution to

$$z_{tt} - z_{yy} = 0, \qquad 0 < y < 1, \quad 0 < t$$

$$z(0, t) = z(1, t) = 0, \qquad 0 < t$$

$$z(y, 0) = \delta(y - \tfrac{1}{2}),$$

$$z_t(y, 0) = 0, \qquad\qquad 0 < y < 1$$

that is, the solution for a pulse wave on a finite string! The fixed ends of the string reflect the pulse wave, but it is a negative reflection. Check Figs. 9.8a and 9.8b again now to verify these effects.

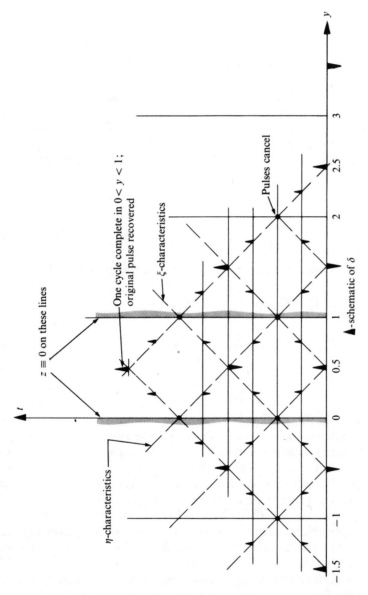

FIGURE 9.9   Dirac δ-function solution to wave equation.

In this section we dealt with a linear hyperbolic equation. It has characteristics as *all* hyperbolic equations do. These characteristics are propagation paths for disturbances or discontinuities in the given data. The characteristic equations for other hyperbolic partial differential equations may be both different and more complex, but the role of the characteristics is not changed.

9.3.3   Numerical Calculations with Characteristics

Although the closed-form solution of the simple wave equation in Sec. 9.3.2 was instructive, the practical matter of computations on more complex equations remains to be explored. As a review, recall that for the quasi-linear equation (9.18) under the condition $b^2 - ac > 0$, there exist two real characteristics through each point of the (x, y) plane and along each of these characteristics a relation involving only total derivatives must hold or no solution exists. Thus, in the (x, y) plane, two sets of characteristic curves are solutions to the ordinary differential equations (9.28):

$$C_1 : \frac{dy_1}{dx} = \frac{b + \{b^2 - ac\}^{1/2}}{a} = \alpha(x, y_1) \tag{9.48a}$$

$$C_2 : \frac{dy_2}{dx} = \frac{b - \{b^2 - ac\}^{1/2}}{a} = \beta(x, y_2) \tag{9.48b}$$

The relation (9.25) must be satisfied on these curves also, and it can be written as

$$C_1 : a \, dp \frac{dy_1}{dx} + c \, dq - F \, dy_1 = 0 \tag{9.49a}$$

$$C_2 : a \, dp \frac{dy_2}{dx} + c \, dq - F \, dy_2 = 0 \tag{9.49b}$$

Finally, the condition

$$dz = p \, dx + q \, dy \tag{9.50}$$

must hold [see (9.19)]. The primary question then is: Given a noncharacteristic strip—that is, $x(l)$, $y(l)$, $z(l)$, $p(l)$, and $q(l)$—can (9.48) to (9.50) be used to construct uniquely the solution to the initial-value problem in the area off the strip?

The answer to this question is obtained through application of a numerical technique. Figure 9.10 shows a schematic of the situation; the points 1, i are taken to be a small distance Δ apart along the prescribed strip I. The solid lines indicate the actual, but unknown, characteristics. No closed-form solution of the general case of (9.48) to (9.50) is possible, so differentials are replaced by their corresponding difference expressions and a numerical solution of the resulting difference equations is obtained in small, but finite, steps.

Derivatives and differentials can be expanded to difference form through application of the Taylor's series (A.1.2) (Appendix 1). For example,

$$y(x_0 + \Delta x) = y(x_0) + \frac{dy}{dx}\bigg|_{x = x_0} \Delta x + O[\Delta x^2]$$

or

$$y(x_0 + \Delta x) - y(x_0) = \frac{dy}{dx}\bigg|_{x = x_0} \Delta x + O[\Delta x^2] \tag{9.51}$$

The approximation becomes exact as $\Delta x \to 0$, and the numerical difference problem converges to the original differential problem similarly. Employing the notation in Fig. 9.10 gives us

$$\Delta x = x_{2,1} - x_{1,1} \quad \text{and} \quad y(x_0 + \Delta x) - y(x_0) = y_{2,1} - y_{1,1}$$

for example. The *forward-difference equation* (9.51) corresponds to replacing the characteristics locally by straight lines with slopes determined at the backward point; we then project forward along the line to the new point 2, 1 from 1, 1, and so on. The approximate construction of characteristics by a sequence of straight lines is illustrated in Fig. 9.10 by the dashed lines. The equations (9.48) and (9.49) for the characteristics through 2, 1 are now

$$C_1 : y_{2,1} - y_{1,1} = \alpha_{1,1}(x_{2,1} - x_{1,1});$$

$$a_{1,1}(p_{2,1} - p_{1,1})\alpha_{1,1} + c_{1,1}(q_{2,1} - q_{1,1}) - F_{1,1}(y_{2,1} - y_{1,1}) = 0 \quad (9.52a)$$

$$C_2 : y_{2,1} - y_{1,2} = \alpha_{1,2}(x_{2,1} - x_{1,2});$$

$$a_{1,2}(p_{2,1} - p_{1,2})\beta_{1,2} + c_{1,2}(q_{2,1} - q_{1,2}) - F_{1,2}(y_{2,1} - y_{1,2}) = 0 \quad (9.52b)$$

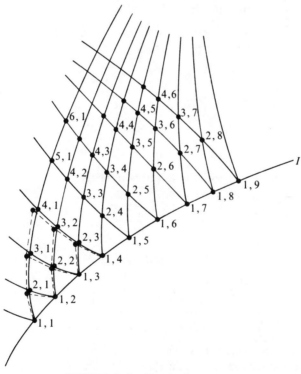

FIGURE 9.10 Characteristic net.

These four equations contain the four unknowns $x_{2,1}$, $y_{2,1}$, $p_{2,1}$, and $q_{2,1}$; thus, with all values at 1, 1 and 1, 2 known, (9.52) can be solved uniquely for these unknowns. But writing (9.50) in difference form produces

$$z_{2,1} - z_{1,1} = \tfrac{1}{2}(p_{1,1} + p_{2,1})(x_{2,1} - x_{1,1}) + \tfrac{1}{2}(q_{1,1} + q_{2,1})(y_{2,1} - y_{1,1}) \quad (9.53)$$

from which $z_{2,1}$ is computed; the average values of p and q along the characteristic are used here because the new values are known when (9.53) is used. By recasting (9.52) and (9.53) for the remaining second-level points $2, i$, we sequentially find x, y, z, p, q at all the points $2, i$. It is then possible to proceed to the third-level points, and so on. From (9.51), we deduce that the order of error in the calculations involving (9.52) and (9.53) is about equal to the square of the spacing between any two adjacent points in the mesh; that is, $O[\Delta x^2 + \Delta y^2]$.

The foregoing procedure is called the *Method of Characteristics*. It is illustrated now by two examples. In the first, (9.52) and (9.53) are used to obtain the "straight-line" characteristic solution in which the actual characteristic segment between two points is replaced by a straight line, as above. In the second example, a method that is very similar to the predictor-corrector method for integration of ordinary differential equations is used. In fact, (9.52) and (9.53) give the first approximation at an advanced level (the predictor); then the approximate values at the advanced level are averaged with the known values at the present level in each equation to yield a more accurate solution (the corrector). The corrector may be repeated several times at a point (each time using the latest advanced-level values available) to further improve the solution.

The following model is treated in the examples:

$$z_{xx} - z^4 z_{yy} = -z, \qquad -\infty < x < \infty, \quad 0 < y \qquad (9.54a)$$

$$z(x, 0) = \begin{cases} 0, & |x| > 10 \\ 1.8, & -10 < x < 0 \\ 0.6(2 + \cos \pi x), & 0 \le x \le 1 \\ 0.6, & 1 < x < 10 \end{cases} \qquad (9.54b)$$

$$z_y(x, 0) = 0, \qquad -\infty < x < \infty \qquad (9.54c)$$

We shall be concerned only with the solution in the region near $x = 0$ and $y = 0$. For this model, (9.48) and (9.49) produce

$$C_1 : \frac{dy_1}{dx} = z^2 \qquad (9.48a')$$

$$dp\, z^2 - z^4\, dq + z\, dy_1 = 0 \qquad (9.49a')$$

$$C^2 : \frac{dy_2}{dx} = -z^2 \qquad (9.48b')$$

$$-dp\, z^2 - z^4\, dq + z\, dy_2 = 0 \qquad (9.49b')$$

and (9.50) is required. The characteristics cannot be computed in advance because they depend on the solution; thus they must develop step by step with the solution itself. Note that within the region of interest (near the origin) there is a weak discontinuity (in the second derivative of z) in the initial condition (specifically at $x = 0$ and $x = 1$).

EXAMPLE 9.4 *Straight-Line Approximation.* Figure 9.11 shows a schematic of the early phases of computation in the region $-0.5 \le x \le 0.5$ with $\Delta = \Delta x$

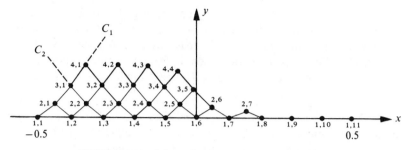

FIGURE 9.11 Schematic of example characteristic net.

$= 0.1$. From (9.48′) and (9.49′), we obtain the difference forms equivalent to (9.52) for calculation of values at $2, i$, using values at $1, i$, and $1, i + 1$:

$$C_1 : y_{2,i} - y_{1,i} = z_{1,i}^2(x_{2,i} - x_{1,i}) \tag{9.55a}$$

$$(p_{2,i} - p_{1,i})z_{1,i}^2 - z_{1,i}^4(q_{2,i} - q_{1,i}) + z_{1,i}(y_{2,i} - y_{1,i}) = 0 \tag{9.55b}$$

$$C_2 : y_{2,i} - y_{1,i+1} = -z_{1,i+1}^2(x_{2,i} - x_{1,i+1}) \tag{9.55c}$$

$$-(p_{2,i} - p_{1,i+1})z_{1,i+1}^2 - z_{1,i+1}^4(q_{2,i} - q_{1,i+1})$$

$$+ z_{1,i+1}(y_{2,i} - y_{1,i+1}) = 0 \tag{9.55d}$$

At point $2, 1$, for example, the values $x_{1,1} = -0.5$, $x_{1,2} = -0.4$, $y_{1,1} = y_{1,2} = 0$, $z_{1,1} = z_{1,2} = 1.8$, $p_{1,1} = p_{1,2} = 0$, $q_{1,1} = q_{1,2} = 0$ are known. Thus (9.55a) and (9.55c) give

$$y_{2,1} = 3.24(x_{2,1} + 0.5)$$

$$y_{2,1} = -3.24(x_{2,1} + 0.4)$$

which yields $y_{1,2} = 0.1620$, $x_{2,1} = -0.4500$. From (9.55b) and (9.55c),

$$3.24p_{2,1} - 10.4976q_{2,1} + 1.8y_{2,1} = 0$$

$$-3.24p_{2,1} - 10.4976q_{2,1} + 1.8y_{2,1} = 0$$

Therefore $p_{2,1} = 0$ and $q_{2,1} = 0.0278$. Finally, applying (9.53), which is the difference form of (9.50), on C_1 gives

$$z_{2,1} - 1.8 = \tfrac{1}{2}(0 + 0)(-0.4500 + 0.5000) + \tfrac{1}{2}(0.0278 - 0)(0.1620 - 0)$$

$$z_{2,1} = 1.8022$$

At $2, 1$, $x = -0.4500$, $y = 0.1620$, $p = 0$, $q = 0.0278$, and $z = 1.8022$. The value for z is reasonable because the initial condition $z_y(x, 0) = 0$ implies that z is constant to the first order near $y = 0$; our computation is accurate to the second order.

In order to compute the remaining second-level points, Eqs. (9.55) are used for successively increasing i to obtain values at $2, 2$; $2, 3$; $2, 4$; etc. Thus for $2, 6$,

$$C_1 : y_{2,6} - y_{1,6} = z_{1,6}^2(x_{2,6} - x_{1,6})$$

$$(p_{2,6} - p_{1,6})z_{1,6}^2 - z_{1,6}^4(q_{2,6} - q_{1,6}) + z_{1,6}(y_{2,6} - y_{1,6}) = 0$$

$$C_2 : y_{2,6} - y_{1,7} = -z_{1,7}^2(x_{2,6} - x_{1,7})$$

$$-(p_{2,6} - p_{1,7})z_{1,7}^2 - z_{1,7}^4(q_{2,6} - q_{1,7}) + z_{1,7}(y_{2,6} - y_{1,7}) = 0$$

Table 9.1a gives a set of values obtained by computing all possible points along the characteristics from the initial line $y = 0$, $-0.5 \le x \le 0.4$, for this example. Why does the number of computed points decrease by one at each level of advance? Using the straight-line approximation technique, the computer (an IBM 360/67) compiles a program and executes it to give Table 9.1a in less than *one* second.

EXAMPLE 9.5 *Predictor-Corrector Computation.* Consider again the initial data (9.54b) and (9.54c) and the characteristic equations (9.48') and (9.49'). Suppose that all values are known at the hth level and we seek to calculate the solution at points $h + 1, i$. In the predictor-corrector computation, we use the straight-line approximation to predict the values at $h + 1, i$. These predicted values at $h + 1, i$ and the known values at h, i are used, then, in a scheme that is equivalent to replacing the characteristics locally by parabolic arcs in lieu of straight lines, to obtain a better

TABLE 9.1a Straight-Line Approximation

Characteristics Solution of Non-linear Wave Equation

		I = 1	2	3	4	5	6	7	8	9	10
J =											
1	X =	−0.5000	−0.4000	−0.3000	−0.2000	−0.1000	0.0000	0.1000	0.2000	0.3000	0.4000
	Y =	0.0000	0.0000	0.0000	0.0000	0.0000	0.0000	0.0000	0.0000	0.0000	0.0000
	Z =	1.8000	1.8000	1.8000	1.8000	1.8000	1.8000	1.7706	1.6854	1.5527	1.3854
	P =	0.0000	0.0000	0.0000	0.0000	0.0000	0.0000	−0.5825	−1.1079	−1.5250	−1.7927
	Q =	0.0000	0.0000	0.0000	0.0000	0.0000	0.0000	0.0000	0.0000	0.0000	0.0000
2	X =	−0.4500	−0.3500	−0.2500	−0.1500	−0.0500	0.0492	0.1475	0.2459	0.3443	
	Y =	0.1620	0.1620	0.1620	0.1620	0.1620	0.1593	0.1490	0.1304	0.1069	
	Z =	1.8022	1.8022	1.8022	1.8022	1.8022	1.7877	1.7321	1.6264	1.4805	
	P =	−0.0000	−0.0000	−0.0000	−0.0000	0.0000	−0.2938	−0.8518	−1.3236	−1.6616	
	Q =	0.0278	0.0278	0.0278	0.0278	0.0278	−0.0634	−0.0591	−0.0487	−0.0281	
3	X =	−0.4000	−0.3000	−0.2000	−0.1000	−0.0012	0.0951	0.1903	0.2856		
	Y =	0.3244	0.3244	0.3244	0.3244	0.3204	0.3062	0.2774	0.2355		
	Z =	1.8090	1.8090	1.8090	1.8090	1.7945	1.7542	1.6802	1.5644		
	P =	−0.0000	−0.0000	−0.0000	−0.0000	−0.2931	−0.5679	−1.0746	−1.4656		
	Q =	0.0555	0.0555	0.0555	0.0555	−0.0354	−0.1234	−0.1086	−0.0779		
4	X =	−0.3500	−0.2500	−0.1500	−0.0516	0.0436	0.1358	0.2266			
	Y =	0.4880	0.4880	0.4880	0.4827	0.4648	0.4314	0.3799			
	Z =	1.8204	1.8204	1.8204	1.8057	1.7658	1.7078	1.6257			
	P =	−0.0000	−0.0000	−0.0000	−0.2931	−0.5652	−0.7968	−1.2227			
	Q =	0.0832	0.0832	0.0832	−0.0073	−0.0949	−0.1746	−0.1395			
5	X =	−0.3000	−0.2000	−0.1020	−0.0079	0.0826	0.1697				
	Y =	0.6537	0.6537	0.6470	0.6254	0.5865	0.5303				
	Z =	1.8364	1.8364	1.8216	1.7818	1.7248	1.6593				
	P =	−0.0000	−0.0000	−0.2939	−0.5640	−0.7913	−0.9505				
	Q =	0.1106	0.1106	0.0208	−0.0662	−0.1453	−0.2074				
6	X =	−0.2500	−0.1524	−0.0593	0.0296	0.1147					
	Y =	0.8223	0.8142	0.7887	0.7443	0.6818					
	Z =	1.8574	1.8422	1.8021	1.7456	1.6816					
	P =	−0.0000	−0.2954	−0.5642	−0.7880	−0.9419					
	Q =	0.1379	0.0490	−0.0372	−0.1157	−0.1774					
7	X =	−0.2028	−0.1107	−0.0233	0.0599						
	Y =	0.9852	0.9556	0.9055	0.8367						
	Z =	1.8678	1.8271	1.7706	1.7073						
	P =	−0.2977	−0.5659	−0.7868	−0.9360						
	Q =	0.0770	−0.0081	−0.0858	−0.1469						
8	X =	−0.1621	−0.0762	0.0054							
	Y =	1.1271	1.0711	0.9956							
	Z =	1.8571	1.8000	1.7368							
	P =	−0.5692	−0.7877	−0.9327							
	Q =	0.0209	−0.0557	−0.1161							
9	X =	−0.1289	−0.0489								
	Y =	1.2418	1.1594								
	Z =	1.8343	1.7704								
	P =	−0.7908	−0.9320								
	Q =	−0.0254	−0.0850								
10	X =	−0.1030									
	Y =	1.3289									
	Z =	1.8085									
	P =	−0.9340									
	Q =	−0.0539									

TABLE 9.1b   Predictor-Corrector Computation
(Corrector used twice)

Characteristics Solution of Nonlinear Wave Equation

I =	1	2	3	4	5	6	7	8	9	10
J =										
1 X =	−0.5000	−0.4000	−0.3000	−0.2000	−0.1000	0.0000	0.1000	0.2000	0.3000	0.4000
Y =	0.0000	0.0000	0.0000	0.0000	0.0000	0.0000	0.0000	0.0000	0.0000	0.0000
Z =	1.8000	1.8000	1.8000	1.8000	1.8000	1.8000	1.7706	1.6854	1.5527	1.3854
P =	0.0000	0.0000	0.0000	0.0000	0.0000	0.0000	−0.5825	−1.1079	−1.5250	−1.7927
Q =	0.0000	0.0000	0.0000	0.0000	0.0000	0.0000	0.0000	0.0000	0.0000	0.0000
2 X =	−0.4500	−0.3500	−0.2500	−0.1500	−0.0500	0.0496	0.1488	0.2480	0.3472	
Y =	0.1622	0.1622	0.1622	0.1622	0.1622	0.1596	0.1495	0.1314	0.1082	
Z =	1.8023	1.8023	1.8023	1.8023	1.8023	1.7877	1.7313	1.6240	1.4760	
P =	−0.0000	−0.0000	−0.0000	−0.0000	−0.0000	−0.2925	−0.8485	−1.3200	−1.6602	
Q =	0.0278	0.0278	0.0278	0.0278	0.0278	−0.0633	−0.0589	−0.0484	−0.0278	
3 X =	−0.4000	−0.3000	−0.2000	−0.1000	−0.0008	0.0968	0.1935	0.2904		
Y =	0.3252	0.3252	0.3252	0.3252	0.3213	0.3075	0.2797	0.2389		
Z =	1.8090	1.8090	1.8090	1.8090	1.7945	1.7537	1.6776	1.5582		
P =	−0.0000	−0.0000	−0.0000	−0.0000	−0.2922	−0.5633	−1.0677	−1.4603		
Q =	0.0555	0.0555	0.0555	0.0555	−0.0352	−0.1230	−0.1081	−0.0772		
4 X =	−0.3500	−0.2500	−0.1500	−0.0512	0.0452	0.1393	0.2324			
Y =	0.4899	0.4899	0.4899	0.4846	0.4671	0.4349	0.3854			
Z =	1.8204	1.8204	1.8204	1.8057	1.7654	1.7061	1.6202			
P =	−0.0000	−0.0000	−0.0000	−0.2926	−0.5613	−0.7884	−1.2139			
Q =	0.0830	0.0830	0.0830	−0.0071	−0.0943	−0.1736	−0.1382			
5 X =	−0.3000	−0.2000	−0.1016	−0.0063	0.0861	0.1757				
Y =	0.6571	0.6571	0.6504	0.6291	0.5914	0.5376				
Z =	1.8366	1.8366	1.8217	1.7813	1.7231	1.6552				
P =	−0.0000	−0.0000	−0.2937	−0.5608	−0.7839	−0.9401				
Q =	0.1103	0.1103	0.0210	−0.0654	−0.1441	−0.2057				
6 X =	−0.2500	−0.1520	−0.0578	0.0330	0.1205					
Y =	0.8277	0.8195	0.7943	0.7511	0.6910					
Z =	1.8577	1.8424	1.8018	1.7440	1.6777					
P =	−0.0000	−0.2956	−0.5617	−0.7815	−0.9326					
Q =	0.1374	0.0491	−0.0364	−0.1142	−0.1752					
7 X =	−0.2024	−0.1092	−0.0200	0.0656						
Y =	0.9930	0.9636	0.9146	0.8480						
Z =	1.8683	1.8271	1.7692	1.7036						
P =	−0.2983	−0.5641	−0.7812	−0.9277						
Q =	0.0770	−0.0074	−0.0841	−0.1445						
8 X =	−0.1606	−0.0729	0.0109							
Y =	1.1380	1.0829	1.0094							
Z =	1.8574	1.7990	1.7335							
P =	−0.5681	−0.7831	−0.9253							
Q =	0.0217	−0.0539	−0.1135							
9 X =	−0.1257	−0.0435								
Y =	1.2569	1.1762								
Z =	1.8336	1.7675								
P =	−0.7871	−0.9256								
Q =	−0.0237	−0.0823								
10 X =	−0.0978									
Y =	1.3494									
Z =	1.8062									
P =	−0.9286									
Q =	−0.0510									

or *corrected* set of values at $h + 1, i$. The corrector step can be repeated until the $h + 1, i$ values no longer change or until they remain unchanged within some fixed-error tolerance.

In order to approximate the characteristics by parabolic arcs, all derivatives and coefficients in (9.48′) and (9.49′) are replaced by the average value of the derivatives and coefficients at the endpoints of the interval considered. The order of error in the averaged difference equations will be $O[(\Delta x^2 + \Delta y^2)^{3/2}]$—that is, much smaller than before. A Taylor series expansion shows this point clearly. For an interval $x_{2,1} - x_{1,1} = \Delta x$, we have, from (A.1.2),

$$y_{2,1} = y_{1,1} + \left.\frac{dy}{dx}\right|_{x=x_{1,1}} (\Delta x) + \left.\frac{d^2 y}{dx^2}\right|_{x=x_{1,1}} (\Delta x)^2 + O[\Delta x^3]$$

and

$$y_{1,1} = y_{2,1} + \frac{dy}{dx}\Bigg|_{x=x_{2,1}}(-\Delta x) + \frac{d^2 y}{dx^2}\Bigg|_{x=x_{2,1}}(-\Delta x)^2 + O[-\Delta x^3]$$

Subtracting the second equation from the first gives [see (9.51)]

$$y_{2,1} - y_{1,1} = \frac{1}{2}\left(\frac{dy}{dx}\Bigg|_{x=x_{1,1}} + \frac{dy}{dx}\Bigg|_{x=x_{2,1}}\right)(x_{2,1} - x_{1,1}) + O[\Delta x^3]$$

because

$$\frac{d^2 y}{dx^2}\Bigg|_{x=x_{2,1}} = \frac{d^2 y}{dx^2}\Bigg|_{x=x_{1,1}} + \frac{d^3 y}{dx^3}\Bigg|_{x=x_{1,1}}\Delta x$$

so

$$\left(\frac{d^2 y}{dx^2}\Bigg|_{x=x_{2,1}} - \frac{d^2 y}{dx^2}\Bigg|_{x=x_{1,1}}\right) = O[\Delta x]$$

The computation equations at each level $h + 1$ (all values are known at h, i points) are

Predictor [generalized from (9.55)]:

$$C_1 : y_{h+1,i}^{(1)} - y_{h,i} = z_{h,i}^2 [x_{h+1,i}^{(1)} - x_{h,i}] \tag{9.56a}$$

$$[p_{h+1,i}^{(1)} - p_{h,i}]z_{h,i}^2 - z_{h,i}^4 [q_{h+1,i}^{(1)} - q_{h,i}] + z_{h,i}[y_{h+1,i}^{(1)} - y_{h,i}] = 0 \tag{9.56b}$$

$$C_2 : y_{h+1,i}^{(1)} - y_{h,i+1} = z_{h,i+1}^2 [x_{h+1,i}^{(1)} - x_{h,i+1}] \tag{9.56c}$$

$$- [p_{h+1,i}^{(1)} - p_{h,i+1}]z_{h,i+1}^2 - z_{h,i+1}^4 [q_{h+1,i}^{(1)} - q_{h,i+1}]$$

$$+ z_{h,i+1}[y_{h+1,i}^{(1)} - y_{h,i+1}] = 0 \tag{9.56d}$$

$$z_{h+1,i}^{(1)} - z_{h,i} = \tfrac{1}{2}[p_{h,i} + p_{h+1,i}^{(1)}][x_{h+1,i}^{(1)} - x_{h,i}]$$

$$+ \tfrac{1}{2}[q_{h,i} + q_{h+1,i}^{(1)}][y_{h+1,i}^{(1)} - y_{h,i}] \tag{9.56e}$$

where the superscript indicates an approximation to the $h + 1$st value, in this case the approximation being the first. The terms without superscript are known at their level from earlier calculation.

Corrector (derivatives and coefficients above are replaced by averages and $j \geq 1$):

$$C_1 : y_{h+1,i}^{(j+1)} - y_{h,i} = \tfrac{1}{2}\{z_{h,i}^2 + [z_{h+1,i}^{(j)}]^2\}^2 [x_{h+1,i}^{(j+1)} - x_{h,i}] \tag{9.57a}$$

$$\tfrac{1}{2}[p_{h+1,i}^{(j+1)} - p_{h,i}]\{z_{h,i}^2 + [z_{h+1,i}^{(j)}]^2\} - \tfrac{1}{2}\{z_{h,i}^4 + [z_{h+1,i}^{(j)}]^4\}[q_{h+1,i}^{(j+1)} - q_{h,i}]$$

$$+ \tfrac{1}{2}[z_{h,i} + z_{h+1,i}^{(j)}][y_{h+1,i}^{(j+1)} - y_{h,i}] = 0 \tag{9.57b}$$

$$C_2 : y_{h+1,i}^{(j+1)} - y_{h,i+1} = \tfrac{1}{2}\{z_{h,i+1}^2 + [z_{h+1,i}^{(j)}]^2\}[x_{h+1,i}^{(j+1)} - x_{h,i+1}] \tag{9.57c}$$

$$\tfrac{1}{2}[p_{h+1,i}^{(j+1)} - p_{h,i+1}]\{z_{h,i+1}^2 + [z_{h+1,i}^{(j)}]^2\} - \tfrac{1}{2}\{z_{h,i+1}^4 + [z_{h+1,i}^{(j)}]^4\}$$

$$\times [q_{h+1,i}^{(j+1)} - q_{h,i+1}] + \tfrac{1}{2}[z_{h,i+1} + z_{h+1,i}^{(j)}][y_{h+1,i}^{(j+1)} - y_{h,i+1}] = 0 \tag{9.57d}$$

$$z_{h+1,i}^{(j+1)} - z_{h,i} = \tfrac{1}{2}[p_{h,i} + p_{h+1,i}^{(j+1)}][x_{h+1,i}^{(j+1)} - x_{h,i}]$$

$$+ \tfrac{1}{2}[q_{h,i} + q_{h+1,i}^{(j+1)}][y_{h+1,i}^{(j+1)} - y_{h,i}] \tag{9.57e}$$

The computation with (9.56) and (9.57) proceeds as follows:

1. Values $x_{h,i}$, $y_{h,i}$, $z_{h,i}$, $p_{h,i}$, and $q_{h,i}$ are known.
2. Equations (9.56) are used to find $x^{(1)}_{h+1,i}$, $y^{(1)}_{h+1,i}$, $p^{(1)}_{h+1,i}$, $q^{(1)}_{h+1,i}$, and $z^{(1)}_{h+1,i}$.
3. Equations (9.57), with $j = 1$, are used to find $x^{(2)}_{h+1,i}$, etc., and the values from step 2 are used.
4. Equations (9.57), with $j = 2, 3$, etc., are used to find $x^{(3)}_{h+1,i}$, $x^{(4)}_{h+1,i}$, etc. as in step 3.

Table 9.1b gives a set of values obtained with the predictor-corrector method and $j = 1, 2, 3$ at each level—that is, one prediction and two corrections. A direct comparison between parts (a) and (b) of Table 9.1 is possible and indicates the effect of the corrector. Also, as an example, Table 9.2 illustrates the effect on the solution at (1, 10) of application of the corrector $j - 1$ times at each step. Clearly, accuracy to five significant figures in z is established with only two applications of the corrector in this case. The computer program, comparable to that used for Table 9.1a, requires less than *two* seconds to compile and execute to give Table 9.1b and hence the results $j = 3$ in Table 9.2.

TABLE 9.2

	$x_{1,10}$	$y_{1,10}$	$z_{1,10}$	$p_{1,10}$	$q_{1,10}$	*Remarks*
$j = 1$	-0.1030	1.3289	1.8085	-0.9340	-0.0539	predictor only
$j = 2$	-0.0976	1.3500	1.8061	-0.9283	-0.0508	corrector once
$j = 3$	-0.0978	1.3494	1.8062	-0.9286	-0.0510	corrector twice
$\vdots$	$\vdots$	$\vdots$	$\vdots$	$\vdots$	$\vdots$	
$j = 5$	-0.0978	1.3494	1.8062	-0.9286	-0.0510	corrector four times at each step

9.4   SUMMARY

This chapter was devoted to examination of characteristics and their role in the solutions to partial differential equations. Characteristics were shown to play a major role for first-order and hyperbolic, second-order equations. They play equivalent roles in higher-order equations, too [3, 4]. Two key properties of characteristics are that discontinuities can occur in the solution across characteristics and that information (e.g., disturbances) propagates along the characteristics.

In some cases, use of characteristics and characteristic coordinates led to a general solution of the partial differential equation; then solutions in closed form to certain initial-value problems were obtained. Perhaps more important, however, was our development of the numerical method of characteristics for second-order equations. By this method, solutions to quite complex problems can be obtained by a straightforward finite-difference scheme employing the characteristic equations. A numerical method of characteristics, although appropriate for first-order equations, was not covered here because it involves only the integration of ordinary differential equations along the base characteristics by standard techniques (see the Problems).

Finally, the concepts and techniques of this chapter apply equally well to systems of equations. For example, the equations governing the motion of long water waves over a horizontal bottom are [2]

$$u_t + uu_x = -gh_x$$
$$h_t + uh_x = -hu_x$$

where h is the distance to the water surface from the bottom and u is the fluid velocity at any point (x, t). There are two unknowns and two equations now; also, we have along a given curve

$$\frac{dh}{dl} = h_t\frac{dt}{dl} + h_x\frac{dx}{dl}$$

$$\frac{du}{dl} = u_t\frac{dt}{dl} + u_x\frac{dx}{dl}$$

But the four equations above constitute a set of four simultaneous equations for the four unknowns u_t, u_x, h_t, and h_x if $x(l)$, $t(l)$, $h(l)$, and $u(l)$ are given on the curve. The discussion of Sec. 9.3.1 can be followed rigorously to generate results for the two-equation system. For example, requiring the determinant of the coefficients of the unknowns to be zero leads to the equations of the characteristics

$$\left(u - \frac{dx}{dt}\right)^2 - gh = 0$$

so the characteristics have the slopes

$$\frac{dx}{dt} = u \pm \sqrt{gh}$$

We deduce directly from this result that the speed of a small wave disturbance on the water surface is $u \pm \sqrt{gh}$. Thus waves moving against the fluid motion travel more slowly than those moving with the fluid motion. Indeed, if the waves are introduced on a stream with velocity $u = \sqrt{gh}$, then no waves can travel upstream!

REFERENCES

1. W. Kaplan, *Advanced Calculus*. Reading, Mass.: Addison-Wesley, 1952.

2. M. B. Abbott, *An Introduction to the Method of Characteristics*. New York: American Elsevier, 1966.

3. P. R. Garabedian, *Partial Differential Equations*. New York: John Wiley & Sons, 1964.

4. R. Courant and D. Hilbert, *Methods of Mathematical Physics*, Vol. II. Partial Differential Equations. New York: Interscience (a division of John Wiley & Sons), 1962.

5. A. G. Webster, *Partial Differential Equations of Mathematical Physics*, 2nd ed., S. J. Plimpton (Ed.). New York: Dover, 1955.

6. D. M. Di Toro, "Stream Equations and Method of Characteristics," New York: *Journal of the Sanitary Engineering Division*, Amer. Soc. Civil Engineers, Proceedings Vol. 95, No. SA4, August 1969, pp. 699–703.

7. D. H. Peregrine, "Calculations of the Development of an Undular Bore," London: *Journal of Fluid Mechanics*, Vol. 25, Part 2, June 1966, pp. 321–330.

8. M. Shiffer, "Analytical Theory of Subsonic and Supersonic Flows," *Handbuch Der Physik*, Band IX, Berlin: Spring-Verlag, 1960.

9. F. E. Hohn, *Elementary Matrix Algebra*. New York: Macmillan, 1958.

10. W. F. Ames, *Nonlinear Partial Differential Equations in Engineering*. New York: Academic Press, 1965.

11. *Handbook of Mathematical Functions*, M. Abramowitz and I. A. Stegun (Eds.). New York: Dover, 1965 (also, Washington, D.C.: National Bureau of Standards, 1964).

12. J. J. Stoker, *Water Waves*. New York: Interscience (a division of John Wiley & Sons), 1957.

PROBLEMS

The notation $r = z_{xx}$, $s = z_{yy}$, $t = z_{yy}$, $p = z_x$, $q = z_y$ is used throughout; when t appears as a subscript, time is implied as an independent variable.

9.1　Find the characteristics for and the general solution to the following:

(a) $p - q = 1$

(b) $p - xq = 0$

(c) $xp + zq = 1$; sketch the base characteristics issuing from the line $x = 1$.

(d) $xp + yq = z$

(e) $yp - xq = 0$

9.2　If $\alpha(x, y, z) = c_1$ and $\beta(x, y, z) = c_2$ are two independent solutions of (9.6), show that $F(\alpha, \beta) = 0$ is the general solution to (9.3), provided only that the arbitrary function F is sufficiently differentiable [10].

9.3　If $p + z^2q = 0$, while $z(x, 0) = \cos x$ on $-\pi < x < \pi$, find $z(x, y)$, plot the base characteristics, and discuss your results.

9.4　Find $z(x, y)$ for $p + zq = 0$ with $z(0, y) = \operatorname{sech} y$ on $-\infty < y < \infty$.

9.5　Given $p + xq = 0$ with $z(x, 0) = f(x)$, find the interval of the initial, base curve $y = 0$ that determines the solution at $y = 5$ for $-\pi < x < 0$.

9.6　For Example 9.3, Sec. 9.2, let $\varepsilon = 0.1$ and draw a properly scaled graph of the base characteristic plane (x, t), showing clearly the zone of nonparallel characteristics and the point at which the solution becomes invalid. What is z there?

9.7　Work Prob. 9.6 with $\varepsilon = -0.1$. In what significant way are the results different from those when $\varepsilon > 0$?

9.8　Find $z(x, y)$ for $p + q = z$ with $z = e^y$ on $x = y$. Discuss your results.

9.9　Find $z(x, y)$ for $xp + yq = 1$ with $z = \ln y$ on $x = y$. Discuss your results.

9.10　The pollution convection problem for concentration $C(x, t)$ is, in some cases [6],

$$C_t + U(x, t)C_x = S(C, x, t), \qquad 0 < x, \quad 0 < t$$

$$C(x, 0) = C_i(x), \qquad 0 < x$$

$$C(0, t) = C_b(t), \qquad 0 < t$$

The problem region is a quadrant of the (x, t) plane bounded by the curve bearing the data.

(a) Find the characteristic equations. Observe that the characteristic equations, plus the data, represent *along each characteristic* a well-posed initial-value problem for an ordinary differential equation.

(b) Use a standard numerical technique for ordinary differential equations (see, e.g., [11]) to find representative results near $x = 0$ if $U(x, t) = (1 + e^{-x})(1 - e^{-t})$, $S(C, x, t) = Cxe^{-t}$, $C_i(x) = 0$, and $C_b(t) = 1 - e^{-t}$.

9.11   Are the conditions $z(x, 0) = f(x)$ and $z_y(x, 0) = g(x)$ on the line $y = 0$, with f and g arbitrary, improper for any of the following equations (explain your answers)?

(a) $r - (1 + x^2 + y^2)t = 0$

(b) $r - 2p - t = 0$

(c) $r = z - t$

(d) $s - 3p + 3q - z = 0$

9.12   Find and sketch the characteristics for the following, and state the condition that must be satisfied along characteristics in each case for a solution to be possible:

(a) $(1 - x^2)r + 2xys + (1 - y^2)t = 0$ with $x^2 + y^2 > 1$—that is, outside the unit circle.

(b) $t - g(ph)_x = 0$, where g is a constant and $h(x) > 0$, but decreases monotonically with increasing x.

(c) $x^2 r + 2xys + (y^2 - 1)t = 0$.

(d) $r - 4x^2 t = 0$ with characteristics from the line $x = 1$.

(e) $r + yt$ for $y < 0$.

(f) $r + xt$ for $x < 0$.

9.13   Find $z(1\frac{1}{2}, 3)$ for the following string model by use of characteristics and images alone:

$$z_{tt} - z_{yy} = 0, \qquad 0 < y, \quad 0 < t$$
$$z(0, t) = 0, \qquad 0 < t$$

$$z(y, 0) = \sin \frac{\pi}{2} y, \qquad 0 < y$$

$$z_t(y, 0) = \sin \frac{\pi}{2} y, \qquad 0 < y$$

Confirm your answer by using the general solution directly.

9.14   Find and plot $z(0, t)$ for the following model by use of the general solution to the wave equation and images:

$$z_{tt} - z_{yy} = 0, \qquad 0 < y, \quad 0 < t$$
$$z_y(0, t) = 0, \qquad 0 < t$$
$$z(y, 0) = 0, \qquad 0 < y$$

$$z_t(y, 0) = \begin{cases} \sin \pi y, & 0 < y < 1 \\ 0, & 1 \le y \end{cases}$$

9.15   The model equation for a string is

$$z_{tt} - 4z_{yy} = 0, \qquad -\infty < y < \infty, \quad 0 < t$$

(a) Find $z(x, 2)$ and $z(x, 4)$ graphically by the method of characteristics in $-8 \leq y \leq 8$ if

$$z(y, 0) = \begin{cases} 0, & |y| > 8 \\ \frac{1}{2}(y + 8), & -8 \leq y \leq -6 \\ \frac{1}{2}(4 - y), & -6 < y \leq -4 \\ 0, & -4 < y < 2 \\ \frac{1}{2}(y - 2), & 2 \leq y \leq 4 \\ 1, & 4 < y < 6 \\ \frac{1}{2}(8 - y), & 6 \leq y \leq 8 \end{cases}$$

$$z_t(y, 0) = 0, \qquad -\infty < y < \infty$$

(b) Find $z(0, 2)$ if $z(y, 0)$ is the same as in (a) but now

$$z_t(y, 0) = \begin{cases} 0, & y < -6 \\ 1, & -6 \leq y \leq 3 \\ 0, & 3 < y \end{cases}$$

For Probs. 9.16 through 9.21 : The flow of current i and the voltage v in a telegraph cable or transmission line are modeled by a pair of simultaneous first-order partial differential equations

$$-i_x = Gv + Cv_t \qquad (\Delta i = \text{losses due to } G \text{ and } C)$$
$$-v_x = Ri + Li_t \qquad (\Delta v = \text{resistive} + \text{inductive drop})$$

where per unit of the length of the line R = the resistance, L = the inductance, C = the capacitance between the line and ground, and G = the conductance between the line and ground.

9.16 Eliminate first i and then v from the first-order system to demonstrate that both satisfy the second-order telegraph equations

$$v_{xx} = LCv_{tt} + (RC + GL)v_t + RGv$$
$$i_{xx} = LCi_{tt} + (RC + GL)i_t + RGi$$

9.17 Consider the equation for v in Prob. 9.16. Let $v = Ve^{-(RC+GL)t/2}$ to obtain a simpler equation. Then find a general solution for V for the special case $RC = GL$.

9.18 For the case $RC = GL$ and given

$$v(x, 0) = v_0 \sin x, \qquad -\infty < x < \infty$$
$$i(x, 0) = i_0 \sin x, \qquad -\infty < x < \infty$$

state the complete mathematical model for voltage and current flow in a telegraph cable of great length. First, do it in terms of the first-order system; then, do it in terms of the second-order equations. [*Hint:* For the second-order equations, you may need to employ the first-order system to get the necessary conditions.]

9.19 Find v and i for all x and t when $RC = GL$ through the use of results from Probs. 9.17 and 9.18. Discuss what happens to the magnitude of a single forward traveling wave.

9.20 Consider a transmission line with $R = 0.1$ ohms/ft, $L = 10^{-2}$ henrys/ft, $C = 10^{-5}$ farads/ft, and $G = 10^{-4}$ ohms/ft. In general, the solution to a transmission-line problem is complicated. However, when $RC = GL$, as in this case, a special and significant type of solution is possible, one called the *distortionless solution.* For the following model, where $\alpha = LC$, $\beta = RC + GL$, and $\delta = RG$:

$$v_{xx} = \alpha v_{tt} + \beta v_t + \delta v, \qquad 0 < x < \infty, \quad 0 < t$$

$$v_x(0, t) = 0$$

$$v(x, 0) = \begin{cases} \cos \pi x, & 0 < x < \frac{1}{2} \\ 0, & x \geq \frac{1}{2} \end{cases}$$

$$v_t(x, 0) = \begin{cases} -\sqrt{\delta/\alpha} \cos \pi x, & 0 < x < \frac{1}{2} \\ 0, & x \geq \frac{1}{2} \end{cases}$$

(a) Use an image technique to formulate an equivalent model for the region $-\infty < x < \infty$.

(b) Let $v(x, t) = V(x, t) \exp[-\sqrt{\delta/\alpha t}]$, and find a simple model for $V(x, t)$.

(c) Use the general solution to the wave equation to describe $V(x, t)$ and thus find $v(x, t)$.

(d) Plot $v(x, t)$ on $0 \leq x$ for $t = 0$ and two other values of t. Do characteristics help here? Does the solution propagate along characteristics? What are the characteristics for the original $v(x, t)$ and derived $V(x, t)$ equations? What happens to the original signal as t increases (any distortion)?

9.21 A distortionless telegraph cable is of length l. The governing equation is

$$v_{xx} = LCv_{tt} + (RC + GL)v_t + RGv, \qquad 0 < x < l, \quad 0 < t$$

where (in proper units) $LC = 10^{-7} \sec^2/\mathrm{ft}^2$, $RC = GL = 10^{-6} \sec/\mathrm{ft}^2$, $RG = 10^{-5} \mathrm{ft}^{-2}$, and $v = $ volts. If the far end $(x = l)$ is insulated, $v_x(l, t) = 0$. A pulse sent down the line from $x = 0$ returns in 10^{-3} sec. How long is the line?

9.22 Using the straight-line approximation, solve the following problem numerically with $\Delta = 0.1$ in $0 < y < 1$:

$$z_{tt} - 4z_{yy} = 0, \qquad -\infty < y < \infty$$

$$z(y, 0) = e^{-y^2/10}, \qquad -\infty < y < \infty$$

$$z_t(y, 0) = ye^{-y^2/10}, \qquad -\infty < y < \infty$$

Why is the predictor-corrector method not needed here? Compare your numerical solution with the analytical solution.

9.23 Stoker [12] shows that the equation

$$\eta_{tt} - g[\eta_x h]_x = 0$$

describes the free-surface elevation η of a small-amplitude (see Sec. 2.2), long water wave moving over shallow water of variable depth $h(x)$. Consider the following problem:

$$\eta_{tt} - gh\eta_{xx} = gh_x\eta_x, \qquad -\infty < x < \infty, \quad 0 < t$$

$$\eta(x, 0) = \begin{cases} 0.1(1 + \cos \pi x), & |x| \leq 1 \\ 0, & |x| > 1 \end{cases}$$

$$\eta_t(x, 0) = \begin{cases} 0.31416g^{1/2} \sin \pi x, & |x| \leq 1 \\ 0, & |x| > 1 \end{cases}$$

with

$$h(x) = \begin{cases} 1, & x \leq 0 \\ 1 - 0.1x, & 0 < x < 5 \\ 0.5, & 5 \leq x \end{cases}$$

and $g = 32.2$ if all lengths are in feet. Use the straight-line approximation to solve numerically for $\eta(x, t)$ with $\Delta x = 0.2$ in the region $0 < x < 2$ at the second and third levels, at least. Discuss your results.

9.24 Calculate and plot representative base characteristics for the model of Prob. 9.23.

9.25 Use the straight-line approximation to obtain a numerical solution by characteristics at the second and third levels in the region $0 < y < 1$ with $\Delta y = 0.2$ for the model

$$z_{xx} - z^2 z_{yy} = z, \qquad -\infty < y < \infty, \quad 1 < x$$

$$z(1, y) = \operatorname{sech}^2 y, \qquad -\infty < y < \infty$$

$$z_y(1, y) = e^{-y^2}, \qquad -\infty < y < \infty$$

9.26 Apply the predictor-corrector technique to Prob. 9.25. A computer would be a good tool here!

9.27 Apply the predictor-corrector technique to Prob. 9.23. A computer should be used!

9.28 Use the straight-line approximation to calculate z at the second, third, and fourth levels with $\Delta y = 0.1$ in the model

$$z_{tt} - z_{yy} = 0, \qquad 0 < y < 1, \quad 0 < t$$

$$z(0, t) = 0, \qquad 0 < t$$

$$z(1, t) = 0, \qquad 0 < t$$

$$z(y, 0) = \sin \pi y, \qquad 0 < y < 1$$

$$z_t(y, 0) = \sin 2\pi y, \qquad 0 < y < 1$$

of an initial-boundary-value problem. Study the action of characteristics at the boundaries carefully; only one characteristic is needed at an advanced point on a boundary because of the boundary condition.

9.29 Solve Prob. 9.28 with the boundary conditions

$$z_y(0, t) = 0, \qquad 0 < t$$

$$z_y(1, t) = 0, \qquad 0 < t$$

replacing those in Prob. 9.28.

9.30 Find the order of the *truncation error*, the error resulting from replacement of differentials by differences, in (9.52) and (9.53).

9.31 Write a computer program to solve Example 9.4, Sec. 9.3.3, for variable Δx. Verify the results of Table 9.1a.

9.32 Write a computer program to solve Example 9.5, Sec. 9.3.3, for variable Δx. Verify the results of Table 9.1b.

CHAPTER 10

NUMERICAL FINITE
DIFFERENCE METHODS

10.1   INTRODUCTION

The analysis of many physical systems leads to mathematical models that are so complex as to preclude the finding of closed-form solutions of any type. Yet in spite of an inability to generate solutions to these models, one can prove or infer the mathematical adequacy—that is, demonstrate the existence, uniqueness, and continuity with respect to the data of the solution—of many models that involve general domains, inhomogeneities, nonlinearities, and so on (see, e.g., Chap. 6 or Ames [1]). In this chapter we study the *method of finite differences* that is universally applicable to linear and nonlinear systems regardless of the domains or inhomogeneities involved. In particular, we shall derive and solve the *numerical models* obtained by this method.

In finite-difference approximations, the derivatives of functions are replaced by their corresponding difference quotients. Referring to the derivative definition in Chap. 1, we can write the following difference approximations for a two-dimensional case, in which we let $\Delta x = h > 0$ and $\Delta y = k > 0$ be small, finite increments:

$$u_x(x, y) \approx \frac{u(x + h, y) - u(x, y)}{h}$$

$$u_x(x, y) \approx \frac{u(x, y) - u(x - h, y)}{h}$$

$$u_x(x, y) \approx \frac{u(x + h, y) - u(x - h, y)}{2h}$$

$$u_y(x, y) \approx \frac{u(x, y + k) - u(x, y - k)}{2k} \tag{10.1}$$

$$u_{xx}(x, y) \approx \frac{u_x(x + h/2, y) - u_x(x - h/2, y)}{h}$$

$$\approx \frac{u(x + h, y) - 2u(x, y) + u(x - h, y)}{h^2}$$

In (10.1) the continuously defined function $u(x, y)$ and its derivatives are represented by values of u defined at particular, discrete points. These are part of a grid of mesh points, say $x = i \Delta x = ih$ and $y = j \Delta y = jk$, that cover the original domain of u. The first two equations of (10.1) give *forward-* and *backward*-difference approximations, respectively. The remaining equations give *central* difference approximations. In Sec. 10.2 the Taylor's series expansion is used to derive the preceding approximations and establish their accuracy.

A *numerical model* is composed of the finite-difference analogs, the *difference equations*, of the differential equation and auxiliary conditions of a mathematical model. While the mathematical model represents the physical system in terms of a dependent variable defined continuously in the domain of the independent variables, the numerical model represents the mathematical model in terms of a dependent variable defined only pointwise on a grid of discrete mesh points that cover the original domain of the mathematical model. The *numerical solution* is a tabulation of numbers, each of which is identified with a point in the grid. This solution is no longer representable as a continuous function of the independent variables, but it must satisfy the difference equations at every point in the grid.

The finite-difference method is applicable to a wide range of complicated systems; yet simple models can be utilized as a basis for the development of the essential techniques and illustration of the major principles involved (see, e.g., [2]). A wealth of advanced information is to be found in the books by Ames [1], Forsythe and Wasow [3], Fox [4], and Richtmyer and Morton [5], as well as in the scientific and engineering journals—the *Journal of Computational Physics*, for example.

The formulation of a well-posed *mathematical model* based on a physical system requires (a) a concise description of the system, (b) reduction of the system to a mathematical model, and (c) demonstration of the adequacy of the model (see Sec. 1.3 and Chap. 6). Formulation of a well-posed *numerical model* requires (a) derivation of a set of difference equations based on a mathematical model and (b) demonstration of the adequacy of the difference equations—namely, the *consistency*, *convergence*, and *stability* of the numerical model. A model that is consistent, converges, and is stable possesses a *stable* or useful *computational scheme*.

10.2   DIFFERENCE SCHEMES

To begin, let us cover the domain of a pair of independent variables (x, y) by a rectangular *grid* or *lattice* of *mesh points* (see Fig. 10.1). The spacing or distance between *node points* is h in the x direction and k in the y direction; the node points are located at the discrete points $x = ih$, $y = jk$, where i and j are integers. For a general region R with boundary C, the points in R are *internal mesh points*, points on C are *boundary points*, and the points outside $\bar{R} = R + C$ are *external mesh points*. Boundary points are either grid nodes or the intersections of C and the lines connecting the nodes—for example, the * points in Fig. 10.1.

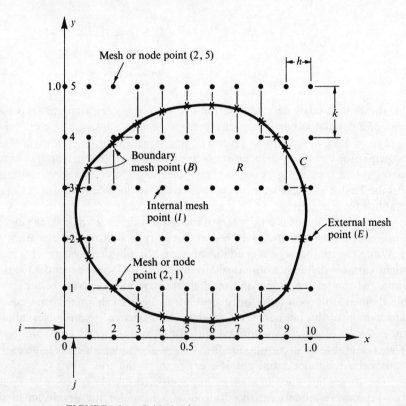

FIGURE 10.1   Grid of mesh or node points on typical region.

Suppose that the continuous function $u(x, y)$ is to be replaced by the *discrete function* $u(ih, jk) = u_{ij}$ that is defined only at the node or boundary points. The Taylor's series (Appendix 1 or [6]) written about (x, y) gives u at $(x + h, y + k)$ in the form

$$
\begin{aligned}
u(x + h, y + k) = \; & u(x, y) + u_x(x, y)h + u_y(x, y)k \\
& + \tfrac{1}{2}\{u_{xx}(x, y)h^2 + 2u_{xy}(x, y)hk + u_{yy}(x, y)k^2\} \\
& + \tfrac{1}{6}\{u_{xxx}(x, y)h^3 + 3[u_{xxy}(x, y)h^2k + u_{xyy}(x, y)hk^2] + u_{yyy}(x, y)k^3\} \\
& + \tfrac{1}{24}\{u_{xxxx}(x, y)h^4 + 4[u_{xxxy}(x, y)h^3k + u_{xyyy}(x, y)hk^3]
\end{aligned}
$$

$$+ 6u_{xxyy}(x, y)h^2k^2 + u_{yyyy}(x, y)k^4\}$$

$$+ \tfrac{1}{120}\{u_{xxxxx}(x, y)h^5 + 5[u_{xxxxy}(x, y)h^4k + u_{xyyyy}(x, y)hk^4]$$

$$+ 10[u_{xxxyy}(x, y)h^3k^2 + u_{xxyyy}(x, y)h^2k^3] + u_{yyyyy}(x, y)k^5\}$$

$$+ O(h^6 + k^6) \tag{10.2}$$

when u and its first five derivatives are assumed to be continuous and the sixth derivatives to be bounded. The last term in (10.2) represents the error made in terminating the series.

Now let us calculate u_{xij}. With $k = 0$ in the Taylor's series (10.2), we have

$$u_{i+1j} = u_{ij} + u_{xij}h + O(h^2) \tag{10.3}$$

if higher-order terms are neglected and $u(x, y)$ is replaced by u_{ij}. Rearrangement of (10.3) yields

$$u_{xij} = \frac{\partial u}{\partial x}(x, y) = \frac{u_{i+1j} - u_{ij}}{h} + O(h) \tag{10.4}$$

The error in this forward-difference approximation of the derivative is of the order of the mesh size h and is the *truncation error* made in replacing differential quantities by their difference equivalents.

The truncation error in (10.4) is $O(h)$; can we do better? Let $k = 0$ in (10.2) and write for $x + h$

$$u_{i+1j} = u_{ij} + u_{xij}h + \tfrac{1}{2}u_{xxij}h^2 + \tfrac{1}{6}u_{xxxij}h^3 + O(h^4) \tag{10.5}$$

and for $x - h$

$$u_{i-1j} = u_{ij} + u_{xij}(-h) + \tfrac{1}{2}u_{xxij}(-h)^2 + \tfrac{1}{6}u_{xxxij}(-h)^3 + O(h^4) \tag{10.6}$$

Now subtract (10.6) from (10.5) to achieve

$$u_{i+1j} - u_{i-1j} = 2hu_{xij} + \tfrac{1}{3}u_{xxxij}h^3 + O(h^4)$$

Because the third derivative of u is at least bounded,

$$u_{xij} = \frac{u_{i+1j} - u_{i-1j}}{2h} + O(h^2) \tag{10.7}$$

This central difference expression has a truncation error that is an order of magnitude smaller than that in (10.4).

Adding (10.5) to (10.6) yields

$$u_{i+1j} + u_{i-1j} = 2u_{ij} + u_{xxij}h^2 + O(h^4)$$

or

$$u_{xxij} = \frac{u_{i+1j} - 2u_{ij} + u_{i-1j}}{2h^2} + O(h^2) \tag{10.8}$$

which is a central difference and has a truncation error equal to that in (10.7). In similar fashion (see the Problems), one finds, for example,

$$u_{yyij} = \frac{u_{ij+1} - 2u_{ij} + u_{ij-1}}{k^2} + O(k^2) \tag{10.9}$$

and

$$u_{xyij} = \frac{u_{i+1j+1} - u_{i+1j-1} - u_{i-1j+1} + u_{i-1j-1}}{4hk} + O(h^2 + k^2) \qquad (10.10)$$

The difference operators corresponding to three common partial differential equations (see Table 2.1) are obtained from differences such as (10.4) and (10.7) to (10.10):

$$[u_{xx} + u_{yy}]_{ij} = \frac{u_{i+1j} - 2u_{ij} + u_{i-1j}}{h^2} + \frac{u_{ij+1} - 2u_{ij} + u_{ij-1}}{k^2}$$

$$+ O(h^2 + k^2) = E_D(u_{ij}) + O(h^2 + k^2) \quad (10.11)$$

$$[u_{xx} - u_{yy}]_{ij} = \frac{u_{i+1j} - 2u_{ij} + u_{i-1j}}{h^2} - \frac{u_{ij+1} - 2u_{ij} + u_{ij-1}}{k^2}$$

$$+ O(h^2 + k^2) = H_D(u_{ij}) + O(h^2 + k^2) \quad (10.12)$$

$$[u_{xx} - u_{y}]_{ij} = \frac{u_{i+1j} - 2u_{ij} + u_{i-1j}}{h^2} - \frac{u_{ij+1} - u_{ij}}{k}$$

$$+ O(h^2 + k) = P_D(u_{ij}) + O(h^2 + k) \quad (10.13)$$

Here E_D, H_D, and P_D are elliptic, hyperbolic, and parabolic *difference operators*. Thus $H_D(u_{ij}) = 0$ is a hyperbolic *difference equation*, which approximates the corresponding differential equation closely when h and k are small. The approximation in P_D is $O(h^2 + k)$ because a forward rather than a central difference approximation was used; the truncation error is apparently larger in (10.13) than in (10.11) or (10.12). However, the use of the central difference in this parabolic difference operator leads to a computational formula that is always *unstable*; that is, the difference equation admits exponentially growing solutions that rapidly swamp the true solution (see Sec. 10.3).

The boundary condition of the first kind, the Dirichlet condition, involves no approximation when it is converted to difference form. The condition

$$u(0, y) = f(y), \qquad y \geq 0$$

becomes

$$u_{0j} = f_j, \qquad j \geq 0 \qquad (10.14)$$

No truncation error is introduced because the discrete and continuous functions coincide at the node points.

Consider the boundary condition of the second kind, the Neumann condition,

$$u_x(0, t) = f(t), \qquad t > 0 \qquad (10.15)$$

for heat flux through the end of a rod, lying in $0 \leq x \leq l$. The condition is applied at the points $(0, j)$, $j > 0$. Employing a central difference (10.7) to achieve a truncation error of $O(h^2)$, we find for (10.15)

$$\left. \frac{u_{i+1j} - u_{i-1j}}{2h} \right|_{0,j} + O(h^2) = f_j$$

or

$$u_{1j} - u_{-1j} = 2hf_j \qquad (10.16)$$

The point $(-1, j)$ is a *fictitious* point that does not lie within the problem domain $0 \le x \le l$. To find u_{0j}, it is necessary to employ the partial difference equation because the central difference representation skips the true boundary points $(0, j)$. The first example in Sec. 10.2.1 illustrates this type of computation.

Boundary conditions of the third kind require only a natural combination of the foregoing results.

The initial conditions for parabolic equations present no problem because only the function value is prescribed, namely,

$$u(x, 0) = U(x), \qquad 0 \le x \le l$$

becomes

$$u_{i0} = U(ih), \qquad i = 0, 1, 2, \ldots, \frac{l}{h} \qquad (10.17)$$

For hyperbolic equations, typically, the function and its first derivative, say z_t, are prescribed, so we have

$$z(y, 0) = Z_0(y),$$
$$z_t(y, 0) = V_0(y), \qquad 0 \le y \le l$$

with

$$z_{tt} - z_{yy} = 0, \qquad 0 < y < l, \quad 0 < t \qquad (10.18)$$

for example. Only the second initial condition is of concern. If a forward difference is used,

$$\frac{z_{i1} - z_{i0}}{k} = V_0(ih) + O(k) \qquad (10.19)$$

but the truncation error is $O(k)$. The computation formula is

$$z_{i1} = z_{i0} + kV_0(ih) + O(k^2) \qquad (10.20)$$

If a central difference is used,

$$\frac{z_{i1} - z_{i-1}}{2k} = V_0(ih) + O(k^2) \qquad (10.21)$$

The truncation error is $O(k^2)$, but in order to remove the fictitious point $(i, -1)$, we must employ the hyperbolic difference equation (10.12) [the difference form of (10.18)] at $(i, 0)$. Writing the difference form of z_{yy} symbolically as $d_{ij}(z_{yy})$, we have

$$\frac{z_{i1} - 2z_{i0} + z_{i-1}}{k^2} = d_{i0}(z_{yy}) + O(k^2 + h^2)$$

so

$$-\frac{z_{i-1}}{2k} = -\frac{2z_{i0}}{2k} + \frac{z_{i1}}{2k} - \frac{k}{2}d_{i0}(z_{yy}) - \frac{k}{2}O(k^2 + h^2)$$

Using this result in (10.21) gives [compare to (10.19)]

$$\frac{z_{i1} - z_{i0}}{k} = V_0(ih) + \frac{k}{2}d_{i0}(z_{yy}) + O(kh^2 + k^2) \tag{10.22}$$

or

$$z_{i1} = z_{i0} + k\left\{V_0(ih) + \frac{k}{2}d_{i0}(z_{yy})\right\} + O(k^3 + k^2h^2) \tag{10.23}$$

If $z_{yy}(y, 0)$ is known analytically from the initial condition $z(y, 0) = Z_0(y)$, then the precise values of $z_{yy}(y, 0)$ can be used in lieu of $d_{i0}(z_{yy}) + O(h^2)$ in (10.23).

10.2.1   A Computational Star—Marching

Consider the physical system of heat conduction in an insulated rod, a system whose behavior is well known to us. Let the right end of the rod be insulated, the left be at a prescribed temperature, and let there be no heat sources present. A mathematical model for $u(x, t)$ is

$$\begin{aligned}
u_t &= u_{xx}, & 0 < x < 1, \quad 0 < t \\
u(0, t) &= f(t), & 0 < t \\
u_x(1, t) &= 0, & 0 < t \\
u(x, 0) &= U_0(x), & 0 \le x \le 1
\end{aligned} \tag{10.24}$$

In order to construct the numerical model, we first establish the grid of mesh points. Let $\Delta x = h$ and $\Delta t = k$; the grid is then

$$G : \begin{cases} 1 \le i \le N \\ 1 \le j \end{cases}$$

where $N = 1 + h^{-1}$ must be an integer, and because many computer compilers do not permit zero subscripts, we use indices greater than zero. Next, we establish the difference expressions corresponding to (10.24). From (10.13), (10.14), (10.16), and (10.17),

$$\frac{u_{ij+1} - u_{ij}}{k} = \frac{u_{i+1j} - 2u_{ij} + u_{i-1j}}{h^2} \qquad \text{in } G$$

$$u_{1j} = f[(j - 1)k], \qquad j \ge 2$$

$$\frac{u_{N+1j} - u_{N-1j}}{2h} = 0, \qquad j \ge 2 \tag{10.25}$$

$$u_{i1} = U_0[(i - 1)h], \qquad 1 \le i \le N$$

From the partial difference equation in (10.25), we obtain the basic computational formula

$$u_{ij+1} = \frac{k}{h^2}(u_{i+1j} + u_{i-1j}) + \left(1 - \frac{2k}{h^2}\right)u_{ij} \tag{10.26}$$

The pattern of mesh points used in this formula is called a *computational star* (Fig. 10.2a) (alternatively, a molecule, template, or stencil [1, 2, 3]). Three points at time j are required to compute the centered value at time $j + 1$. At $i = 2$, the pattern is the same except that the values of u_{1j} are prescribed, while for $j > 2$, the u_{2j} and u_{3j} must be calculated from prior time levels (Fig. 10.2b).

At $i = N$ we combine (10.26) and the third of equations (10.25) to remove the fictitious point $(N + 1, j)$. The result is, with (10.26) applied at N,

$$u_{Nj+1} = \left(1 - \frac{2k}{h^2}\right)u_{Nj} + \frac{2k}{h^2}u_{N-1j} \tag{10.27}$$

The resulting star is shown in Fig. 10.2c.

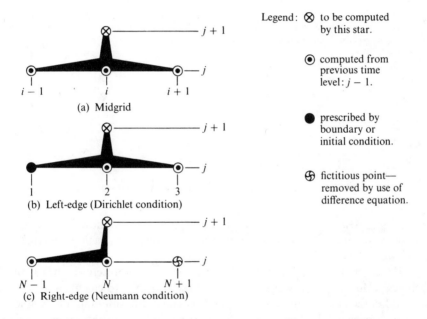

Legend: ⊗ to be computed by this star.

◉ computed from previous time level: $j - 1$.

● prescribed by boundary or initial condition.

⊕ fictitious point— removed by use of difference equation.

(a) Midgrid

(b) Left-edge (Dirichlet condition)

(c) Right-edge (Neumann condition)

FIGURE 10.2   Computational stars for explicit parabolic computation.

The computational formulas, the mesh and the computing sequence are illustrated in Fig. 10.3. All values of u_{i1} are known from the initial condition; using the stars of Fig. 10.2 yields the values u_{i2}, $2 \leq i \leq N$, while u_{12} is prescribed. With u_{i2} known, u_{i3} can be calculated, and so forth. With this numerical model, the computation *marches* forward in time with each new value in time given *explicitly* in terms of known values at the immediately preceding time. From a given, restricted base region, say $2 \leq i \leq 10$, only a pyramid of new values can be constructed in the time-space domain (see Fig. 10.3).

For $k \leq \frac{1}{2}h^2$, the marching formula (10.26) computes the new value of u_{ij+1} as a weighted average of the positive coefficients of the three values in the previous time step. Indeed, for $k \leq \frac{1}{2}h^2$, if $|u_{ij}| < M_j$ for all i, then (10.26) gives $|u_{ij+1}| \leq M_j$, and by induction

$$|u_{ij+1}| \leq |u_{ij}| \leq M_{j-1} \leq \cdots \leq M_0$$

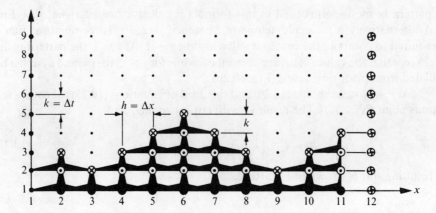

(a) Grid of mesh points and typical computational stars.
(b) Computational formulas

	Symbol
$u_{i1} = U_0[(i - 1)h]$, $\quad 1 \le i \le 11$	●
$u_{1j} = f[(j - 1)k]$, $\quad 2 \le j$	●
$u_{ij+1} = \dfrac{k}{h^2}(u_{i+1j} + u_{i-1j}) + \left(1 - \dfrac{2k}{h^2}\right)u_{ij}$	$\otimes$, $\odot$
$u_{Nj+1} = \left(1 - \dfrac{2k}{h^2}\right)u_{Nj} + \dfrac{2k}{h^2}u_{N-1j}$	$\otimes$, $\odot$

FIGURE 10.3 An explicit, marching computational sequence.

where $|u_0(x)| \le M_0$. Similarly, if $|u_0(x)| \ge m_0$, $|u_{ij+1}| \ge m_0$, so the difference equation (10.26) obeys a maximum-minimum principle as does its analog in (10.24) (see Chap. 6, Sec. 6.3.3).

If $k > \frac{1}{2}h^2$, $(1 - 2k/h^2) < 0$, and a portion of u_{ij} is subtracted in the calculation of each new value u_{ij+1}. However, as we shift the star over to calculate u_{i+1j+1}, the u_{ij} now add in the calculation of u_{i+1j+1} and the maximum-minimum principle cited above is no longer valid. This effect of alternate addition and subtraction leads to an unstable computation scheme (see Sec. 10.3.1). Accordingly, the coefficients in the computation formula must be nonnegative and $k \le \frac{1}{2}h^2$.

EXAMPLE 10.1 *Heat Conduction in an Insulated Rod.* Consider (10.24) with $f(t) = \exp(-9\pi^2 t/4)$ and $u_0(x) = 1$. According to the methods of Sec. 5.1, the analytic solution is (see the Problems)

$$u(x, t) = e^{-9\pi^2 t/4} - \frac{9}{2\pi}(e^{-9\pi^2 t/4} - e^{-\pi^2 t/4})\sin\frac{\pi x}{2} + 3\pi t e^{-9\pi^2 t/4}\sin\frac{3\pi}{2}x$$

$$+ \frac{36}{\pi}\sum_{n=2}^{\infty}\frac{[e^{-9\pi^2 t/4} - e^{(2n+1)\pi^2 t/4}]}{(2n+1)[(2n+1)^2 - 9]}\sin(2n+1)\frac{\pi}{2}x$$

The numerical solution is given by application of the formulas in Fig. 10.3b—namely, $u_{i1} = 1$, $1 \le i \le 11$; $u_{1j} = \exp[-2.25\pi^2 k(j - 1)]$, $2 \le j$; and so forth. Results for $h = 0.1$ and $k = 0.005$ (i.e., $k/h^2 = \frac{1}{2}$), are tabulated in Table 10.1. Figure 10.4 shows

TABLE 10.1   Numerical Solution for Parabolic Equation,
$h = 0.1$, $k = 0.005$ (rounded to nearest 0.001)

t

j	$i=1$	2	3	4	5	6	7	8	9	10	11
750	0.000	0.000	0.000	0.000	0.000	0.000	0.000	0.000	0.000	0.000	0.000
500	0.000	0.001	0.001	0.001	0.002	0.002	0.002	0.003	0.003	0.003	0.003
	·	·	·	·	·	·	·	·	·	·	·
	·	·	·	·	·	·	·	·	·	·	·
250	0.000	0.010	0.020	0.030	0.039	0.047	0.053	0.059	0.063	0.065	0.066
200	0.000	0.019	0.038	0.056	0.072	0.087	0.099	0.109	0.116	0.121	0.122
150	0.000	0.036	0.070	0.103	0.134	0.161	0.184	0.203	0.216	0.225	0.227
100	0.000	0.066	0.131	0.192	0.248	0.299	0.342	0.376	0.401	0.417	0.422
	·	·	·	·	·	·	·	·	·	·	·
50	0.004	0.131	0.253	0.367	0.470	0.561	0.636	0.696	0.739	0.765	0.773
40	0.013	0.162	0.302	0.432	0.545	0.643	0.721	0.783	0.825	0.852	0.860
30	0.040	0.219	0.382	0.526	0.646	0.744	0.818	0.873	0.910	0.932	0.938
20	0.121	0.341	0.526	0.674	0.785	0.866	0.920	0.955	0.975	0.986	0.988
10	0.368	0.615	0.784	0.892	0.950	0.981	0.993	0.998	0.999	1.000	1.000
	·	·	·	·	·	·	·	·	·	·	·
	·	·	·	·	·	·	·	·	·	·	·
5	0.641	0.845	0.950	0.987	1.000	1.000	1.000	1.000	1.000	1.000	1.000
4	0.717	0.900	0.974	1.000	1.000	1.000	1.000	1.000	1.000	1.000	1.000
3	0.801	0.948	1.000	1.000	1.000	1.000	1.000	1.000	1.000	1.000	1.000
2	0.895	1.000	1.000	1.000	1.000	1.000	1.000·	1.000	1.000	1.000	1.000
$j = 1$	1.000	1.000	1.000	1.000	1.000	1.000	1.000	1.000	1.000	1.000	1.000

$\longrightarrow x$

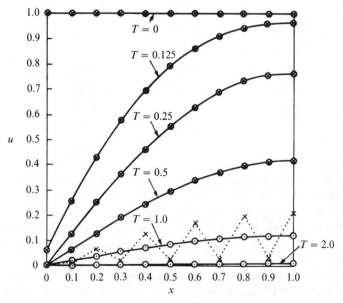

FIGURE 10.4   Comparison of analytic and numerical solutions of parabolic equation. (—— Analytic; ⊙ $k/h^2 = 0.5$; × $k/h^2 = 0.51$.)

both analytic (with 10 terms evaluated and summed) and numerical solutions. Even for the coarse grid used (only 11 points), the numerical solution accurately approximates the analytic solution. In Table 10.1 it is easy to see the change in temperature at $x = 0$ ($i = 1$) being transmitted over the pyramid of computation values (see Fig. 10.3a) and with finite speed in the x direction. This conflicts with the analysis in Chap. 7, where the speed of propagation of a temperature pulse was shown to be infinite for the differential equation in (10.24). Yet the error in the numerical solution is small. The propagation of information takes place at a speed $\Delta x/\Delta t = h/k = 2h^{-1}$ $\to \infty$ as h and $k \to 0$, so the numerical and analytic results agree in the limit (recall that $k/h^2 = \frac{1}{2}$ as $h \to 0$).

The largest values of the analytic and numerical solutions occur at $x = 1.0$, and by looking there we can see the effect of changing k most clearly. We let $k = h^2/6$, $k = h^2/2$, and $k = h^2/2 + 0.0001$. Table 10.2 shows the effect on the results. Clearly, the smallest $k = 0.00166\ldots$ yields the most accurate answers. Use of the Taylor's series (left as an exercise) shows that the specific choice of $k = h^2/6$ yields an order-of-magnitude decrease in the truncation error for the parabolic equation studied here. However, three times as much time is required to evaluate the solution to a given time for this smaller k and the improvement, although of "academic" interest, is not of practical value in this case.

TABLE 10.2   Solutions at $x = 1.0$
(three significant digits retained)

		Explicit Numeric ($h = 0.1$)		
t	*Analytic* (10 *terms*)	$k = h^2/2$ = 0.005	$k = h^2/6$ = 0.00166...	$k = h^2/2 + 0.0001$ = 0.0051
0.0	1.000	1.000	1.000	1.000
0.005	1.000	1.000	1.000	1.000
0.010	1.000	1.000	1.000	1.000
0.020	1.000	1.000	1.000	1.000
0.040	1.000	1.000	1.000	1.000
0.080	0.993	0.996	0.993	0.995
0.160	0.913	0.917	0.913	0.917
0.320	0.648	0.649	0.648	0.644
0.640	0.295	0.295	0.295	0.284
0.995	0.122	0.122	0.122	0.036
1.000	0.121	0.121	0.121	0.209
1.005	0.119	0.119	0.119	0.029
1.010	0.118	0.118	0.118	0.211

Table 10.2 and Fig. 10.4 also show the disastrous result of using $k = h^2/2 + 0.0001$—that is, k/h^2 very slightly greater than one-half. It is obvious that for this largest value of k the numerical solution is oscillating and inaccurate at $t = 1$. This unstable calculation has generated oscillations beyond the scope of the computer before $t = 2.0$. Thus, as predicted earlier, the computational scheme is stable only for $k/h^2 \le \frac{1}{2}$.

Several exercises are given at the chapter's end to illustrate these results further, and the reader can easily verify the early parts of Table 10.1 by hand calculations. Interestingly, evaluation and summation of ten terms of the analytic solution require five times as much time per time step as the numerical solution for $k/h^2 = \frac{1}{2}$.

10.2.2   Normalization of a Model

Normalization is the process of nondimensionalizing the equations and auxiliary conditions of a mathematical model in terms of the significant scales of the model—for example, the initial maximum temperature and the length of a rod conducting heat. The process reduces classes of models to a standard form so that only one numerical computation need be made to obtain answers for a range of conditions. When closed-form solutions are available, such considerations are not paramount; however, it is wasteful to recompute solutions for each individual length of a rod conducting heat when, for similar auxiliary conditions, a single computation may be sufficient for all rods of arbitrary length and material (see the Problems and below).

An interesting example to consider is the simplest convection-diffusion equation (see Sec. 8.3.2). The convection equation

$$O_t + UO_x = 0 \tag{10.28}$$

for the convection of dissolved oxygen through the fluid of a river flowing at speed U was introduced in Sec. 9.2. It is reasonable that the oxygen is diffused (or transported) also by the random (Brownian) motion of the fluid molecules and by the turbulent motion of the fluid in which the oxygen is dissolved. Based on the hypothesis that the rate of transfer of diffusing substance is proportional to the concentration gradient (see Sec. 2.2.1 on heat conduction and Sec. 8.3), the diffusion flux rate can be represented by $f_x = -D\partial O/\partial x$, where D is the diffusivity constant for *Fickian* diffusion. In direct analogy with the Fourier heat law, a conservation of diffusing mass equation, including diffusion and convection, can be derived; when diffusion is included (10.28) becomes

$$O_t + UO_x = DO_{xx} \tag{10.29}$$

and a key question arises as to the relative importance of convection and diffusion.

Suppose that (10.29) is applied to a section of river of length L and that the maximum possible concentration of dissolved oxygen determined by the river water temperature is O_m. In order to normalize (10.29), we define a new set of nondimensional variables, namely,

$$0 \le \Omega = \frac{O}{O_m} \le 1$$

$$0 \le T = \frac{t}{\tau} \tag{10.30}$$

$$0 \le X = \frac{x}{L} \le 1$$

According to the chain rule of partial differentiation,

$$O_t = \frac{\partial}{\partial T}(O_m\Omega)\frac{dT}{dt} = \frac{O_m}{\tau}\Omega_T, \quad O_x = \frac{\partial}{\partial X}(O_m\Omega)\frac{dX}{dx} = \frac{O_m}{L}\Omega_X, \quad O_{xx} = \frac{O_m}{L^2}\Omega_{XX}$$

From these results, (10.29) becomes

$$\Omega_T + \frac{U\tau}{L}\Omega_X = \frac{D\tau}{L^2}\Omega_{XX} \tag{10.31}$$

Now $0 \leq t \leq \infty$; however, the time required for a particle of fluid to span the section of the river is L/U and is a natural time scale. With $\tau = L/U$, (10.31) becomes

$$\Omega_T + \Omega_X = \mathscr{D}\Omega_{XX} \tag{10.32}$$

where the nondimensional diffusion coefficient $\mathscr{D} = D/UL$. If $\mathscr{D} = O(1)$, then the diffusion and convection terms in (10.32) are in balance. If $\mathscr{D} \gg 1$, diffusion dominates. If $\mathscr{D} \ll 1$, convection dominates. For a given set of initial and boundary conditions, solution of (10.32) for a representative range of $\mathscr{D}$ provides nondimensional solutions for all possible combinations of values of D, U, and L covered by the range of $\mathscr{D}$. For specific D, U, and L, the dimensional solution is then $O(x, t) = O_m\Omega(x/L, tU/L; \mathscr{D})$.

The auxiliary conditions of a model are also normalized with the variables defined above. Henceforth our examples should be considered as normalized (non-dimensional) examples of general models.

10.2.3   The Hyperbolic Star

Consider a normalized model for the small transverse vibrations of a string of finite length (from Sec. 2.2.2):

$$z_{tt} - z_{yy} = 0, \qquad 0 < y < 1, \quad 0 < t$$
$$z_y(0, t) = z(1, t) = 0, \qquad 0 \leq t$$
$$z(y, 0) = Z_0(y), \qquad \qquad \qquad 0 < y < 1 \tag{10.33}$$
$$z_t(y, 0) = V_0(y),$$

The boundary condition at $y = 0$ requires a fictitious point at the left edge of the grid of mesh points. Let $\Delta y = h$ and $\Delta t = k$; the grid is then

$$G : \begin{cases} 1 \leq i \leq N = 2 + h^{-1} & (N \text{ must be integer}) \\ 1 \leq j \end{cases}$$

The difference expressions corresponding to (10.33) are

$$\frac{z_{ij+1} - 2z_{ij} + z_{ij-1}}{k^2} - \frac{z_{i+1j} - 2z_{ij} + z_{i-1j}}{h^2} = 0, \qquad 2 \leq i \leq N - 1, \quad j \geq 2$$

$$\frac{z_{3j} - z_{1j}}{2h} = 0, \qquad j \geq 1$$

$$z_{Nj} = 0, \qquad j \geq 1 \tag{10.34}$$

$$z_{i1} = Z_0[(i - 2)h], \qquad 2 \leq i \leq N - 1$$

$$z_{i2} = z_{i1} + k\left\{V_0[(i - 2)h] + \frac{k}{2}d_{i1}(z_{yy})\right\}, \qquad 2 \leq i \leq N - 1$$

At the corners $(0, 0)$ and $(1, 0)$ of the y-t plane, it is best to obtain the values at the initial fictitious points $(1, 1)$ and $(1, 2)$ and initial boundary points $(N, 1)$ and $(N, 2)$ from the boundary conditions rather than by arbitrary extension of the initial conditions. This is done in (10.34) and the mathematical model (10.33). The truncation errors in (10.34) are $O(h^2 + k^2)$ or smaller.

From the partial difference equation in (10.34), the basic computational formula is

$$z_{ij+1} = 2\left(1 - \frac{k^2}{h^2}\right)z_{ij} - z_{ij-1} + \frac{k^2}{h^2}(z_{i+1j} + z_{i-1j}), \qquad j \geq 2 \qquad (10.35)$$

The computational star for this formula is shown in Fig. 10.5a. At $i = 2$, the relation $z_{1j} = z_{3j}$ from (10.34) is incorporated in (10.35) to give (Fig. 10.5b)

$$z_{2j+1} = 2\left(1 - \frac{k^2}{h^2}\right)z_{2j} - z_{2j-1} + 2z_{3j} \qquad (10.36)$$

At $i = N - 1$, values of z_{Nj} are known, so computation may proceed (Fig. 10.5c) and (10.35) need not be applied at (N, j).

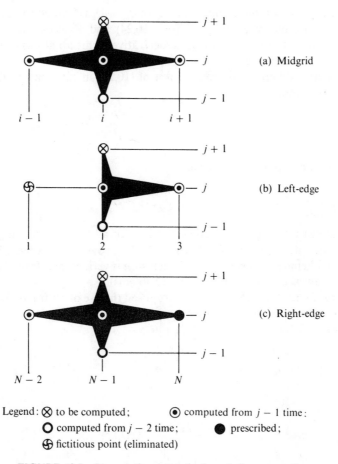

Legend: ⊗ to be computed;   ⊙ computed from $j - 1$ time:
        ○ computed from $j - 2$ time;   ● prescribed;
        ⊕ fictitious point (eliminated)

FIGURE 10.5   Computational stars for hyperbolic computation.

The computation proceeds as follows. All values of z_{i1}, $1 \leq i \leq N$, are computed from the initial condition on z_{i1} and the boundary conditions given in (10.34). Then the last of (10.34) and the boundary conditions give z_{i2}, $1 \leq i \leq N$, with $d_{i1}(z_{yy})$ being computed analytically if possible. For $j \geq 2$, application of (10.35) or

(10.36) as appropriate for $2 \leq i \leq N - 1$ gives z_{ij} provided that the z_{ij-1} have been calculated. You should construct a star diagram similar to Fig. 10.3a to confirm that computation is possible on a forward *marching* scheme with new values *explicitly* given in terms of old as for the parabolic equation. Does the pyramid restriction still hold?

From (10.35) for $k^2 \leq h^2$, the marching formula computes the new value z_{ij+1} as a weighted average of four known values at previous times, all weighting coefficients being positive. For $k^2 > h^2$, the coefficient of z_{ij} is negative. Following the reasoning ennunciated for the parabolic case, we require $k \leq h$. We see in Sec. 10.3 that, indeed, for $k > h$ the computational scheme outlined above is not stable.

10.2.4   An Implicit Calculation

The explicit computational scheme for $u_t = u_{xx}$ is limited to small time steps because it is unstable when $k > \frac{1}{2}h^2$ [see (10.24) and Example 10.1]. A forward difference was used to represent the time-derivative term; a natural suggestion is to try a central time difference.

A central difference representation of (10.24) in time and space yields the Richardson equation

$$\frac{u_{ij+1} - u_{ij-1}}{2k} = \frac{u_{i+1j} - 2u_{ij} + u_{i-1j}}{h^2} \tag{10.37}$$

The Richardson computational formula is

$$u_{ij+1} = u_{ij-1} + \frac{2k}{h^2}(u_{i+1j} - 2u_{ij} + u_{i-1j}) \tag{10.38}$$

which has a negative weighting coefficient on u_{ij} for all values of k and h. According to our heuristic rule of positive coefficients, (10.38) provides an explicit, but *unstable*, computation scheme for all k or h. This conclusion is verified by a formal convergence or stability analysis (see Sec. 10.3 and the Problems).

In 1947 Crank and Nicolson [7] proposed the use of central differences about $(i, j + \frac{1}{2})$ (their Method III). Let us examine this idea for the model (10.24). The Taylor's series (10.2) gives at $(x, t + k/2) = (i, j + \frac{1}{2})$

$$u_{xx} = \frac{u_{i+1j+\frac{1}{2}} - 2u_{ij+\frac{1}{2}} + u_{i-1j+\frac{1}{2}}}{h^2} + O(h^2)$$

and

$$u_t = \frac{u_{ij+1} - u_{ij}}{k} + O(k^2)$$

Thus the truncation error in representing $u_t = u_{xx}$ about $(i, j + \frac{1}{2})$ is $O(k^2 + h^2)$. However, the values of u are known only at the grid points (i, j). Terms like $u_{ij+\frac{1}{2}}$ must be replaced by their average value $(u_{ij} + u_{ij+1})/2$. A subtle question of whether or not the averaging process introduces a lower-order truncation error arises. If $u(x, t)$ is sufficiently differentiable, use of the Taylor's series shows that the error remains $O(k^2 + h^2)$. Forsythe and Wasow [3, Sec. 17.2] discuss this point in some detail.

Using the foregoing difference forms and replacing undefined values by their averages give, for $u_t = u_{xx}$,

$$\frac{u_{ij+1} - u_{ij}}{k} = \frac{u_{i+1j+1} - 2u_{ij+1} + u_{i-1j+1} + u_{i+1j} - 2u_{ij} + u_{i-1j}}{2h^2}$$

When rearranged, this equation becomes

$$u_{i-1j+1} - 2\left(1 + \frac{h^2}{k}\right)u_{ij+1} + u_{i+ij+1} = 2u_{ij}\left(1 - \frac{h^2}{k}\right) - u_{i+1j} - u_{i-1j}$$

(10.39)

or, for each i in the space domain of the model,

$$A_i u_{i-1j+1} + B_i u_{ij+1} + C_i u_{i+1j+1} = D_i \qquad (10.40)$$

where

$$A_i = 1, \quad B_i = -2\left(1 + \frac{h^2}{k}\right), \quad C_i = 1, \quad D_i = 2u_{ij}\left(1 - \frac{h^2}{k}\right) - u_{i+1j} - u_{i-1j}$$

The A_i, B_i, C_i, and D_i are known at time j, but three unknown values of u appear on the left-hand side of (10.40). Thus it gives u_{ij+1}, *not* explicitly in terms of known values but *implicitly* in terms of known values at time j and two unknown values at $i - 1$ and $i + 1$ at time $j + 1$. The computational star is shown in Fig. 10.6a (see Fig. 10.2a for the explicit computation).

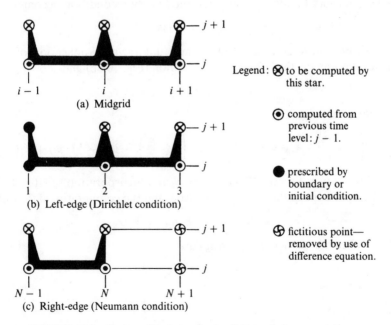

Legend: ⊗ to be computed by this star.

◉ computed from previous time level: $j - 1$.

● prescribed by boundary or initial condition.

⊕ fictitious point— removed by use of difference equation.

(a) Midgrid

(b) Left-edge (Dirichlet condition)

(c) Right-edge (Neumann condition)

FIGURE 10.6   Computational stars for implicit parabolic computation.

Clearly, (10.40) *cannot* be solved by marching ahead (in j) point by point in the technique used in Sec. 10.2.1 (and, therefore, requiring only a finite pyramid of values to be known behind the most advanced point, e.g., see Fig. 10.3). Indeed, for fixed j, (10.40) is a matrix equation representing a system of simultaneous, linear, algebraic equations for the u_{ij+1}, $2 \le i \le N$.

Suppose that we begin at $i = p$ and use the computational star in Fig. 10.6a at $i = p$, $i = p \pm 1$, $i = p \pm 2$, and so on. For $i = p$, Fig. 10.6a and (10.40) yield one equation for the three unknowns u_{p-1j+1}, u_{pj+1}, u_{p+1j+1}. By adding the two stars at $i = p \pm 1$, we gain two equations *and* two additional unknowns, giving three equations and five unknowns. Continuing the process always adds two equations and two unknowns; the number of unknowns always exceeds the number of equations by two for a computation in an unbounded region. This implicit technique is not usable for infinite space domains, for the number of equations must equal the number of unknowns in order for a unique solution of the set of linear equations to exist.

Is the technique usable in finite domains? The two boundary conditions in (10.24) must yield two equations but no new unknowns if the total linear system is to be solvable. For the implicit case where differences are centered on $(i, j + \frac{1}{2})$, the conditions are

$$u_{ij+\frac{1}{2}} = f\left[k\left(j + \frac{1}{2} - 1\right)\right] \quad \text{and} \quad \frac{u_{N+1j+\frac{1}{2}} - u_{N-1j+\frac{1}{2}}}{2h} = 0$$

For the derivative form,

$$u_{N+1j+1} = u_{N-1j+1} + u_{N-1j} - u_{N+1j} \tag{10.41}$$

when averages are used to replace $j + \frac{1}{2}$ values. As u_{ij} is known and equal to $f[(j - 1)k]$, at every boundary point $(1, i)$ the Dirichlet condition becomes

$$u_{1j+1} = f(jk) \tag{10.42}$$

which gives one more equation and no new unknowns. Application of (10.40) at $i = 2$ gives the star for the left-edge of the region (Fig. 10.6b) and

$$B_2 u_{2j+1} + C_2 u_{3j+1} = D_2$$

where *in the present case*

$$B_2 = -2\left(1 + \frac{h^2}{k}\right), \quad C_2 = 1, \quad D_2 = 2u_{2j}\left(1 - \frac{h^2}{k}\right) - u_{3j} - \{f(jk) + f[(j-1)k]\}$$

Now, application of (10.40) at $i = N$ and incorporation of (10.41) yield the star for the right-edge of the region (Fig. 10.6c) and the computational formula

$$A_N u_{N-1j+1} + B_N u_{Nj+1} = D_N \tag{10.43}$$

with the coefficients being *in the present case*

$$A_N = 1 + C_N = 2$$

$$B_N = -2\left(1 + \frac{h^2}{k}\right)$$

$$D_N = 2u_{Nj}\left(1 - \frac{h^2}{k}\right) - 2u_{N-ij}$$

Thus u_{N+1j} does not appear in the calculation and may be ignored. Use of the derivative boundary condition provides the second new equation without additional unknowns.

In summary, application of the stars in Fig. 10.6 and their related equations (10.40), (10.42), and (10.43) provides a set of $N - 1$ equations and $N - 1$ unknowns. Clearly, this technique is usable for finite domains. In matrix form, the problem is posed as a linear system $AU = D$, where

$$A = \begin{bmatrix} B_2 & C_2 & & & & & \\ A_3 & B_3 & C_3 & & & \Large 0 & \\ & A_4 & B_4 & C_4 & & & \\ & & \cdot & \cdot & \cdot & \cdot & \\ & \Large 0 & & \cdot & \cdot & \cdot & \cdot \\ & & & A_{N-1} & B_{N-1} & C_{N-1} \\ & & & & A_N & B_N \end{bmatrix} \qquad (10.44)$$

$$U = \begin{bmatrix} u_{2j+1} \\ u_{3j+1} \\ u_{4j+1} \\ \vdots \\ u_{N-1j+1} \\ u_{Nj+1} \end{bmatrix} \qquad D = \begin{bmatrix} 2u_{2j}\left(1 - \dfrac{h^2}{k}\right) - u_{3j} - \{f(jk) + f[(j-1)k]\} \\ 2u_{3j}\left(1 - \dfrac{h^2}{k}\right) - u_{4j} - u_{2j} \\ 2u_{4j}\left(1 - \dfrac{h^2}{k}\right) - u_{5j} - u_{3j} \\ \vdots \\ 2u_{N-1j}\left(1 - \dfrac{h^2}{k}\right) - u_{Nj} - u_{N-2j} \\ 2u_{Nj}\left(1 - \dfrac{h^2}{k}\right) - 2u_{N-1j} \end{bmatrix} \qquad (10.45)$$

and the A_i, B_i, and C_i are given above. The key to the solution of the linear system is that A is a special type of *banded sparse matrix* because there is only one line of coefficients to each side of the diagonal of the matrix and most of its elements are zero. The *tridiagonal matrix* A is nonsingular (its determinant is nonzero) for the Crank–Nicolson formulation. It follows [8] that the set of equations $AU = D$ has a unique, nonzero solution provided that $D \neq 0$.

The oldest systematic method of obtaining the solution to the linear equations

$$AU = D \qquad (10.46)$$

where A is nonsingular, is Gaussian elimination and back-substitution [8, pp. 60 ff]. The elimination of all A_i in (10.46) is accomplished [see (10.44)] by subtracting the appropriate multiple of a given row (or equation) from the row (or equation) just below it. When carried out for $2 < i \leq N$, the process produces a set of equations, each with only two unknowns (A becomes an upper-triangular, bidiagonal matrix), except the last (the $N - 1$th), which has the form

$$\tilde{B}_N u_{Nj+1} = \tilde{D}_N$$

Thus u_{Nj+1} can be found. As the $N - 2$th equation contains only u_{N-1j+1} and u_{Nj+1}, we find u_{N-1j+1} by back-substitution of u_{Nj+1}. This process can be repeated sequentially for smaller i until all u_{ij+1} are known. The value of j is increased and the next set of u_{ij+1} are found. The computation is easy to program for the computer and very rapid.

Computationally, the Gauss method requires us to

1. Define and compute (at each time level if necessary) the A_i, B_i, C_i, and D_i of (10.44) and (10.45) for $2 \le i \le N$. For *the present case*, $A_2 = C_N = 0$.

2. Carry out the elimination. This step is best done by normalizing the B_i before elimination in the next equation. Let

$$b_2 = \frac{B_2}{B_2} = 1, \quad c_2 = \frac{C_2}{B_2}, \quad d_2 = \frac{D_2}{B_2}$$

Now, multiplying equation 2 by A_3 and subtracting it from equation 3 to eliminate A_3, we have

$$\tilde{a}_3 = A_3 - A_3 = 0, \quad \tilde{b}_3 = B_3 - c_2 A_3, \quad \tilde{c}_3 = C_3, \quad \tilde{d}_3 = D_3 - A_3 d_2$$

Normalizing b_3 gives

$$a_3 = 0, \quad b_3 = 1, \quad c_3 = \frac{C_3}{(B_3 - c_2 A_3)}, \quad d_3 = \frac{D_3 - A_3 d_2}{B_3 - c_2 A_3}$$

By induction, we obtain the recursion formulas

$$c_2 = \frac{C_2}{B_2} \qquad d_2 = \frac{D_2}{B_2}$$

and for $2 < i \le N$,

$$a_i = 0, \quad b_i = 1, \quad c_i = \frac{C_i}{B_i - c_{i-1}A_i}, \quad d_i = \frac{D_i - A_i d_{i-1}}{B_i - A_i c_{i-1}}$$

Recall that $A_2 = C_n = 0$, so $a_2 = c_N = 0$.

3. Carry out the back-substitution. The last equation is, after elimination, $u_{Nj+1} = d_N$; the next to last is $u_{N-1j+1} + c_{N-1}u_{Nj+1} = d_{N-1}$ or $u_{N-1j+1} = d_{N-1} - c_{N-1}u_{Nj+1}$. By induction, for $2 < i < N$,

$$u_{i-1j+1} = d_{i-1} - c_{i-1}u_{ij+1}$$

For the Crank–Nicolson procedure, $B_2 \ne 0$ and the denominator $B_i - c_{i-1}A_i \ne 0$ ($B_i - A_i c_{i-1} \ge \frac{3}{2}$ for any k/h^2). Thus the procedure does not suffer from excessive accumulation of round-off errors caused by large values of c_i or d_i arising from small denominators (see [3, p. 105]).

EXAMPLE 10.2 *Heat Conduction in an Insulated Rod.* We employ the implicit scheme on the model in Example 10.1. With $k/h^2 = 2$ (not $\frac{1}{2}$) and $h = 0.1$, the implicit results are indistinguishable from the analytic results shown in Fig. 10.4. Table 10.3 shows the analytic, explicit, and implicit results at $x = 1.0$. The implicit solution agrees within ± 1 in the third significant digit with the analytic solution and the most accurate explicit numerical solution. Because it can be shown that there is no limit on k for computational stability for the implicit scheme, we used $k = 2h^2$, and the implicit scheme reaches a given time value in approximately one-third the time required by the explicit scheme with $k = 0.5h^2$ ($h = 0.1$ in each case), thus showing the value of the implicit scheme in computation speed.

TABLE 10.3   Solutions at $x = 1.0$

| t | Analytic (10 *terms*) | *Numeric* ($h = 0.1$) | | Implicit $k/h^2 = 2$ |
		Explicit $k/h^2 = \frac{1}{6}$	$k/h^2 = \frac{1}{2}$	
0	1.000	1.000	1.000	1.000
0.04	1.000	1.000	1.000	1.000
0.08	0.993	0.993	0.996	0.992
0.16	0.913	0.913	0.917	0.913
0.32	0.648	0.648	0.649	0.648
0.64	0.295	0.295	0.295	0.296
1.00	0.121	0.121	0.121	0.122

Approximate Normalized Computation Time to $t = 1.0$
(based on specific computer runs)

1.0	0.70	0.20	0.06

10.3   CONSISTENCY, CONVERGENCE, AND STABILITY OF INITIAL-BOUNDARY-VALUE MODELS

A mathematical model is well posed if it has one and only one solution that varies continuously with the auxiliary data (Chaps. 1 and 6) and, except in rare cases, is bounded. A numerical model must meet certain criteria also. These criteria were implicit in our successes (and failure) with numerical models to this point.

First, the difference equations and auxiliary conditions of the numerical model must be *consistent* with the differential equations and auxiliary conditions of the mathematical model. The numerical model is consistent if the truncation errors vanish as the grid spacings approach zero—that is, as $k \to 0$ and $h \to 0$. This condition ensures that the difference operators accurately represent their corresponding differential operators. Second, the difference between the exact solutions of the numerical and mathematical models should vanish as the grid spacings approach zero; that is, the difference solution should *converge* to the differential solution as $h \to 0$ and $k \to 0$. Finally, we must be able to carry out a practical computation. As computers can store only a finite number of digits to represent each number (of the order of 7 to 15 decimal digits), *round-off errors* can occur at each step of the computation. For a practical computation, the cumulative growth of the round-off errors must not swamp the true difference solution. If the growth of these errors is reasonable or controlled, the computation is *stable*.

Thus a numerical model with consistent equations, convergent solution, and stable error propagation yields a *computationally stable scheme* whose results can closely approximate the exact solution to the mathematical model, as Examples 10.1 and 10.2 showed. In the following section we define consistency, convergence, and stability more precisely and test the initial-boundary-value models developed previously (actually, only the main difference equations are usually significant in this regard and are examined in the text). The Taylor's series expansion and Fourier series concepts form the basis of our tests. We assume that all mathematical models are well posed and that their solutions are continuous with as many continuous and bounded derivatives as required.

10.3.1   Testing the Numerical Model

There are three types of error, the *truncation error* T_{ij} representing the errors made by replacing differential operators with difference operators, the *discretization error* D_{ij} (so named by Forsythe and Wasow [3]), which is the difference between the exact solution u_{ij} of the numerical model and that $u(x, y)$ of the mathematical model, and the *round-off error* e_{ij} whose cumulative value $\hat{e}_{ij}$ is the difference between the computed solution u_{ij}^c and u_{ij}. *As h and k approach zero*, a numerical model is *consistent* if $T_{ij} \to 0$, *convergent* if $D_{ij} \to 0$, and *stable* if $\hat{e}_{ij}$ does not grow exponentially for fixed $t = jk$ (or, equivalently, $\hat{e}_{ij}$ does not grow exponentially for fixed h, k as $j \to \infty$).

Consistency

In Sec. 10.2 difference expressions for various differential operators were obtained by use of the Taylor's series. From these expressions and reconstruction of the analysis leading to them, we obtain the truncation error T_{ij} in each case. The method is the same for initial-boundary-value and pure boundary-value models in the case of consistency.

From (10.11),

$$T_{ij} = [u_{xx} + u_{yy}]_{ij} - \left[\frac{u_{i+1j} - 2u_{ij} + u_{i-1j}}{h^2} + \frac{u_{ij+1} - 2u_{ij} + u_{ij-1}}{k^2} \right]$$

$$= E[u] - E_D[u_{ij}]$$

$$= \frac{1}{12}(u_{xxxx}h^2 + u_{yyyy}k^2)_{ij} + O(h^4 + k^4) = O(h^2 + k^2) \qquad (10.47)$$

As h and $k \to 0$, $T_{ij} \to 0$; $E_D[u_{ij}]$ is a consistent difference representation for the elliptic operator $E[u]$. From (10.12),

$$T_{ij} = H[u] - H_D[u_{ij}] = -\frac{1}{12}(u_{yyyy}k^2 - u_{xxxx}h^2)_{ij} + O(h^4 + k^4)$$

$$= O(h^2 + k^2) \qquad (10.48)$$

Clearly, $H_D[u_{ij}]$ is consistent with the hyperbolic or wave operator $H[u]$. From (10.13),

$$T_{ij} = P[u] - P_D[u_{ij}] = \frac{1}{12}(u_{xxxx}h^2 - 6u_{tt}k)_{ij} + O(h^4 + k^2) = O(h^2 + k)$$

$$(10.49)$$

Accordingly, $P_D[u_{ij}]$ is consistent with $P[u]$.

Two other difference forms were used in Sec. 10.2.4 to represent $P[u] = 0$.

The unstable Richardson formula (10.37) yields

$$T_{ij} = P[u] - \left[\frac{u_{i+1j} - 2u_{ij} + u_{i-1j}}{h^2} - \frac{u_{ij+1} - u_{ij-1}}{2k} \right]$$

$$= \frac{1}{12}(u_{xxxx}h^2 + 2u_{ttt}k^2)_{ij} + O(h^4 + k^3) = O(h^2 + k^2) \qquad (10.50)$$

and is consistent! The Crank–Nicholson equation (10.39) is also consistent (see the Problems).

Thus all the difference representations that we have proposed are consistent. But although Richardson's scheme (10.37) is consistent, it is neither convergent nor stable, since (10.37) admits exponentially growing solutions (see the Problems). In 1953 Du Fort and Frankel [9] sought to improve the Richardson equation (10.37) by replacing u_{ij} by the average of the forward and backward values $\frac{1}{2}(u_{ij+1} + u_{ij-1})$. Then the computational formula (10.38) becomes

$$u_{ij+1}\left(\frac{1 + 2k}{h^2} \right) = \frac{2k}{h^2}(u_{i+1j} + u_{i-1j}) + u_{ij-1}\left(\frac{1 - 2k}{h^2} \right) \qquad (10.51)$$

This scheme is convergent and stable for any $k/h^2 < \infty$ (see the Problems), but is only conditionally consistent for $P[u]$.

Reversing our previous approach, we obtain the differential representation of (10.51) by expanding each term in a Taylor's series about (i, j). This step leads to

$$P_{D_D-F}[u_{ij}] = \left(u_{xx} - u_t + \frac{1}{12}u_{xxxx}h^2 - u_{tt}\frac{k^2}{h^2} - \frac{1}{12}u_{tttt}\frac{k^4}{h^2} - \frac{1}{6}u_{ttt}k^2 \right)_{ij} + O(k^4 + h^4)$$

Hence

$$T_{ij} = P[u] - P_{D_D-F}[u_{ij}] = u_{ttij}\left(\frac{k^2}{h^2} \right) + O(k^2 + h^2) \qquad (10.52)$$

As $k \to 0$ and $h \to 0$, $T_{ij} \to u_{ttij}(k^2/h^2) = c^{-2}u_{tt}$ if $h/k = c$. Unless the "wave speed" $c \to \infty$ as $h \to 0$—that is, unless $k = o(h)$, (10.51) is actually consistent with the hyperbolic equation

$$u_{tt} + c^2u_t = c^2u_{xx}$$

The DuFort–Frankel scheme (10.51) is *conditionally consistent* with $P[u]$—that is, consistent if $k = o(h)$ as $h \to 0$ and $k \to 0$. Although this scheme is explicit, a special starting technique is needed initially, for the difference scheme requires initial conditions appropriate to *hyperbolic equations*; in other words, the first two rows must be known.

Convergence

The discretization error is

$$D_{ij} = u(x, t) - u_{ij} \qquad (10.53)$$

where $x = ih$ and $t = jk$. Writing $u_{ij} = u - D_{ij}$, introducing this definition in the difference equations of various models, and expanding the exact solution by the Taylor's series lead in each case to an equation for the D_{ij} that can be examined as h and $k \to 0$.

For the explicit numerical model (10.25) and its mathematical analog (10.24), use of (10.53) leads directly to

$$\frac{D_{ij+1} - D_{ij}}{k} - \frac{D_{i+1j} - 2D_{ij} + D_{i-1j}}{h^2} = T_{ij} \tag{10.54}$$

where

$$T_{ij} = \frac{1}{12}\left(u_{xxxx}h^2 - \frac{1}{2}u_{tt}k\right)_{ij} + O(h^4 + k^4) = O(h^2 + k)$$

[follow the derivation leading to (10.49) above]. Solving (10.54) for D_{ij+1} yields

$$D_{ij+1} = \frac{k}{h^2}(D_{i+1j} + D_{i-1j}) + \left(1 - 2\frac{k}{h^2}\right)D_{ij} + kT_{ij} \tag{10.55}$$

When $0 < s \leq \frac{1}{2}$, where $s = k/h^2$, the coefficients of the D values on the right of (10.55) are positive and their sum $s + s + (1 - 2s) = 1$. Thus for $0 < s \leq \frac{1}{2}$,

$$|D_{ij+1}| \leq s|D_{i+1j}| + s|D_{i-1j}| + (1 - 2s)|D_{ij}| + k|T_{ij}|$$

Defining

$$|D_{ij}| \leq D_j = |D_{ij}|_{\max} \quad \text{and} \quad |T_{ij}| \leq T_j = |T_{ij}|_{\max}$$

for all i in the relevant range and at "time" j gives

$$D_{j+1} = |D_{ij+1}|_{\max} \leq sD_j + sD_j + (1 - 2s)D_j + kT_j = D_j + kT_j$$

It follows that

$$D_{j+1} \leq D_j + kT_j \leq D_{j-1} + kT_{j-1} + kT_j$$

The $T_j = |T_{ij}|_{\max}$ are bounded and $O(h^2 + k)$, and there exists a $T = O(h^2 + k)$ such that

$$T_j \leq T \qquad \text{for all } j$$

Consequently, by induction,

$$D_{j+1} \leq D_0 + (j + 1)kT$$

As $D_0 = |D_{i0}|_{\max}$, $D_0 = 0$ because $D_{i0} = u(ih, 0) - u_{i0} = 0$ (the difference solution and the differential solution agree exactly at the mesh points at $t = 0$). At any time $t = jk$, the maximum discretization error is then

$$D_j \leq jkT = tT = tO(h^2 + k)$$

and $D_j \to 0$ as h and $k \to 0$. Therefore the explicit numerical representation of the heat equation converges when $s = k/h^2 \leq \frac{1}{2}$.

For $s > \frac{1}{2}$, we show that the difference equation admits exponentially growing solutions u_{ij} for fixed $t = jk$ as $h \to 0$ (as $j \to \infty$). Then, as Isaacson and Keller [10] show, $D_{ij} = u(x, t) - u_{ij}$ cannot generally go to zero because the solution $u(x, t)$ of the differential equation is bounded.

The difference equation (10.26) is

$$u_{ij+1} = s(u_{i+1j} + u_{i-1j}) + (1 - 2s)u_{ij} \tag{10.56}$$

Let us seek Fourier component solutions of the form

$$\hat{u}_{ij} = A_\lambda e^{\hat{\imath}\lambda x} e^{\gamma t} = A_\lambda e^{\hat{\imath}\lambda ih} e^{\gamma jk} \tag{10.57}$$

where $\hat{\imath} = (-1)^{1/2}$, $\lambda > 0$ is real, and $e^{\hat{\imath}\lambda x + \gamma t} = e^{\gamma t}(\cos \lambda x + \hat{\imath} \sin \lambda x)$ is a complex Fourier component. A general initial condition is the real (or imaginary) part of the sum of all possible component solutions:

$$u_{0ij} = \begin{cases} \operatorname{Re}\left(\sum_\lambda A_\lambda e^{\hat{\imath}\lambda x}\right) = \sum_\lambda A_\lambda \sin \lambda x \\ \operatorname{Im}\left(\sum_\lambda A_\lambda e^{\hat{\imath}\lambda x}\right) = \sum_\lambda A_\lambda \cos \lambda x \end{cases}$$

What values of λ and γ make $\hat{u}_{ij}$ a solution of (10.56)? Introducing (10.57) into (10.56) gives

$$A_\lambda e^{\hat{\imath}\lambda ih} e^{\gamma jk} e^{\gamma k} = A_\lambda e^{\gamma jk} s[e^{\hat{\imath}\lambda h(i+1)} + e^{\hat{\imath}\lambda h(i-1)}] + A_\lambda e^{\gamma jk} e^{\hat{\imath}\lambda ih}(1 - 2s)$$

Cancelling equivalent terms produces

$$e^{\gamma k} = 1 - 2s + 2s\left\{\frac{e^{\lambda \hat{\imath} h} + e^{-\lambda \hat{\imath} h}}{2}\right\}$$

$$= 1 - 2s(1 - \cos \lambda h)$$

As $1 - \cos \lambda h = 2 \sin^2 (\lambda h/2)$, $\hat{u}_{ij}$ is a solution to (10.56) if

$$e^{\gamma k} = 1 - 4s \sin^2 \frac{\lambda h}{2} = \omega$$

that is, if

$$\hat{u}_{ij} = A_\lambda e^{\hat{\imath}\lambda ih}\left(1 - 4s \sin^2 \frac{\lambda h}{2}\right)^j = A_\lambda e^{\hat{\imath}\lambda ih} \omega^j \tag{10.58}$$

For $0 < s \leq \frac{1}{2}$, $|\omega| \leq 1$, while $|\omega|$ can exceed unity when $s > \frac{1}{2}$. Clearly, $|\omega^j| = |\omega|^j$ is always bounded as $j \to \infty$ for $0 < s \leq \frac{1}{2}$, while for $s > \frac{1}{2}$, $|\omega|^j$ will grow exponentially* if for some component solution in the sum over values of λ

$$1 \geq \sin^2 \frac{\lambda h}{2} > \frac{1}{2s} \tag{10.59}$$

As s increases, such a possibility becomes more likely. And since the λ can be considered as a set of eigenvalues, it is highly probable that at least one component in every series will satisfy the inequality (10.59) as k and $h \to 0$. Then $|\omega| > 1$ and $|\omega^j| = |\omega|^j \to \infty$ as $j \to \infty$.

For $s > \frac{1}{2}$, the difference equation (10.56) admits possibly unbounded solutions of the form (10.58) because, for fixed time $t = jk$, the absolute value of u_{ij} may approach infinity as k and $h \to 0$ (for then $j \to \infty$). Accordingly, D_{ij} cannot approach zero as the grid spacing vanishes, and this difference scheme does not converge for $s > \frac{1}{2}$. Isaacson and Keller [10, p. 504] exhibit an explicit example of an unbounded solution for $s > \frac{1}{2}$.

* If $|\omega| > 1$, $|e^{\gamma k}| > 1$, so either $\gamma > 0$ or $\gamma = \alpha + i\beta$ and $\alpha > 0$. Thus $|\omega| > 1$ leads to a positive real exponential term, and so $w^j = e^{\gamma kj}$ grows without bound.

The difference scheme (10.26) is *conditionally convergent* for $s \le \frac{1}{2}$. A similar analysis shows the explicit, hyperbolic scheme (10.35) to be conditionally convergent for $k/h \le 1$ (see the Problems).

For the Crank–Nicolson scheme, a matrix analysis of the D_{ij}, based on the actual computation matrix formulas (10.43) to (10.46), shows the convergence of the scheme for $s < \infty$; Isaacson and Keller [10] have carried out such an analysis explicitly. In our brief introduction here, we have not used the matrix treatments.

Stability

Round-off errors e_{ij} can occur at each step of a numerical computation because only a limited number of decimal digits can be retained. As the computation proceeds, the computed solution u_{ij}^c to the difference equations departs from the true solution u_{ij} as a result of the cumulative effect of the e_{ij} and their subsequent propagation in the calculation. In linear systems the effects of the e_{ij} are additive.

We call $\hat{e}_{ij} = u_{ij} - u_{ij}^c$ the *cumulative departure* of the computed solution from the true numerical solution caused by all round-off errors. For a practical (useful) computation, $|\hat{e}_{ij}| \ll |u_{ij}|$; that is, the cumulative growth of round-off errors must not swamp the true difference solution. When $|\hat{e}_{ij}| \ll |u_{ij}|$ for all relevant i and $j < \infty$ in initial-value problems, the computation is termed *stable*. Then, because

$$u(x, t) = u_{ij}^c + D_{ij} + \hat{e}_{ij}, \qquad x = ih, \quad t = jk$$

the difference between the exact solution u of the mathematical model and the computed solution u_{ij}^c of the numerical model depends primarily on the discretization error D_{ij}. Thus it is the dominant part of the *total error* $D_{ij} + \hat{e}_{ij}$ in a stable computation with a consistent and convergent numerical model.

Unfortunately, it is difficult to determine an estimate or upper bound for $|\hat{e}_{ij}|$. Also, an error e_{ij} may not be damped or diffused by further calculation; it may simply persist or grow very slowly, leading to a constant or (relatively) slowly growing $\hat{e}_{ij}$ even in stable computations (where $|\hat{e}_{ij}| \ll |u_{ij}|$ still holds). Fortunately, experience has shown [3] that $|\hat{e}_{ij}|$ grows slowly (or decays) in a stable computation but grows exponentially in an unstable one. A practical definition of stability for initial-boundary-value problems is then: given that $|e_{ij}| < \varepsilon$, the difference equations are stable for fixed h and k if $|\hat{e}_{ij}| \to 0$ as $\varepsilon \to 0$ and $|\hat{e}_{ij}|$ does not increase exponentially as $j \to \infty$. If $|u(x, t)| < \infty$, the latter part of the definition can be replaced by $|\hat{e}_{ij}| < \infty$ as $j \to \infty$.

For linear equations, it is sufficient to study a single line of errors along, say, $j = J$ because the effects of errors at other $j \ne J$ are similar and merely additive. Indeed, if $|\hat{e}_{ij}|_J \le \delta_J$ is the cumulative effect at j of errors on the line J only, then at $t = jk$ the $\sum_J |\hat{e}_{ij}|_J$ of all errors at all $J \le t/k$ is $O(\delta_J k^{-1})$ as $k \to 0$ (i.e., $j \to \infty$) because each row of errors is additive and there are approximately k^{-1} rows of errors as $k \to 0$. If the maximum round-off error δ_J is fixed by the computer, attempts to reduce the total error by refining the grid spacing so $D_{ij} \to 0$ may be foiled by an increase in $\hat{e}_{ij}$ produced by $k \to 0$!

There are two well-known ways of studying the stability of linear difference equations. In the *matrix method*, the difference equations and boundary conditions are expressed in matrix form, e_{ij} is introduced, and the propagation of an initial line of e_{i0} is investigated (see Sec. 10.2.4 for an idea of how such a calculation might proceed). The *Fourier (component) method* employs elemental Fourier components in exponential form to study the growth of a Fourier-series-representable initial error distribution, whose greatest absolute value is less than, say, ε. The Fourier method is simple to use and interpret, but it is strictly applicable only to linear equations with constant coefficients. It ignores the boundary conditions, but this lack of rigor is rarely of serious consequence (see Ames [11, p. 48]). Equations with variable coefficients and nonlinear equations must be reduced to linear, constant coefficient form if the Fourier method is to be used (see Sec. 10.4).

We treat only the Fourier method here. Smith [2] and Ames [11] discuss both methods. The concepts, methods, and consequences of stability analysis are covered in detail in the well-known books by Forsythe and Wasow [3] and Richtmyer and Morton [5].

The Fourier method is attributed to John von Neumann, who did not publish any detailed version of his work. However, O'Brien, Hyman, and Kaplan [12] used his material with permission in a study of the heat-conduction-equation difference scheme (see the historical note by Strelkoff [13] in his paper on differencing for a pair of nonlinear hyperbolic equations). The basic idea of the Fourier stability method is to represent an initial set of errors at the mesh points $(i, 1)$ by a complex Fourier series (a finite series can be used if the range of i is finite) and then to study the growth of the solution to the difference equations that has the initial errors as an initial condition.

Let us examine the difference equation (10.26) for the explicit marching scheme of Sec. 10.2.1. The only round-off error is assumed to be made initially, so for $j > 1$ (recall that $j = 1$ is the initial line), the computed solution u_{ij}^c satisfies the difference equation as does u_{ij}. Accordingly, the propagating round-off error e_{ij} from the single line of errors at $j = 1$ satisfies (10.26), namely,

$$e_{ij+1} = s(e_{i+1j} + e_{i-1j}) + (1 - 2s)e_{ij} \tag{10.60}$$

where $s = k/h^2$ and

$$e_{i1} = \sum_{n=1}^{N} e_n e^{i\lambda_n x} = \sum_{n=1}^{N} e_n e^{i\lambda_n ih} \tag{10.61}$$

For an arbitrary error distribution e_{i1} at the N points, $1 \leq n \leq N$, (10.61) provides N equations for the unknowns e_n if we let $\lambda_n^2 = (n\pi/l)^2$ be the "eigenvalues" for the interval $0 \leq x \leq l = (N - 1)h$ (see Sec. 10.2.1 for the relation of this interval and N and h).*

Again we seek particular Fourier component solutions

$$e_{ij} = e^{i\lambda_n ih} e^{\gamma jk} = e^{i\lambda_n ih} \omega^j \tag{10.62}$$

that can be linearly superposed to satisfy both (10.60) and (10.61). Now γ can be complex, so if $\gamma = \alpha + i\beta$,

$$e^{\gamma jk} = e^{j\alpha k}(\cos jk\beta + i \sin jk\beta)$$

For $|\omega| > 1$, α must be positive; if $\alpha < 0$, $|e^{j\alpha k}| \leq 1$ because $1 \leq j$ and $0 < k$. When $|\omega| < 1$, (10.62) is an exponentially decaying error that oscillates in sign if $\beta \neq 0$.

---

*Alternatively, the error distribution could be assigned a continuous functional form and represented in an infinite series using the eigenfunctions of the mathematical model. The ultimate results are unaffected.

When $|\omega| > 1$, (10.62) is an exponentially growing error as $e^{\alpha k j} \to \infty$ for $j \to \infty$ because $\alpha > 0$; this solution oscillates if $\beta \neq 0$. When $|\omega| = 1$, $\alpha = 0$ and the error persists and oscillates in sign if $\beta \neq 0$. Clearly, stability requires that the difference (or error) equation admit *no* solutions with $|\omega| > 1$. Thus a *necessary condition for the stability of a linear difference scheme with constant coefficients is that it admit only solutions of the form* (10.62) *with* $|\omega| \leq 1$.

In the section on convergence we carried out (equivalently) the substitution of (10.62) in (10.60) with the result that (10.60) admits solutions of the form

$$e_{ij} = e^{i\lambda_n ih}\left(1 - 4s \sin^2 \frac{\lambda_n h}{2}\right)^j = e^{i\lambda_n ih}\omega^j$$

The complete solution of (10.60) and (10.61) has the form

$$e_{ij} = \sum_{n=1}^{N} e_n e^{i\lambda_n ih}\left(1 - 4s \sin^2 \frac{\lambda_n h}{2}\right)^j$$

From (10.61), it is clear that if $|e_{i1}| < \varepsilon$ at each mesh point, $|e_n| \to 0$ as $\varepsilon \to 0, j < \infty$. Thus if

$$|\omega| = \left|1 - 4s \sin^2 \frac{\lambda_n h}{2}\right| \leq 1$$

the difference scheme is stable. We know $|\omega| \leq 1$ for $s \leq \frac{1}{2}$. The stability criteria is $k/h^2 \leq \frac{1}{2}$. This is precisely the result empirically determined in Example 10.1 *and* is the criteria for convergence of the difference scheme also.

A numbergram is an ideal way of illustrating the propagation of a single initial error e. Using (10.60) with $s = \frac{1}{2}$ and 1, $e_{i1} = 0$ for $i \neq 6$, and $e_{61} = e$, we obtain Fig. 10.7. The boundary conditions from (10.25) are applied without introducing additional error, so

$$e_{ij} = 0, \qquad j \geq 2$$
$$e_{N+1 j} = e_{N-1 j}, \qquad j \geq 2, \quad N = 11$$

In the stable case (a) in Fig. 10.7, the error decays. The situation in Fig. 10.7b needs little further amplification! Check Fig. 10.4 again.

There is a connection between the convergence and stability of a difference scheme, as the parabolic scheme results suggest. This connection was formally proved by Lax (see [5], [10], [11]) and is normally stated as

The Lax Equivalence Theorem. Given a well-posed, *linear*, initial-boundary-value problem (mathematical model) and a finite-difference approximation (numerical model) to it that is consistent, then stability is a necessary and sufficient condition for convergence and conversely.

10.3.2   Hyperbolic Equations

Consider first the numerical model (10.34) for the mathematical model (10.33). The difference equation in (10.34) is consistent with the differential equation in (10.33) [see (10.48)]. The convergence of the difference equation is demonstrated

i	1	2	3	4	5	6	7	8	9	10	11	12
7	0	$\frac{5}{64}e$	0	–	–	–	–	–	–	$\frac{7}{64}e$	0	$\frac{7}{64}e$
6	0	0	$\frac{5}{32}e$	0	$\frac{5}{16}e$	0	$\frac{5}{16}e$	0	$\frac{5}{32}e$	0	$\frac{1}{16}e$	0
5	0	$\frac{1}{16}e$	0	$\frac{1}{4}e$	0	$\frac{3}{8}e$	0	$\frac{1}{4}e$	0	$\frac{1}{16}e$	0	$\frac{1}{16}e$
4	0	0	$\frac{1}{8}e$	0	$\frac{3}{8}e$	0	$\frac{3}{8}e$	0	$\frac{1}{8}e$	0	0	0
3	0	0	0	$\frac{1}{4}e$	0	$\frac{1}{2}e$	0	$\frac{1}{4}e$	0	0	0	0
2	0	0	0	0	$\frac{1}{2}e$	0	$\frac{1}{2}e$	0	0	0	0	0
1	0	0	0	0	0	e	0	0	0	0	0	0

j

(a) $s = k/h^2 = \frac{1}{2}$, stable

i	1	2	3	4	5	6	7	8	9	10	11	12
7	0	$20e$	–	–	–	$141e$	–	–	–	$22e$	$12e$	–
6	0	$-5e$	$15e$	$-30e$	$45e$	$-51e$	$45e$	$-30e$	$15e$	$-5e$	$2e$	$-5e$
5	0	e	$-4e$	$10e$	$-16e$	$19e$	$-16e$	$10e$	$-4e$	e	0	0
4	0	0	e	$-3e$	$6e$	$-7e$	$6e$	$-3e$	e	0	0	0
3	0	0	0	e	$-2e$	$3e$	$-2e$	e	0	0	0	0
2	0	0	0	0	e	$-e$	e	0	0	0	0	0
1	0	0	0	0	0	e	0	0	0	0	0	0

j

(b) $s = k/h^2 = 1$, unstable

FIGURE 10.7   Numbergrams for marching, explicit, parabolic model ($N = 11$, $h = 0.1$).

precisely as outlined in Sec. 10.3.1 with the result that *conditional convergence* occurs for $s = k/h \le 1$ (see the Problems). For $s > 1$, the difference equation admits exponentially growing solutions.

We can confirm the convergence result by a stability analysis employing the Fourier (von Neumann) method. For errors introduced at the initial line only, the errors subsequently satisfy the difference equation; from (10.35), the error equation is

$$e_{ij+1} = 2(1 - s^2)e_{ij} + e_{ij-1} + s^2(e_{i+1j} + e_{i-1j}) \tag{10.63}$$

Solutions are sought in the form [see (10.62)]

$$e_{ij} = e^{i\lambda_n ih}\omega^j \tag{10.64}$$

If $|\omega| > 1$ is possible for solutions to (10.63) of form (10.64), the difference equation admits exponentially growing solutions and is unstable.

Introducing (10.64) in (10.63) produces (using the trigonometric identities as before)

$$\omega + \omega^{-1} = 2 - 4s^2 \sin^2 \frac{\lambda_n h}{2}$$

In standard quadratic form, this equation becomes

$$\omega^2 + 2b\omega + 1 = 0 \tag{10.65}$$

where $b = 1 - 2s^2 \sin^2 (\lambda_n h/2) \leq 1$ [see (9.26) to (9.27)]. Now (10.65) has the solutions

$$\omega_\pm = b \pm (b^2 - 1)^{1/2} \qquad (10.66)$$

There are, as we know, three possible cases—namely, $b^2 - 1 \gtrless 0$. If $b^2 - 1 > 0$, $b^2 > 1$; but as $b \leq 1$ for all s, $b^2 > 1$ implies $b < -1$. Then, clearly, $|\omega_-| > 1$ and this solution is unstable. For $b^2 - 1 \leq 0$, $b^2 \leq 1$ and (10.66) can be written

$$\omega_\pm = b \pm i(1 - b^2)^{1/2}$$

so

$$|\omega_\pm| = [b^2 + (1 - b^2)]^{1/2} = 1$$

The difference equation is precisely stable for

$$b^2 = \left(1 - 2s^2 \sin^2 \frac{\lambda_n h}{2}\right)^2 \leq 1$$

or

$$-1 \leq 1 - 2s^2 \sin^2 \frac{\lambda_n h}{2} \leq 1 \qquad (10.67)$$

As $\sin^2 (\lambda_n h/2) \leq 1$, it follows that (10.67) is met when $s = k/h \leq 1$. This result is in agreement with the convergence result, and the simple wave equation has an explicit difference scheme that is stable provided that $k/h \leq 1$. A numbergram (see Fig. 10.7) can be used to demonstrate this criterion.

The ratio $s = k/h \leq 1$ has a particular significance for hyperbolic equations. First, recall that in Sec. 9.3.2 we defined the domain of dependence for the wave equation. This domain, for a solution at a point (y_0, t_0) in the y–t plane, was a portion of the initial data bounded by the characteristics running through (y_0, t_0) and backward to the initial line. Only the *initial data* lying on and between the two characteristics affected the solution at (y_0, t_0). For $c^2 = 1$, the magnitude of the slope of the characteristics was $C_S = |dt/dx| = 1$, so the speed of propagation of information in the mathematical model (10.33) is $c = C_S^{-1} = |dx/dt| = 1$. From the computational star (Fig. 10.5) for the numerical model (10.34) and construction of a sequence diagram such as Fig. 10.3, it is clear that the numerical solution at (i, j) also has a domain of dependence along the initial data. The magnitude of the slope of the implied *numerical characteristics* is $s = k/h = \Delta t/\Delta x$; the speed of propagation of information in the numerical model is $c = h/k = s^{-1}$.

As $s \leq 1$ for stability, the magnitude of the slope of the numerical characteristics must be less than or equal to the magnitude of the slope of the characteristics (of the mathematical model). In other words, the dependence ratio $D_R = s/C_S \leq 1$. Working back from a point $(i, j) = (y, t) = (ih, jk)$, we see that the numerical characteristics spread as fast or faster than the characteristics; thus when the initial data are reached, *the numerical domain of dependence must always contain the mathematical domain of dependence for stability.* This result can be extended broadly to all numerical schemes involving hyperbolic-type equations, both linear and nonlinear [3, 5, 10, 13], and is often called the *Courant Condition.*

Finally, we see that $s = 1$ gives a computational net that precisely coincides with characteristics. This result suggests that a numerical calculation along the characteristics of the mathematical model is the most efficient. This point is true, in general, for it leads to propagation of disturbances at precisely the correct speeds. However, unless the characteristics are straight lines, the computer programming can be difficult and the results are not usually obtained at locations on a convenient grid (see Sec. 9.3.3).

EXAMPLE 10.3   *The Vibrating Membrane.* In Example 8.3 we obtained, by separation of variables and eigenfunction expansion, the solution to a model of the vibration of a large, circular membrane. The differential equation was

$$z_{tt} = c^2 \left(z_{rr} + \frac{1}{r} z_r \right), \qquad 0 < r < R, \quad 0 < t \tag{10.68}$$

with the condition that (see Sec. 2.2.2)

$$z_{tt} = 2c^2 z_{rr}, \qquad r \to 0, \quad 0 < t \tag{10.69}$$

What are the stability criteria? Note that (10.68) is linear but has variable coefficients.

First normalize (10.68) and (10.69). Let $z = Z_0 u$, $r = Rx$, $t = \tau T$. Then (10.68) and (10.69) become

$$u_{TT} = \frac{\tau^2 c^2}{R^2} \left(u_{xx} + \frac{1}{x} u_x \right) \qquad u_{TT} = \frac{2\tau^2 c^2}{R^2} u_{xx}$$

Choosing $\tau = R/c$, a natural time scale equal to the time for a wave to reach the center from the edge of the membrane, gives the normalized differential equations

$$u_{TT} = u_{xx} + \frac{1}{x} u_x, \qquad 0 < x < 1, \quad 0 < T \tag{10.70}$$

$$u_{TT} = 2u_{xx}, \qquad x \to 0, \quad 0 < T \tag{10.71}$$

Explicit difference schemes for (10.70) and (10.71) are easy to write by using central differences on a grid of $\Delta x = h$ and $\Delta T = k$. The difference equation for (10.71) is used at the origin [say for $i = 1$ where $x = h(i - 1)$]. Unfortunately, (10.70) has a variable coefficient x^{-1}, and so it is not possible to use the Fourier method to test the stability of the difference scheme. Fortunately, the characteristics of an equation are determined by only the highest-order terms (Chap. 9). The characteristics of (10.70) are the same as those of the simple wave equation $u_{TT} = u_{xx}$ and $C_S = 1$. From the Courant condition, $D_R = s/C_S \le 1$; therefore $s = k/h \le 1$ is the criterion for stability of a calculation in which the domain of dependence of the differential equation is contained within that of the difference equation.

With the mesh ratio $s = 1$, a computation for the full numerical model is unstable (Fig. 10.8)! Why? To find the reason, we look to the apparently innocuous center condition (10.71). It is also a wave equation, but with a wave speed of $2^{1/2}$ (not 1). Thus, for this equation, $C_S = |dt/dx| = 2^{-1/2}$; and from $D_R \le 1$, $s \le 2^{-1/2} \approx 0.707 < 1$! We must, accordingly, retain $s \le 2^{-1/2}$ throughout the entire calculation for stability (Fig. 10.8). Otherwise the solution progressively deteriorates after $t \approx 1.0$, as the figure shows, because although the computation is stable for $x \ne 0$, the exponentially growing error at $x = 0$ propagates through the solution.

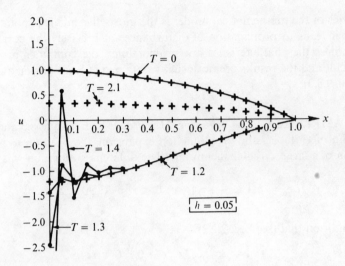

FIGURE 10.8   Vibration of circular membrane ($\longrightarrow$: $s = 1$, $+ + +$: $s = 2^{-1/2}$).

10.4   NONLINEAR INITIAL-VALUE PROBLEMS

When the partial differential equation of a mathematical model is nonlinear, solutions for general auxiliary conditions can no longer be obtained by any of the series or integral methods that we have developed because they all depend on linear superposition (see Sec. 2.4). However, the finite-difference method and the method of characteristics (see Chap. 9) are both applicable to nonlinear problems. In principle, nonlinearity makes no change in the method of finite differences; however, consistency and convergence may be more difficult to prove. The Fourier (and matrix) methods for stability analysis are no longer applicable, since they, too, rely on linearity.

In the conduction of heat in solids, the thermal conductivity K often depends linearly [14] on temperature u; we usually assume that K is constant, whereas $K = K_0(1 + \beta u)$ may be more accurate, β being small generally. The one-dimensional heat equation (2.20) becomes in this case

$$u_t = [k_0(1 + \beta u)u_x]_x \tag{10.72}$$

that is, nonlinear. With regard to the diffusion equation

$$Q_t = DQ_{xx} \tag{10.73}$$

discussed in Sec. 8.3.2, Crank [15] offers several examples in which D is not constant but depends on the concentration Q of the diffusing substance; then (10.73) must be written as

$$Q_t = (DQ_x)_x$$

which is nonlinear if $D = D(Q)$. One specific example cited by Crank [15] involves $D = D_0 \exp(2.3Q/Q_0)$ (see the Problems).

In heat conduction, even if K is constant, the boundary conditions may be nonlinear. For example, if natural convection replaces cooling by forced convection at a surface $\bar{S}$ of a body, (2.25) (a linear relation) is replaced by

$$K\frac{\partial u}{\partial n} + H(u - u_S)^{5/4} = 0 \text{ on } \bar{S}, \qquad t > 0$$

a nonlinear law [14]. If black-body radiation occurs from $\bar{S}$, then

$$K\frac{\partial u}{\partial n} = \sigma E(u^4 - u_S^4) \text{ on } \bar{S}, \qquad t > 0$$

where σ is the Stefan–Boltzmann constant and 0.05 (polished metal) $< E < 0.98$ (soot) is the emissivity of the surface [14]. Although nonlinear boundary conditions prevent use of linear superposition to obtain model solutions, the analysis of difference equations can be carried out as usual if the partial differential equation remains linear, under the (rather good) assumption that the boundary conditions do not have a serious effect on the stability criteria.

In fluid mechanics, the Euler equations of motion (2.65) and (2.66) for an ideal fluid are a coupled, nonlinear pair. If the fluid is viscous (with viscosity μ), the terms $(\mu/\rho)\nabla^2 u$ and $(\mu/\rho)\nabla^2 v$ must be added to the right of (2.65) and (2.66), respectively, and the velocity potential ϕ no longer exists. An equation representing the key nonlinear problems arising in fluid mechanics is the Burgers' equation

$$u_t + uu_x = vu_{xx} \tag{10.74}$$

where $v = \mu/\rho = $ constant. This equation was employed by Burgers in a heuristic mathematical model of turbulence in fluid flow.

EXAMPLE 10.4   *Nonlinear Vibration of a Long String.* Section 9.3.3 gave a method of characteristics solution for the model (let $x \to y$ and $y \to t$)

$$z^4 z_{tt} - z_{yy} = z, \qquad -\infty < y < \infty, \quad 0 < t$$

$$z(y, 0) = f(y) \neq 0, \qquad -\infty < y < \infty \tag{10.75}$$

$$z_t(y, 0) = 0, \qquad -\infty < y < \infty$$

Let us try to determine the consistency, convergence, and stability of a numerical model for (10.75). Assume that $z \neq 0$; then the differential equation (a wave equation) has characteristics given by $dt/dx = \pm z^2$ and the speed of propagation of disturbances is $c = z^{-2}$, so that the shape of the characteristics and c depend on the unknown $z(x, t)$ at each point.

The difference model for (10.75) is, with $h = \Delta y$ and $k = \Delta t$,

$$(z_{ij})^4 \frac{z_{ij+1} - 2z_{ij} + z_{ij-1}}{k^2} - \frac{z_{i+1j} - 2z_{ij} + z_{i-1j}}{h^2} = z_{ij}, \qquad 2 < j, \quad \text{all } i$$

$$z_{i1} = f(ih), \qquad \text{all } i \tag{10.76}$$

$$z_{i2} = z_{i1} + \frac{h^2}{2}\left[\frac{d_{i1}(z_{yy})}{z_{i1}^4} + \frac{1}{z_{i1}^3}\right]$$

which is nonlinear but explicit for z_{ij+1}. The computation formula, with $s = k/h$, is

$$z_{ij+1} = 2z_{ij} - z_{ij-1} + \frac{s^2}{z_{ij}^4}(z_{i+1j} - 2z_{ij} + z_{i-1j}) + \frac{k^2}{z_{ij}^3}, \qquad z_{ij} \neq 0$$

In order to determine if the difference equation in (10.76) is consistent, we use the Taylor's series expansion about (i, j) to obtain the truncation error

$$T_{ij} = -\frac{1}{12}(z^4 z_{tttt} k^2 - z_{yyyy} h^2)_{ij} + O(z^4 k^4 + h^4) = O(k^2 + h^2)$$

provided that z and the fourth derivatives are bounded. The difference equation is consistent because $T_{ij} \to 0$ as k and $h \to 0$.

Introduction of the discretization error $D_{ij}(z_{ij} = z - D_{ij})$ in the difference equation leads to a complex nonlinear equation involving the unknown, exact solution z at (i, j), and the method that we have used previously fails. Similarly, an attempt to do a Fourier-method stability analysis fails because the difference equation (satisfied by the error e_{ij}) is nonlinear and superposition is not possible. Is there a way out of this dilemma? Yes, two.

First, we can assume that over any given time step (in particular, between $j - 1$ and $j + 1$) and spatially (from say $i - 1$ to $i + 1$) the value of z_{ij} does not change significantly (e.g., $|\Delta z|/|z| \ll 1$). Then, where z_{ij} appears nonlinearly, it can be treated for convergence and stability analyses as a constant, albeit unknown. This effectively linearizes the problem, introduces a constant parameter $F = s^2/z^4$, and brings the Fourier method back into use. Such an approach of linearization is the most widely used means of analyzing nonlinear models, but it is valid strictly only as k and $h \to 0$. Serious instabilities have been known to arise in "theoretically" stable computations with nonlinear equations because k was effectively finite.

Second, for hyperbolic equations, there is a direct way out of our dilemma. We rely on the assumption that the *Lax Equivalence Theorem* (Sec. 10.3.1) applies. Then we use the *Courant* (domain of dependence) *Condition* (Sec. 10.3.2). Here $C_S = |dt/dy| = 1/c = z^2$, while $s = k/h = \Delta t/\Delta y$. For the domain of dependence of the numerical model to contain that of the mathematical model, $D_R = s/C_S \leq 1$; that is, $s \leq z^2$. Unfortunately, the characteristics are now *curved*, so this result depends on the unknown z at each point. The stability criterion $k/h \leq z^2$ is thus applicable only locally—that is, between say $j - 1$ and $j + 1$—*and* only as k and $h \to 0$. If k is finite, the slope of the characteristics C_S computed at (i, j) may change sufficiently as we move away from this point so that the straight-sided numerical domain of dependence does not include the mathematical domain blocked out by curving characteristics (see Fig. 10.9).

For a computation, one might require $k \leq hz_j^2$, where $z_j = |z_{ij}|_{\min}$ at each j, when computing z_{ij+1}. Clearly, a new feature of nonlinear equations is that the stability criterion depends not only on the grid-mesh-spacing ratio but on the solution as well. Great care is needed in treating nonlinear initial-value problems.

EXAMPLE 10.5   *A Nonlinear Parabolic Equation—a Stability Analysis.*
Consider (10.74), whose linear equivalent is the convection-diffusion equation (Secs.

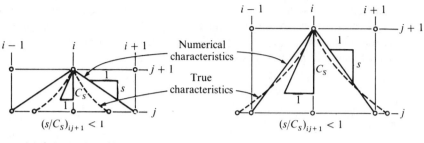

$(s/C_S)_{ij+1} < 1$ $(s/C_S)_{ij+1} < 1$

k infinitesimal: *stable* k finite: *unstable*

FIGURE 10.9   The effect of curved characteristics on the Courant condition.

8.3 and 10.2.2). With $h = \Delta x$ and $k = \Delta t$, the explicit difference representation of (10.74), where $v \geq 0$ and $u(x, t)$ is the unknown, is

$$\frac{u_{ij+1} - u_{ij}}{k} + u_{ij}\frac{u_{i+1j} - u_{i-1j}}{2h} = v\frac{u_{i+1j} - 2u_{ij} + u_{i-1j}}{h^2} \tag{10.77}$$

We assume as before that an initial line of round-off errors e_{i1} ($j = 1$ corresponds to $t = 0$ as usual) is introduced, but no further errors are made; therefore the computed solution u_{ij}^c satisfies the difference equation, as does u_{ij}, for $j > 1$. If the initial-value problem for $e_{ij} = u_{ij} - u_{ij}^c$ admits exponentially growing solutions of the form

$$e_{ij} = e^{i\lambda ih}e^{\gamma jk} = e^{i\lambda ih}\omega^j \tag{10.78}$$

that is, if $|\omega| > 1$ is permissible—the scheme (10.77) is unstable. Introducing $u_{ij} = u_{ij}^c + e_{ij}$ in (10.77) yields

$$\frac{u_{ij+1}^c - u_{ij}^c}{k} + \frac{e_{ij+1} - e_{ij}}{k} + (u_{ij}^c + e_{ij})\frac{u_{i+1j}^c - u_{i-1j}^c}{2h} + (u_{ij}^c + e_{ij})\frac{e_{i+1j} - e_{i-1j}}{2h}$$

$$= v\frac{u_{i+1j}^c - 2u_{ij}^c + u_{i-1j}^c}{h^2} + v\frac{e_{i+1j} - 2e_{ij} + e_{i-1j}}{h^2} \tag{10.79}$$

Because u_{ij}^c satisfies (10.77) for $j > 1$, the difference equation for e_{ij} is obtained by subtracting (10.77) from (10.79):

$$\frac{e_{ij+1} - e_{ij}}{k} + (u_{ij}^c + e_{ij})\frac{e_{i+1j} - e_{i-1j}}{2h} + e_{ij}\frac{u_{i+1j}^c - u_{i-1j}^c}{2h}$$

$$= v\frac{e_{i+1j} - 2e_{ij} + e_{i-1j}}{h^2} \tag{10.80}$$

This equation is nonlinear and involves the difference derivative of the solution u_{ij}^c. The only systematic way to proceed is to employ an extension of the Fourier (von Neumann) method. We *assume* that the change in u_{ij}^c over an i or j step is small compared to u_{ij}^c; that is, $|\Delta u_{ij}^c| \ll |u_{ij}^c|$ and that the derivatives

$$\frac{u_{i+1j}^c - u_{i-1j}^c}{2h} \quad \text{and} \quad \frac{e_{i+1j} - e_{i-1j}}{2h}$$

are, as a consequence, also small, namely, $O(e_{ij})$. Now (10.80) is examined and only $O(e_{ij})$ terms are retained; we are actually constructing a stability analysis for vanishingly small errors [terms in $(e_{ij})^2$ are negligible] and h and $k \to 0$ (changes in u_{ij}^c and e_{ij} are small over a few grid points). Thus

$$e_{ij} \frac{u_{i+1j}^c - u_{i-1j}^c}{2h} = O(e_{ij}^2)$$

and is neglected, as is

$$e_{ij} \frac{e_{i+1j} - e_{i-1j}}{2h} = O(e_{ij}^2)$$

The *linear* result from (10.80) is

$$\frac{e_{ij+1} - e_{ij}}{k} + u_{ij}^c \frac{e_{i+1j} - e_{i-1j}}{2h} = v \frac{e_{i+1j} - 2e_{ij} + e_{i-1j}}{h^2} \tag{10.81}$$

The growth or decay of the error e_{ij} according to this equation is now investigated for Fourier component forms (10.78). If $|\omega| > 1$ is possible, we conclude that (10.81) is unstable and *infer* that the original difference approximation (10.77) is also unstable.

Putting (10.78) in (10.81) gives

$$\frac{\omega - 1}{k} + u_{ij}^c \frac{e^{\hat{\imath}\lambda h} - e^{-\hat{\imath}\lambda h}}{2h} = v \frac{e^{\hat{\imath}\lambda h} - 2 + e^{-\hat{\imath}\lambda h}}{h^2}$$

Using trigonometric identities to replace the exponentials yields

$$\omega = 1 - \frac{4vk}{h^2} \sin^2 \frac{\lambda h}{2} - i \frac{u_{ij}^c k}{h} \sin \lambda h$$

Accordingly, (10.81) admits solutions of the form (10.78) with this ω. For stability, $|\omega| \leq 1$. As $\omega = \alpha + i\beta$, $|\omega| = (\alpha^2 + \beta^2)^{1/2}$, and $|\omega|^2 \leq 1$ is equivalent to $|\omega| \leq 1$. Therefore we require

$$\left(1 - \frac{4vk}{h^2} \sin^2 \frac{\lambda h}{2}\right)^2 + \left(\frac{u_{ij}^c k}{h}\right)^2 \sin^2 \lambda h \leq 1 \tag{10.82}$$

Suppose that $\sin \lambda h = 0$ for some component with specific λ and given h; then $\sin \lambda h/2$ is either 0 or ± 1. If it is not zero, we require

$$\left(1 - \frac{4vk}{h^2}\right)^2 \leq 1 \quad \text{or} \quad \frac{vk}{h^2} \leq \frac{1}{2} \tag{10.83}$$

But if $\sin \lambda h/2 = 0$, then $\sin \lambda h = 0$ always, and (10.82) is satisfied. Assume that $\sin \lambda h \neq 0$ and expand (10.82); this gives

$$\left(\frac{4vk}{h^2} \sin^2 \frac{\lambda h}{2}\right)\left(-2 + \frac{4vk}{h^2} \sin^2 \frac{\lambda h}{2} + u_{ij}^{c2} \frac{k}{v} \cos^2 \frac{\lambda h}{2}\right) \leq 0$$

since

$$\sin^2 \lambda h = 4 \sin^2 \frac{\lambda h}{2} \cos^2 \frac{\lambda h}{2}$$

When $\sin \lambda h/2 \neq 0$, we require

$$-2 + \frac{4vk}{h^2} \sin^2 \frac{\lambda h}{2} + u_{ij}^{c2} \frac{k}{v} \cos^2 \frac{\lambda h}{2} \leq 0 \qquad (10.84)$$

The largest allowable value of $vk/h^2 = \frac{1}{2}$, so (10.84) must hold for $vk/h^2 = \frac{1}{2}$; that is,

$$\sin^2 \frac{\lambda h}{2} + \frac{u_{ij}^{c2} k}{2v} \cos^2 \frac{\lambda h}{3} \leq 1$$

But $\sin^2 (\lambda h/2) + \cos^2 (\lambda h/2) = 1$, so

$$\sin^2 \frac{\lambda h}{2} + \frac{u_{ij}^{c2} k}{2v} \cos^2 \frac{\lambda h}{2} \leq \sin^2 \frac{\lambda h}{2} + \cos^2 \frac{\lambda h}{2}$$

and we conclude that *another stability criteria* exists, namely,

$$\frac{1}{2} (u_{ij}^c)^2 \frac{k}{v} \leq 1 \qquad (10.85)$$

Thus the difference equation (10.77) is *conditionally stable* according to linear theory provided that the *two* criteria

$$\frac{vk}{h^2} \leq \frac{1}{2}, \qquad (u_{ij}^c)^2 k \leq 2v \qquad (10.86)$$

are met. The criteria for the nonlinear equation (10.77) depend on the solution, as now expected. The first criterion $vk/h^2 \leq \frac{1}{2}$ is related to the diffusion part of the differential equation, for it is precisely the same as that obtained for the normalized equation $u_t = u_{xx}$ (set $v = 1$). The slope of the characteristics for the convection equation $u_t + uu_x = 0$ is (Example 9.1, Chap. 9) u^{-1}; the Courant condition is then

$$\left(\frac{k}{h}\right)^2 \leq \frac{1}{(u_{ij}^c)^2}$$

for the "wavelike" portion of our equation. Combining the diffusion and convection criteria deduced here produces, when $vk/h^2 = \frac{1}{2}$,

$$\frac{k^2}{h^2} \leq \frac{1}{(u_{ij}^c)^2} \quad \text{or} \quad k^2 (u_{ij}^c)^2 \leq h^2 = 2vk$$

Hence

$$\frac{1}{2} (u_{ij}^c)^2 \frac{k}{v} \leq 1$$

which is the second criterion (10.85). Often stability criteria can be deduced in this heuristic manner by considering the physically different parts from which an equation is composed.

10.5   ELLIPTIC EQUATIONS

Elliptic equations are associated with mathematical models of equilibrium or steady-state physical processes in spatial domains. In the widespread and varied applications involving such models, the space domains are often irregular, thereby making numerical solution of the models necessary.

The classic and simplest elliptic equations, the Laplace equation

$$\nabla^2 u = u_{xx} + u_{yy} = 0 \tag{10.87}$$

and the Poisson equation

$$\nabla^2 u = f(x, y) \qquad f(x, y) < \infty \tag{10.88}$$

illustrate the key features of elliptic equations, yet have current applications ([1, 3, 11] and Sec. 2.2.3). Indeed, a most difficult mathematical problem remains the accurate solution of these equations in arbitrary regions with specified boundary conditions dictated by the physical system.

Elliptic equations of all orders, linear and nonlinear, share two key features. First, the domain R of an elliptic model (i.e., a model including an elliptic equation) is surrounded by a *closed* boundary C (compare this to the boundary for parabolic and hyperbolic models, which is open to infinity in the time dimension). Second, specification of a single boundary condition at every point of C is sufficient to determine uniquely the solution to a second-order elliptic model (Sec. 6.3). There are no initial conditions to be satisfied; the problem to be solved is a pure boundary-value problem. As a consequence, numerical marching procedures cannot be used; a numerical procedure must seek to satisfy the difference equation and boundary conditions of an elliptic numerical model simultaneously at every internal and boundary mesh point of the grid (see, e.g., Fig. 10.1). To begin, we formulate representative numerical models of the classic Dirichlet and Neumann mathematical models involving the two-dimensional Laplace equation on the region R with a boundary condition prescribed on the boundary C shown in Fig. 10.1.

The Dirichlet model for $u(x, y)$ is

$$\nabla^2 u = 0 \qquad \text{in } R \tag{10.89}$$

$$u = g(x, y) \qquad \text{on } C \tag{10.90}$$

This model has a unique solution for all reasonable $g(x, y)$ (see Chap. 6). As before, construction of a numerical model begins with R being covered by a grid of mesh points (Fig. 10.1). There are no stability criteria to meet in an elliptic computation, so the grid-spacing ratio $s = k/h$ plays no significant role and we let $s = 1$ or $k = h$ for convenience. Mesh points or nodes within C are internal (I) points and those outside C are external (E) points. The boundary (B) points are those nodes lying on C, *plus* those points of C lying on lines connecting I and E nodes (Fig. 10.1). The difference representation of the boundary condition (10.90) is

$$u_p = g(x_p, y_p), \qquad x_p, y_p \quad \text{on } C \tag{10.91}$$

where (x_p, y_p) are the coordinates of the B points (some suitable numbering system must be devised in a computation to identify these points precisely).

The simple central difference operator E_D, defined in (10.11), is usually adequate to represent the Laplacian ∇^2 at all I points *having four I neighbors*. The difference equation can be written as the "five-point" expression ($k = h$)

$$u_{ij} = \tfrac{1}{4}(u_{i+ij} + u_{ij+1} + u_{i-1j} + u_{ij-1}), \qquad (i \pm 1, j \pm 1) \in I \tag{10.92}$$

This "regular" computational star is shown in Fig. 10.10. The regular star gives the value of u_{ij} as the average of the four surrounding values of the discrete function. The first application of (10.92) produces *one* equation and *five* unknowns; subsequent applications that use the nodes from the corners of the previous stars as centers produce on average *one* equation and *two* new unknowns. Clearly, this method is of no use in unbounded domains!

Near C the regular star cannot be applied because the stars centered at I points with three or fewer I neighbors have legs that intersect C where boundary values are specified. Three "irregular" stars are shown for a sample boundary-region orientation in Fig. 10.10. A new representation of the Laplacian must be derived for the irregular stars to link I points to B points where u is prescribed in this Dirichlet problem; a different special treatment near C is required for Neumann problems.

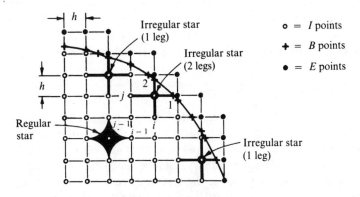

FIGURE 10.10   Section of region R and boundary C for elliptic model.

Consider the irregular star with two short legs in Fig. 10.10. The B points at the ends of the short legs are numbered 1 and 2 in a counterclockwise direction; the lengths of these legs are $\alpha_1 h$ and $\alpha_2 h$, respectively, where $0 < \alpha_1 \le 1$ and $0 < \alpha_2 \le 1$. To obtain an expression for an irregular Laplace difference operator at (i, j), we use the Taylor's series (10.2). For example,

$$u_1 = u_{ij} + u_{xij}\alpha_1 h + \tfrac{1}{2}u_{xxij}\alpha_1^2 h^2 + \tfrac{1}{6}u_{xxxij}\alpha_1^3 h^3 + O(h^4)$$

$$u_{i-1j} = u_{ij} + u_{xij}(-h) + \tfrac{1}{2}u_{xxij}h^2 + \tfrac{1}{6}u_{xxxij}(-h)^3 + O(h^4)$$

To find u_{xxij}, we multiply the second equation by α_1 and add the equations to eliminate u_{xij}:

$$u_1 + \alpha_1 u_{i-1j} = (1 + \alpha_1)u_{ij} + \tfrac{1}{2}u_{xxij}\alpha_1 h^2(1 + \alpha_1)$$

$$+ \tfrac{1}{6}u_{xxxij}\alpha_1 h^3(\alpha_1^2 - 1) + O(h^4)$$

Then

$$u_{xxij} = \frac{2}{\alpha_1 h^2}\left(\frac{u_1}{1 + \alpha_1} - u_{ij} + \frac{\alpha_1 u_{i-1j}}{1 + \alpha_1}\right) + \frac{h}{3}(\alpha_1 - 1)u_{xxxij} + O(h^2)$$

It follows that u_{yyij} is given by a similar expression (see the Problems), so

$$[\nabla^2 u]_{ij} = \frac{1}{h^2}\left[\frac{2u_1}{\alpha_1(1+\alpha_1)} + \frac{2u_2}{\alpha_2(1+\alpha_2)} - 2\left(\frac{1}{\alpha_1} + \frac{1}{\alpha_2}\right)u_{ij} + \frac{2u_{i-1j}}{1+\alpha_1} + \frac{2u_{ij-1}}{1+\alpha_2}\right]$$

$$+ \frac{h}{3}[(\alpha_1 - 1)u_{xxx} + (\alpha_2 - 1)u_{yyy}]_{ij} + O(h^2) \qquad (10.93)$$

The truncation error for (10.93) is

$$T_{ij} = \frac{h}{3}[(\alpha_1 - 1)u_{xxx} + (\alpha_2 - 1)u_{yyy}]_{ij} + O(h^2) = O(h) + O(h^2) \qquad (10.94)$$

if the third derivatives are bounded and $\alpha_1 \neq 1$. If $\alpha_1 \to 1$ and $\alpha_2 \to 1$, then $u_1 \to u_{i+1j}$ and $u_2 \to u_{ij+1}$, so $T_{ij} = O(h^2)$ and (10.93) is equivalent to the regular star expression [see (10.11) and (10.47)]. Use of the irregular stars leads to a first-order truncation error. An alternative is to use regular stars and apply the boundary values at the nodes nearest to C. This process leads to first-order errors as well.

The computation formula derived from (10.93) for irregular stars is

$$u_{ij} = \frac{\alpha_1\alpha_2}{\alpha_1 + \alpha_2}\left[\frac{u_1}{\alpha_1(1+\alpha_1)} + \frac{u_2}{\alpha_2(1+\alpha_2)} + \frac{u_{i-1j}}{1+\alpha_1} + \frac{u_{ij-1}}{1+\alpha_2}\right] \qquad (10.95)$$

(Another form is needed if the short legs are other than 1 and 2 in Fig. 10.10.) Now, the linear, algebraic equations (10.92) and (10.95) provide simultaneous equations for the u_{ij} at all possible I points in R, while (10.91) gives u values at the B points (Fig. 10.1). Because C is a closed boundary, there is *one* linear, algebraic equation for *each* unknown at an interior point. If the I points are numbered sequentially—for example, from left to right and upward—we can write the set of linear simultaneous equations formally in a matrix form $AU = D$ with $U = (u_1 \ldots u_N)^{T*}$ being the u_{ij} values at the numbered I points, $D = (d_1 \ldots d_N)^T$, where $d_n = 0$ unless an irregular star is involved and boundary values enter the expression, and N being the total number of I points. Thus D contains all the g values that are prescribed. In each linear equation, $u_n = u_{ij}$ is given in terms of other unknown interior values or known boundary values. The number of equations equals the number of unknowns, and this linear set of simultaneous equations is nonhomogeneous—that is, $D \neq 0$—if $g(x_p, y_p) \neq 0$ on C. We expect, consequently, to find a unique solution to the set $AU = D$. Before answering the obvious questions raised by this paragraph, let us examine the changes in formulation that occur if a Neumann problem is considered.

Let the Neumann model for $u(x, y)$ be

$$\nabla^2 u = 0 \qquad \text{in } R \qquad (10.96)$$

$$\frac{\partial u}{\partial n} = g(x, y) \qquad \text{on } C \qquad (10.97)$$

with $\oint_C g(x, y)\, ds = 0$ for compatibility. Consider Fig. 10.11 and the boundary condition (10.97). Several approaches are possible—for example, using the layout of Fig. 10.10 and constructing normals at each B point. We have chosen a simpler one.

$*(u_1 \quad u_2)^T = \begin{pmatrix} u_1 \\ u_2 \end{pmatrix}$; that is, the transpose exchanges rows and columns.

Only regular stars are used *at each I point* and the normal derivative is evaluated along a perpendicular to C from the *closest* node, which is taken as a B point. These nodes are numbered consecutively in Fig. 10.11. The left-hand vertical boundary that coincides with the nodes offers no problem. We apply the regular star formula (10.92) at $(2, j)$, together with the central difference representation

$$\frac{u_{3j} - u_{1j}}{.2h} = g(x_2, y_j)$$

to eliminate the fictitious point u_{1j} and obtain the star shown at 17.

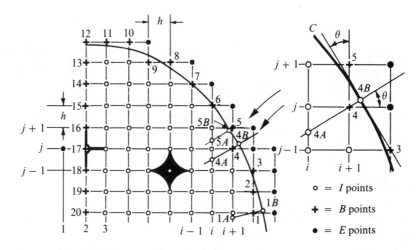

FIGURE 10.11   Section of region R and boundary C for Neumann model.

Looking at point 4, we have the derivative representation

$$\frac{u_4 - u_{4A}}{h/\cos \theta} + O(h) = (u_n)_{4B} = g(x_{4B}, y_{4B})$$

obtained by use of the Taylor's series about $4B$. Formulas of this type can be derived for all points on the curved boundary. As u_{4A} is not defined, we interpolate linearly between (i, j) and $(i, j - 1)$; that is,

$$u_{4A} = u_{ij}(1 - \tan \theta) + u_{ij-1} \tan \theta$$

so, finally, as $u_4 = u_{i+1j}$,

$$u_{ij}(\cos \theta - \sin \theta) = u_{i+1j} \cos \theta + u_{ij-1} \sin \theta - hg(x_{4B}, y_{4B}) \qquad (10.98)$$

Equation (10.92) is applied to all internal nodes having no boundary neighbors; (10.92) is used together with (10.98) at (i, j) points involving the boundary to produce a single star and computation formula involving the five points (i, j) and $(i \pm 1, j \pm 1)$. As a result, there are an equal number of equations and unknowns. However, as the solution to a pure Neumann problem is unique only up to an undetermined constant (Chap. 6), there must be an infinity of solutions to the finite-difference problem, all differing by a constant. Indeed, the system of linear equations is redundant because one equation can be expressed as a linear combination of the others. The methodology for solution of a pure Neumann difference model is not well established, but pragmatic methods work [3].

Now we return to the Dirichlet numerical model, represented by (10.91), (10.92), and (10.95), to prove that it is consistent and convergent. By proving the existence and uniqueness of the solution in the process, we deduce a specific means of solving the model.

First, are the difference equations consistent? For the regular star represented by (10.92), the truncation error is [Sec. 10.3, (10.50); recall that $k = h$ here]

$$T_{ij} = [\nabla^2 u]_{ij} - \left(\frac{u_{i+1j} - 2u_{ij} + u_{i-1j}}{h^2} + \frac{u_{ij+1} - 2u_{ij} + u_{ij-1}}{h^2} \right)$$

$$= E[u] - E_D[u_{ij}] = O(h^2) \tag{10.99}$$

The truncation error for the irregular star formula (10.95) or (10.93) was, according to (10.94), $T_{ij} = O(h)$ if $\alpha_1 \neq 1$ or $\alpha_2 \neq 1$. Otherwise $T_{ij} = O(h^2)$. As $h \to 0$, $T_{ij} \to 0$ in both cases; the difference equations are consistent.

Second, is the difference model convergent—that is, does $D_{ij} = u(x, y) - u_{ij}$ vanish as $h \to 0$? In Sec. 6.3.1 a maximum-minimum principle was the key to proofs of uniqueness for the Dirichlet model. Here such a principle is also the basis for our results.

THEOREM 10.1   A solution u_{ij} of the difference representation of the Laplace equation in a region R takes its maximum and minimum values at the boundary points on C or u_{ij} is constant on $\bar{R} = R + C$.

Proof: For later use, we prove by contradiction a more general result that includes the theorem. Let $\nabla^2 u_{ij} = E_D[u_{ij}] \geq 0$ in R. For example, (10.92) becomes

$$u_{ij} \leq \tfrac{1}{4}(u_{i+1j} + u_{ij+1} + u_{i-1j} + u_{ij-1}) \tag{10.100}$$

and in (10.95) $\leq$ replaces $=$. Suppose that the maximum value $u_{pq} = M$ occurs strictly in R, not on C, at the I point (p, q). According to (10.100), u_{pq} must be less than or equal to the average of the surrounding values [if the star includes B points, (10.95) is used]. Therefore the maximum value M must be taken at all four surrounding points also because although u_{pq}, as the maximum value, cannot be less than any of the values at the surrounding points, (10.100) cannot be valid if one of the values is less than u_{pq}. Repetition of this argument successively outward from (p, q) over all I points governed by (10.100) shows that the maximum value M must be taken at all such points. Near the boundary at those I points connected to B points, (10.95) holds with $\leq$ replacing $=$. The foregoing argument is still valid because (10.95) gives u_{ij} as a weighted average of the neighboring values with positive coefficients whose sum is unity. The maximum M must continue to be taken at surrounding points, which now include all the boundary points. This contradicts the supposition that the maximum is taken strictly in the interior.

Thus if $\nabla^2 u_{ij} = E_D[u_{ij}] \geq 0$, the maximum value of u_{ij} is taken at the boundary C of R or the maximum is taken everywhere in R; that is, u_{ij} is constant. The proof that the minimum of u_{ij} must occur on C or u_{ij} is constant when $\nabla^2 u_{ij} = E_D[u_{ij}] \leq 0$ follows by using $U_{ij} = -u_{ij}$ and the maximum result. These general inequality results prove the theorem as a special case—that is, when $\nabla^2 u_{ij} = E[u_{ij}] = 0$.   Q.E.D.

If $g(x_p, y_p) \equiv 0$ on C in the Dirichlet difference model for the Laplace equation given by (10.91), (10.92), and (10.95), the resulting set of simultaneous equations is homogeneous; that is, $AU = 0$. In this case, Theorem 10.1 requires $U = 0$ because both the maximum and the minimum are zero on the boundary and hence the constant value of u_{ij} is zero. Because this homogeneous system of simultaneous equations has the unique solution zero, *a unique nonzero solution exists* [8] for the nonhomogeneous system $AU = D$ representing the Dirichlet model when $g \neq 0$ on C. This fact proves the existence and uniqueness of the solution to the Dirichlet numerical, finite-difference model for the Laplace equation for g, which must at least be defined and bounded at points on C. Similar proofs can be made for Poisson's equation. If we can now prove that u_{ij} converges to $u(x, y)$ as $h \to 0$, we shall have effectively constructed an existence proof for the Dirichlet mathematical model for the Laplace equation in a general closed region R for arbitrary boundary values $g(x, y)$ (see Sec. 6.2).

The general maximum-minimum results proved above are the basis for the convergence proof. We employ a technique used in Sec. 6.3.1. Let $D_{ij} = u(x, y) - u_{ij}$ be the discretization error, where, as before, $x = ih$ and $y = jh$. For any sufficiently smooth u, (10.99) yields

$$E[u] - E_D[u_{ij}] = T_{ij}$$

The existence of bounded derivatives up to the order necessary to estimate T_{ij} is assumed. As $E[u] = \nabla^2 u = 0$, introduction of D_{ij} in the difference relations (10.92) or (10.95) produces

$$0 = E_D[u - D_{ij}] = E_D[u] - E_D[D_{ij}] = E[u] - T_{ij} - E_D[D_{ij}]$$

or

$$E_D[D_{ij}] = -T_{ij} = \begin{cases} O(h^2) & \text{for (10.92)} \\ O(h) & \text{for (10.95)} \end{cases} \tag{10.101}$$

while $D_{ij} \equiv 0$ on C—that is, at B points.

Define

$$\phi(x, y) = \tfrac{1}{4}T(x^2 + y^2)$$

where $T = \max \{|T_{ij}|\}$ in R. Let the origin of (x, y) lie in R, so $0 \leq \phi(x, y) \leq \tfrac{1}{4}T\rho^2$, where ρ is the diameter of the smallest circle enclosing R with center at $(0, 0)$; ρ is less than or equal to the maximum distance across R. If $d_{ij} = D_{ij} + \phi$,

$$E_D[D_{ij}] = E_D[d_{ij}] - E_D[\phi] = E_D[d_{ij}] - T = -T_{ij}$$

because the third and higher derivatives of ϕ are zero; that is, $E_D[\phi] = E[\phi]$. Accordingly,

$$E_D[d_{ij}] = -T_{ij} + T \geq 0$$

and d_{ij} takes its maximum value on C because of the maximum result proved earlier. As $D_{ij} \equiv 0$ on C, $d_{ij} = \phi$ on C, and as $\phi \leq \tfrac{1}{4}T\rho^2$, $d_{ij} \leq \tfrac{1}{4}T\rho^2$ in R. But $d_{ij} = D_{ij} + \phi$; hence

$$D_{ij} \leq \tfrac{1}{4}T\rho^2 - \phi = \tfrac{1}{4}T\rho^2 - \tfrac{1}{4}T(x^2 + y^2) \leq \tfrac{1}{4}T\rho^2 \tag{10.102}$$

If $d_{ij} = -D_{ij} + \phi$,

$$E_D[D_{ij}] = -E_D[d_{ij}] + T = -T_{ij}$$

and

$$E_D[d_{ij}] = T + T_{ij} \geq 0$$

Again, $d_{ij} \leq \frac{1}{4}T\rho^2$ in R, so

$$D_{ij} \geq \phi - \frac{T}{4}\rho^2 \geq -\frac{T}{4}\rho^2 \qquad (10.103)$$

From (10.102) and (10.103),

$$-\frac{T}{4}\rho^2 \leq D_{ij} \leq \frac{T}{4}\rho^2$$

or

$$|D_{ij}| \leq \tfrac{1}{4}\rho^2 T = \tfrac{1}{4}\rho^2 \cdot \begin{cases} O(h) & \text{for (10.95)} \\ O(h^2) & \text{for (10.92)} \end{cases}$$

The discretization error vanishes as $h \to 0$ and $u_{ij} \to u(x, y)$; therefore the difference model is convergent.

We have proved that our Dirichlet numerical model is consistent and convergent and has a unique solution. Indeed, the solution can be obtained directly by solving a set of linear, algebraic, simultaneous equations $AU = D$. As the Problems show, the nonsingular coefficient matrix A is sparse (many zeros) and banded (nonzero coefficients appear in bands parallel to the main diagonal). Most computer centers now offer standard programs that can solve $AU = D$ efficiently when A is as described. It remains only for the user to bring his equations and matrices to the proper input form. This step can always be done but is often time consuming. Moreover, the direct method, which essentially involves inversion of the matrix A, may not be economical unless a number of similar problems (with the same A but differing D) are to be solved. However, the direct method does give the exact solution to the difference equations except for a computational round-off error whose effect is made negligible in well-devised programs. For the Neumann model, A is singular and special treatment is needed.

Three successive-approximation or iteration methods are described in the following section. They are conceptually simple, easy to program for even an arbitrary region, and widely used. But they introduce the additional question of the convergence of the iteration and yield only approximate answers.

10.5.1   Iterative Methods

The three standard iterative or successive-approximation techniques are the Jacobi, Gauss–Seidel, and Successive Overrelaxation or SOR Methods. In an iterative technique a first approximation $u_{ij}^{(1)}$ is assumed for the solution u_{ij} to a difference model in a region $\bar{R} = R + C$. A simple formula based on the difference equations is used to calculate the second approximation $u_{ij}^{(2)}$ from the first, the third from the second, and so on. The methods described here calculate $u_{ij}^{(n+1)}$ explicitly in terms of approximate values at (i, j) and the surrounding four I or B points of the region R; the same formula is used for every level of approximation.

An iterative procedure is convergent if

$$\lim_{n \to \infty} u_{ij}^{(n)} = u_{ij}$$

The iteration yields the exact solution u_{ij} of the difference equations only as the limit of a convergent sequence of successive approximations. Because of round-off errors e_{ij} in the computation, it is only possible to obtain

$$|u_{ij}^{(n)} - u_{ij}| = O(e_{ij})$$

even for very large n, so there is a residual error that cannot be eliminated [but $e_{ij} = O(10^{-7}$ to $10^{-15})$, which is normally negligible]. Finally, a practical iteration technique must converge rapidly (see Example 10.6 below).

Suppose that we seek the solution to the two-dimensional Dirichlet model for the Poisson equation (10.88) in a region R with boundary C (Fig. 10.1). The difference equations for regular and irregular stars are [see, (10.92) and (10.95)]

$$u_{ij} = \tfrac{1}{4}(u_{i+1\,j} + u_{i\,j+1} + u_{i-1\,j} + u_{i\,j-1} - h^2 f_{ij}) \tag{10.104}$$

and

$$u_{ij} = \frac{\alpha_1 \alpha_2}{\alpha_1 + \alpha_2} \left[\frac{u_1}{\alpha_1(1 + \alpha_1)} + \frac{u_2}{\alpha_2(1 + \alpha_2)} + \frac{u_{i-1\,j}}{1 + \alpha_1} + \frac{u_{ij-1}}{1 + \alpha_2} - \frac{h^2}{2} f_{ij} \right] \tag{10.105}$$

Consider (10.104) [the analysis applies equally to (10.105)] and write it as

$$u_{ij}^{(n+1)} = u_{ij}^{(n)} + c_{ij}^{(n)} \tag{10.106}$$

with

$$c_{ij}^{(n)} = \tfrac{1}{4}[u_{i+1\,j}^{(n)} + u_{i\,j+1}^{(n)} + u_{i-1\,j}^{(n)} + u_{ij-1}^{(n)} - 4u_{ij}^{(n)} - h^2 f_{ij}] \tag{10.107}$$

where (n) refers to the nth approximation. Here (10.106) and (10.107) are effectively

$$u_{ij}^{(n+1)} = \tfrac{1}{4}[u_{i+1\,j}^{(n)} + u_{i\,j+1}^{(n)} + u_{i-1\,j}^{(n)} + u_{ij-1}^{(n)} - h^2 f_{ij}]$$

which corrects $u_{ij}^{(n)}$, so it satisfies the difference equation (10.104). However, use of $c_{ij}^{(n)}$ is informative and convenient, because it is the residual error at each node at the nth approximation attempt.

The Jacobi Method

The Jacobi method employs (10.106) and (10.107) to find $u_{ij}^{(n+1)}$ over R, using only values from the nth approximation. The correction of an iterative approximation $u_{ij}^{(n)}$ by the amount of the residual error $c_{ij}^{(n)}$ is generally called *relaxation*, although classical relaxation used a slightly different procedure and was done by hand. The Jacobi iteration is convergent as the following theorem shows.

THEOREM 10.2   For the Dirichlet difference model for the Poisson equation, represented by (10.91), plus (10.104) and (10.105), the Jacobi method is convergent.

Proof: Define the error $U_{ij}^{(n)} = u_{ij} - u_{ij}^{(n)}$, where u_{ij} is the exact solution of the difference equations and $u_{ij}^{(n)}$ is the nth Jacobi approximation for (i, j) in R. We need to prove that $|U_{ij}^{(n)}| \to 0$ as $n \to \infty$.

For the boundary points B on C, $U_p^{(n)} \equiv 0$; that is, the prescribed Dirichlet values and the approximate values coincide. In order to use this result, we categorize the mesh points or nodes I in the region R (see Figs. 10.1 or 10.10). Irregular stars connect the B points to the first layer of I nodes, called *first-order nodes*. These are at the center of a star containing one or more B points. Regular stars connect all the remaining I points, which are now sequentially ordered in layers inward from the boundary C until all nodes in R are accounted for. The *second-order nodes* are those that have *at least one* first-order node in their regular star; *third-order nodes* have *at least one* second-order node in their regular star but no first-order nodes, and so forth. Because R is a finite region with closed boundary C and $h > 0$, the number of orders or layers of nodes required to account for all nodes is finite, say N.

As u_{ij} satisfies (10.104) or (10.105), $u_{ij}^{(n)}$ satisfies the regular star iteration formula

$$u_{ij}^{(n+1)} = \tfrac{1}{4}[u_{i+1\,j}^{(n)} + u_{ij+1}^{(n)} + u_{i-1\,j}^{(n)} + u_{ij-1}^{(n)} - h^2 f_{ij}] \tag{10.108}$$

or, for example, the typical irregular star iteration formula

$$u_{ij}^{(n+1)} = \frac{\alpha_1 \alpha_2}{\alpha_1 + \alpha_2}\left[\frac{u_1^{(n)}}{\alpha_1(1+\alpha_1)} + \frac{u_2^{(n)}}{\alpha_2(1+\alpha_2)} + \frac{u_{i-1\,j}^{(n)}}{1+\alpha_1} + \frac{u_{ij-1}^{(n)}}{1+\alpha_2} - \frac{h^2}{2}f_{ij}\right] \tag{10.109}$$

with $0 < \alpha_1 \le 1$, $0 < \alpha_2 \le 1$. It follows that $U_{ij}^{(n)}$ satisfies the homogeneous formula

$$U_{ij}^{(n+1)} = \frac{\alpha_1 \alpha_2}{\alpha_1 + \alpha_2}\left[\frac{U_1^{(n)}}{\alpha_1(1+\alpha_1)} + \frac{U_2^{(n)}}{\alpha_2(1+\alpha_2)} + \frac{U_{i-1\,j}^{(n)}}{1+\alpha_1} + \frac{U_{ij-1}^{(n)}}{1+\alpha_2}\right] \tag{10.110}$$

at the first-order nodes and

$$U_{ij}^{(n+1)} = \tfrac{1}{4}[U_{i+1\,j}^{(n)} + U_{ij+1}^{(n)} + U_{i-1\,j}^{(n)} + U_{ij-1}^{(n)}] \tag{10.111}$$

at second- and higher-order nodes.

Let $M_n = \max\{|U_{ij}^{(n)}|\}$. From (10.110), $|U_{ij}^{(n+1)}| \le \beta_{ij} M_n$ for $0 \le \beta_{ij} < 1$ as either $U_1^{(n)}$ or $U_2^{(n)}$ or both are zero because first-order nodes contain at least one B point where the error is zero. Thus, the normal sum of positive coefficients

$$\frac{\alpha_1 \alpha_2}{\alpha_1 + \alpha_2}\left[\frac{1}{\alpha_1(1+\alpha_1)} + \frac{1}{\alpha_2(1+\alpha_2)} + \frac{1}{1+\alpha_1} + \frac{1}{1+\alpha_2}\right] = 1$$

is reduced by the appropriate deletion of

$$\frac{\alpha_1 \alpha_2}{\alpha_1 + \alpha_2}\left[\frac{1}{\alpha_1(1+\alpha_1)}\right] > \frac{2}{2(1+\alpha_2)} > 0 \quad \text{or} \quad \frac{\alpha_1 \alpha_2}{\alpha_1 + \alpha_2}\left[\frac{1}{\alpha_2(1+\alpha_2)}\right] > \frac{1}{2(1+\alpha_1)} > 0$$

or both because $0 < \alpha_1 \le 1$, $0 < \alpha_2 \le 1$. Letting $\beta = \max\{\beta_{ij}\} < 1$ yields

$$|U_{ij}^{(n+1)}| \le \beta M_n, \qquad 0 \le \beta < 1 \tag{10.112}$$

at the first-order nodes.

At the second-order nodes, at least one value in the regular star to estimate $U_{ij}^{(n+2)}$ comes from a first-order node. Then (10.111) produces

$$|U_{ij}^{(n+2)}| \le \tfrac{1}{4}(3M_{n+1} + \beta M_n) \le [1 - \tfrac{1}{4}(1-\beta)]M_n \tag{10.113}$$

because from (10.111) $M_{n+1} \le M_n$. At the third-order nodes, one second-order value enters the star; from (10.111) and (10.113),

$$|U_{ij}^{(n+3)}| \le \tfrac{1}{4}[3M_{n+2} + \{1 - \tfrac{1}{4}(1 - \beta)\}M_n] \le [1 - \tfrac{1}{16}(1 - \beta)]M_n$$

$$= \left[1 - \frac{1}{4^2}(1 - \beta)\right]M_n$$

Proceeding sequentially upward one in approximation level and one in node order to the Nth-order nodes yields, by induction,

$$|U_{ij}^{(n+N)}| \le \left[1 - \frac{1}{4^{N-1}}(1 - \beta)\right]M_n \qquad (10.114)$$

for the Nth-order nodes. Clearly, there is a cone of nodes and approximation levels for $n < N$ where no estimate of the bound on the error $U_{ij}^{(n)}$ has been made. This fact is of no consequence;

$$\left[1 - \frac{1}{4^{m-1}}(1 - \beta)\right] \le \left[1 - \frac{1}{4^{N-1}}(1 - \beta)\right]$$

for $m \le N$ and (10.114) bounds the error for all nodes in R for $n \ge 1$—that is, from the $N + 1$st approximation.

From (10.114), we have directly for $n \ge 1$,

$$M_{n+N} \le \left[1 - \frac{1}{4^{N-1}}(1 - \beta)\right]M_n$$

for all nodes in R and, in particular,

$$M_{N+1} \le \left[1 - \frac{1}{4^{N-1}}(1 - \beta)\right]M_1$$

where M_1 is surely finite because the assumed first iterate $u_{ij}^{(1)}$ can only differ from the finite u_{ij} by a finite amount. Now, the maximum error at the $(mN + 1)$st iteration is

$$M_{mN+1} \le \left[1 - \frac{1}{4^{N-1}}(1 - \beta)\right]M_{(m-1)N+1} \le \left[1 - \frac{1}{4^{N-1}}(1 - \beta)\right]^2 M_{(m-2)N+1} \cdots$$

or by induction

$$M_{mN+1} \le \left[1 - \frac{1}{4^{N-1}}(1 - \beta)\right]^m M_1$$

where

$$\left[1 - \frac{1}{4^{N-1}}(1 - \beta)\right] < 1$$

because $0 \le \beta < 1$ and N is finite. Then

$$\lim_{m \to \infty} \left[1 - \frac{1}{4^{N-1}}(1 - \beta)\right]^m = 0$$

Accordingly,

$$\lim_{m \to \infty} M_{mN+1} = \lim_{m \to \infty} \{\max |U_{ij}^{(mN+1)}|\} = 0$$

The error $U_{ij}^{(mN+1)}$ vanishes as $m \to \infty$ $[(mN+1) \to \infty$, too] and the Jacobi method is convergent.   Q.E.D.

The Gauss–Seidel Method

The convergence of the Jacobi method is slow and the method rarely used in practice. However, when (10.106) and (10.107) are used, it is normal to apply them sequentially across the range of i values for fixed j, then across i values for $j+1$, and so on. Thus at (i, j) the values $u_{i-1,j}^{(n+1)}$ and $u_{ij-1}^{(n+1)}$ have already been calculated (or are boundary values and known in a Dirichlet problem). The Gauss–Seidel method uses these new data immediately in each successive step; (10.106) remains the same but (10.107) becomes

$$c_{ij}^{(n)} = \tfrac{1}{4}[u_{i+1,j}^{(n)} + u_{ij+1}^{(n)} + u_{i-1,j}^{(n+1)} + u_{ij-1}^{(n+1)} - 4u_{ij}^{(n)} - h^2 f_{ij}] \qquad (10.115)$$

If, in a particular case, the Jacobi method converges, the Gauss–Seidel method's rate of convergence is *twice* as fast as that of the Jacobi method [1, 2, 3].

The Successive Overrelaxation Method [1, 2, 3]

With (10.106) the convergence of the iteration is faster if $c_{ij}^{(n)}$ is given by the Gauss–Seidel (10.115) rather than by the Jacobi (10.107). Young and Frankel proposed to further accelerate convergence toward the solution by overcorrecting at each step—that is, by "overrelaxation." When applied with the Gauss–Seidel $c_{ij}^{(n)}$, the method is "successive overrelaxation" or SOR; we replace (10.106) by

$$u_{ij}^{(n+1)} = u_{ij}^{(n)} + \omega c_{ij}^{(n)} \qquad (10.116)$$

where, for $0 < \omega \le 2$, the iteration can be shown to converge if the Jacobi method converges for the same case. An optimum value ω_{opt} can be estimated from the geometry of the region R and the number of I points in R for certain simple regions; ω_{opt} can also be estimated from the eigenvalues of the coefficient matrix A of the Jacobi method. In practice, ω_{opt} is often found by testing the computer program in actual operation; SOR convergence rates 10 to 50 times faster than the Jacobi rate are not uncommon.

EXAMPLE 10.6   *The Dirichlet Model for Poisson's Equation in a Quadrant of a Circle.* Consider,* for $u(x, y)$,

$$\nabla^2 u = 12xy \qquad \text{in } R$$

$$u = xy \qquad \text{on } C$$

where $\bar{R} = R + C : x^2 + y^2 \le 1, 0 \le \tan^{-1} y/x \le \infty$. Figure 10.12 is a scale drawing of $\bar{R}$ with a grid of mesh points superimposed; $h = 0.05$. The SOR solution values (times 10^3), obtained with $\omega = 1.70$ and iteration carried on until $|c_{ij}^{(n)}| \le 10^{-5}$, are noted near each node. For the residual error tolerance of 10^{-5}, the three iterative methods agreed to at least three decimal digits with the exact solution

$$u(x, y) = xy^3 + x^3 y$$

* This model represents, for example, steady heat conduction in a plate with heat sources present and temperature specified at the boundary (see Secs. 2.2.1 and 2.2.3).

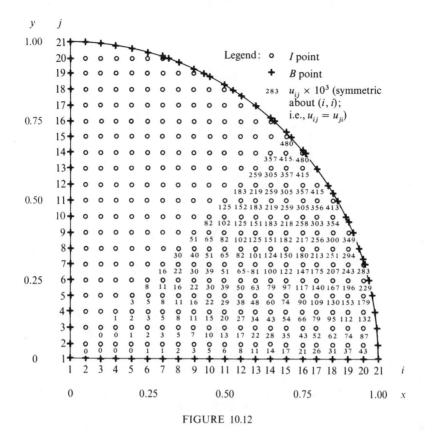

FIGURE 10.12

The most accurate answer is obtained if iteration is continued until $|c_{ij}^{(n)}| \leq$ (computer round-off error). This criterion should be used when computer time is available for the large number of iterations required.

Figure 10.13 is a plot of the number of iterations N_R required to meet the error criteria by each method. The superiority of optimum SOR is clear, since it is 5 times faster than the Gauss–Seidel method and 8.5 times faster than the Jacobi method.

Figure 10.14 is a flow chart for the computer program that made the calculations of $u_{ij}^{(n)}$. The notation includes

$$x_c(j) = \text{the } x \text{ distance to } C \text{ at } y = (j-1)h$$

$$y_c(i) = \text{the } y \text{ distance to } C \text{ at } x = (i-1)h$$

$$u_{ij}^{(n+1)} = u_{ij}^{(n)} + \omega c_{ij}^{(n)}$$

If the Jacobi or Gauss–Seidel procedures are used, $\omega = 1$ and the proper $c_{ij}^{(n)}$ formula is chosen. For SOR, ω is prescribed and the Gauss–Seidel $c_{ij}^{(n)}$ is used. When a computation is made at (i, j) its coordinates are x_i, y_j. If $x_{i+1} \geq x_c(j), \alpha_1 \leq 1$; if $y_{j+1} \geq y_c(j)$, $\alpha_2 \leq 1$. These inequalities mean that an irregular star is needed. If $x_{i+1} \geq x_c(j)$, the horizontal sweep (over i at fixed j) has reached C and we start the next sweep at $(2, j + 1)$.

For convenience and simplicity, $u_{ij}^{(1)} = 0$ for $(i, j) \in R$, not C. The appropriate boundary values are always used for points on C.

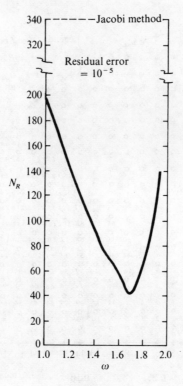

FIGURE 10.13

10.5.2   Nonlinear Equations

Nonlinear elliptic equations are frequently found in equilibrium models of physical systems, for example, when the small amplitude assumption is dropped in membrane displacement models or the variation of thermal conductivity with temperature is included in heat conduction models (see, also, Sec. 10.4 and Ames [1]).

If we write the general two-dimensional, quasi-linear, partial differential equation (1.6)

$$\alpha_1 u_{xx} + \alpha_2 u_{xy} + \alpha_3 u_{yy} + \alpha_4 = 0$$

in the symbolic form

$$\phi(x, y, u_x, u_y, u_{xx}, u_{xy}, u_{yy}) = 0 \tag{10.117}$$

where $\alpha_i = \alpha_i(x, y, u, u_x, u_y)$, we know from Sec. 2.6 that (10.117) is elliptic if $\alpha_2^2 - 4\alpha_1\alpha_3 < 0$. If (10.117) is represented on a region R by finite differences, the difference equation takes the symbolic form

$$\phi_i(U) = 0, \qquad i = 1, 2, 3, \ldots, N \tag{10.118}$$

of a set of N *nonlinear*, simultaneous, algebraic equations, where $U = (u_1, u_2, u_3, u_4, \ldots, u_N)^T$ is a column vector with the N elements representing the solutions u_i at the N interior nodes of R. Of course, the linear-based direct and iterative methods previously covered are of no use.

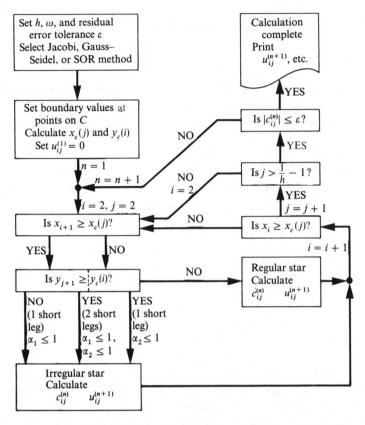

FIGURE 10.14   Flow chart for iterative program for elliptic equation (Example 10.6).

The problem of finding U according to (10.118) with, say, specified boundary conditions on C (a Dirichlet model) is equivalent to finding the root U of the N equations $\phi_i = 0$. This suggests the possibility of adapting a root-finding technique for algebraic equations. Ames [1] summarizes the work and literature in this field to 1965. We outline only the *nonlinear SOR method* here.

First, recall Newton's process for a given function of one variable $\phi(u)$. We seek values of u such that $\phi(u) = 0$. The process is iterative. Suppose that $u^{(n)}$ is known, but the actual solution is

$$\phi[u^{(n+1)}] = \phi[u^{(n)} + \varepsilon^{(n)}] = 0 \tag{10.119}$$

where $\varepsilon^{(n)}$ is the remaining error in $u^{(n)}$ and we want $u^{(n+1)}$ to equal the true root u_r. If ϕ and its first derivative are continuous functions of u and $\partial^2\phi/\partial u^2$ is bounded, a Taylor's series expansion of (10.119) about $u^{(n)}$ yields

$$\phi[u^{(n+1)}] = 0 = \phi[u^{(n)}] + \frac{\partial\phi}{\partial u}[u^{(n)}]\varepsilon^{(n)} + \frac{\partial^2\phi}{\partial u^2}[u_A]\frac{[\varepsilon^{(n)}]^2}{2}$$

where $u^{(n)} \leq u_A \leq u^{(n+1)}$. This result gives

$$\varepsilon^{(n)} = -\frac{\phi[u^{(n)}]}{\partial\phi/\partial u[u^{(n)}]} + O\{[\varepsilon^{(n)}]^2\}$$

The Newton process uses this result to calculate

$$u^{(n+1)} = u^{(n)} - \frac{\phi[u^{(n)}]}{\partial\phi/\partial u[u^{(n)}]} \tag{10.120}$$

Now, actually, $u_r = u^{(n+1)} + O\{[\varepsilon^{(n)}]^2\}$; $u^{(n+1)}$ is not the true root, just a closer approximation than $u^{(n)}$. However, the error decreases by an order of magnitude at each step of approximation under the present assumptions if the process is convergent [10].

For the elliptic numerical model there are N equations $\phi_i = 0$ and N unknowns u_i. Accordingly, (10.120) must be applied N times at each iteration to gain a new estimate; that is, using the common notation $\partial\phi_i/\partial u_j = \phi_{ij}$, we write

$$u_1^{(n+1)} = u_1^{(n)} - \frac{\phi_1[u_1^{(n)}, u_2^{(n)}, u_3^{(n)} \ldots u_N^{(n)}]}{\phi_{11}[u_1^{(n)}, u_2^{(n)}, u_3^{(n)} \ldots u_N^{(n)}]} \tag{10.121a}$$

$$u_2^{(n+1)} = u_2^{(n)} - \frac{\phi_2[u_1^{(n)}, u_2^{(n)}, u_3^{(n)} \ldots u_N^{(n)}]}{\phi_{22}[u_1^{(n)}, u_2^{(n)}, u_3^{(n)} \ldots u_N^{(n)}]} \tag{10.121b}$$

$$\vdots$$

$$u_N^{(n+1)} = u_N^{(n)} - \frac{\phi_N[u_1^{(n)}, u_2^{(n)}, u_3^{(n)} \ldots u_N^{(n)}]}{\phi_{NN}[u_1^{(n)}, u_2^{(n)}, u_3^{(n)} \ldots u_N^{(n)}]} \tag{10.121c}$$

Clearly, if $\phi_{ii} = 0$ for any i, the method fails.

If ϕ_i is linear, (10.121) reduce to the Jacobi method for the given equation $\phi = 0$. Thus we may expect to improve the convergence rate by putting the latest estimates in each equation and by using an overrelaxation factor ω. This step leads to (10.121) reducing to the Gauss–Siedel and SOR methods, respectively, if ϕ is linear. For the equivalent nonlinear SOR, (10.121) are

$$u_i^{(n+1)} = u_i^{(n)} - \omega\frac{\phi_i[u_1^{(n+1)}, u_2^{(n+1)} \ldots u_{i-1}^{(n+1)}, u_i^{(n)} \ldots u_N^{(n)}]}{\phi_{ii}[u_1^{(n+1)}, u_2^{(n+1)} \ldots u_{i-1}^{(n+1)}, u_i^{(n)} \ldots u_N^{(n)}]} \tag{10.122}$$

for $1 \leq i \leq N$ and $0 < \omega < 2$. For all common ϕ_i, $\phi_{ii} \neq 0$.

The nonlinear Jacobi method [Eqs. (10.121)] and the nonlinear SOR method [Eqs. (10.122)] were proposed by Lieberstein,* while Bers* analyzed the nonlinear Gauss–Seidel method [Eqs. (10.122) with $\omega = 1$]. Several successful calculations have been made with (10.122), but there is little supporting theory [1].

10.6   SUMMARY

We began with well-posed and normalized mathematical models of physical systems. The continuously-defined solution function and its derivatives for the model were replaced by function values and derivatives defined only on a grid of mesh points or nodes covering the region of the original problem. Under the assumption that the mathematical model has a continuous solution with the necessary continuous

---

* See J. M. Ortega and W. C. Rheinboldt, *Iterative Solution of Nonlinear Equations in Several Variables*, New York: Academic Press, Inc., 1970 (Sec. 7.4), and H. M. Lieberstein, *A Course in Numerical Analysis*, New York: Harper & Row, Publishers, Inc., 1968 (Chap. 6).

and/or bounded derivatives, use of the Taylor's series provided the formal technique for the derivation of difference forms from differentials, as well as estimates of the error made in this discretization process.

The method of deriving the difference equations of the numerical model was the same in every case. However, the technique of solution of the numerical models depended on the nature of the original mathematical model. Hyperbolic and parabolic equations have timelike models—that is, models with initial conditions or, equivalently, models whose solutions at a point depend on auxiliary data prescribed for only smaller values of one of the independent variables (the past). In these cases, one variable naturally has a semi-infinite range $(0 - \infty)$ with auxiliary conditions arising only at zero; solution of timelike numerical models was a step-by-step progression or marching sequence beginning at zero "time." Elliptic equations led to spacelike mathematical models whose auxiliary conditions were only boundary conditions specified naturally on a closed boundary (even if the boundary is taken to infinity as an approximation) and whose solutions depended on all the data prescribed at the boundary. Solutions of numerical models of spacelike systems had to be obtained simultaneously at every point internal to the boundary by direct solution of simultaneous algebraic equations or by iteration.

In all cases, a well-posed numerical model could be shown to be consistent with its mathematical model and to have a numerical solution that converged to the mathematical solution as the grid of mesh points was refined. For the marching-solution technique, a further requirement was the stability of the computation scheme against error growth, whereas convergence of the iteration was needed for iteration schemes.

The main emphasis of the chapter was on linear models, but it was demonstrated that the method of finite differences can treat nonlinear models in arbitrary regions. Indeed, nonlinearity scarcely alters the derivation of the numerical model or the computation of a solution. Nonlinearity does make adequacy tests of numerical models more difficult, however, and in some cases an actual computation is the only means of verifying the model's adequacy.

For higher-order equations in two independent variables, the techniques for derivation and solution of the numerical models are unchanged. Of course, the detailed form of the difference equations and the numbers and forms of auxiliary conditions do change. Examples included in the Problems are the vibration of an elastic beam, whose differential equation is

$$z_{tt} + \frac{EI}{\rho} z_{yyyy} = q$$

and the purely elastic bending of a uniform plate whose differential equation is the *biharmonic* equation

$$\nabla^2(\nabla^2 z) = z_{xxxx} + 2z_{xxyy} + z_{yyyy} = \frac{q}{D}$$

When the number of independent variables is greater than two, the difference-equation derivation and the general form of the numerical model are unchanged. For linear models, even the solution techniques remain generally the same, and the adequacy tests for consistency, convergence, and stability (or convergence of an iteration) can be carried out as before (with due regard for the extra dimensions).

However, the actual computation of a solution is often tedious because of the large number of nodes involved in a marching scheme or iteration.

For example, for the Laplace equation in three dimensions, the computation formula for a regular star is the seven-point equation ($\Delta x = \Delta y = \Delta z = h$)

$$u_{ijk} = \tfrac{1}{6}(u_{i+1jk} + u_{i-1jk} + u_{ij+1k} + u_{ij-1k} + u_{ijk+1} + u_{ijk-1})$$

which requires either direct inversion of the large banded matrix obtained by sequentially numbering all nodes in the three-dimensional region or iteration; both methods require great computer storage and large amounts of time.

For the vibration of a thin, flexible membrane, the differential equation is (Sec. 5.2.2)

$$z_{tt} = c^2(z_{xx} + z_{yy}) = c^2 \nabla^2 z$$

The explicit-difference computation formula is ($\Delta x = \Delta y = \Delta$)

$$z_{ijk+1} = 2z_{ijk} - z_{ijk-1} + \left(\frac{c\,\Delta t}{\Delta}\right)^2 (z_{i+1jk} - 2z_{ijk} + z_{i-1jk} + z_{ij+1k} - 2z_{ijk} + z_{ij-1k})$$

Under the Courant stability condition $c\,\Delta t/\Delta \leq 1$, computation with this equation is stable and straightforward. However, the model of heat conduction in a plate (Sec. 5.2.1) has the parabolic differential equation

$$u_t = k\nabla^2 u = k(u_{xx} + u_{yy}) \tag{10.123}$$

Computation with the explicit-difference formula ($\Delta x = \Delta y = \Delta$)

$$u_{ijn+1} = u_{ijn} + \frac{k\,\Delta t}{\Delta^2}(u_{i+1jn} - 2u_{ijn} + u_{i-1jn} + u_{ij+1n} - 2u_{ijn} + u_{ij-1n}) \tag{10.124}$$

is convergent and stable only when $k\,\Delta t/\Delta^2 \leq \tfrac{1}{4}$. If adequate resolution is obtained in the space dimensions, Δt must be small and calculations with (10.124) are time consuming. Application of the Crank–Nicolson method (Sec. 10.2.4) to (10.123) gives an implicit-difference equation containing five unknown values at time $n + 1$. This leads over the x-y plane to a set of simultaneous algebraic equations to be solved at each time step, which is equivalent to solving the Poisson difference equation by direct or iterative means at each time step.

A well-known alternative to the Crank–Nicolson formulation above, or indeed for the SOR iterative technique for two-dimensional elliptic equations, is the *Alternating Direction Implicit Method* or ADI [2, 3]. ADI was proposed by Peaceman, Douglas, and Rachford in 1955 and 1956 for rectangular spatial regions related to both elliptic equations and the three-dimensional parabolic equation (10.123). Consider the regular star difference equation for the Laplace equation $u_{xx} + u_{yy} = 0$ in the rectangle R; that is,

$$\frac{u_{i+1j} - 2u_{ij} + u_{i-1j}}{\Delta^2} + \frac{u_{ij+1} - 2u_{ij} + u_{ij-1}}{\Delta^2} = 0$$

for $\Delta x = \Delta y = \Delta$. This equation is often solved iteratively (Sec. 10.5.1). In the ADI procedure, each iteration step is taken in two parts. The basic idea is to treat the equation implicitly in alternating directions, in the x direction in the first part and in the y direction in the second part. The first part after the nth iteration is

$$\frac{u_{i+1j}^{(n+1/2)} - 2u_{ij}^{(n+1/2)} + u_{i-1j}^{(n+1/2)}}{\Delta^2} + \frac{u_{ij+1}^{(n)} - 2u_{ij}^{(n)} + u_{ij-1}^{(n)}}{\Delta^2} = 0$$

or

$$u_{i+1j}^{(n+1/2)} - 2u_{ij}^{(n+1/2)} + u_{i-1j}^{(n+1/2)} = -u_{ij+1}^{(n)} + 2u_{ij}^{(n)} - u_{ij-1}^{(n)} \qquad (10.125)$$

Application of (10.125) over R yields a set of linear simultaneous equations; the set has a tridiagonal coefficient matrix and is solved by the method of Sec. 10.2.4. The second part is given by

$$\frac{u_{i+1j}^{(n+1)} - 2u_{ij}^{(n+1)} + u_{i-1j}^{(n+1)}}{\Delta^2} + \frac{u_{ij+1}^{(n+1/2)} - 2u_{ij}^{(n+1/2)} + u_{ij-1}^{(n+1/2)}}{\Delta^2} = 0$$

or

$$u_{i+1j}^{(n+1)} - 2u_{ij}^{(n+1)} + u_{i-1j}^{(n+1)} = -u_{ij+1}^{(n+1/2)} + 2u_{ij}^{(n+1/2)} - u_{ij-1}^{(n+1/2)} \qquad (10.126)$$

As the $u_{ij}^{(n+1/2)}$ are known, the method of Sec. 10.2.4 gives $u_{ij}^{(n+1)}$ from the implicit relation (10.126).

Overrelaxation factors are used in ADI to accelerate convergence. They can be introduced by writing (10.125) and (10.126) in the iteration form (10.106), namely,

$$u_{ij}^{(n+1/2)} = u_{ij}^{(n)} + \omega_n[u_{i+1j}^{(n+1/2)} - 2u_{ij}^{(n+1/2)} + u_{i-1j}^{(n+1/2)} + u_{ij+1}^{(n)} - 2u_{ij}^{(n)} + u_{ij-1}^{(n)}] \qquad (10.127)$$

$$u_{ij}^{(n+1)} = u_{ij}^{(n+1/2)} + \omega_n[u_{i+1j}^{(n+1/2)} - 2u_{ij}^{(n+1/2)} + u_{i-1j}^{(n+1/2)} + u_{ij+1}^{(n+1)}$$
$$- 2u_{ij}^{(n+1)} + u_{ij-1}^{(n+1)}] \qquad (10.128)$$

where $\omega_n > 0$ is the relaxation parameter. The ω_n is usually changed with n to maximize the rate of convergence, and some formulas for ω_n have been determined [2, 3]. ADI using an optimum choice of ω_n is superior to SOR for Laplace and Poisson equations on a rectangle.

Noting the similarity of (10.127), (10.128), and (10.124) if $\omega_n = k\,\Delta t/\Delta^2$, we see that ADI can be applied with equal success to solve the parabolic-elliptic equation (10.123). In this case, ADI gives a method that is stable for any $k\,\Delta t/\Delta^2 < \infty$, relaxing thereby the stringent limit on Δt imposed by the explicit scheme (10.124).

For models with two or more space variables (with or without a time variable), the space region of the physical system is often not a simple rectangle or circle. Then the great power of the numerical finite difference is clear as our analytic methods fail, with the possible exception of the Green's function and characteristics methods. But these methods are dependent on the determination of the Green's function for each equation and region and on the determination of the characteristics and characteristic compatibility equations, respectively—never an easy task in general cases. (Indeed, the triangle is the simplest region for which none of our analytic methods works conveniently.) Another numerical technique with current applications for equilibrium problems and with great overall promise is the Finite-Element Method [16], which achieved its first widespread recognition in the late 1960s.

The finite-element method differs from the finite-difference method in two key ways. Consider the region R in Fig. 10.15, and assume that the partial differential equation and boundary conditions

$$\phi(u, u_x, u_{xx}, u_y, u_{yy}, u_{xy}, x, y) = 0 \qquad \text{in } R$$

$$\psi(u, u_x, u_y) = 0 \qquad \text{on } C$$

are to be satisfied on $\bar{R} = R + C$ for $u(x, y)$. First, in lieu of a mesh of grid points, the finite-element method employs a series of "finite elements," connected at discrete nodes on their boundaries and covering R. The triangles in Fig. 10.15 are typical; note that the location of nodes i is flexible and can be adjusted to optimize the fit of the elements to the shape of R. The known x_i and y_i of each node and the unknown u are the basic parameters of the problem. A function (usually linear) is chosen to represent u within each element (which is small, with sides of the same order h as the mesh spacing used in finite differences) in terms of its nodal values. The values u_i then uniquely define u *continuously* throughout R. Second, the partial differential equation $\phi = 0$ is replaced in R by its equivalent (integral) functional form (Sec. 7.2) whose value is to be minimized according to the Calculus of Variations.

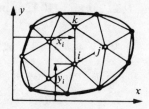

FIGURE 10.15

For example,

$$\frac{T}{\rho}\nabla^2 z + F = 0 \qquad \text{in } R$$

is the equation for the equilibrium displacement z in R of a membrane acted on by a force F per unit mass. The equivalent functional is the potential energy (Chap. 5, Prob. 5.51) of position

$$\text{PE} = \iint_R \left[\frac{T}{2}(z_x^2 + z_y^2) - \rho F z \right] dx\, dy \qquad (10.129)$$

The natural shape taken by the membrane is that which minimizes PE. In this case, the derivative of PE with respect to any variable must be zero (recall the definition of a minimum of a function). If z is replaced by its representation in each element by a function of the unknown nodel values, (10.129) becomes

$$\text{PE} = \text{PE}(z_1, z_2, z_3, \ldots, z_i, z_j, z_k, \ldots z_N)$$

where N is the number of element nodes. If PE is to take on its minimum value,

$$\frac{\partial P}{\partial z_i} = 0, \qquad i = 1, 2, \ldots, N \tag{10.130}$$

is required. Actually, only the few elements adjacent to each node contribute to $\partial P/\partial z_i$ for each i, so (10.130) yield a set of linear simultaneous equations whose coefficient matrix is banded and sparse; this fact facilitates direct solution by inversion of the matrix. The method gives excellent results, particularly for irregular regions, but it requires an equivalent number of nodes to that of finite-difference methods and the treatment of other than Dirichlet boundary conditions is equally difficult by either method.

REFERENCES

1. W. F. Ames, *Nonlinear Partial Differential Equations in Engineering*. New York: Academic Press, 1965.

2. G. D. Smith, *Numerical Solution of Partial Differential Equations*. London: Oxford University Press, 1965.

3. G. E. Forsythe and W. R. Wasow, *Finite-Difference Methods for Partial Differential Equations*. New York: John Wiley & Sons, 1960.

4. L. Fox, *Numerical Solution of Ordinary and Partial Differential Equations*. Reading, Mass.: Addison-Wesley, 1962.

5. R. D. Richtmyer and K. W. Morton, *Difference Methods for Initial-Value Problems*, 2nd ed. New York: Interscience (a division of John Wiley & Sons), 1967.

6. W. Kaplan, *Advanced Calculus*, Reading, Mass.: Addison-Wesley, 1952.

7. J. Crank and P. Nicolson, "A Practical Method for Numerical Evaluation of Solutions of Partial Differential Equations of the Heat Conduction Type," *Proc. Cambridge Phil. Soc.*, Vol. 43, Cambridge: The University Press, 1947, pp. 50–67.

8. J. N. Franklin, *Matrix Theory*. Englewood Cliffs, N.J.: Prentice-Hall, 1968.

9. E. C. DuFort and S. P. Frankel, "Stability Conditions in the Numerical Treatment of Parabolic Differential Equations," *Math. Tables and Other Aids to Computation*, Vol. VII, No. 43, Washington, D.C., July 1953, pp. 135–152.

10. E. Isaacson and H. B. Keller, *Analysis of Numerical Methods*. New York: John Wiley & Sons, 1966.

11. W. F. Ames, *Numerical Methods for Partial Differential Equations*. London: Thomas Nelson and Sons, Ltd., 1969.

12. G. G. O'Brien, M. A. Hyman, and S. Kaplan, "A Study of the Numerical Solution of Partial Differential Equations," *Journal of Mathematics and Physics*, Vol. 29, 1950, pp. 223–251.

13. T. Strelkoff, "Numerical Solution of Saint-Venant Equations," *Journal of the Hydraulics Division*, ASCE, Vol. 96, No. HY1, Proc. Paper 7043, January 1970, pp. 223–252.

14. H. S. Carslaw and J. C. Jaeger, *Conduction of Heat in Solids*. London: Oxford University Press, 1959.

15. J. Crank, *Mathematics of Diffusion*. London: Oxford University Press, 1956.

16. O. C. Zienkiewicz, *The Finite Element Method in Structural and Continuum Mechanics*. London: McGraw-Hill Ltd., 1967.

PROBLEMS

10.1 Use a Taylor's series expansion about (i, j) to obtain the central difference expressions and their truncation errors for the following:

(a) u_{yy}

(b) u_{xy}

(c) $z_{tt} + z_{yyyy} = 0$

(d) $z_{xxxx} + 2z_{xxyy} + z_{yyyy} = 0$

(e) $u_t = u_{xx} + u_{yy}$. Use a forward time difference.

10.2 A nine-point approximation to the Laplacian is

$$\nabla^2 u = \{4u_{i+1j} + u_{i+1j+1} + 4u_{ij+1} + u_{i-1j+1} + 4u_{i-1j} + u_{i-1j-1} + 4u_{ij-1} + u_{i+1j-1}$$
$$- 20u_{ij}\}/6h^2$$

Find the truncation error.

10.3 Derive a central difference approximation for the boundary condition of the third kind $u_x(1, t) + h(t)u(1, t) = g(t)$, $0 < t$. What is the computational star at the boundary if $u_t = ku_{xx}, 0 < x < 1, 0 < t$?

10.4 Show that in (10.23)

$$d_{i0}(z_{yy}) + O(h^2) = z_{yy}(y, 0)$$

10.5 Derive explicit-marching numerical models and give a physical interpretation of the following mathematical models:

(a) $u_t = ku_{xx} + q(x, t)$, $0 < x < 1$, $0 < t$
    $u(0, t) = u_x(1, t) + h(t)u(1, t) = 0$, $0 < t$
    $u(x, 0) = 0$, $0 \le x \le 1$

(b) $u_t = ku_{xx}$, $0 < x < 1$, $0 < t$
    $u_x(0, t) = A$,
    $u_x(1, t) = B$, $0 < t$
    $u(x, 0) = x(1 - x)$, $0 < x < 1$

(c) Prob. 5.6(a).

(d) Prob. 5.6(b).

(e) Prob. 5.6(d).

10.6 Find the analytic solution to Example 10.1, and evaluate it on the computer to verify the results in Fig. 10.4.

10.7 Write a computer program to solve the numerical model of Example 10.1 and to verify the results in Tables 10.1 and 10.2.

10.8 Use the Taylor's series to obtain the truncation error for the difference representation of $u_t = u_{xx}$ when $\Delta t = (\Delta x)^2/6$.

10.9 Using Example 10.1 as a basis, discuss the relative merits of analytic and numeric solutions. When is it advantageous to have an analytic solution? Does this depend on its complexity or the rate of convergence of series?

10.10   Normalize the following mathematical models, and give a physical interpretation of the time scales in each case:

(a) Prob. 5.4(a)

(b) Prob. 5.21

(c) Prob. 5.65

(d) $u_t = k \nabla^2 u,$ $0 < x < X, 0 < y < Y,$ $0 < t$
$u = 0$ on the boundary
$u(x, y, 0) = u_0(x, y),$ $0 \leq x \leq X,$ $0 \leq y \leq Y$

(e) Prob. 2.24. Consider how to establish relative sizes of terms in the boundary condition at lead ball.

10.11   Derive a normalized numerical model for Prob. 2.6. Write a computer program to solve the model.

10.12   Repeat Prob. 10.11 for the system of Prob. 2.24.

10.13   Derive mathematical and explicit numerical models for the small vibrations of a string of length l and density ρ under a tension T if

(a) no external force acts on the string but one end is fixed and a sinusoidally varying force of amplitude F and frequency ω is applied at the other laterally restrained end.

(b) both ends are fixed but gravity and a force per unit mass $F = F_0 z \sin \omega t$ act on the string.

10.14   Write a computer program to solve Prob. 10.13(a) and (b).

10.15   Construct a star diagram similar to Fig. 10.3a for the model (10.34) and stars shown in Fig. 10.5.

10.16   Derive a Crank–Nicolson difference equation for the normalized convection-diffusion equation (10.32).

10.17   Derive an implicit-difference equation for (10.24) by using central space differences centered at $(i, j + 1)$ and a backward-time difference from $(i, j + 1)$.

10.18   Derive a general difference scheme for the parabolic equation (10.24) centered at $(i, j + \theta)$, $0 \leq \theta \leq 1$. Replace discrete values at undefined points by linearly interpolated values from defined points. Show how $\theta = 0, \frac{1}{2},$ and 1 correspond to the forward-explicit, Crank–Nicholson, and backward-implicit difference schemes, respectively.

10.19   Derive an implicit-difference equation for the differential wave equation in (10.33) by using a weighted average of central space differences with coefficients $(1, 2, 1)$, respectively, at $j + 1, j, j - 1$.

10.20   Construct computer programs to verify the results given in Example 10.2.

10.21   Derive an implicit, Crank–Nicolson numerical model, lay out a computational procedure including the necessary matrices, and write a computer program to solve the mathematical model:

$u_t = k u_{xx} + au,$ $0 < x < l,$ $0 < t$
$u_x(0, t) = 0,$
$k u_x(l, t) + u(l, t) = 0,$ $0 < t$
$u(x, 0) = U_0,$ $0 \leq x \leq l$

Discuss the parameter values for which you must make computations, the selection of Δt and Δx, and compare results obtained from a range of cases.

10.22   Repeat Prob. 10.21 using a backward-difference scheme (see Prob. 10.17).

10.23   Derive and solve explicit and implicit (Prob. 10.19) numerical models for the following hyperbolic model:

$$z_{tt} = c^2 z_{yy}, \qquad 0 < x < l, \quad 0 < t$$

$$z(0, t) = a \sin \omega t,$$
$$z_y(l, t) = 0, \qquad\qquad t > 0$$

$$z(y, 0) = z_t(y, 0) = 0, \qquad 0 \le y \le l$$

Compare results for various Δy, Δt, and $\omega l/c$. How do these results agree with the analytic solution?

10.24   Solve

$$u_t = u_{xx}, \qquad 0 < x, \quad 0 < t$$

$$u(0, t) = 0, \qquad 0 < t$$

$$u(x, 0) = 1, \qquad 0 < x$$

by numerical finite differences. Compare your results for various Δt and Δx to the exact solution

$$u(x, t) = \mathrm{erf}\left(\frac{x}{2t^{1/2}}\right)$$

10.25   Find the truncation error T_{ij} for the explicit parabolic difference operator $P_D[u]$, and prove that for $s = k/h^2 = \frac{1}{6}$

$$T_{ij} = O(k^2 + h^4) = O(h^4)$$

10.26   Use the Taylor's series with remainder to prove (10.47) and (10.48).

10.27   Prove that the Crank–Nicolson equation (10.39) is consistent by use of the Taylor's series. [*Hint:* Derive (10.39) directly by use of the two-dimensional Taylor's series about $(i, j + \frac{1}{2})$.]

10.28   Use the Taylor's series to prove the DuFort–Frankel result (10.51). Show that for

$$\Delta t = (\Delta x)^2/12^{1/2}$$
$$T_{ij} = O(k^2 + h^4) = O(h^4)$$

10.29   Solve Example 10.1 by using the DuFort–Frankel scheme. Determine at least two alternative starting procedures; try both and compare the results against Fig. 10.4 and Table 10.1 for various $s = k/h^2$.

10.30   Verify (10.54) for the discretization error D_{ij}.

10.31   Use D_{ij} to prove that the hyperbolic difference equation in (10.34) is conditionally convergent for $k/h \le 1$.

10.32   Show that the Richardson equation (10.37) admits unbounded Fourier component solutions for all k/h^2 and thus is not the basis for a convergent scheme.

10.33   The backward-difference scheme derived in Prob. 10.17 satisfies a maximum-minimum principle because if the equation is written

$$u_{ij+1} = u_{ij} + \frac{k}{h^2}(u_{i+1j+1} - 2u_{ij+1} + u_{i-1j+1})$$

the terms in parentheses are negative at a maximum and positive at a minimum. Use induction to show that $u_{i,j+1}$ is bounded by the initial values or boundary values for $t \leq (j + 1)k$. Formulate a model for D_{ij}, and use the preceding results to show that $|D_{ij}| \leq t|T_{ij}|_{max}$ and hence that the backward-difference scheme is convergent for all $k/h^2 < \infty$.

10.34 Use the Fourier component (von Neumann) method to test the stability (and hence convergence) of the following difference equations:

(a) the Crank–Nicolson (10.39). For what values of k/h^2 can you prove convergence directly using D_{ij}? Why does this not agree with the stability analysis? [*Hint:* Stability analysis leads to form $\omega = -(\alpha - \beta)/(\alpha + \beta)$. This means $|\omega| \leq 1$, why?]

(b) the implicit hyperbolic equation in Prob. 10.19. Then solve Prob. 2.24 for various values of key nondimensional parameters.

(c) the equation derived in Prob. 10.18.

(d) the Richardson equation (10.37).

(e) the DuFort–Frankel equation (10.51).

(f) the backward-difference equation derived in Prob. 10.17. (Prove stability also by a maximum-minimum principle; see Prob. 10.33.) Then solve Example 10.1 for various $k = \Delta t$.

10.35 Construct numbergrams for the following difference equations for pure initial-value models:

(a) the Richardson equation (10.37) with $k/h^2 = 1, \frac{1}{2}$, and $\frac{1}{6}$.

(b) the DuFort–Frankel equation (10.51) with $k/h^2 = \frac{1}{6}$ and $\frac{1}{12}$.

(c) the explicit parabolic equation (10.26) with $k/h^2 = \frac{1}{6}$ (compare to Fig. 10.7).

(d) the hyperbolic equation (10.35) with $k/h = \frac{1}{2}, 1$, and 2.

Discuss the implications of your results.

10.36 Introduce (10.64) in (10.63) to show

$$\omega + \omega^{-1} = 2[1 - 2s^2 \sin^2 (\lambda_n h/2)]$$

10.37 Construct computational sequence diagrams (see Fig. 10.3) for the stars of the difference equation (10.35) for a pure initial-value problem with $k/h = \frac{1}{2}, 1$, and 2. Sketch in the numerical characteristics and the characteristics of the wave equation in (10.33) passing through the peak of the sequence pyramid. How do the domains of dependence relations correlate with the convergence and stability criteria?

10.38 Derive and solve a numerical model for Example 8.3. Verify the results of Example 10.3 by appropriate use of your computer program.

10.39 An experiment is being run in which some initial data can be measured and the variable value at a point can be measured up to time t_0. If the variable value at the point as a function of time is to be computed numerically up to t_0 by a program using an explicit formulation and a space increment h and to be compared then to the experimentally determined value, over what region must initial data be measured for input to the program?

(a) For heat conduction in a rod with material values K, ρ, c.

(b) For vibration of a string under tension T and with density ρ.

10.40   Derive difference equations for explicit, marching computation for

(a) the heat equation (10.72).

(b) the diffusion equation $Q_t = [D_0 e^{xQ} Q_x]_x$, where α is constant.

(c) the boundary condition

$$-Ku_x(0, t) = \sigma E[u^4(0, t) - u_S^4], \qquad 0 < t$$

(d) Burgers' equation (10.74).

10.41   Formulate and solve a numerical model for the heat model

$$u_t = [(1 + \beta u)u_x]_x, \qquad -\infty < x < \infty$$
$$u(x, 0) = e^{-x^2}, \qquad -\infty < x < \infty$$

with $\beta = 0, 0.01$, and -0.01. Discuss the influence of β, the stability criteria, etc.

10.42   Formulate and solve a numerical model for the vapor concentration uptake in a sheet of absorbent material [15] described by the model:

$$Q_t = [DQ_x]_x, \qquad 0 < x < l, \quad 0 < t$$
$$Q(0, t) = Q(l, t) = Q_0, \qquad 0 < t$$
$$Q(x, 0) = 0, \qquad 0 < x < l$$

where Q_0 is constant and $D = D_0 \exp(2.3Q/D_0)$. What stability criteria are required? [*Hint:* Do normalize first!]

10.43   Consider the model

$$u_t = ku_{xx}, \qquad 0 < x, \quad 0 < t$$
$$-Ku_x(0, t) = \sigma E[u^4(0, t) - u_S^4], \qquad 0 < t$$
$$u(x, 0) = 1000\,°F, \qquad 0 < x$$

Let $E = 1$ and $u_S = 750\,°F$; select a suitable metal and find K and σ in appropriate units; formulate and solve the resulting numerical model.

10.44   Derive from first principles the numerical model (10.76). Also, obtain the truncation error T_{ij} of the difference equation.

10.45   Prove the convergence and stability of the difference equation in (10.76) under the assumption that nonlinear factors can be treated as constants.

10.46   Determine the appropriate Courant condition for stability in numerical models of the following equations:

(a) $z_{yy} = z_{tt} + z_t + \varepsilon z^3$

(b) $v_{xx} = v_{tt} + (1 + 2v)v_t$

(c) $\rho z_{tt} = [T_0(1 + z^2)z_y]_y \qquad \rho, T_0 > 0$

10.47   Prove that the explicit-difference scheme (10.77) is consistent with (10.74).

10.48   Determine stability criteria for finite-difference representations of the following equations by linearization and the Fourier component method:

(a) $u_t = (u^3)_{xx}$; explicit scheme.

(b) $u_t = u_{xx} + au^2$; explicit scheme.

(c) $Q_t + UQ_x = [D_0(1 + Q)Q_x]_x$ for U, D_0 constant; explicit scheme.

(d) $Q_t + UQ_x = [D_0 e^{\alpha Q}Q_x]_x$ for U, α, D_0 constant; explicit scheme.

(e) $u_t = uu_x$; implicit, backward time-difference scheme.

(f) $u_t + uu_x = vu_{xx}$ for the Crank–Nicolson implicit scheme.

10.49 Formulate and solve a numerical model for

$$Q_t + Q_x = [(1 + Q)Q_x]_x - \alpha Q, \qquad 0 < x, \quad 0 < t$$

$$Q(0, t) = 1, \qquad 0 < t$$

$$Q(x, 0) = 0, \qquad 0 \le x$$

with $\alpha = 0$, 0.1, and 1. Discuss the influence of α. What would happen if $\alpha < 0$? Calculate appropriate stability criteria and verify them in your computations.

10.50 Formulate and solve a numerical, finite-difference model for equations (9.54). Compare your answers to those given in Chap. 9.

10.51 Derive an expression for an irregular Laplace difference operator at (i, j) in Fig. 10.51P.

FIGURE 10.51P

10.52 Derive expressions for the regular star Laplace difference operator at an interior point (i, j) in

(a) cartesian coordinates (x, y, z):

$$u_{xx} + u_{yy} + u_{zz} = 0$$

(b) cylindrical polar coordinates (r, θ, z):

$$u_{rr} + r^{-1}u_r + r^{-2}u_{\theta\theta} + u_{zz} = 0$$

(c) spherical coordinates (r, θ, ϕ):

$$u_{rr} + 2r^{-1}u_r + (r \sin \theta)^{-2}u_{\phi\phi} + r^{-2}u_{\theta\theta} + r^{-2}\cot \theta u_\theta = 0$$

10.53 Formulate a numerical model for

$$\nabla^2 u = 0, \qquad 0 < x < 1, \quad 0 < y < 1$$

$$u(x, 0) = u(x, 1) = u(1, y) = 0, \qquad 0 \le x \le 1, \quad 0 \le y \le 1$$

$$u(0, y) = \sin \pi y, \qquad 0 \le y \le 1$$

Now, for $h = \frac{1}{3}$, set up the matrix form $AU = D$ for solution, and find U by a hand calculation using Cramer's rule [8].

10.54 Use finite differences to solve directly the model shown in Fig. 10.54P when

(a) $h = k = \frac{1}{3}$ and irregular stars are used.

(b) $k = h \tan \pi/3 = \frac{1}{3} \tan \pi/3$ and nodes lie on the boundary.

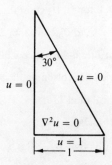

FIGURE 10.54P

10.55 Repeat Prob. 10.54(b) with $u_n = 0$ along the hypotenuse. Use the Taylor's series to derive the Neumann difference condition.

10.56 Derive a difference Neumann representation equivalent to (10.98) for points 2 and 3 on the boundary shown in Fig. 10.56P.

FIGURE 10.56P

10.57 Solve the following Neumann model by finite differences with $h = \frac{1}{3}$:

$$\nabla^2 u = xy, \qquad 0 < x < 1, \quad 0 < y < 1$$

$$u_x(0, y) = u_x(1, y) = 0, \qquad 0 < y < 1$$

$$u_y(x, 1) = 0, \qquad 0 \le x \le 1$$

$$u_y(x, 0) = \frac{\pi}{8} \sin \pi x, \qquad 0 < x < 1$$

10.58 Complete the proof of Theorem 10.1 for the minimum value of u_{ij} on $\bar{R}$.

10.59 Prove the existence and uniqueness of the solution to the model

$$\nabla^2 u = f(x, y) \text{ in } R$$

$$u = g(x, y) \text{ on } B$$

for $\bar{R} = R + B$, where B is a piecewise-smooth, simple closed boundary and $(f, g) \in C$.

10.60 Solve the following models by finite differences using several values of h and your computer center's linear equation solver that takes advantage of the banded nature of the coefficient matrix:

(a) $\nabla^2 u = 0, \qquad 0 < x < 1, \quad 0 < y < 2$
$u(x, 0) = \sin \pi x, \qquad 0 < x < 1$

$u(0, y) = -\sin \frac{\pi}{2} y, \qquad 0 < y < 2$

$u(1, y) = u(x, 2) = 0, \qquad 0 \le x \le 1, \quad 0 \le y \le 2$

(b) $\nabla^2 u = 2u,$ $0 < x < 1,$ $0 < y < 1$
   $u(x, 0) = e^x,$ $0 \le x \le 1$
   $u(x, 1) = e^{x+1},$ $0 \le x \le 1$
   $u(0, y) = e^y,$ $0 < y < 1$
   $u(1, y) = e^{y+1},$ $0 < y < 1$
   $[u(x, y) = e^{x+y}$ is the exact solution.]

(c) $\nabla^2 u = 0,$ $0 < x < 1,$ $0 < y < 1$
   $u_x(0, y) = 0,$ $0 < y < 1$
   $u_y(x, 0) = 0,$ $0 < x < 1$
   $u(1, y) = 1 - y^2,$ $0 \le y \le 1$
   $u(x, 1) = x^2 - 1,$ $0 \le x \le 1$
   $[u(x, y) = x^2 - y^2$ is the exact solution.]

(d) $\nabla^2 u = 2,$ $0 < x < 1,$ $0 < y < 1$
   $u_x(0, y) = u_y(x, 0) = 0,$
   $u(1, y) = 1 + y^2$ $u(x, 1) = 1 + x^2,$ $0 \le x \le 1,$ $0 \le y \le 1$
   $[u(x, y) = x^2 + y^2$ is the exact solution.]

10.61 Solve the following models by finite differences using $h = 0.05$ and iteration. In each case, write a program easily modified to do all three types of iteration, and construct a graph similar to Fig. 10.13 for a residual error tolerance of 10^{-5}. For ω_{opt}, test the effect of varying the tolerance $|c_{ij}|_{max}$ from 10^{-2} to the level of 10^{-1} times the round-off error of your machine (in single-precision arithmetic); plot the number of iterations required and the maximum difference between the solutions as a function of $|c_{ij}|_{max}$. What is a reasonable $|c_{ij}|_{max}$?

(a) Prob. 10.60(a)

(b) Prob. 10.60(b)

(c) Prob. 10.60(d)

(d) Example 10.6

(e) The model in Fig. 10.61P
   [Can you calculate the flux u_n across cde?]

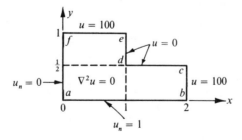

FIGURE 10.61P

(f) $\nabla^2 u = x^2 + y^2$ in R
   $u = 0$ on B
   where $\bar{R} = R + B$: the ellipse $x^2/4 + y^2/1 \le 1.$
   (Can you work on only part of the region?)

(g) The region of Example 10.6 with $\nabla^2 u = 0$ in R; $u_n = 0$ on $x^2 + y^2 = 1$; $u_x(0, y) = \sin \pi y$ on $0 < y < 1$; and $u_y(x, 0) = -\sin \pi x$ on $0 < x < 1.$

10.62   A maximum-minimum principle can be derived for parabolic as well as elliptic equations (see Sec. 10.2.1). Derive a maximum-minimum principle for the Crank–Nicolson difference operator (10.39) on the region $0 < x < 1$, $0 < t \leq T$, where T is finite. Use this principle to conclude that a solution of the difference equation is always bounded by the initial and boundary values. Try to infer the convergence and stability of the Crank–Nicolson scheme for all $k/h^2 < \infty$.

10.63   Prove that if $\phi = u_{xx} + u_{yy}$, (10.121) reduce to the Jacobi iteration scheme.

10.64   Verify that nonlinear SOR reduces to SOR if ϕ is a linear relationship.

10.65   Solve the following models by nonlinear SOR, and determine ω_{opt} in each case:

(a) $\nabla^2 u - e^u = 0$ in R
     $u = 1$ on C
     where $\bar{R} = R + C$: $0 \leq x \leq 1$, $0 \leq y \leq 1$. (This equation has several physical applications in heat, electricity, and fluids [1].)

(b) $\dfrac{\partial}{\partial x}\left[(1 + \beta u)\dfrac{\partial u}{\partial x}\right] + \dfrac{\partial}{\partial y}\left[(1 + \beta u)\dfrac{\partial u}{\partial y}\right] = 0,$

    $u(0, y) = u(x, 0) = 0,$ $0 < x < 1,$

    $u_x(1, y) = 0,$ $0 < y < 1$

    $u(x, 1) = \sin \pi x,$

    for $\beta = 0.01, 0.1$, and -0.01 (steady-state heat conduction; see Sec. 10.4).

(c) $\dfrac{\partial}{\partial x}\left[D\dfrac{\partial Q}{\partial x}\right] + \dfrac{\partial}{\partial y}\left[D\dfrac{\partial Q}{\partial y}\right] = 0,$

    $Q(-1, y) = Q(1, y) = Q(x, 1) = 0,$ $-1 < x < 1,$ $0 < y < 1$

    $Q_y(x, 0) = \begin{cases} 0, & |x| > \frac{1}{5}, \\ 1, & |x| \leq \frac{1}{5}, \end{cases}$

    where $D = e^{\alpha Q}$ for $\alpha = 0, 1$. Compare the results (steady diffusion of pollutant input).

10.66   Solve the model for steady-state heat conduction in a long cylinder if $K = 1 + \beta u$ and the top half of the cylinder is at temperature $u = 0$ while on the bottom half

$$u(1, \theta) = \sin \theta, \qquad \pi < \theta < 2\pi$$

Use polar coordinates (r, θ) and $\beta = 0$ and ± 0.1. [Hint: Be careful at the center!]

10.67   Formulate and solve explicit or implicit numerical models for the vibration of an elastic beam, where

$$z_{tt} + z_{yyyy} = q, \qquad 0 < y < 1, \quad 0 < t$$

if

(a) the beam is pinned at the ends so z and z_{yy} are zero there, $q \equiv 0$, and $z(y, 0) = y(1 - y)$ while $z_t(y, 0) = 0$.

(b) the beam is cantilevered so $z(0, t) = z_y(0, t) = z_{yy}(1, t) = z_{yyy}(1, t) = 0$; $q = y \sin 2\pi t$ and $z(y, 0) = z_t(y, 0) = 0$.

10.68   Formulate and solve by iteration a numerical model for the bending of an elastic plate under load where $\nabla^2(\nabla^2 z) = Q$, $0 < x < 1$, $0 < y < 1$, where $Q = q/D$. Here q is the load per unit area, D is the flexural rigidity of the material, and z is the plate deflection. Let

(a) $Q = 0$ and the plate be supported with moments applied along all edges so that

$$z(0, y) = z(1, y) = z(x, 0) = z(x, 1) = 0$$
$$z_{xx}(0, y) = -z_{xx}(1, y) = 1$$
$$z_{yy}(x, 0) = -z_{yy}(x, 1) = 1$$

(b) the plate be simply supported with $Q = \sin \pi x \sin \pi y$.

10.69 Solve by finite differences and iteration the Poisson equation $\nabla^2 u = f$ in R with $u = 0$ on C if

(a) $\bar{R}$ is the unit cube and $f = -(1 + \rho)^{-1}$, where $\rho = (x^2 + y^2 + z^2)^{1/2}$.

(b) $\bar{R}$ is the unit radius sphere and $f = -\sin \theta \sin \phi e^{-r}$ in spherical coordinates.

(c) $\bar{R}$ is a unit radius cylinder of unit length and $f = -e^{-(r+z)} \sin \theta$ in cylindrical polar coordinates.

10.70 Use the Fourier component method to establish stability criteria for the explicit-difference representations of

(a) the membrane vibration equation $z_{tt} = c^2 \nabla^2 z$ with $z(x, y, t)$.

(b) the heat equation $u_t = k \nabla^2 u$ with $u(x, y, t)$.

10.71 Formulate, test the adequacy of, and solve explicit numerical models for the mathematical models

(a) comprised of Eqs. (5.60) to (5.62) with $U_0(x, y) = xy(1 - x)(1 - y)$.

(b) comprised of Eqs. (5.89) to (5.91) with $z(x, y, 0) = 0$ and $z_t(x, y, 0) = 1$.

(c) used in Prob. 5.39.

(d) used in Prob. 5.40.

(e) used in Prob. 5.43 with $q(x, y) = \sin \pi x \sin \pi y$ and $U_0 = 0$.

(f) used in Prob. 5.22(a).

10.72 Use the ADI method to solve Prob. 10.71(e). Try several Δt values and compare with analytic or explicit numerical results.

SUMMARY OF USEFUL RESULTS
OF CALCULUS

The material summarized here should already be in the repertoire of the reader. It is the base on which much of the main text is built. The objective of this summary is to provide both a convenient reference to key concepts, definitions, and theorems and a list of references in which the various results can be pursued in more detail if a refresher is needed. As usual, the numbers in brackets refer to the references listed at the end of the appendixes.

A.1.1   SYMBOLS AND DEFINITIONS

Limits and Continuous Functions [1]

By the symbolism

$$\lim_{x \to x_0} f(x) = L$$

we mean that, for every $\varepsilon > 0$, there exists a $\delta > 0$ such that whenever $|x - x_0| < \delta$, $|f(x) - L| < \varepsilon$. Similarly,

$$\lim_{x \to x_0^+} f(x) = L_r$$

means that, for $\varepsilon > 0$, there exists a $\delta > 0$ such that whenever $0 < x - x_0 < \delta$, $|f(x) - L_r| < \varepsilon$. Thus we approach x_0 only from the right through $x > x_0$ and find the *limit from the right*. Finally,

$$\lim_{x \to x_0^-} f(x) = L_l$$

is the *limit from the left* with $-\delta < x - x_0 < 0$.

A function $f(x)$, defined in the open interval $a < x < b$, is termed continuous at a point x_0 in the interval if

$$\lim_{x \to x_0} f(x) = f(x_0)$$

that is, if for each $\varepsilon > 0$, there is a $\delta > 0$ so whenever $|x - x_0| < \delta$,

$$|f(x) - f(x_0)| < \varepsilon$$

In like manner, a function may be termed *continuous from the left* or *the right* in appropriate circumstances.

A function $f(x)$ is called *piecewise continuous* in an interval $a \leq x \leq b$ if there are only a finite number of discontinuities of $f(x)$ at $x_1, x_2, \ldots, x_n$ for $a \leq x_i \leq b$ and if $f(x)$ has finite limits from the left and from the right at each discontinuity.

Definitions similar to the preceding ones hold for greater numbers of independent variables.

Function Classes [2, 3]

It is often convenient to talk of classes of functions. For example, suppose that f is a real-valued function on some interval I. Then if f has derivatives of every order at each point of I, we say that f belongs to the class C^∞ of all functions with derivatives of every order on I; that is, $f \in C^\infty$ on I. Such a function is termed analytic.

If f is only continuous on I, we write $f \in C^0$ or, equivalently, $f \in C$ on I. Were f twice continuously differentiable on I, then we would have $f \in C^2$ on I, and so on.

Note that if $f' \in C^1$, then at least piecewise $f \in C^2$. If f' is only piecewise continuous on I, it may be that $f \in C$ on I. The converse does not necessarily follow, of course.

Just as it is useful to talk in terms of classes of continuous functions, it is useful to define function classes in terms of integral measures. Thus we say that $f \in L^p(R)$—that is, f belongs to the class L^p on the region R—if

$$\int_R |f|^p \, dR < \infty$$

For an absolutely integrable function $f(x)$, we write $f(x) \in L^1(a, b)$ if

$$\int_a^b |f(x)| \, dx < \infty$$

that is, the integral exists. A square-integrable function $f(x, y)$ on the rectangle $R: a \leq x \leq b, c \leq y \leq d$ satisfies

$$\iint_R |f(x, y)|^2 \, dA = \int_c^d \int_a^b |f(x, y)|^2 \, dx \, dy < \infty$$

so $f(x, y) \in L^2(R)$.

Order Symbols [4]

The symbols O and o are used to describe the rate at which a function approaches a limit. If $f(x) = x$, we know that

$$\lim_{x \to 0} f(x) = 0$$

To describe the rate at which $f(x)$ approaches zero, we write

$$f(x) = O[x] \qquad \text{as } x \to 0$$

meaning

$$\lim_{x \to 0} \frac{f(x)}{x} < \infty$$

To generalize the above, we follow Van Dyke [4] and define some selected gage function $\mathit{6}(x)$ against which the behavior of $f(x)$ is measured [above $\mathit{6}(x) = x$]. Then we define the following relations:

$$f(x) = O[\mathit{6}(x)] \qquad \text{as } x \to x_0$$

if

$$\lim_{x \to x_0} \frac{f(x)}{\mathit{6}(x)} < \infty$$

$$f(x) = o[\mathit{6}(x)] \qquad \text{as } x \to x_0$$

if

$$\lim_{x \to x_0} \frac{f(x)}{\mathit{6}(x)} = 0$$

Finally, a function $f(x)$ is said to be of *exponential order* as x tends to infinity if a constant $\alpha < \infty$ exists such that

$$e^{-\alpha x} |f(x)| = O[1] \qquad \text{as } x \to \infty$$

It follows that

$$f(x) = O[e^{\alpha x}] \qquad \text{as } x \to \infty$$

that is, $\mathit{6}(x) = e^{\alpha x}$.

A.1.2   SERIES

Infinite Series [1, 2, 5]

Let

$$PS_k = \sum_{n=1}^{k} f_n(x)$$

be the kth partial sum of the infinite series

$$\sum_{n=1}^{\infty} f_n(x) \tag{A.1.1}$$

of continuous functions $f_n(x)$, defined on the interval $I : a \leq x \leq b$.

Convergence. The series (A.1.1) is pointwise convergent to a sum $f(x)$ in I if, for each $\varepsilon > 0$, there exists an integer N_x^ε such that $|f(x) - PS_k| < \varepsilon$ for $k \geq N_x^\varepsilon$. Here N_x^ε may depend on x and does depend on ε.

Uniform Convergence. The series (A.1.1) is uniformly convergent to $f(x)$ in I if, for each $\varepsilon > 0$, there exists an integer N^ε, not dependent on x, such that $|f(x) - PS_k| < \varepsilon$ for $k \geq N^\varepsilon$ and all x in I.

Properties of Uniformly Convergent Series of Functions.

1. The sum $f(x)$ of a uniformly convergent series, say (A.1.1), of continuous functions $f_n(x)$ is continuous.

2. A uniformly convergent series of continuous functions can be integrated term by term; the integral of the sum equals the sum of the integrated terms.

3. The sum, difference, or product of two uniformly convergent series is also uniformly convergent.

4. A uniformly convergent series of functions $f_n(x)$ can be differentiated term by term provided that $f_n(x) \in C^1$ in I and that the series of derivatives is uniformly convergent in I; the sum of the series $\sum_{n=1}^{\infty} f'_n(x)$ is $f'(x)$.

The Weierstrass M-Test. If there exists a *majorizing* or *dominating* series of constants M_n, such that $|f_n(x)| \leq M_n$ for all n and x in I, and the series of positive constants $\sum_{n=1}^{\infty} M_n$ is convergent, the series (A.1.1) is absolutely convergent for each x and is uniformly convergent in I.

Abel's Test for Functions. If $\sum_{n=1}^{\infty} f_n(x)$ is uniformly convergent in I and $g_n(y)$ is a bounded, positive, monotomic decreasing function (not increasing) of n for y in the interval I, the series $\sum_{n=1}^{\infty} g_n(y) f_n(x)$ is also uniformly convergent in the region $R = I + I$!

Tests for Series of Constants. There are a large number of such tests; two of the most useful are listed here.

1. *The harmonic series:* The series

$$\sum_{n=1}^{\infty} \frac{1}{n^\alpha} = 1 + \frac{1}{2^\alpha} + \frac{1}{3^\alpha} + \cdots$$

converges for $\alpha > 1$ and diverges for $\alpha \leq 1$.

2. *The ratio test:* Let M_n be a set of nonzero constants, $\sum_{n=1}^{\infty} M_n$ be a series of these constants and the ratio

$$R = \lim_{n \to \infty} \left| \frac{M_{n+1}}{M_n} \right|$$

If $R < 1$, the series is absolutely convergent; if $R > 1$, the series diverges; and if $R = 1$, the test fails.

Taylor's Series [1, 2]

The Taylor's series is a power series expansion about a point. Let the real-valued function $f(x) \in C^{\infty}$ in $I: a \le x \le b$; then the Taylor's series expansion about x_0 in I is

$$f(x) = \sum_{n=0}^{\infty} \frac{f^{(n)}(x_0)}{n!}(x - x_0)^n \tag{A.1.2}$$

where $f^{(n)}(x) = d^n f(x)/dx^n$. For equality to hold in (A.1.2), it is necessary and sufficient [2] that the remainder term

$$R_n = \frac{f^{(n)}(x_1)}{n!}(x - x_0)^n$$

where x_1 lies between x_0 and x, approach zero as $n \to \infty$—that is, that

$$\lim_{n \to \infty} R_n = 0$$

In two dimensions, if $f(x, y) \in C^{\infty}$ in a domain D of the x–y plane, then [1]

$$f(x, y) = f(x_0, y_0) + [f_x(x_0, y_0)(x - x_0) + f_y(x_0, y_0)(y - y_0)]$$

$$+ \frac{1}{2!}[f_{xx}(x_0, y_0)(x - x_0)^2 + 2f_{xy}(x_0, y_0)(x - x_0)(y - y_0)$$

$$+ f_{yy}(x_0, y_0)(y - y_0)^2] + \cdots + \frac{1}{n!}\left[\frac{\partial^n F}{\partial x^n}(x_0, y_0)(x - x_0)^n + \ldots\right] + \ldots$$

Asymptotic Series [4, 6, 7]

The series

$$f(x) \sim \sum_{n=0}^{\infty} c_n x^n \tag{A.1.3}$$

is called an *asymptotic series* for $f(x)$ if, for fixed k,

$$\lim_{x \to 0} \frac{\left[\sum_{n=0}^{k} c_n x^n - f(x)\right]}{x^k} = 0$$

Although the series (A.1.3) may not even converge for any value of x, the error in the kth partial sum is less than the first neglected term; that is,

$$\left| f(x) - \sum_{n=0}^{k} c_n x^n \right| < c_{k+1} x^{k+1}$$

The asymptotic series (A.1.3) is often useful in calculations, even when it diverges.

The convergent power series

$$f(x) = \sum_{n=0}^{\infty} a_n x^n \tag{A.1.4}$$

exists if, for fixed x,

$$\lim_{k \to \infty} \left[f(x) - \sum_{n=0}^{k} a_n x^n \right] = 0$$

Thus (A.1.4) is also an asymptotic series as

$$\lim_{x \to 0} \frac{\left[f(x) - \sum_{n=0}^{k} a_n x^n \right]}{x^k} = \lim_{x \to 0} \sum_{n=k+1}^{\infty} a_n x^{n-k} = 0$$

The converse regarding (A.1.3) is not true except in special cases; that is, an asymptotic series is not, in general, a convergent power series.

A.1.3   VECTORS [8]

Definitions

A *vector* is a quantity that can be represented in terms of its magnitude and direction. Typically, the vector f can be expressed in terms of its components along the axes of the cartesian system x, y, z; that is,

$$f = f_x i + f_y j + f_z k$$

where f_x, f_y, f_z are the projections of the magnitude of f along the x, y, z axes, respectively. The unit vectors i, j, and k lie along the mutually perpendicular coordinate axes.

It follows that the absolute value

$$|f| = (f_x^2 + f_y^2 + f_z^2)^{1/2}$$

is the *magnitude* of f.

Vector Operations

The Scalar Product. $f \cdot g = |f| |g| \cos \theta$, where θ is the angle between the vectors f and g.

If n is a unit vector normal to a surface, the component of the vector f along n is

$$f_n = f \cdot n$$

The Vector Product.

$$f \times g = \begin{vmatrix} i & j & k \\ f_x & f_y & f_z \\ g_x & g_y & g_z \end{vmatrix}$$

Derivatives. Let the vector f and scalar g be functions of the parametric variable s or of x, y, and z as necessary. Then

$$\frac{df}{ds} = \frac{df_x}{ds}i + \frac{df_y}{ds}j + \frac{df_z}{ds}k$$

$$\frac{dgf}{ds} = f\frac{dg}{ds} + g\frac{df}{ds}$$

$$\text{grad } g = \frac{\partial g}{\partial x}i + \frac{\partial g}{\partial y}j + \frac{\partial g}{\partial z}k$$

$$\left(\text{grad} = \nabla = \frac{\partial}{\partial x}i + \frac{\partial}{\partial y}j + \frac{\partial}{\partial z}k \text{ is called the gradient operator}\right)$$

$$\text{div} f = \nabla \cdot f = \frac{\partial f_x}{\partial x} + \frac{\partial f_y}{\partial y} + \frac{\partial f_z}{\partial z} \quad \text{(called the divergence)}$$

$$\nabla^2 g = \nabla \cdot \nabla g = \text{div grad } g = \frac{\partial^2 g}{\partial x^2} + \frac{\partial^2 g}{\partial y^2} + \frac{\partial^2 g}{\partial z^2}$$

A.1.4   INTEGRAL RELATIONS

The Gauss integral theorem and the Green's identities that are derived from it form the key set of integral relations for this text. The integral theorem transforms line integrals to surface integrals or surface integrals to volume integrals. The Green's identities are particularly useful because they transfer derivative operations between two functions.

In the following material we let the arbitrary vector field $v \in C^1$ in some domain D of the appropriate space. Similarly, the functions f and $g \in C^2$ in D. Here, as before, n is the outward unit normal vector to the curve C or the surface $\bar{S}$ as appropriate and where f and $g \in C^1$.

Two Dimensions [1, 8]

Let C be a piecewise-smooth, simple, closed curve in the domain D of the x–y plane, while R is the region enclosed in C. Then

$$\oint_C v \cdot n \, ds = \iint_R \text{div } v \, dx \, dy \quad \text{(Gauss' theorem)} \tag{A.1.5}$$

where $\oint$ indicates the counterclockwise line integral over the whole boundary curve C.

By letting $v = f\nabla g$ in (A.1.5), one may obtain

$$\oint_C f\frac{\partial g}{\partial n} \, ds = \iint_R f \, \nabla^2 g \, dx \, dy + \iint_R (\nabla f \cdot \nabla g) \, dx \, dy \quad \text{(Green's First Identity)} \tag{A.1.6}$$

for the two functions f and g. Here

$$\frac{\partial g}{\partial n} = \nabla g \cdot \boldsymbol{n}$$

By exchanging the roles of f and g in (A.1.6), we obtain a second identity. Subtracting the second from the first produces

$$\oint_C \left(f \frac{\partial g}{\partial n} - g \frac{\partial f}{\partial n} \right) ds = \iint_R (f \nabla^2 g - g \nabla^2 f) \, dx \, dy \qquad \text{(Green's Second Identity)}$$

Three Dimensions [1, 8]

Let $\bar{S}$ be the piecewise-smooth bounding surface of a bounded, closed volume V in D. Then

$$\iint_{\bar{S}} v_n \, dS = \iiint_V \operatorname{div} \boldsymbol{v} \, dV \qquad \text{(Gauss' theorem)} \qquad \text{(A.1.7)}$$

where $v_n = \boldsymbol{v} \cdot \boldsymbol{n}$.

Again, by setting $\boldsymbol{v} = f \nabla g$ in (A.1.7), one may obtain

$$\iint_{\bar{S}} f \frac{\partial g}{\partial n} \, dS = \iiint_V f \nabla^2 g \, dV + \iiint_V (\nabla f \cdot \nabla g) \, dV \qquad \text{(Green's First Identity)}$$
$$\text{(A.1.8)}$$

Exchanging the roles of f and g produces a second equation. Subtracting the second equation from (A.1.8) yields

$$\iint_{\bar{S}} \left(f \frac{\partial g}{\partial n} - g \frac{\partial f}{\partial n} \right) dS = \iiint_V (f \nabla^2 g - g \nabla^2 f) \, dV \qquad \text{(Green's Second Identity)}$$
$$\text{(A.1.9)}$$

REVIEW OF ORDINARY
DIFFERENTIAL EQUATION THEORY

Several excellent texts are available for the study of ordinary differential equations [9–11]. The following discussion is not comprehensive; rather it is heavily slanted toward those concepts and methods that are of immediate use in the developments in this book. Many of the results are stated without proof, which, of course, can be found in the references.

A.2.1 BASIC CONCEPTS AND DEFINITIONS

The general first-order, linear, ordinary differential equation has the standard form

$$X' + \beta_1(x)X = \beta_2(x) \tag{A.2.1}$$

in which $X(x)$ is the dependent variable and β_1 and β_2 are assumed to be continuous functions. This equation is solved by use of an integrating factor

$$I(x) = \exp\left[\int^x \beta_1(\eta)\,d\eta\right] = \exp\left[\int^x \beta_1\,d\eta\right] \tag{A.2.2}$$

where η is a dummy variable and $\int^x$ indicates an indefinite integral with respect to the variable x.

Multiplying (A.2.1) by (A.2.2) produces

$$\frac{d}{dx}\left(X \exp\left[\int^x \beta_1\, d\eta \right] \right) = \exp\left[\int^x \beta_1\, d\eta \right]\beta_2(x)$$

Integration of this equation yields the general solution to (A.2.1)

$$X(x) = \exp\left[-\int^x \beta_1(\eta)\, d\eta \right] C + \int^x \beta_2(\tau) \exp\left[\int^\tau \beta_1(\eta)\, d\eta \right] d\tau \qquad \text{(A.2.3)}$$

It has one arbitrary constant C.

The reader may verify by direct substitution that

$$C \exp\left[-\int^x \beta_1(\eta)\, d\eta \right]$$

is the so-called *complementary solution* to the homogeneous equation

$$X' + \beta_1 X = 0$$

while the remainder of (A.2.3) is a particular solution to the inhomogeneous equation (A.2.1).

The structure of second-order equations is analogous to that of the first-order equation. Thus

$$X'' + P_1(x)X' + P_2(x)X = P_3(x) \qquad \text{(A.2.4)}$$

is a standard form for the general, linear, ordinary differential equation of second order defined on some x-interval (a, b). Equation (A.2.4) is called *homogeneous* when $P_3(x) \equiv 0$; otherwise (A.2.4) is an *inhomogeneous* equation. A function $X(x)$ is a solution to (A.2.4) if it becomes an identity in x upon substitution of X and its appropriate derivatives. The *general solution* of (A.2.4) is the collection of all solutions and contains two arbitrary constants.

When $P_3(x) \equiv 0$, the resulting equation

$$X''(x) + P_1(x)X'(x) + P_2(x)X = 0 \qquad \text{(A.2.5)}$$

is called the *complementary* homogeneous equation to (A.2.4). The general solution to (A.2.5) is given by

$$X_c = c_1 X_1 + c_2 X_2 \qquad \text{(A.2.6)}$$

where X_1 and X_2 are two linearly independent solutions to (A.2.5) and c_1 and c_2 are a pair of arbitrary, free constants. We recall that the two solutions X_1 and X_2 are *linearly independent* if one cannot be written as a linear function of the other. If X_1 and X_2 are *linearly dependent*, then a constant c exists such that for x on (a, b), where (A.2.5) is defined,

$$X_1 - cX_2 \equiv 0$$

Now, in view of the above and the linearity of (A.2.4), it follows that if X_p is any particular solution of (A.2.4) and X_c is the general solution of the complementary equation (A.2.5), then

$$X = X_p + X_c \qquad \text{(A.2.7)}$$

is the general solution to (A.2.4), where X_c as given by (A.2.6) contains the required two arbitrary constants. In this case, X_c is called the *complementary solution*.

Finally, the fundamental existence theorem [9] for the general equation (A.2.4) states

THEOREM A.1   For (A.2.4), under the conditions that P_1, P_2, and P_3 are bounded, continuous functions on $a \leq x \leq b$, there exists a unique solution $X(x)$, valid over the entire interval, such that

$$X(x_0) = A$$

$$X'(x_0) = B$$

where x_0 is a point in the interval and A and B are real constants. It follows that:

THEOREM A.2   If $P_3 \equiv 0$ and $A = B = 0$ in the above, then the unique solution is $X(x) \equiv 0$.

A.2.2   METHODS OF SOLUTION

The Power Series Method

A power series can be used to solve the general homogeneous equation (A.2.5) under certain conditions, in particular, near ordinary and regular singular points in the domain $a \leq x \leq b$. Any point $x = x_0$ in (a, b) at which $P_1(x)$ and $P_2(x)$ are analytic* is called an *ordinary point* of (A.2.5); all other points are called *singular points*. A singular point $x = x_s$ is called a *regular* singular point if the functions

$$Q_1(x) = P_1(x)(x - x_s)^{-1} \quad \text{and} \quad Q_2(x) = P_2(x)(x - x_s)^{-2}$$

are analytic at $x = x_s$; otherwise x_s is an *irregular* singular point.

A *power* series is an infinite series of the form

$$\sum_{n=0}^{\infty} c_n x^n = c_0 + c_1 x + c_2 x^2 + \cdots + c_n x^n + \cdots$$

where the c_i are constants. For an expansion about $x = x_0$, the series is

$$\sum_{n=0}^{\infty} c_n(x - x_0)^n = c_0 + c_1(x - x_0) + \cdots + c_n(x - x_0)^n + \cdots \qquad \text{(A.2.8)}$$

Each power series has a *convergence interval* that lies along the x axis and is centered about $x = x_0$; that is, the interval is the region $|x - x_0| < R$, where R is the *radius of convergence* and is given by [11]

$$R = \lim_{n \to \infty} \left| \frac{c_n}{c_{n+1}} \right|, \qquad \text{if the limit exists}$$

---

* Recall from Sec. 2.6 that a function is analytic in an interval if it can be represented by a power series in the given interval.

or

$$R = \lim_{n \to \infty} \frac{1}{\sqrt[n]{|c_n|}}, \qquad \text{if the limit exists}$$

Whenever $R > 0$ and $|x - x_0| < R$, the series (A.2.8) converges absolutely and uniformly [1]. A convergent power series can be integrated or differentiated term by term. Within the convergence interval of the orignal series, the series of integrated or differentiated terms converges to the integral or derivative of the sum of the original series. Finally, two convergent power series can be added and multiplied together term by term to form new series whose radius of convergence is as large as the smaller of the radii of the original series.

Suppose now that $x = 0$ is an ordinary point (A.2.5) so that P_1 and P_2 can be represented by power series in powers of x with $R > 0$; then [9, 11]:

THEOREM A.3   Every solution $X(x)$ of (A.2.5) can be represented by a power series in powers of x with $R > 0$.

The formal method of solution consists of
(a) writing $X = \sum_{n=0}^{\infty} c_n x^n$, where the c_n are constants to be determined.
(b) expanding P_1 and P_2 in power series—for example,

$$P_i = \sum_{n=0}^{\infty} p_{in} x^n$$

where the p_{in} are known.
(c) introducing the series from (a) and (b) into (A.2.5), performing the indicated multiplications to achieve a new power series, and, finally, equating the coefficients of like powers of x equal to zero. This last step is justified because if a power series has $R > 0$ and zero sum, every coefficient of the series must be zero. The method is illustrated with two simple but significant examples.

EXAMPLE A.1   Find the general solution to

$$X'' + \lambda^2 X = 0 \tag{A.2.9}$$

Solution: Here $x = 0$ is a regular point of (A.2.9) and λ^2 is a constant. Write

$$X(x) = \sum_{n=0}^{\infty} c_n x^n$$

and introduce it into (A.2.9) to achieve

$$\sum_{n=0}^{\infty} n(n-1)c_n x^{n-2} + \lambda^2 \sum_{n=0}^{\infty} c_n x^n = 0$$

We shift the index of the second series by replacing n by $n - 2$ and obtain

$$\sum_{n=0}^{\infty} n(n-1)c_n x^{n-2} + \lambda^2 \sum_{n=2}^{\infty} c_{n-2} x^{n-2} = 0 \tag{A.2.10}$$

For (A.2.10) to be satisfied, the sum of the coefficients of x^{n-2} for each n must be zero. Accordingly, for $n < 2$, only the left-hand series in (A.2.10) contributes terms, and so when

$$n = 0, \qquad 0(0 - 1)c_0 = 0 \rightarrow c_0 \text{ is arbitrary}$$

$$n = 1, \qquad 1(1 - 1)c_1 = 0 \rightarrow c_1 \text{ is arbitrary}$$

When $n \geq 2$, both series in (A.2.10) contribute terms, and so for

$$n \geq 2, \qquad n(n - 1)c_n + \lambda^2 c_{n-2} = 0$$

or

$$c_n = \frac{-\lambda^2}{n(n - 1)} c_{n-2}$$

which is called the *recursion formula*. Accordingly, the general solution to (A.2.9) is

$$X(x) = c_0 \sum_{n=0}^{\infty} \frac{1}{(2n)!} (\lambda x)^{2n} + \frac{c_1}{\lambda} \sum_{n=0}^{\infty} \frac{1}{(2n + 1)!} (\lambda x)^{2n+1} \tag{A.2.11}$$

because c_0 and c_1 are arbitrary constants and the two series are linearly independent. In fact,

$$\cos \lambda x = \sum_{n=0}^{\infty} \frac{1}{(2n)!} (\lambda x)^{2n}$$

and

$$\sin \lambda x = \sum_{n=0}^{\infty} \frac{1}{(2n + 1)!} (\lambda x)^{2n+1}$$

Thus (A.2.11) can be written as

$$X(x) = c_0 \cos \lambda x + c_1 \frac{\sin \lambda x}{\lambda} \tag{A.2.12}$$

EXAMPLE A.2   Find the general solution to

$$(1 - x^2)X'' - 2xX' + \lambda(\lambda + 1)X = 0 \tag{A.2.13}$$

which is called the *Legendre equation* when λ is a real number; (A.2.13) has wide application for boundary-value problems associated with spherical bodies.

Solution: Here $x = 0$ is an ordinary point, whereas $x = \pm 1$ are regular singular points. It can be shown, as a consequence, that if the solution is

$$X = \sum_{n=0}^{\infty} c_n x^n \tag{A.2.14}$$

the series converges in $|x| < 1$.

Introduction of (A.2.14) into (A.2.13) leads first to

$$(1 - x^2) \sum_{n=0}^{\infty} n(n - 1)c_n x^{n-2} - 2x \sum_{n=0}^{\infty} nc_n x^{n-1} + \lambda(\lambda + 1) \sum_{n=0}^{\infty} c_n x^n = 0$$

and then to

$$\sum_{n=0}^{\infty} n(n-1)c_n x^{n-2} - \sum_{n=0}^{\infty} n(n-1)c_n x^n - \sum_{n=0}^{\infty} 2nc_n x^n + \sum_{n=0}^{\infty} \lambda(\lambda+1)c_n x^n = 0$$

We now replace n by $n-2$ in each of the series containing x^n to obtain

$$\sum_{n=0}^{\infty} n(n-1)c_n x^{n-2} + \sum_{n=2}^{\infty} [-(n-2)(n-3)c_{n-2} - 2(n-2)c_{n-2}$$

$$+ \lambda(\lambda+1)c_{n-2}]x^{n-2} = 0 \qquad (A.2.15)$$

As before, when $n < 2$, only the first series in (A.2.15) contributes terms, so when

$$n = 0, \qquad 0(0-1)c_0 = 0 \rightarrow c_0 \text{ is arbitrary}$$

$$n = 1, \qquad 1(1-1)c_1 = 0 \rightarrow c_1 \text{ is arbitrary}$$

When $n \geq 2$,

$$n(n-1)c_n + [-(n-2)(n-3) - 2(n-2) + \lambda(\lambda+1)]c_{n-2} = 0$$

or

$$c_n = \frac{(n-1)(n-2) - \lambda(\lambda+1)}{n(n-1)}c_{n-2}, \qquad n \geq 2$$

which again is a recursion formula whereby all the coefficients can be calculated. Thus

$$c_0, c_2 = -\frac{\lambda(\lambda+1)}{2!}c_0, \quad c_n = (-1)^{n/2}\frac{\lambda(\lambda+1)(\lambda-2)(\lambda+n-1)\cdots}{n!}c_0,$$

$$n = 4, 6, \ldots$$

and

$$c_1, c_3 = -\frac{(\lambda-1)(\lambda+2)}{3!}c_1, \quad c_n = (-1)^{(n-1)/2}\frac{(\lambda-1)(\lambda+2)(\lambda-n+2)\cdots}{n!}c_1,$$

$$n = 5, 7, \ldots$$

Consequently, the general solution to (A.2.13) is

$$X(x) = c_0 X_0(x) + c_1 X_1(x) \qquad (A.2.16)$$

where c_0 and c_1 are arbitrary,

$$X_0 = 1 - \frac{\lambda(\lambda+1)}{2!}x^2 + \frac{\lambda(\lambda+1)(\lambda-2)(\lambda+3)}{4!}x^4$$

$$- \frac{\lambda(\lambda+1)(\lambda-2)(\lambda+3)(\lambda-4)(\lambda+5)}{6!}x^6 + - + \cdots \qquad (A.2.17)$$

and

$$X_1 = x - \frac{(\lambda-1)(\lambda+2)}{3!}x^3 + \frac{(\lambda-1)(\lambda+2)(\lambda-3)(\lambda+4)}{5!}x^5 - + - \cdots \qquad (A.2.18)$$

Q.E.D.

The series (A.2.17) and (A.2.18) are each solutions of the Legendre equation. Their properties when λ is a positive integer are interesting. When λ is an even integer, we see from (A.2.17) that the series X_0 is truncated to a polynomial of degree λ. When λ is an odd integer, the series X_1 of (A.2.18) is truncated to a polynomial of degree λ. Thus when λ is a positive integer, there always exists a polynomial solution P_λ to Legendre's equation (A.2.13) and the general solution can be written

$$X(x) = AP_\lambda(x) + BQ_\lambda(x)$$

where $Q_\lambda(x)$ can be determined from (A.2.16). These polynomial solutions are of great value and are discussed further in Appendix 3.

Now we return to (A.2.5) and suppose that $x = 0$ is a regular singular point of the equation and, in accordance with our definition of a singular point, that the functions P_1 and P_2 can be expanded in series of the form

$$P_1(x) = \frac{p_{10}}{x} + p_{11} + \sum_{n=2}^{\infty} p_{1n}x^{n-1} \tag{A.2.19}$$

and

$$p_2(x) = \frac{p_{20}}{x^2} + \frac{p_{21}}{x} + p_{22} + \sum_{n=3}^{\infty} p_{2n}x^{n-2} \tag{A.2.20}$$

Because of the singular nature of the differential equation, we expand our solution in the form

$$X(x) = \sum_{n=0}^{\infty} c_n^k x^{n+k} \tag{A.2.21}$$

where now both the c_n^k and k are to be found. Here k represents the expectation that the solution of a singular equation is different; since k is unknown, c_0^k is taken to be the coefficient of the smallest power of x in the solution, so $c_0^k \neq 0$.

We introduce (A.2.19) to (A.2.21) into (A.2.5). Our first result is

$$\sum_{n=0}^{\infty} (n+k)(n+k-1)c_n^k x^{n+k-2} + \left[\sum_{n=0}^{\infty} p_{1n}x^{n-1}\right]\left[\sum_{n=0}^{\infty} (n+k)c_n^k x^{n+k-1}\right]$$

$$+ \left[\sum_{n=0}^{\infty} p_{2n}x^{n-2}\right]\left[\sum_{n=0}^{\infty} c_n^k x^{n+k}\right] = 0$$

Carrying out the indicated multiplications but writing only the first few terms gives us

$$k(k-1)c_0^k x^{k-2} + (k+1)kc_1^k x^{k-1} + (k+2)(k+1)c_2^k x^k \cdots$$

$$+ p_{10}kc_0^k x^{k-2} + [p_{10}(k+1)c_1^k + p_{11}kc_0^k]x^{k-1} \cdots$$

$$+ p_{20}c_0^k x^{k-2} + [p_{20}c_1^k + p_{21}c_0^k]x^{k-1} \cdots = 0$$

Equating the coefficients of like powers of x to zero gives [10]

$$[k(k-1) + p_{10}k + p_{20}]c_0^k = 0 \tag{A.2.22}$$

and in general

$$c_n^k = \frac{-1}{[(n + k)(n + k - 1) + (n + k)p_{10} + p_{20}]} \sum_{m=0}^{n-1} c_m^k [(m + k)p_{1q} + p_{2q}] \qquad \text{(A.2.23)}$$

where $q = n - m$.

As $c_0^k \neq 0$, (A.2.22) gives a quadratic equation for k:

$$k(k - 1) + p_{10}k + p_{20} = 0 \qquad \text{(A.2.24)}$$

This is called the *indicial equation*. As (A.2.24) is a quadratic in k, there are two possible roots k_1 and k_2. The solution of (A.2.5) takes several forms that depend on k_1 and k_2: (a) k_1 and k_2 differ by a number that is not an integer, (b) $k_1 = k_2 = k_r$; that is, (A.2.24) has a double root, or (c) k_1 and k_2 differ by an integer. These cases are discussed in detail in [9, 10]. We comment on each here and work an example.

(a) If k_1 and k_2 differ by a nonintegral number, then two linearly independent solutions of (A.2.5) are given by

$$X_1 = \sum_{n=0}^{\infty} c_n^{k_1} x^{n + k_1}$$

and

$$X_2 = \sum_{n=0}^{\infty} c_n^{k_2} x^{n + k_2}$$

The solutions X_1 and X_2 can be used in the usual manner to form a general solution.

(b) If (A.2.24) has a double root k_r, then two linearly independent solutions of (A.2.5) are given by

$$X_1 = \sum_{n=0}^{\infty} c_n x^{n + k_r}$$

and

$$X_2 = X_1 \ln x + x^{k_r} \sum_{n=1}^{\infty} c_n x^n$$

Here $X_1 \ln x$ replaces the $n = 0$ term in the series for X_2. Again a general solution is obtained from a combination of X_1 and X_2.

(c) If k_1 and k_2 differ by an integer, then the root k_1 [the root with the larger real part if the solution to (A.2.24) is complex] gives a solution

$$X_1 = \sum_{n=0}^{\infty} c_n^{k_1} x^{n + k_1}$$

while to k_2 there corresponds

$$X_2 = c_2 X_1 \ln x + x^{k_2} \sum_{n=0}^{\infty} c_n^{k_2} x^n$$

In this case, the constant c_2 is obtained as a part of the calculation [10, 12] leading to evaluation of the power series coefficients; c_2 may be zero in some cases.

We illustrate means of generating some of these solutions in the following example in which we discuss the important *Bessel equation* [12]

$$X'' + \frac{1}{x}X' + \left(1 - \frac{n^2}{x^2}\right)X = 0 \qquad (A.2.25)$$

EXAMPLE A.3   We seek to generate solutions to (A.2.25) for various values of n that are real and positive. Clearly, (A.2.25) has a regular singular point at $x = 0$, and from the above

$$p_{10} = 1 \qquad p_{1i} = 0, \qquad \text{for } i \geq 1$$

and

$$p_{20} = -n^2, \quad p_{21} = 0, \quad p_{22} = 1; \qquad p_{2i} = 0 \qquad \text{for } i \geq 3$$

Thus, from (A.2.24), if we expand our solution in the form (A.2.21)

$$k(k - 1) + k - n^2 = 0$$

or

$$(k + n)(k - n) = 0$$

If $n = 0$, the indicial equation has a double root. If n is an integer, $k_1 = n$ and $k_2 = -n$ differ by an integer $2n$; otherwise $k_1 - k_2 \neq$ integer. Thus we may study three separate cases associated with (A.2.25).

   Case 1. $k_1 = k_2 = 0$; that is, $n = 0$. n
The Frobenuis method uses

$$X_k = \sum_{m=0}^{\infty} c_m^k x^{m+k} \qquad (A.2.26)$$

where k is an unknown as are the c_m^k. By substituting (A.2.26) in the differential equation being solved, one can find c_m^k as a function of c_0^k and k. There is one value of k for which (A.2.26) solves the differential equation. Then if X_k is differentiated with respect to k and $(\partial X_k/\partial k)$ is introduced into the differential equation, a second, linearly independent solution can be found.

   We begin by substituting (A.2.26) in (A.2.25) to obtain

$$k^2 c_0^k x^{k-2} + (k + 1)^2 c_1^k x^{k-1} + [(k + 2)^2 c_2^k + c_0^k]x^k + [(k + 3)^2 c_3^k + c_1^k]x^{k+1} \cdots = 0$$

$$(A.2.27)$$

From (A.2.27),

$$c_0^k k^2 = 0$$

$$(k + 1)^2 c_1^k = 0$$

$$(k + 2)^2 c_2^k + c_0^k = 0$$

$$(k + 3)^2 c_3^k + c_1^k = 0, \text{ etc.}$$

Ignoring the first relation for the moment, we see

$$c_1^k = c_3^k = c_5^k = c_7^k \cdots = 0$$

while

$$c_2^k = -\frac{c_0^k}{(k+2)^2}, \qquad c_4^k = -\frac{c_2^k}{(k+4)^2} = \frac{c_0^k}{(k+2)^2(k+4)^2}, \cdots$$

Accordingly,

$$X_k = c_0^k x^k \left[1 + \sum_{m=1}^{\infty} \frac{(-1)^m x^{2m}}{[(k+2)^2(k+4)^2 \cdots (k+2m)^2]} \right] \qquad (A.2.28)$$

Clearly, introduction of (A.2.28) into (A.2.25) gives, for $n = 0$,

$$X_k'' + \frac{1}{x}X_k' + X_k = c_0^k k^2 x^{k-2} \qquad (A.2.29)$$

For $k = 0$, X_0 is a solution. In particular, setting $c_0^0 = 1$ gives

$$X_0 = 1 - \frac{x^2}{2^2} + \frac{x^4}{2^2 \cdot 4^2} - \frac{x^6}{2^2 \cdot 4^2 \cdot 6^2} + \cdots$$

The values of X_0, or, more commonly, $J_0(x)$, have been tabulated because of their importance;

$$J_0(x) = \sum_{m=0}^{\infty} (-1)^m \frac{x^{2m}}{2^{2m}(m!)^2} \qquad (A.2.30)$$

is called *Bessel's function of zero order* and it is a solution of *Bessel's equation of zero order*

$$X'' + \frac{1}{x}X' + X = 0 \qquad (A.2.31)$$

However, partial differentiation of (A.2.29) with respect to k produces

$$\frac{\partial}{\partial k}\left(X_k'' + \frac{1}{x}X_k' + X_k \right) = c_0^k(2kx^{k-2} + k^2 x^{k-2} \ln x) \qquad (A.2.32)$$

and then

$$\left(\frac{\partial X_k}{\partial k}\right)'' + \frac{1}{x}\left(\frac{\partial X_k}{\partial k}\right)' + \left(\frac{\partial X_k}{\partial k}\right) = c_0^k\left[2k\left(x^{k-2} + \frac{1}{2}kx^{k-2}\ln x\right)\right] \qquad (A.2.33)$$

Again, for $k = 0$,

$$\left.\frac{\partial X_k}{\partial k}\right|_{k=0}$$

is the solution to (A.2.31). From (A.2.28),

$$\frac{1}{c_0^k}\frac{\partial X_k}{\partial k} = \frac{X_k \ln x}{c_0^k} + x^k \sum_{m=1}^{\infty} (-1)^m x^{2m} \frac{\partial}{\partial k}\left[\frac{1}{(k+2)^2(k+4)^2 \cdots (k+2m)^2}\right] \qquad (A.2.34)$$

By evaluating (A.2.34) at $k = 0$ and using standard notation, we achieve, with $c_0^0 = 1$,

$$N_0(x) = J_0(x) \ln x + \frac{x^2}{2^2} - \frac{x^4}{2^2 \cdot 4^2}\left(1 + \frac{1}{2}\right) + \frac{x^6}{2^2 \cdot 4^2 \cdot 6^2}\left(1 + \frac{1}{2} + \frac{1}{3}\right) - + \cdots \quad \text{(A.2.35)}$$

which is the *Bessel function of the second kind of zero order* and a solution to (A.2.31).

The J_0 and N_0 functions are linearly independent; hence the general solution to (A.2.31) is

$$X = AJ_0(x) + BN_0(x) \quad \text{(A.2.36)}$$

where A and B are constants.

Case 2. $k_1 = n$, $k_2 = -n$ with n being an integer.

The method used in Case 1 is employed again. Both desired, linearly independent solutions are found from the root $k_1 = n$. Bowman [12] demonstrates another technique and also shows that the general solution to (A.2.25) for $n = $ integer is

$$X_n = AJ_n(x) + BN_n(x) \quad \text{(A.2.37)}$$

where

$$J_n(x) = \sum_{m=0}^{\infty} (-1)^m \frac{x^{n+2m}}{2^{n+2m} m!(n+m)!} \quad \text{(A.2.38)}$$

and

$$N_n(x) = J_n(x) \int \frac{dx}{x J_n^2(x)} = J_n(x)(a_0 \ln x + b_0) + \frac{1}{x^n}(c_0 + c_1 x^2 \cdots) \quad \text{(A.2.39)}$$

where only b_0 is arbitrary in (A.2.39).

Case 3. $k_1 = n$, $k_2 = -n$, where n is not an integer.

The standard technique works in this case, so let

$$X_k = \sum_{m=0}^{\infty} c_m^k x^{m+k} \quad \text{(A.2.40)}$$

Introducing (A.2.40) into (A.2.25) gives the indicial equation

$$k(k - 1) + k - n^2 = 0$$

when $c_0^k \neq 0$, and the following additional equations:

$$k(k + 1)c_1^k + (k + 1)c_1^k - n^2 c_1^k = 0, \qquad m = 1$$

$$(k + 2)(k + 1)c_2^k + (k + 2)c_2^k + c_0 - n^2 c_2^k = 0, \qquad m = 2$$

$$\vdots \qquad\qquad \vdots \qquad\qquad \vdots$$

$$(m + k)(m + k - 1)c_m^k + (m + k)c_m^k - n^2 c_m^k + c_{m-2}^k = 0, \qquad m = n$$

Since $k = \pm n$, it follows that $c_1^k = 0$. But then $c_3^k = 0$, $c_5^k = 0$, and so on. Now, $c_0^k \neq 0$ and c_0^k is arbitrary, so with $k = n$,

$$c_2^n = -\frac{1}{2^n(1 + n)}c_0^n \quad \text{(A.2.41)}$$

and, in general,

$$c_m^n = \frac{-c_{m-2}^n}{m(m + 2n)}, \qquad m = 2, 4, 6, \ldots. \tag{A.2.42}$$

or

$$c_{2m}^n = \frac{-c_{2m-2}^n}{2^2 m(m + n)}, \qquad m = 1, 2, 3, \ldots \tag{A.2.43}$$

It is customary to set

$$c_0^n = \frac{1}{2^n \Gamma(1 + n)}$$

where $\Gamma(1 + n)$ is the *Gamma function* [10, 13]

$$\Gamma(1 + n) = \int_0^\infty e^{-\beta} \beta^n \, d\beta \tag{A.2.44}$$

Thus (A.2.41) becomes

$$c_2^n = -\frac{1}{2^{2+n}(1 + n)\Gamma(1 + n)} = -\frac{1}{2^{2+n}\Gamma(1 + n + 1)}$$

From (A.2.42), we then get

$$c_4^n = \frac{1}{2^{4+n}2(2 + n)\Gamma(n + 2)} = \frac{1}{2^{4+n}2\Gamma(n + 2 + 1)}$$

or from (A.2.43)

$$c_{2m}^n = \frac{(-1)^m}{2^{2m+n}m!\Gamma(n + m + 1)}, \qquad m = 1, 2, 3, 4, \ldots \tag{A.2.45}$$

The solution to (A.2.25) for $k = n$ is given by (A.2.40) and (A.2.45) as

$$X_n = \sum_{m=0}^\infty \frac{(-1)^m x^{2m+n}}{2^{2m+n}m!\Gamma(m + n + 1)} \tag{A.2.46}$$

In more common notation, $X_n = J_n(x)$, which is the tabulated *Bessel's function of order n* and a solution of *Bessel's equation of order n* (A.2.25).

Another solution to (A.2.25) is found for $k = -n$. In fact, because n appears only as n^2 in the indicial equation, the second solution is

$$X_{-n} = J_{-n}(x) = \sum_{m=0}^\infty \frac{(-1)^m x^{2m-n}}{2^{2m-n}m!\Gamma(m - n + 1)} \tag{A.2.47}$$

Clearly, $J_{-n}(x)$ and $J_n(x)$ are linearly independent, since the lowest-order term of $J_n(x)$ is $O(x^n)$, whereas the lowest-order term of $J_{-n}(x)$ is $O(x^{-n})$. Thus when n is non-integral, the general solution to (A.2.25) is given by

$$X = AJ_n(x) + BJ_{-n}(x) \tag{A.2.48}$$

where A and B are constants.

Methods for Inhomogeneous Equations

Two direct methods that can be used to generate particular solutions to inhomogeneous ordinary differential equations are the method of *undetermined coefficients* and the method of *variation of parameters*. Only the latter is discussed here.

The variation of parameters method can be applied directly to (A.2.4) provided only that all the indicated integrations exist in the development that follows. In operator notation, (A.2.4) becomes the linear, second-order equation

$$L_1[X] = P_3(x) \tag{A.2.49}$$

Equation (A.2.49) has a complementary solution X_{1c} of the form

$$X_{1c} = c_1 X_{11} + c_2 X_{12}$$

The method of variation of parameters consists of replacing c_1 and c_2 with two variable, but unknown, parameters (functions) $C_1(x)$ and $C_2(x)$ and then requiring that

$$X_p = C_1(x)X_{11} + C_2(x)X_{12} \tag{A.2.50}$$

(A.2.49), and the added condition (its usefulness becomes obvious below)

$$C_1' X_{11} + C_2' X_{12} = 0 \tag{A.2.51}$$

all be satisfied. This is possible, since there are three unknowns X_p, C_1, and C_2 in this set of three equations.

The unknown X_p is eliminated from (A.2.49) by use of (A.2.50). First, from (A.2.50),

$$X_p' = C_1' X_{11} + C_2' X_{12} + C_1 X_{11}' + C_2 X_{12}'$$

or by virtue of (A.2.51),

$$X_p' = C_1 X_{11}' + C_2 X_{12}'$$

Next

$$X_p'' = C_1' X_{11}' + C_2' X_{12}' + C_1 X_{11}'' + C_2 X_{12}''$$

Then (A.2.49) becomes

$$C_1 X_{11}'' + C_2 X_{12}'' + C_1' X_{11}' + C_2' X_{12}' + P_1 C_1 X_{11}' + P_1 C_2 X_{12}' + P_2 C_1 X_{11}$$
$$+ P_2 C_2 X_{12} = P_3$$

and since X_{11} and X_{12} are each solutions of (A.2.49) when $P_3 = 0$,

$$C_1(\overbrace{X_{11}'' + P_1 X_{11}' + P_2 X_{11}}^{0}) + C_2(\overbrace{X_{12}'' + P_1 X_{12}' + P_2 X_{12}}^{0})$$
$$+ C_1' X_{11}' + C_2' X_{12}' = P_3$$

The result is

$$C_1' X_{11}' + C_2' X_{12}' = P_3 \tag{A.2.52}$$

Equations (A.2.51) and (A.2.52) constitute a pair of simultaneous algebraic equations for the unknowns C_1' and C_2'. As X_{11} and X_{12} are linearly independent, the determinant

$$\begin{vmatrix} X_{11} & X_{12} \\ X_{11}' & X_{12}' \end{vmatrix} \tag{A.2.53}$$

of the coefficients in the equation set (A.2.51) and (A.2.52) is always nonzero [9]. It follows from (A.2.51) to (A.2.53) that nontrivial solutions $C_1(x)$ and $C_2(x)$ can be found to

$$\begin{aligned} X_{11}C_1' + X_{12}C_2' &= 0 \\ X_{11}'C_1' + X_{12}'C_2' &= P_3 \end{aligned} \tag{A.2.54}$$

EXAMPLE A.4   Find a particular solution to

$$L_1[T] = T''(t) + \omega^2 T(t) = f(t)$$

Solution:

$$T_{11}(t) = \sin \omega t$$

and

$$T_{12}(t) = \cos \omega t$$

are a pair of linearly independent solutions of the complementary equation. Thus we seek

$$T_p = C_1(t) \sin \omega t + C_2(t) \cos \omega t$$

and (A.2.54) become

$$\sin \omega t C_1' + \cos \omega t C_2' = 0$$
$$\omega \cos \omega t C_1' - \omega \sin \omega t C_2' = f(t)$$

We find

$$C_1(t) = \frac{1}{\omega} \int^t f(\tau) \cos \omega \tau \, d\tau$$

$$C_2(t) = -\frac{1}{\omega} \int^t f(\tau) \sin \omega \tau \, d\tau$$

Thus

$$T_p = \frac{1}{\omega} \sin \omega t \int^t f(\tau) \cos \omega \tau \, d\tau - \frac{1}{\omega} \cos \omega t \int^t f(\tau) \sin \omega \tau \, d\tau \tag{A.2.55}$$

Q.E.D.

SPECIAL FUNCTIONS

A.3.1 INTRODUCTION

The solutions to ordinary differential equations that arise in the method of separation of variables are rarely elementary functions. Even the simple equation $X'' + \lambda^2 X = 0$, which is a basis for much of this book, has power series solutions that are well-known trigonometric functions and that are tabulated under the symbolic names sine and cosine. Separation of variables in mathematical models written in cylindrical or spherical coordinates gives rise to ordinary differential equations that also have well-known and tabulated power series solutions. These are three of the *special functions*—Bessel functions, Legendre polynomials, and associated Legendre functions.

The formal power series solutions of the Bessel and Legendre equations were obtained in the previous appendix (Examples A.2 and A.3 of Sec. A.2.2). Using these solutions as a base, we summarize here the key properties and relations needed to employ the special functions in generalized Fourier series solutions (see Sec. 4.5) of mathematical models. Bowman [12] and Watson [14] treat Bessel functions in depth; Churchill [15] and Courant and Hilbert [6] treat Bessel and Legendre functions. Erdélyi [16] gives the transforms of Bessel functions; Abramowitz and Stegun [17] provide tables of the functions and polynomials and their properties.

A.3.2   BESSEL FUNCTIONS

Consider the mathematical model for the small transverse vibrations $z(r, \theta, t)$ of a circular membrane with fixed circumference [see (2.62) and the model (2.63)]:

$$z_{tt} = c^2\left(z_{rr} + \frac{1}{r}z_r + \frac{1}{r^2}z_{\theta\theta}\right), \qquad 0 < r < a, \quad -\pi < \theta < \pi, \quad 0 < t$$

$$
\begin{aligned}
z(a, \theta, t) &= 0, \\
&\qquad\qquad\qquad\qquad -\pi \le \theta < \pi, \quad 0 < t \qquad\qquad \text{(A.3.1)} \\
|z(r, \theta, t)| &< \infty,
\end{aligned}
$$

$$
\begin{aligned}
z(r, \theta, 0) &= \phi(r, \theta), \\
&\qquad\qquad\qquad 0 \le r < a, \quad -\pi \le \theta < \pi \\
z_t(r, \theta, 0) &= \psi(r, \theta),
\end{aligned}
$$

Separation of variables based on a product-form solution $z(r, \theta, t) = R(r)\Theta(\theta)T(t)$ leads to

$$T'' + c^2\lambda^2 T = 0, \qquad T = c_0 \cos c\lambda t + \frac{c_1}{c\lambda}\sin c\lambda t \qquad \text{(A.3.2)}$$

$$\Theta'' + n^2\Theta = 0, \quad \Theta(-\pi) = \Theta(\pi), \quad \Theta'(-\pi) = \Theta'(\pi)$$

$$
\begin{aligned}
\Theta_{1n} &= \cos n\theta, \\
&\qquad\qquad n = 0, 1, 2, 3, \ldots \qquad\qquad \text{(A.3.3)} \\
\Theta_{2n} &= \sin n\theta,
\end{aligned}
$$

and with $\lambda^2 > 0$,

$$R'' + \frac{1}{r}R' + \left(\lambda^2 - \frac{n^2}{r^2}\right)R = 0, \quad R(a) = 0, \quad |R(r)| < \infty \qquad \text{(A.3.4)}$$

Letting $X(x) = R(r)$ with $x = \lambda r$ in (A.3.4) gives the nth-order Bessel equation [see (A.2.25)]

$$X'' + \frac{1}{x}X' + \left(1 - \frac{n^2}{x^2}\right)X = 0, \qquad 0 < x < \lambda a \qquad \text{(A.3.5)}$$

with the auxiliary conditions

$$X(\lambda a) = 0, \quad |X(x)| < \infty, \quad 0 \le x \le \lambda a \qquad \text{(A.3.6)}$$

The equations for R or X constitute an eigenvalue problem; a series of the product-form solutions is used to solve (A.3.1) after the eigenvalue problem (A.3.4) is solved.

Solutions of Bessel's Equation

There are two linearly independent solutions, *called Bessel functions,* of the nth-order Bessel equation (A.3.5); they were obtained by a power series expansion and the Method of Frobenius in Example A.3 of Appendix 2.

If n is zero,

$$J_0(x) = \sum_{m=0}^{\infty} (-1)^m \frac{x^{2m}}{2^{2m}(m!)^2} \qquad \text{(A.3.7)}$$

and

$$N_0(x) = J_0(x) \ln x + \frac{x^2}{2^2} - \frac{x}{2^2 4^2}\left(1 + \frac{1}{2}\right) + \frac{x^6}{2^2 4^2 6^2}\left(1 + \frac{1}{2} + \frac{1}{3}\right) - \cdots \quad \text{(A.3.8)}$$

are the linearly independent, zeroth-order Bessel functions of the first and second kind, respectively. Commonly, $N_0(x)$ is incorporated with $J_0(x)$ in the Neumann form [14, 17]

$$Y_0(x) = \frac{\pi}{2}[N_0(x) - (\ln 2 - \gamma)J_0(x)] \quad \text{(A.3.9)}$$

where the Euler constant

$$\gamma = \lim_{N \to \infty} \left(\sum_{n=1}^{N} \frac{1}{n} - \ln N\right) = 0.5772\ldots$$

(A.3.9) is used to obtain the tabulated values of the Bessel functions of the second kind.

If n is a nonzero integer,

$$J_n(x) = \sum_{m=0}^{\infty} (-1)^m \frac{x^{n+2m}}{2^{n+2m} m!(n+m)!} \quad \text{(A.3.10)}$$

and

$$Y_n(x) = \frac{2}{\pi} \ln \frac{x}{2} J_n(x) + O(x^{-n}) + O(x^n) \quad \text{(A.3.11)}$$

are the linearly independent nth-order Bessel functions of the first and second (Neumann) kind, respectively.

If n is neither an integer nor zero,

$$J_n(x) = \sum_{m=0}^{\infty} \frac{(-1)^m x^{n+2m}}{2^{n+2m} m! \Gamma(m+n+1)} \quad \text{(A.3.12)}$$

and

$$J_{-n}(x) = \sum_{m=0}^{\infty} \frac{(-1)^m x^{-n+2m}}{2^{-n+2m} m! \Gamma(m-n+1)} \quad \text{(A.3.13)}$$

are the two linearly independent Bessel functions satisfying (A.3.5).

If $\lambda^2 < 0$ in (A.3.4), the transformation $x = i\Lambda r$, where $i = (-1)^{1/2}$, is used; $\Lambda^2 = -\lambda^2$ then and (A.3.5) is replaced by

$$X'' + \frac{1}{x}X' - \left(1 - \frac{n^2}{x^2}\right)X = 0 \quad \text{(A.3.14)}$$

whose solutions are the modified Bessel functions I_n and K_n. These are related to the Bessel functions; for example,

$$I_0(x) = J_0(ix) = \sum_{m=0}^{\infty} \frac{x^{2m}}{2^{2m}(m!)^2} \quad \text{(A.3.15)}$$

and

$$K_0(x) = -\left(\ln \frac{x}{2} + \gamma\right) I_0(x) + O(x^2) \tag{A.3.16}$$

Typical Bessel functions are plotted in Figs. A.3.1 and A.3.2. Table A.3.1 gives the zeros of several functions (see [17] or your local computation center to obtain a complete tabulation). Clearly, J_n and Y_n behave much as the sine and cosine, except that the Bessel functions oscillate with decreasing amplitude and vanish at infinity; Y_n is unbounded as $x \to 0$. As with the sine and cosine, the Bessel functions have no common zeros. Neither I_0 nor K_0 oscillate; K_0 is unbounded as $x \to 0$, while I_0 is unbounded as $x \to \infty$.

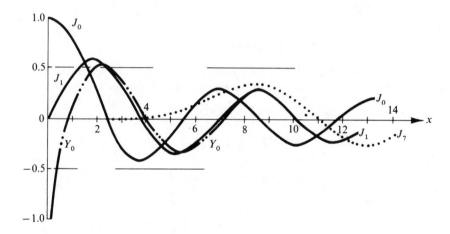

FIGURE A.3.1   Bessel functions.

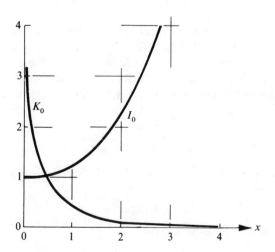

FIGURE A.3.2   Modified Bessel functions.

TABLE A.3.1   Zeros of Bessel functions [17]

Root α_i	J_0	J_1	J_2	J_7	Y_0
1	2.4048	3.8319	5.1356	11.0864	0.8936
2	5.5201	7.0156	8.4172	14.8213	3.9577
3	8.6537	10.1735	11.6198	18.2876	7.0861
4	11.7915	13.3237	14.7960	21.6415	10.2223
5	14.9309	16.4706	17.9598	24.9349	13.3611
6	18.0711	19.6159	21.1170	28.1912	16.5010
7	21.2116	22.7601	24.2701	31.4228	19.6413
⋮	⋮	⋮	⋮	⋮	⋮
19	58.9070	60.4695	62.0162	69.5497	57.3362
20	62.0485	63.6114	65.1593	72.7066	60.4777
	$[J_0(\alpha_i) = 0]$	$[J_1(\alpha_i) = 0]$	$[J_2(\alpha_i) = 0]$	$[J_7(\alpha_i) = 0]$	$[Y_0(\alpha_i) = 0]$

Asymptotic and Integral Relations

The asymptotic behavior of the Bessel functions is of importance in eigenvalue problems and in construction of the Hankel transform. As $x \to 0$,

$$J_0(x) = 1 - O(x^2)$$

$$Y_0(x) = \frac{\pi}{2} \ln x + O(x^2 \ln x)$$

$$J_n(x) = O(x^n), \qquad n \neq 0$$

$$J_{-n}(x) = O(x^{-n}), \qquad n \neq 0$$

$$Y_n(x) = O(x^{-n}), \qquad n \neq 0$$

$$I_0(x) = 1 + O(x^2)$$

$$K_0(x) = -\ln \frac{x}{2} + O(x^2 \ln x)$$

Clearly, $J_0, J_{n,n>0}$, and I_0 are well behaved as $x \to 0$; however, the usual boundedness condition on eigenfunctions will exclude $Y_0, J_{-n,n>0}$, and K_0 if the origin is a point of the problem region (see Example 4.7 in Chap. 4 and Example 8.3 in Chap. 8).

For large $x \to \infty$, the behavior of Bessel functions is deduced by examining the Bessel equations (A.3.5) and (A.3.14). In (A.3.5), introduction of $\phi = x^{1/2} X$ leads to

$$\phi'' + \left(1 - \frac{4n^2 - 1}{x^2}\right)\phi = 0 \tag{A.3.17}$$

We can neglect terms of $O(x^{-2})$ as $x \to \infty$. The solution to $\phi'' + \phi = 0$, and hence to (A.3.17), as $x \to \infty$, has the form

$$\phi = A \cos(x + \varepsilon)$$

where ε is a phase angle. Thus as $x \to \infty$,

$$J_n, N_n, Y_n, J_{-n} \sim \frac{1}{x^{1/2}} \cos(x + \varepsilon)$$

Examination of the actual expansion of the functions for large x yields [17]

$$J_n(x) = \left(\frac{2}{\pi x}\right)^{1/2}\left[\cos\left(x - \frac{n\pi}{2} - \frac{\pi}{4}\right) + O(|x|^{-1})\right] \tag{A.3.18}$$

$$Y_n(x) = \left(\frac{2}{\pi x}\right)^{1/2}\left[\sin\left(x - \frac{nx}{2} - \frac{\pi}{4}\right) + O(|x|^{-1})\right] \tag{A.3.19}$$

Similarly, as $x \to \infty$ [17],

$$I_0(x) = (2\pi x)^{-1/2}e^x\{1 - O(|x|^{-1})\}$$

$$K_0(x) = \left(\frac{2}{\pi x}\right)^{1/2}e^{-x}\{1 + O(|x|^{-1})\}$$

For $n = \pm\frac{1}{2}$, (A.3.17) has the exact general solution

$$\phi = A\cos x + B\sin x$$

It follows, with prescription of the arbitrary constants A and B, that

$$J_{1/2}(x) = \left(\frac{2}{\pi x}\right)^{1/2}\sin x$$

$$J_{-1/2}(x) = \left(\frac{2}{\pi x}\right)^{1/2}\cos x$$

are two linearly independent solutions of (A.3.5) for $n^2 = \frac{1}{4}$. Similarly,

$$I_{1/2}(x) = \left(\frac{2}{\pi x}\right)^{1/2}\sinh x$$

$$I_{-1/2}(x) = \left(\frac{2}{\pi x}\right)^{1/2}\cosh x$$

are the modified Bessel functions satisfying (A.3.14) for $n^2 = \frac{1}{4}$.

The Bessel functions can also be expressed as integrals of trigonometric functions [12, 15, 17]. These may be useful in the evaluation of the Bessel functions. Bessel's integral for $J_n(x)$, with n being any integer, is

$$J_n(x) = \frac{1}{\pi}\int_0^\pi \cos(x\sin\theta - n\theta)\,d\theta \tag{A.3.20}$$

Watson [14] notes that Bessel used this integral as a definition of J_n and derived the other properties of the functions from this definition. For example, from (A.3.20),

$$|J_n(x)| \le 1$$

and

$$\frac{d^k J_n(x)}{dx^k} = -\frac{1}{\pi}\int_0^\pi \begin{cases} (-1)^{(k-1)/2}\sin(x\sin\theta - n\theta)\sin^k\theta \\ (-1)^{(k/2)+1}\cos(x\sin\theta - n\theta)\sin^k\theta \end{cases} d\theta \qquad \begin{array}{l}(k\text{ odd}) \\ (k\text{ even})\end{array}$$

It follows that

$$\left|\frac{d^k}{dx^k}J_n(x)\right| \le 1, \qquad k \ge 0$$

The actual derivatives are obtained by differentiating the series for J_n term by term. This leads directly to the formulas

$$\frac{d}{dx}[x^n J_n(x)] = x^n J_{n-1}(x) \tag{A.3.21}$$

and

$$\frac{d}{dx}[x^{-n} J_n(x)] = -x^{-n} J_{n+1}(x) \tag{A.3.22}$$

These, in turn, produce the recurrence formulas

$$x J_n'(x) + n J_n(x) = x J_{n-1}(x) \tag{A.3.23a}$$

$$x J_n'(x) - n J_n(x) = -x J_{n+1}(x) \tag{A.3.23b}$$

$$J_{n-1}(x) - J_{n+1}(x) = 2 J_n'(x) \tag{A.3.23c}$$

$$x[J_{n-1}(x) + J_{n+1}(x)] = 2n J_n(x) \tag{A.3.23d}$$

for J_n and its first derivatives. Also, from (A.3.21),

$$\int_0^x \xi^n J_{n-1}(\xi) \, d\xi = x^n J_n(x), \qquad n > 0$$

For example,

$$\int_0^x \xi J_0(\xi) \, d\xi = x J_1(x)$$

or

$$\frac{d}{dx}[x J_1(x)] = x J_0(x) \tag{A.3.24}$$

while

$$\frac{d}{dx}[J_0(x)] = -J_1(x) \tag{A.3.25}$$

from (A.3.22).

By using (A.3.23) it is easy to show that

$$\frac{d}{dx}\{x^2[J_n^2(x) - J_{n-1}(x) J_{n+1}(x)]\} = 2x J_n^2(x) \tag{A.3.26}$$

For $n = 0$, (A.3.23d) gives

$$x[J_{-1}(x) + J_1(x)] = 0$$

or $J_{-1}(x) = (-1)J_1(x)$, which is a particular form of the general result for integer n:

$$J_{-n}(x) = (-1)^n J_n(x)$$

Thus, for $n = 0$, (A.3.26) yields

$$\frac{d}{dx}\{x^2[J_0^2(x) + J_1^2(x)]\} = 2x J_0^2(x) \tag{A.3.27}$$

which is a result needed in the Fourier–Bessel expansion of a function in terms of J_0.

Generalized Fourier Series

The general solution to the ordinary differential equation in (A.3.4) is

$$R(r) = AJ_n(\lambda r) + BY_n(\lambda r) \tag{A.3.28}$$

for the case where n is an integer (as in the vibration problem). From Sec. 4.4, we find that the Bessel's equation of order n is a singular Sturm–Liouville case with standard form

$$\frac{d}{dr}\left(r\frac{dR}{dr}\right) + \left(-\frac{n^2}{r} + \lambda^2 r\right)R = 0$$

According to the theorems of Sec. 4.4, it follows that for the eigenvalue problem (A.3.4):

1. an infinite set of real eigenvalues $\lambda_0^2,\ \lambda_1^2,\ \lambda_2^2, \ldots$ exist such that $0 < \lambda_0^2 < \lambda_1^2 < \lambda_2^2 \cdots$ and $\lambda_m^2 \to \infty$ as $m \to \infty$. An infinite set of corresponding eigenfunctions R_m on $0 < r < a$ exists also. Indeed, the boundary conditions of (A.3.4) require $B = 0$ and hence $J_n(\lambda_m a) = 0$, $m \geq 0$. The zeros α_m of the Bessel function provide the eigenvalues λ_m^2/a^2; the eigenfunctions are

$$R_m(r) = J_n\left(\frac{\alpha_m}{a}r\right) = J_n(\lambda_m r)$$

2. the eigenfunctions R_p and R_q corresponding to the distinct eigenvalues λ_p^2 and λ_q^2 are orthogonal with respect to the weight function r. Accordingly,

$$\int_0^a rJ_n(\lambda_p r)J_n(\lambda_q r)\, dr = 0, \qquad p \neq q$$

3. the generalized Fourier series, called the Fourier–Bessel series in this case,

$$\sum_{m=0}^{\infty} J_n(\lambda_m r)\left[\frac{\int_0^a \rho\phi(\rho)J_n(\lambda_m \rho)\, d\rho}{\int_0^a \rho J_n^2(\lambda_m \rho)\, d\rho}\right] \tag{A.3.29}$$

converges absolutely and uniformly on $0 < r < a$ to $\phi(r)$ if $\phi(r) \in C^2$. If ϕ is piecewise continuous and $\int_0^a r\phi'^2\, dr < \infty$, the series converges uniformly at points of continuity and to $\frac{1}{2}[\phi(r^+) + \phi(r^-)]$ at points of discontinuity.

The normalizing constants in (A.3.29) are

$$N_m = \int_0^a \rho J_n^2(\lambda_m \rho)\, d\rho = \frac{1}{\lambda_m^2}\int_0^{\lambda_m a} xJ_n^2(x)\, dx$$

$$= \frac{1}{2\lambda_m^2}\{x^2[J_n^2(x) - J_{n-1}(x)J_{n+1}(x)]\}_0^{\lambda_m a}$$

$$= -\frac{a^2 J_{n-1}(\lambda_m a)J_{n+1}(\lambda_m a)}{2} = \frac{a^2 J_{n+1}^2(\lambda_m a)}{2} > 0$$

from (A.3.26) and (A.3.23d), because $J_n(\lambda_m a) = 0$ in the present case and because the Bessel functions have no common roots.

Applications

To complete the solution of the model (A.3.1), we form a Fourier-Bessel series to sum over the λ_m^2 and sum that series over the eigenvalues n^2 of the eigenvalue problem (A.3.3). Using the appropriate orthogonality relations (which is left to the Problems) determines A_{mn}, B_{mn}, C_{mn}, and D_{mn} in the final form

$$z(r, \theta, t) = \sum_{n=0}^{\infty} \sum_{m=0}^{\infty} J_n(\lambda_m^{(n)}r)\left[\cos c\lambda_m^{(n)}t(A_{mn}\cos n\theta + B_{mn}\sin n\theta)\right.$$
$$\left. + \frac{\sin c\lambda_m^{(n)}t}{c\lambda_m^{(n)}}(C_{mn}\cos n\theta + D_{mn}\sin n\theta)\right]$$

where

$$[\lambda_m^{(n)}]^2 = \left(\frac{\alpha_m}{a}\right)^2 \qquad \text{with } J_n(\alpha_m) = 0$$

Heat conduction in a finite cylinder with prescribed boundary temperatures is described by the Dirichlet model with the Laplace equation, namely, by

$$\nabla^2 u = u_{rr} + \frac{1}{r}u_r + u_{zz}, \qquad 0 < r < a, \quad 0 < z < l$$

$$u(a, z) = T_s(z), \qquad 0 < z < l$$

$$u(r, 0) = T_B(r), \qquad \qquad \qquad \qquad \text{(A.3.30)}$$
$$\qquad\qquad\qquad\qquad 0 \le r < a$$
$$u(r, l) = T_T(r),$$

$$|u(r, z)| < \infty, \quad 0 \le r < a, \quad 0 < z < l$$

when the surface temperatures are not a function of θ. If $T_s \equiv 0$, separation of variables and eigenfunction expansion yield a solution of the form

$$u(r, z) = \sum_{m=0}^{\infty} J_0(\lambda_m r)\left(c_{0m}\cosh\lambda_m z + \frac{c_{1m}}{\lambda_m}\sinh\lambda_m z\right)$$

where $\lambda_m^2 = \alpha_m^2/a^2$ with $J_0(\alpha_m) = 0$. If $T_B \equiv T_T \equiv 0$, the solution form is

$$u(r, z) = \frac{l}{\pi}\sum_{n=1}^{\infty} c_{1n}I_0\left(\frac{n\pi}{l}r\right)\sin\frac{n\pi}{l}z$$

The details are left to the supplementary problems at the end of this appendix.

A.3.3 LEGENDRE POLYNOMIALS AND ASSOCIATED FUNCTIONS

Legendre polynomials and the associated Legendre functions have applications in models involving the Laplacian in spherical coordinates—models for electrostatic and gravitational potentials and heat conduction in a sphere. The model for steady-state heat conduction in a sphere is used as a base for this section [see (3.3)]:

$$\nabla^2 u = (r^2 u_r)_r + \frac{1}{\sin \phi}(\sin \phi u_\phi)_\phi + \frac{1}{\sin^2 \phi} u_{\theta\theta} = 0,$$

$$u(1, \theta, \phi) = T(\theta, \phi),$$

$$|u(r, \theta, \phi)| < \infty,$$

$$0 \le r \le 1, \quad -\pi < \theta \le \pi$$
$$0 \le \phi \le \pi$$

$$\text{(A.3.31)}$$

where the relation between spherical and cartesian coordinates is

$$x = r \sin \phi \cos \theta, \quad y = r \sin \phi \cos \theta, \quad z = r \cos \phi$$

$$x^2 + y^2 + z^2 = r^2$$

In Sec. 3.1 we proposed a product-form solution $u(r, \theta, \phi) = R(r)\Theta(\theta)\Phi(\phi)$ to separate variables in the differential equation in (A.3.31). This solution yields

$$r^2 R'' + 2rR' - n(n+1)R = 0, \quad |R(r)| < \infty, \quad 0 \le r \le 1 \quad \text{(A.3.32)}$$

$$\Theta'' + \lambda^2 \Theta = 0, \quad \Theta(-\pi) = \Theta(\pi), \quad \Theta'(-\pi) = \Theta'(\pi), \quad -\pi \le \theta \le \pi \quad \text{(A.3.33)}$$

and

$$\sin^2 \phi \Phi'' + \sin \phi \cos \phi \Phi' + [n(n+1)\sin^2 \phi - \lambda^2]\Phi = 0$$

$$\Phi(0) \quad \text{and} \quad \Phi(\pi) \quad \text{continuous}, \quad 0 \le \phi \le \pi \quad \text{(A.3.34)}$$

when the necessary continuity of temperature and flux is imposed at the bounding zones established by the coordinates in the solid. In Sec. 3.1 it was noted that (A.3.32) is an Euler- or Cauchy-type equation with general solution

$$R_n = C_n r^n + D_n r^{-1-n}$$

As R must be bounded at the center of the sphere, $D = 0$ and

$$R_n(r) = r^n, \quad n \ge 0 \quad \text{(A.3.35)}$$

The solutions to the eigenvalue problem (A.3.33) are

$$\Theta(\theta) = \begin{cases} \sin m\theta, \\ \cos m\theta, \end{cases} \quad m \ge 0 \quad \text{(A.3.36)}$$

with $\lambda^2 = m^2$, m being an integer.

Using these results and the transformation $X(x) = \Phi(\phi)$ for $x = \cos \phi$ gives, from (A.3.34), the associated Legendre equation (see Prob. 3.3)

$$(1 - x^2)X'' - 2xX' + \left[n(n+1) - \frac{m^2}{1 - x^2}\right]X = 0, \quad -1 < x < 1 \quad \text{(A.3.37)}$$

and the boundary conditions

$$X(-1) \quad \text{and} \quad X(1) \quad \text{continuous} \quad \text{(A.3.38)}$$

In Example A.2 of Sec. A.2.2, the solution to (A.3.37) for $\lambda^2 = m^2 = 0$ was found. If n is a positive integer or zero, there always exists a polynomial solution to

(A.3.37) [see the series (A.2.17) and (A.2.18)]. It can be shown by induction that these *Legendre polynomials* $P_n(x)$, satisfying

$$(1 - x^2)X'' - 2xX' + n(n + 1)X = 0 \tag{A.3.39}$$

are given by

$$P_n(x) = \frac{1}{2^n} \sum_{i=0}^{N} \frac{(-i)^i(2n - 2i)!}{i!(n - 2i)!(n - 1)!} x^{n-2i}, \qquad n \geq 0$$

where

$$N = \begin{cases} \dfrac{n}{2}, & n \text{ even} \\[2ex] \dfrac{(n - 1)}{2}, & n \text{ odd} \end{cases}$$

or by the Rodrigues' formula [17]

$$P_n(x) = \frac{1}{2^n n!} \frac{d^n}{dx^n}[(x^2 - 1)^n], \qquad n \geq 0 \tag{A.3.40}$$

For example,

$$P_0(x) = 1$$

$$P_1(x) = x = \cos \phi$$

$$P_2(x) = \frac{(3x^2 - 1)}{2} = \frac{1}{4}(3 \cos 2\phi + 1)$$

$$P_3(x) = \frac{(5x^3 - 3x)}{2} = \frac{1}{8}(5 \cos 3\phi + 3 \cos \phi)$$

$$P_9(x) = \frac{(1260x - 18480x^3 + 72072x^5 - 102960x^7 + 48620x^9)}{512}$$

The highest power of x in P_n is x^n, and the polynomials P_n are continuous and bounded on $|x| \leq 1$. It follows that the eigenvalue problem (A.3.34) has, for $\lambda^2 = m^2 = 0$, the eigenvalues $n(n + 1)$, with integers $n \geq 0$, and the eigenfunctions $P_n(\cos \phi)$ corresponding to $m = 0$.

Rodrigues' formula also provides a means [18] for determining the recurrence relations

$$(1 - x^2)P'_n(x) = (n + 1)[xP_n(x) - P_{n+1}(x)] \tag{A.3.41a}$$

$$(1 - x^2)P'_m(x) = n[P_{n-1}(x) - xP_n(x)] \tag{A.3.41b}$$

$$P'_{n+1}(x) - P'_{n-1}(x) = (2n + 1)P_n(x) \tag{A.3.41c}$$

$$(n + 1)P_{n+1}(x) + nP_{n-1}(x) = (2n + 1)xP_n(x) \tag{A.3.41d}$$

Now, to find the eigenvalues and eigenfunctions for (A.3.34) when $\lambda^2 = m^2 \geq 0$, we differentiate (A.3.39) m times with respect to x to obtain

$$(1 - x^2)X^{(m+2)} - 2m(x + 1)X^{(m+1)} + [n(n + 1) - m(m + 1)]X^{(m)} = 0$$

Defining

$$P_n^m(x) = (1 - x^2)^{m/2} X^{(m)} = (1 - x^2)^{m/2} \frac{d^m}{dx^m} P_n(x)$$

because the $P_n(x)$ are solutions of (A.3.39) and introducing $P_n^m(x)$ in the preceding equation leads to

$$(1 - x^2) \frac{d^2}{dx^2} P_n^m - 2m \frac{d}{dx} P_n^m + \left[n(n + 1) - \frac{m^2}{1 - x^2} \right] P_n^m = 0$$

that is, the P_n^m are solutions of the associated Legendre equation (A.3.37) and the

$$P_n^m(x) = (1 - x^2)^{m/2} \frac{d^m P_n}{dx^m} \tag{A.3.42}$$

are called the *associated Legendre functions*. From Rodrigues' formula (A.3.40),

$$P_n^m(x) = \frac{1}{2^n n!} (1 - x^2)^{m/2} \frac{d^{m+n}}{dx^{m+n}} [(x^2 - 1)^n] \tag{A.3.43}$$

If $m > n$, $P_n^m(x) = 0$ as $P_n = O(x^n)$ only. Again $P_n^m(x)$ are continuous, bounded, polynomials on $-1 \le x \le 1$ or $0 \le \phi \le \pi$ for $x = \cos \phi$. Accordingly, with $\lambda^2 = m^2$ and m and n being nonnegative integers, $P_n^m(\cos \phi)$ are all the eigenfunctions for the eigenvalue problem (A.3.34).

Spherical Harmonics

The product-form solutions $u(r, \theta, \phi) = R(r)\Theta(\theta)\Phi(\phi)$ of Laplace's equation are called *spherical harmonics*. From above, for example, the spherical harmonics for the region interior to the unit sphere are

$$u(r, \theta, \phi) = r^n \begin{Bmatrix} \cos m\theta \\ \sin m\theta \end{Bmatrix} P_n^m(\cos \phi), \qquad n, m \ge 0 \tag{A.3.44}$$

The functions

$$S_n^m(\theta, \phi) = \begin{Bmatrix} \cos m\theta \\ \sin m\theta \end{Bmatrix} P_n^m(\cos \phi)$$

are called *surface harmonics*. For $-\pi \le \theta \le \pi$, $0 \le \phi \le \pi$, they are continuous functions on the surface of the unit sphere.

If the boundary data in (A.3.31) are not dependent on θ, $m^2 = \lambda^2 = 0$ [check (A.3.36)] and

$$u(r, \phi) = r^n P_n(\cos \phi)$$

are the product-form solutions. We found in Sec. 4.4 that the Legendre equation (A.3.39), whose solutions are $P_n(x)$, had the Sturm–Liouville form

$$\frac{d}{dx} \left[(1 - x^2) \frac{dX}{dx} \right] + n(n + 1)X = 0, \qquad -1 < x < 1$$

If follows that $n(n + 1)$ are the eigenvalues of the equation and that the eigenfunctions $P_n(x)$ are orthogonal on $|x| < 1$ with respect to the weight function $p = 1$; that is,

$$\int_{-1}^{1} P_r(x)P_s(x)\, dx = 0, \qquad s \neq r$$

In fact,

$$\int_{-1}^{1} P_r^m(x)P_s^m(x)\, dx = 0, \qquad s \neq r$$

holds; that is, the associated functions are orthogonal on $|x| < 1$ also because the P_n^m satisfy an equation with Sturm–Liouville form

$$\frac{d}{dx}\left[(x^2 - 1)\frac{dX}{dx}\right] + \left[n(n + 1) - \frac{m^2}{1 - x^2}\right]X = 0$$

and are orthogonal for the eigenvalues $n(n + 1)$ without need for specified boundary conditions. It is easily shown by use of the original differential equation, integration by parts, and the orthogonality relations that

$$N_m^n = \int_{-1}^{1} [P_m^n(x)]^2\, dx = \frac{2(n + m)!}{(2n + 1)(n - m)!}$$

It follows now from Sec. 4.5 that functions can be expanded in Fourier–Legendre series of Legendre polynomials or associated Legendre functions. In particular, as (A.3.34) satisfy the Laplace equation and all the conditions on boundedness and continuity derived from (A.3.31), the formal solution to (A.3.31) is

$$u(r, \theta, \phi) = \sum_{n=0}^{\infty} \sum_{m=0}^{\infty} r^n P_n^m(\cos \phi)\{c_{0mn} \cos m\theta + c_{1mn} \sin m\theta\}$$

and the c_{0mn} and c_{1mn} are determined by use of the orthogonality relations for $\cos m\theta$, $\sin m\theta$, and $P_m^n(\cos \phi)$.

SUPPLEMENTARY PROBLEMS (related to Chapters 4 and 5)

A.1   Study the behavior of the Bessel functions of zero order by

(a) plotting $J_2(x)$ and $Y_2(x)$, using, first, five terms in their expansions (use 50 if a computer is available) and, second, tabulated values.

(b) finding the first two zeros of each function from your expansions.

(c) comparing the computational results found above with tabulated results.

A.2   Show that I_0 and K_0 behave as $Cx^{-1/2}e^x$ and $Cx^{-1/2}e^{-x}$, respectively, as $x \to \infty$.

A.3   Show that

$$I_{1/2}(x) = \left(\frac{2}{\pi x}\right)^{1/2} \sinh x$$

$$I_{-1/2}(x) = \left(\frac{2}{\pi x}\right)^{1/2} \cosh x$$

A.4   Prove that

$$\frac{d^k J_n(x)}{dx^k} = -\frac{1}{\pi} \int_0^\pi \left[\begin{array}{l} (-1)^{(k-1)/2} \sin(x \sin\theta - n\theta) \sin^k\theta \\ (-1)^{(k/2)+1} \cos(x \sin\theta - n\theta) \sin^k\theta \end{array} \right] d\theta \qquad \begin{array}{l} (k \text{ odd}) \\ (k \text{ even}) \end{array}$$

A.5   Using the power series for J_n, show that

$$\frac{d}{dx}[x^n J_n(x)] = x^n J_{n-1}(x)$$

A.6   Derive the recurrence relations (A.3.23).

A.7   Prove the identity (A.3.26).

A.8   Expand the following in terms of the indicated Bessel function on $0 < r < 1$:

(a) 1 in terms of $J_0(\alpha_i r)$ for $J_0(\alpha_i) = 0$.

(b) r^2 in terms of $J_0(\alpha_i r)$ for $J_0(\alpha_i) = 0$.

(c) r^n in terms of $J_n(\alpha_i r)$ for $J_n(\alpha_i) = 0$.

(d) 1 in terms of $J_0(\alpha_i r)$ for $J_0'(\alpha_i) = 0$.

A.9   Complete the formal solution to (A.3.1).

A.10   Solve the model

$$\nabla^2 u = 0, \qquad 0 < r < a, \ \ 0 < z < l$$
$$u(a, z) = T_s(z), \qquad 0 < z < l$$
$$u_x(r, 0) = u_x(r, l) = 0, \qquad 0 \le r < a$$
$$|u(r, z)| < \infty, \qquad 0 \le r < a, \ \ 0 < z < l$$

A.11   Complete the formal solution of (A.3.30) with

(a) $T_s \equiv 0, T_B \equiv 0$ (b) $T_B \equiv 0, T_T \equiv 0$

A.12   Derive the series expression for the Legendre polynomials $P_n(x)$, and verify that it is equivalent to the Rodrigues' formula (A.3.40).

A.13   Find and plot

(a) P_4, P_5, and P_{10}

(b) $P_1^1, P_2^1, P_2^2, P_2^3$

A.14   Derive the recurrence relations (A.3.41).

A.15   Prove

$$\int_{-1}^1 P_r(x)P_s(x)\, dx = 0, \qquad s \ne r$$

and

$$\int_{-1}^1 P_r^m(x)P_s^m(x)\, dx = 0, \qquad s \ne r$$

A.16   Show that

$$N_n^m = \int_{-1}^1 [P_n^m(x)]^2\, dx = \frac{2(m+n)!}{(2n+1)(n-m)!}$$

and

$$\int_{-1}^{1} P_n^r(x)P_n^s(x)(1 - x^2)^{-1}\,dx = 0, \qquad r \neq s$$

A.17 Formally expand $\cos(\pi/2)x$ on $-1 < x < 1$ in terms of a series of Legendre polynomials. Establish the accuracy of the Legendre series representation.

A.18 The mathematical model for the potential induced in the interior of a unit sphere by a distributed charge on the surface is

$$\nabla^2 V = 0, \quad 0 \le r < 1, \quad -\pi < \theta < \pi, \quad 0 \le \phi < \pi$$

$$V(1, \theta, \phi) = \bar{V}(\theta)$$

Find $V(r, \theta, \phi)$ in the interior of the sphere.

A.19 The temperature u on the surface of a unit sphere of a conducting material is $0\,°C$ on the bottom half and $100\,°C$ on the top half. Find $u(r, \theta, \phi)$.

A.20 Find the formal solution for the potential in a region, free of sources, *exterior* to the unit sphere if $V = \bar{V}(\theta, \phi)$ on the sphere.

TABLES OF
INTEGRAL TRANSFORMS

The following is a tabulation of a few Fourier, Hankel, and Laplace transforms for immediate reference. Transforms for a range of representative functions and the basic transform relations derived in Chap. 8 are included. Most of the transforms were adapted from the comprehensive tables [16] edited by Erdélyi.* These tables are readily available to readers, so the present list is not extensive and the reader should not expect to find all the transforms that he needs listed here. References [13, 17, 18] are also good sources of transforms. Care should always be taken to adjust to the varying standard forms used in the published tables.

Our tables are used from left to right across the columns to find transforms of functions and from right to left to find inverses. However, the Hankel transforms are self-reciprocal, so either column can be used as a transform or inverse as desired. With due regard for the factors $1/2\pi$ and $2/\pi$, the same can be said for the Fourier transforms (the sign of i must be changed in the exponential transforms).

* From *Tables of Integral Transforms*, Vols. I and II, by A. Erdélyi (Ed.). Copyright © 1954 by McGraw-Hill Book Company. Used with permission of McGraw-Hill Book Company.

A.4.1   NOTATION

$$\text{erf}\, x = \text{error function}$$

$$\text{erfc}\, x = \text{complementary error function}$$

$$\exp x = e^x$$

$$F(\lambda), c(\lambda), s(\lambda), H_0(\lambda), \Phi(p) = \text{transforms}$$

$$f(x), a(x), b(x), \phi(x) = \text{original functions or inverses}$$

$$H(x) = \begin{cases} 1, x \geq 0 \\ 0, x < 0 \end{cases} ; \text{Heaviside unit function of } x$$

$$i = (-1)^{1/2}$$

$$J_n(x) = \text{Bessel function of first kind of order } n \text{ (Appendix 3)}$$

$$p = \text{variable of integration or real parameter}$$

$$r, \rho = \text{real variables in Hankel transform}$$

$$x = \text{real variable in Fourier and Laplace transforms}$$

$$Y_n(x) = \text{Weber's Bessel function (Neumann form) of second kind of order } n \text{ (Appendix 3;}$$

$$Y_0(x) = \frac{2}{\pi}\{N_0(x) - (\ln 2 - \gamma)J_0(x)\},$$

where Euler's constant $\gamma =$

$$\lim_{N \to \infty} \left(\sum_{n=1}^{N} \frac{1}{n} - \ln N \right) = 0.5772\ldots)$$

$$\alpha, \beta, \mu = \text{real constants}$$

$$\gamma_n = \text{exponent in } e^{\gamma_n x}, \text{ where } n\text{th derivative of } \phi \text{ is of exponential order } e^{\gamma_n x}$$

$$\delta(x) = \text{Dirac } \delta\text{-function}$$

$$\xi = \text{dummy variable of integration}$$

$$\lambda = \text{variable of integration or real parameter}$$

A.4.2   FOURIER TRANSFORMS

EXPONENTIAL TRANSFORMS

$$f(x) = \int_{-\infty}^{\infty} F(\lambda)e^{-i\lambda x}\, d\lambda \qquad\qquad F(\lambda) = \frac{1}{2\pi}\int_{-\infty}^{\infty} f(\xi)e^{i\lambda \xi}\, d\xi$$

$f'(x)$	$-i\lambda F(\lambda)$
$f''(x)$	$-\lambda^2 F(\lambda)$
$f^{(n)}(x)$	$(-i\lambda)^n F(\lambda)$

$f(\alpha x), \alpha > 0$ $\qquad\qquad\qquad\qquad \dfrac{1}{\alpha} F\left(\dfrac{\lambda}{\alpha}\right)$

$f(x - \mu)$ $\qquad\qquad\qquad\qquad e^{i\lambda\mu} F(\lambda)$

$e^{i\mu} f(x)$ $\qquad\qquad\qquad\qquad F(\lambda - \mu)$

$a * b = \displaystyle\int_{-\infty}^{\infty} a(\xi) b(x - \xi)\, d\xi$ $\qquad\qquad 2\pi A(\lambda) B(\lambda)$

$\qquad = \displaystyle\int_{-\infty}^{\infty} a(x - \xi) b(\xi)\, d\xi$

$\delta(x)$ $\qquad\qquad\qquad\qquad (2\pi)^{-1}$

$(1 + x^2)^{-1}$ $\qquad\qquad\qquad \frac{1}{2} e^{-|\lambda|}$

$e^{-\alpha x^2}, \alpha > 0$ $\qquad\qquad\qquad (4\pi\alpha)^{-1/2} \exp\left(\dfrac{-\lambda^2}{4\alpha}\right)$

COSINE TRANSFORMS

$f(x) = \displaystyle\int_0^{\infty} c(\lambda) \cos \lambda x\, d\lambda$ $\qquad\qquad c(\lambda) = \dfrac{2}{\pi} \displaystyle\int_0^{\infty} f(\xi) \cos \lambda\xi\, d\xi$

$f'(x)$ $\qquad\qquad\qquad\qquad \dfrac{2}{\pi} f(0) + \lambda s(\lambda)$

$f''(x)$ $\qquad\qquad\qquad\qquad -\dfrac{2}{\pi} f'(0) - \lambda^2 c(\lambda)$

$f(\alpha x), a \neq 0$ $\qquad\qquad\qquad \alpha^{-1} c\left(\dfrac{\lambda}{\alpha}\right)$

$f(\alpha x) \cos \beta x, \alpha, \beta > 0$ $\qquad \dfrac{\alpha^{-1}}{2}\left[c\left(\dfrac{\lambda + \beta}{\alpha}\right) + c\left(\dfrac{\lambda - \beta}{\alpha}\right) \right]$

$\delta(x)$ $\qquad\qquad\qquad\qquad \dfrac{2}{\pi}$

$H(\alpha - x)$ $\qquad\qquad\qquad \left(\dfrac{2}{\pi\lambda}\right) \sin \alpha\lambda$

$x^{-1/2}$ $\qquad\qquad\qquad\qquad \left(\dfrac{2}{\pi\lambda}\right)^{1/2}$

$(x^2 + \alpha^2)^{-1}, \alpha > 0$ $\qquad\qquad \dfrac{1}{\alpha} e^{-\alpha\lambda}$

$e^{-\alpha x^2}, \alpha > 0$ $\qquad\qquad\qquad \dfrac{1}{(\pi\alpha)^{1/2}} \exp\left[\dfrac{-\lambda^2}{4\alpha}\right]$

$(x^2 + \beta^2)^{-1} e^{-\alpha x^2}, \alpha, \beta > 0$ $\qquad \dfrac{1}{2\beta} e^{\alpha\beta^2}\left[e^{-\beta\lambda} \operatorname{erfc}\left(\alpha^{1/2}\beta - \dfrac{\lambda}{2\alpha^{1/2}}\right) \right.$

$\qquad\qquad\qquad\qquad\qquad\qquad \left. + e^{\beta\lambda} \operatorname{erfc}\left(\alpha^{1/2}\beta + \dfrac{\lambda}{2\alpha^{1/2}}\right)\right]$

$\ln\left[\dfrac{\alpha^2 + x^2}{\beta^2 + x^2}\right], \alpha, \beta > 0$ $\qquad \dfrac{2}{\lambda}(e^{-\beta\lambda} - e^{-\alpha\lambda})$

$\dfrac{\sin \alpha x}{x}, \alpha > 0$ $\qquad\qquad\qquad H(\alpha - \lambda)$

$$\left.\begin{array}{l}(\alpha^2 - x^2)^{-1/2}\cos{[\beta(\alpha^2 - x^2)^{-1/2}]}, \; 0 < x < \alpha \\ \qquad\qquad 0, \qquad\qquad \alpha < x < \infty\end{array}\right\} \qquad J_0[\alpha(\beta^2 + \lambda^2)^{1/2}]$$

$\operatorname{sech}\alpha x, \alpha > 0 \qquad\qquad\qquad\qquad \alpha^{-1}\operatorname{sech}\left(\dfrac{\pi\lambda}{2\alpha}\right)$

$J_0(\alpha x), \alpha > 0 \qquad\qquad\qquad\qquad \dfrac{2}{\pi}(\alpha^2 - \lambda^2)^{-1/2}H(\alpha - \lambda)$

$Y_0(\alpha x), \alpha > 0 \qquad\qquad\qquad\qquad -\dfrac{2}{\pi}(\lambda^2 - \alpha^2)^{-1/2}H(\lambda - \alpha)$

$J_0(\alpha x^{1/2}), \alpha > 0 \qquad\qquad\qquad \dfrac{2}{\pi\lambda}\sin\left(\dfrac{\alpha^2}{4\lambda}\right)$

$x^{-1/2}J_1(\alpha x^{1/2}), \alpha > 0 \qquad\qquad \dfrac{8}{\pi\lambda}\sin^2\dfrac{\alpha^2}{8\lambda}$

SINE TRANSFORMS

$$f(x) = \int_0^\infty s(\lambda)\sin\lambda x\, d\lambda \qquad\qquad s(\lambda) = \frac{2}{\pi}\int_0^\infty f(\xi)\sin\lambda\xi\, d\xi$$

$f'(x) \qquad\qquad\qquad\qquad\qquad -\lambda c(\lambda)$

$f''(x) \qquad\qquad\qquad\qquad\qquad \dfrac{2}{\pi}\lambda f(0) - \lambda^2 s(\lambda)$

$f(\alpha x), \alpha \neq 0 \qquad\qquad\qquad\quad \alpha^{-1}s\left(\dfrac{\lambda}{\alpha}\right)$

$f(\alpha x)\cos\beta x, \alpha, \beta > 0 \qquad\qquad \dfrac{\alpha^{-1}}{2}\left[s\left(\dfrac{\lambda + \beta}{\alpha}\right) + s\left(\dfrac{\lambda - \beta}{\alpha}\right)\right]$

$H(\alpha - x) \qquad\qquad\qquad\qquad\quad \dfrac{2}{\pi\lambda}\{1 - \cos\lambda\alpha\}$

$x^{2n}f(x) \qquad\qquad\qquad\qquad\quad (-1)^n\dfrac{d^{2n}s(\lambda)}{d\lambda^{2n}}$

$x^{-1/2} \qquad\qquad\qquad\qquad\qquad \left(\dfrac{2}{\pi\lambda}\right)^{1/2}$

$x^{-1} \qquad\qquad\qquad\qquad\qquad\quad 1$

$x(x^2 + \alpha^2)^{-1}, \alpha > 0 \qquad\qquad\quad e^{-\alpha\lambda}$

$x^{-1}e^{-\alpha x}, \alpha > 0 \qquad\qquad\qquad \dfrac{2}{\pi}\tan^{-1}\dfrac{\lambda}{\alpha}$

$x^{-1}e^{-\alpha x^2}, \alpha\ \text{real} \qquad\qquad\qquad \operatorname{erf}\dfrac{\lambda}{2\alpha^{1/2}}$

$x^{-2}\sin\alpha x, \alpha > 0 \qquad\qquad\qquad \alpha H(\lambda - \alpha) + \lambda H(\alpha - \lambda)$

$x^{-1}\cos\alpha x, \alpha > 0 \qquad\qquad\qquad H(\lambda - \alpha)$

$x^{-2}\sin\dfrac{\alpha^2}{x}, \alpha > 0 \qquad\qquad\quad \dfrac{\lambda^{1/2}}{\alpha}J_1(2\alpha\lambda^{1/2})$

$J_0(\alpha x), \alpha > 0 \qquad\qquad\qquad\qquad \dfrac{2}{\pi}(\lambda^2 - \alpha^2)^{-1/2}H(\lambda - \alpha)$

$J_0(\alpha x^{1/2}), \alpha > 0 \qquad\qquad\qquad \dfrac{2}{\pi\lambda}\cos\left(\dfrac{\alpha^2}{4\lambda}\right)$

A.4.3   HANKEL TRANSFORMS (OF ZERO ORDER)

$$f(r) = \int_0^\infty \lambda H_0(\lambda) J_0(\lambda r) \, d\lambda \qquad\qquad H_0(\lambda) = \int_0^\infty \rho f(\rho) J_0(\lambda \rho) \, d\rho$$

$f'' + \dfrac{1}{r} f'$	$-\lambda^2 H_0(\lambda)$
$f(\alpha r)$	$\dfrac{1}{\alpha} H_0\!\left(\dfrac{\lambda}{\alpha}\right)$
$r^{1/2} f(r)$	$\dfrac{d}{\lambda d\lambda}[\lambda^{1/2} H_1(\lambda)]$
r^{-1}	λ^{-1}
$(r^2 + \alpha^2)^{-1/2}, \alpha > 0$	$\lambda^{-1} e^{-\alpha\lambda}$
$(\alpha^2 - r^2)^{-1/2} H(\alpha - r), \alpha > 0$	$\lambda^{-1} \sin \alpha\lambda$
$(r^2 - \alpha^2)^{-1/2} H(r - \alpha), \alpha > 0$	$\lambda^{-1} \cos \alpha\lambda$
$(r^2 + \alpha^2)^{-3/2}, \alpha > 0$	$\alpha^{-1} e^{-\alpha\lambda}$

A.4.4   LAPLACE TRANSFORMS

$$\phi(x) = \frac{1}{2\pi i} \int_{\gamma - i\infty}^{\gamma + i\infty} \Phi(p) e^{px} \, dp, \ \operatorname{Re} p > \gamma \qquad\qquad \Phi(p) = \int_0^\infty \phi(x) e^{-px} \, dx$$

(p assumed real in this column)

$\phi'(x)$	$-\phi(0) + p\Phi(p)$
$\phi^{(n)}(x), p > \gamma_n$	$-\displaystyle\sum_{i=2}^n p^{n-i} \phi^{(i-1)}(0) - p^{n-1}\phi(0) + p^n \Phi(p)$
$\phi(x - \mu)$	$e^{-p\mu} \Phi(p)$
$e^{\mu x} \phi(x)$	$\Phi(p - \mu)$
$\delta(x - \alpha), \alpha, p > 0$	$e^{-p\alpha}$
$H(x - \alpha), \alpha, p > 0$	$\dfrac{1}{p} e^{-p\alpha}$
$x^n \phi(x)$	$(-1)^n \dfrac{d^n}{dp^n} \Phi(p)$
$\displaystyle\int_0^x \phi(\tau) \, d\tau$	$p^{-1} \Phi(p)$
$\displaystyle\int_0^x \int_0^\tau \phi(\eta) \, d\eta \, d\tau$	$p^{-2} \Phi(p)$
$a * b = \displaystyle\int_0^x a(\xi) b(x - \xi) \, d\xi = \int_0^x a(x - \xi) b(\xi) \, d\xi$	$A(p) B(p)$
$1, p > 0$	p^{-1}
$x^n, p > 0$	$\begin{cases} \dfrac{\Gamma(1 + n)}{p^{n+1}}, n > -1 \\[2mm] \dfrac{n!}{p^{n+1}}, n \text{ integer} \end{cases}$

$x^{-1/2}H(x-\alpha), \alpha, p > 0$ $\qquad\qquad\left(\dfrac{\pi}{p}\right)^{1/2}\operatorname{erfc}(\alpha^{1/2}p^{1/2})$

$(x+\alpha)^{-1/2}, \alpha, p > 0$ $\qquad\qquad\left(\dfrac{\pi}{p}\right)^{1/2}e^{\alpha p}\operatorname{erfc}(\alpha^{1/2}p^{1/2})$

$e^{\alpha x}, p > \alpha$ $\qquad\qquad (p-\alpha)^{-1}$

$xe^{-\alpha x}, p > \alpha > 0$ $\qquad\qquad (p+\alpha)^{-2}$

$\dfrac{\alpha\kappa-\mu}{\alpha-\beta}e^{-\alpha x}+\dfrac{\beta\kappa-\mu}{\beta-\alpha}e^{-\beta x}$ $\qquad\qquad \dfrac{\kappa p+\mu}{(p+\alpha)(p+\beta)}$

$\operatorname{erf}\left(\dfrac{x}{2\alpha}\right), p > 0$ $\qquad\qquad p^{-1}e^{\alpha^2 p^2}\operatorname{erfc}\alpha p$

$\operatorname{erfc}\left(\dfrac{\alpha}{2x^{1/2}}\right), p > 0$ $\qquad\qquad \dfrac{1}{p}e^{-\alpha p^{1/2}}$

$\operatorname{erf}(\alpha^{1/2}x^{1/2}), p > -\alpha; \alpha > 0$ $\qquad\qquad \alpha^{1/2}p^{-1}(p+\alpha)^{-1/2}$

$\cos\alpha x, p > 0$ $\qquad\qquad p(p^2+\alpha^2)^{-1}$

$\sin\alpha x, p > 0$ $\qquad\qquad \alpha(p^2+\alpha^2)^{-1}$

$\cosh\alpha x, p > \alpha$ $\qquad\qquad p(p^2-\alpha^2)^{-1}$

$\sinh\alpha x, p > \alpha$ $\qquad\qquad \alpha(p^2-\alpha^2)^{-1}$

$2x^{-1}\sinh\alpha x, p > \alpha$ $\qquad\qquad \ln\left|\dfrac{p+\alpha}{p-\alpha}\right|$

$J_0(\alpha x)$ $\qquad\qquad (p^2+\alpha^2)^{1/2}$

$xJ_0(\alpha x)$ $\qquad\qquad p(p^2+\alpha^2)^{-3/2}$

$J_0(2\alpha^{1/2}x^{1/2}), p > 0$ $\qquad\qquad p^{-1}e^{-\alpha p^{-1}}$

$x^{1/2}J_1(2\alpha^{1/2}x^{1/2}), p > 0$ $\qquad\qquad \alpha^{1/2}p^{-2}e^{-\alpha p^{-1}}$

REFERENCES

1. W. Kaplan, *Advanced Calculus*. Reading, Mass.: Addison-Wesley, 1952.

2. T. M. Apostol, *Mathematical Analysis*. Reading, Mass.: Addison-Wesley, 1957.

3. E. C. Titchmarsh, *Introduction to the Theory of Fourier Integrals*, 2nd ed. London: Oxford University Press, 1948.

4. M. Van Dyke, *Perturbation Methods in Fluid Mechanics*. New York: Academic Press, 1964.

5. J. M. Hyslop, *Infinite Series*, 5th ed. New York: Interscience (a division of John Wiley & Sons), 1954.

6. R. Courant and D. Hilbert, *Methods of Mathematical Physics*, Vol. 1. New York: Interscience (a division of John Wiley & Sons), 1953.

7. F. B. Hildebrand, *Advanced Calculus for Applications*. Englewood Cliffs, N.J.: Prentice-Hall, 1963.

8. R. B. McQuistan, *Scalar and Vector Fields*. New York: John Wiley & Sons, 1965.

9. W. Leighton, *Ordinary Differential Equations*. Belmont, Calif.: Wadsworth, 1963.

10. E. D. Rainville, *Elementary Differential Equations*, 3rd ed. New York: Macmillan, 1964.

11. E. D. Rainville, *Intermediate Differential Equations*, 2nd ed. New York: Macmillan, 1964.

12. F. Bowman, *Introduction to Bessel Functions*. New York: Dover, 1958.

13. C. R. C. *Standard Mathematical Tables*, 20th ed. Cleveland: Chemical Rubber Publishing Co., 1972.

14. G. N. Watson, *A Treatise on the Theory of Bessel Functions*, 2nd ed. London: Cambridge University Press, 1944.

15. R. V. Churchill, *Fourier Series and Boundary Value Problems*, 2nd ed. New York: McGraw-Hill, 1963.

16. A. Erdélyi (Ed.), *Tables of Integral Transforms*, Vols. I & II. New York: McGraw-Hill, 1954.

17. M. Abramowitz and I. A. Stegun (Eds.), *Handbook of Mathematical Functions*. New York: Dover, 1965.

18. R. V. Churchill, *Operational Mathematics*, 2nd ed., New York: McGraw-Hill, 1958.

INDEX

Robert L. Street received his M.S. and Ph.D. from Stanford University, where he is currently Professor of Fluid Mechanics and Applied Mathematics and Chairman of the Department of Civil Engineering. His main areas of interest are fluid mechanics, applied hydrodynamics, ocean and coastal engineering, and computer simulation. His favorite pastimes include returning to his birthplace of Honolulu, body surfing at Makapuu Point, and finishing the day off with a Mai Tai at sunset on the lanai at the Halekalani Hotel on Waikiki Beach.